Instructor's Resource Manual
with Full Solutions

to accompany

Reconceptualizing Mathematics for Elementary School Teachers

Second Edition

Judith Sowder
Larry Sowder
Susan Nickerson

W. H. Freeman and Company
A Macmillan Higher Education Company
New York

ISBN-13: 978-1-4641-0900-3
ISBN-10: 1-4641-0900-1

First printing

W.H. Freeman and Company
41 Madison Avenue
New York, NY 10010
Houndmills, Basingstoke
RG21 6XS England

www.whfreeman.com

Contents

4. SOLUTIONS TO EXERCISES 169

Introduction

Mathematics programs for prospective (elementary) teachers must emphasize the intellectual depth of the elementary mathematics curriculum and provide the pedagogical tools to effectively teach this critical material to elementary school children. (Mathematical Association of America—Committee on the Undergraduate Program in Mathematics, p. 41, 2004)

There is today a greater awareness that elementary mathematics is rich in important ideas and that its instruction requires far more than simply knowing the "math facts" and a handful of algorithms. Teachers are expected to support their students' development of concepts, procedures, processes, and proficiencies in doing mathematics. Mathematics courses for teachers must reflect the intellectual depth and challenge of the elementary school curriculum. The Conference Board of Mathematical Sciences (CBMS) recommends that the preparation of the mathematics teachers include courses that develop a "deep understanding of the mathematics they teach," that are designed to "develop careful reasoning and 'common sense' in analyzing conceptual relationships, . . . that develop the habits of mind of a mathematical thinker and that demonstrate flexible, interactive styles of teaching" (CBMS, 2001, pp. 7–8).

We recognize and accept the challenge of presenting mathematics to teachers in a manner that addresses these recommendations. In doing so, we provide instruction that will lead teachers of mathematics to *reconceptualize* the mathematics they often think they already know, thus allowing them to develop a deep understanding of the mathematics they will teach. As the Common Core State Standards (CCSS) authors (2010) suggest, *Reconceptualizing Mathematics* has and in this newest edition continues to stress conceptual understanding of key ideas and organizing principles such as place value and properties of numbers. Furthermore, we believe that teachers must know mathematics differently than most people do. Teachers need to know the mathematics they teach in a way that allows them to hold conversations about mathematical ideas and mathematical thinking with their students.

Future teachers must be mathematically proficient if they are to be successful in developing mathematical proficiency in their own students. They must understand that mathematical proficiency is multifaceted, as described by the Mathematics Learning Study Committee (National Research Council, 2001) to include:

- conceptual understanding—comprehension of mathematical concepts, operations, and relations

- procedural fluency—skill in carrying out procedures flexibly, accurately, efficiently, and appropriately

- strategic competence—ability to formulate, represent, and solve mathematical problems

- adaptive reasoning—capacity for logical thought, reflection, explanation, and justification

- productive disposition—habitual inclination to see mathematics as sensible, useful, and worthwhile, coupled with a belief in diligence and one's own efficiency (p. 116)

These strands of mathematical proficiency are interwoven and should develop together. The authors of the CCSS similarly describe process and proficiencies in the *Standards for Mathematical Practice.* Teachers are expected to develop this expertise in these students and instructors of these courses can rely on the *Reconceptualizing Mathematics* text to address these competencies in an integrated fashion. CCSS authors (2010) also state: "One hallmark of mathematical understanding is the ability to justify, in a way appropriate to the students' mathematical maturity, why a particular mathematical statement is true or where a mathematical rule comes from." (p. 14). Instructors of preservice teachers need to develop norms for their students and users *Reconceptualizing Mathematics* will see support for this in the text. Additionally, the work of this group was based on a thorough review of research on learning mathematics. Such research continues. For example, a recent study (Rittle-Johnson & Mathews, 2009) showed that teaching children the concepts that underlie mathematics was more useful than focusing instruction on procedures. With conceptual instruction, (students) are able to come up with the procedures on their own.

The CCSS authors developed the Standards grounded in research on how students' mathematical knowledge develops over time. Our text puts children's thinking central and we integrate revisions that reflect what is known about research on children's mathematical thinking. The second edition of *Reconceptualizing Mathematics* reflects some of these changes, notably a revised Chapter 10 encompasses recent research on students' conceptions of negative numbers.

A common axiom is that teachers teach the way they were taught. Prospective teachers are unlikely to demonstrate flexible, interactive styles of teaching unless they have experienced mathematics taught this way. Instructors of the *Reconceptualizing Mathematics* courses, however, may not have experienced this type of instruction themselves. Thus, we provide many forms of instructional assistance intended to help instructors to better understand the mathematics that their prospective teachers need to know, to begin to model teaching strategies that these prospective teachers will be expected to use in their own classrooms, and to assist them in many ways throughout the course. For example, we provide short videos of teachers teaching from these materials along with questions for reflecting on this teaching.

This program is appropriate for both elementary and middle school teachers, although middle school teachers need additional coursework. "The mathematics needed by prospective middle-grades teachers encompasses the mathematics needed by teachers in the lower grades, but extended in several important ways to reflect the more sophisticated mathematics curriculum of the middle grades" (CBMS, 2001, p. 99).

For both instructors and students, we offer:

➢ A *Message to Prospective and Practicing Teachers* that lays out expectations of students as participants in learning. This section should be assigned reading on the first day and then discussed in class so that students know what is expected of them. This section also provides students information on the structure of the book.

➢ A *focus on sense-making*, with regular expectations to include explanations and justifications. Students should learn not to expect to be shown "*the* right way," as though imitation is the only way one can learn mathematics and as though there is only one way in which certain tasks can be accomplished.

➤ A variety of elements in each chapter described in the *Message to Prospective and Practicing Teachers* that include activities, discussion items, examples, think abouts, information boxes, take-away messages, end-of-chapter check yourself lists, learning exercises, and supplementary learning exercises

- *Activities* within lessons that can be undertaken in pairs or groups during class and then discussed as a full class. The activities provide opportunities to explore, guess, test, estimate, argue, and justify (National Research Council, 1989). Many of the activities are rich tasks that invite problem solving while others provide needed practice.

- *Discussion* items for whole classroom interactions that can, with some guidance from the instructor, lead to rich conversations that provoke learning through the sharing of ideas and insights.

- *Take Away Messages* that summarize the major points made in each section and that can serve as a partial way of reviewing for examinations.

- *Learning Exercises* for each chapter section that provide opportunities to practice, consolidate what has been learned from a lesson, extend and explore ideas in new ways, develop new insights and understandings, connect to previous learning, and at times foreshadow lessons yet to come. Many of the exercises and discussion questions are rich enough that different solution methods are possible and even likely.

- *Supplementary Learning Exercises* with that provide additional opportunities for review and consolidation.

- *Issues for Learning* sections at the end of most chapters that examine some of what is known from research about the learning of one or more topics in that chapter. In many instances, the issues discussed apply to both elementary students and prospective teachers.

➤ *Examples of children's ways* of doing mathematics throughout the text. Many times children's solutions are highly original and exemplify the reasons why teachers need to understand mathematics and student thinking in deeper ways than people who do not teach.

➤ Pages from *elementary school mathematics textbooks* that relate to the chapter sections where they appear.

➤ A *glossary* of important terms used in the course.

➤ An *Appendix: A Review of Some "Rules"* is available at the Book Companion site for students who do not remember basic arithmetic that is assumed in this course.

➢ An inexpensively produced text for students to write in and keep as a reference, rather than as a resale item after the final exam. We recommend that instructors urge their students to write in the texts and they keep it to use as a resource as they teach.

For the instructors of *Reconceptualizing Mathematics* courses we offer additionally:

➢ Textbook pages that are identical to the students' pages, except that in the instructor text marginal notes provide explanations, sometimes answers, and sometimes suggestions for teaching a particular topic. The margins are left blank in the student version for note-taking.

➢ Additional, separate instructor notes in this Manual that offer more background and detail than can be placed in margins. At times, we suggest ways to approach a lesson. At times, we provide background on particular lessons that can be useful in understanding the point of the lesson, or research about the particular topic.

➢ *Information* in the margins of the text about which exercise answers are not included in the student text.

➢ *Appropriate technology* incorporated into lessons in each part of the book, with instructions on how to use the technology when deemed necessary.

➢ *Lists of special materials needed* for each section. Some of the materials can be obtained from the pages for cut-outs in the appendices. Other materials are common-place items. Only a few items would need to be purchased, and they are optional although recommended.

➢ A *research-based curriculum.* The authors have studied the learning and teaching of mathematics in elementary and middle school for many years, and that work has influenced decisions made while developing these materials.

➢ A *classroom-tested curriculum.* These text materials have been used and refined in San Diego State University classes for preservice elementary teachers for the past fifteen years, and in our Professional Development Collaborative for twelve years. They have also been used at thousands of other universities and colleges throughout these years. The text materials have been through a rigorous review process.

Alignment Issues. We have attempted to do more than simply reorganize the usual content of mathematics courses for elementary and middle grade teachers. We have selected and developed topics and problems that exemplify mathematical reasoning and problem solving, make mathematical connections clear, clarify and overcome common misconceptions, provide opportunities to communicate mathematically, and promote greater confidence in one's ability to deal with mathematics—in short, to develop proficiencies as described in the *Standards for Mathematical Practice.* The materials here align with the content goals of the *Common Core State Standards.* They reflect the CBMS document *The Mathematics Education of Teachers* (2001) and with the MAA-CUPM document *Undergraduate Programs and Courses in the Mathematical Sciences* (2004). The vision of school mathematics found in the NCTM *Standards* (1989, 2000) documents also guided us as we developed and revised these text materials. The level B *Guidelines for Assessment and Instruction in Statistics Education* (GAISE) align well with our Part IV: *Reasoning about Chance and Data*. In addition, a study of state mathematics frameworks and credentialing requirements show that teachers who know the content in *Reconceptualizing Mathematics* will be prepared to pass credentialing tests for elementary school teachers (assuming that they also know basic algebraic symbol manipulation). We believe that with the adaptation of the testing to address the demands of the CCSS, and our close alignment with the goals of these standards, the materials will continue to meet this need.

The Role of Problem Solving. Problem solving is "not only a goal of learning mathematics but a major means of doing so. Students should have frequent opportunities to formulate, grapple with, and solve complex problems that require a significant amount of effort and should then be encouraged to reflect on their thinking" (National Council of Teachers of Mathematics, 2000, p. 52). We agree with O'Brien and colleagues who state that problem solving can be seen as "causing learning to take place." Problems permeate these course materials, rather than being relegated to sections called problem solving.

At times a focus on problem solving is prominent. For example: In *Reasoning with Numbers and Quantities,* problems are solved by analyzing their quantitative structures. In *Reasoning about Algebra and Change*, describing graphs qualitatively is fundamental to the notion of change. In *Reasoning about Shapes and Measurement,* there are rich problems that explore and develop spatial reasoning. In *Reasoning about Chance and Data,* some of the misconceptions about probability are explored. There are many other instances and types of problems throughout that are non-trivial and go beyond application of skills.

Some Common Themes. In addition to the common themes of reasoning and sense-making that permeate this text, there are other common themes worth mentioning. Proportional reasoning is recognized as a cornerstone of the elementary and middle school curriculum, and this topic runs throughout the different parts: Chapters 1, 8, and 9 in Part I, Chapter 13 in Part II, and Chapter 20 in Part III all focus on some aspect of proportional reasoning. The ability to reason proportionally is assumed in Part IV. A second common content theme is that of the fundamental role of fractions in elementary school mathematics, and the different aspects of understanding of fractions permeate all four Parts. A third common theme is the use of models, such as the number line and rectangular array, to illustrate mathematical properties and operations.

A fourth common theme is the demonstration of how the content in this text is related to what is taught in elementary school. This can be seen in the elementary mathematics textbook pages in each chapter, in the inclusion of student work when feasible, and in the attention given to curriculum issues in the *Issues for Learning* sections in each part, particularly those that focus on related publications of the *Principles and Standards of School Mathematics* and *Curriculum Focal Points for Prekindergarten through Grade 8 Mathematics: A Quest for Coherence,* both published by the National Council of Teachers of Mathematics. We have found this focus to be very motivational. Note however, that we leave the *how* to teach to courses on methods of teaching mathematics. Here, we focus on content—the content of elementary school mathematics.

Your Students. This information may be useful to you if you have never taught preservice or practicing K–8 teachers. Their mathematics backgrounds and confidence levels cover an enormous range; some should be math majors, others are still struggling with fractions and decimal points; some welcome any challenging problem, others feel that they should be expected only to imitate worked-out examples. As with most required mathematics classes, your toughest jobs will be to convince the "weaker" students that they can indeed succeed and to inspire the indifferent students to admire and enjoy mathematics and mathematical thinking.

Sometimes, students are expecting a methods-of-teaching course. Although there are indirect messages about teaching methods built into the materials (for example, some work in small groups, hands-on manipulatives, explanations as a part of mathematics), the concern here is building understanding *of* mathematical content, *not* of *how to teach* this content. Most likely, your students will be taking a methods of teaching mathematics course if they are seeking a teaching credential.

The Use of Technology.   Each of the four parts uses technology in a different way. We highly recommend using this technology, but it is not required in any of the four parts.

> ➤ For *Part I: Reasoning about Numbers and Quantities*, we include video clips of interviews of elementary students working on number tasks. The seven clips are highly motivating. When prospective teachers have a close-up look at how elementary students think about mathematics, they realize that just knowing procedures is not enough—they themselves *must* understand the mathematics, that is, they must reconceptualize the mathematics if they are to develop the deep understanding of mathematics needed to teach well. Appendix A contains commentary and suggested questions for prospective teachers upon viewing. We also discuss the appropriate use of calculators in an *Issues for Learning* section and recommend internet applets appropriate for this content. (Unfortunately, we do not have free access to videos of student work in other content areas.)

> ➤ In *Part II: Reasoning about Algebra and Change,* we provide an applet called "Over and Back" that allows students to explore the important concept of average rate, and we discuss with the instructor the incorporation of the motion detector (to be purchased) as a way to visualize the graphing of motion. Applets appropriate for this content are also recommended.

> ➤ *Part III: Reasoning about Shapes and Measurement* contains an optional unit that introduces the *Geometer's Sketchpad* (from Key Curriculum Press). These lessons build on the content of Part III and provide not only information on making some standard geometric figures, but reflection questions that help solidify understanding of geometric concepts. The set of lessons here were developed by Dr. Janet Bowers, who has also designed the online course for *Geometer's Sketchpad* for Key Curriculum Press. In addition, applets appropriate for this content are recommended. With the second edition, we now include five more videos clips of interviews of elementary students working on geometry and measurement tasks.

> ➤ *Part IV: Reasoning About Chance and Data* is perhaps the part most dependent on software. We recommend Fathom (a computer program available from Key Curriculum Press) or the TI-73 Explorer (a calculator available from Texas Instruments). Some of

the statistical work can be done using Excel if neither Fathom nor the TI-73 is available. Data sets are available at www.whfreeman.com/reconceptmath for Fathom and Excel, or students can type in data sets. The lessons in Part IV are developed independently of any software so that whatever is available can be used. Appendices explain how to use each of the types of software mentioned here. Here, again we also recommend the use on online applets.

Classwork. The activities and discussions are expected to be done in class, although you may decide to assign some. Or you may decide to discuss selected Learning Exercises in class as part of the instruction. Some of the exercises or discussion questions are fertile enough that different solution methods are possible and even likely; a variety of approaches or thinking sometimes comes up in group work, and such occurrences should be noted to the class in a positive fashion.

Your questioning will be a key to developing the students' sensitivity to sense-making. Some of your planning might involve thinking of a few "good" questions to ask; others will arise in the flow of discussions (do not feel that *you* have to answer every question that students ask). Be aware of your "wait-times"—(1) the interval between the asking of a question and the calling for a response and (2) the interval after a question is answered but before the discussion continues. Longer wait-times naturally allow more time for thought, time that might be needed for a large part of the class. When teachers extend their wait-times to 5 to 10 seconds from the commonly observed *one* second, participation increases, both quantitatively and qualitatively. This observation makes sense; of course the really fast students, by definition, will give answers quickly. But other students may also be capable of figuring something out if given just a bit more time. Similarly, the post-answer wait-time gives students time to evaluate a response and not just to rely on your reaction.

Every theory of learning assumes that the student is engaged. Keep that in mind when you are planning a class. Discussions usually lead to more involvement than does only note-taking during lectures. Questions calling on manipulative materials seem to accomplish the same thing. You can punctuate any lecturing you do with questions and "do this now" exercises or explorations. Explaining what students should get from homework reading and exercises may be helpful in adding to their engagement there; an attitude of "What can I learn from the homework?" is much better than a "What can I do to finish this as quickly as possible?" posture. "Engagement in what?" is, however, the ultimate concern. Exercises in sense-making, not only exercises in memory retrieval, should be routine. Although work on knowledge of vocabulary and other conventions is not unimportant, work that focuses on conceptual development and explanations is perhaps more important for prospective teachers.

Our intention is to help you, the instructor, move beyond lecturing to incorporate group work and whole class work. Prospective teachers should experience mathematical pedagogy that will be appropriate for them to use as teachers. We recognize, however, that there may be times when you may find lecturing is necessary and appropriate.

Students usually do take notes during lectures (a cautionary rule of thumb: If *you* don't write it down, it will not appear in the students' notes). Students should also be encouraged to take notes during Discussions, during work with manipulatives, and when vocabulary and general results are encountered in the exercises. These appear to be occasions when students fail to put into reviewable form those items that require consolidation or review. For example, some result that may be clear at the time of work during class may be forgotten if there is no written record or highlighting of the result.

An important aspect of the formatting used here is that each text page has a wide outer margin. In the instructor version, this space is used for notes for the instructor, and in the students version, there is empty space deliberately provided for notes. This has proved to be an attractive feature for many students and encourages them to write in their text and keep it for future reference rather than selling it back to a bookstore.

Homework and the Design of the Learning Exercises. It is probably accurate to say that it is when doing homework that a student *really* learns the material. *You* know the importance of homework; some students apparently do not. Indeed, in some cases you may well decide to devote class time to topics in exercises. Some exercise lists contain too many exercises for a session-to-session assignment, so you will have to pick and choose. You may also wish to "save" some exercises, or parts of exercises, for assignments later in the course, to build in an ongoing review of the earlier topics.

The format and content of the majority of Learning Exercises are somewhat different than the end-of-chapter exercises that prospective teachers may have experienced in other courses. We know that most students coming into our classes have the belief that a homework exercise takes at most a few minutes to complete. But most good mathematical problems take more time. Schoenfeld, in an often-quoted reference, has said:

> We have done a serious disservice to any student who emerges from the classroom thinking that mathematics only applies to situations that can be solved in just a few minutes—and that if you can't solve a problem in a short amount of time, you should simple give up" (1988, p. 160).

In the video study associated with the Trends in International Mathematics and Science Study (TIMSS), countries that achieved higher scores than those in the United States used instructional methods quite different from ours. In Japan, teachers often focused on one problem, with extensions and explanations, for the entire class period, whereas in the United States teachers gave multiple problems or just practice on definitions that did not require much thought (Stigler & Hiebert, 1999). Some of the more recently published K–12 curricula also sometimes focus on one problem for a relatively long period of time. Prospective teachers should experience problems that require more than a few minutes to solve if they are going to be able to teach from such textbooks.

The exercises are called *Learning Exercises* for a reason. They are intended to help students parse the material in a manner that will lead to a deeper understanding of the content of that section. Of course, skill development is provided, with the recognition that skills must be developed. There are, however, fewer practice exercises on topics where skill development is not necessary. For example, computing with different bases is intended to help prospective teachers better understand our place-value system and its importance in developing algorithms for computing. But prospective teachers will not be teaching computation in bases other than ten, and therefore do not need to develop expertise in computation with numbers displayed in other bases.

Students have answers to parts of the Learning Exercises, but a substantial number of answers are not included, and instructors have information telling them which answers are provided for students. (Instructors have all answers.) Keep in mind the fact that even when answers are included, the process of reaching the answer often is not. Learning often takes place in the middle ground between problems and answers.

Supplementary Learning Exercises for each section are similar in design to the regular Learning Exercises, but students have answers for all of these exercises in the optional Students' Solutions Manual. They can be used for consolidation of learning or for review for exams, and they provide additional opportunities for learning. We suggest that they not necessarily be assigned, but that students who feel the need for additional exercises be encouraged to do them.

The Role of Explaining. Students are told that the overall goal of these courses is to come to understand the mathematics deeply enough to participate in meaningful conversations about this mathematics and its applications, and that being capable of solving a problem or performing a procedure, by itself, will not enable them to add value to the school experience of their students. But when they are able to converse with their students about mathematical ideas, reasons, goals, and relationships, their students can come to make sense of the mathematics. Opportunities for explaining occur during Activities and Discussions in class, and in Learning Exercises outside of class.

Testing. Most instructors will use standard quizzes or tests as at least part of their evaluation of students. An assortment of items used by our instructors and colleagues at other universities is available on the W.H. Freeman Web site. On tests we try always to include at least one item, and preferably more, requiring that the students provide an explanation. (The latter do require more time to grade.)

How to Use These Four Parts of *Reconceptualizing Mathematics*

There are four parts to *Reconceptualizing Mathematics*: *Part I: Reasoning about Numbers and Quantities, Part II: Reasoning about Algebra and Change, Part III: Reasoning about Shapes and Measurement,* and *Part IV: Reasoning about Chance and Data.* The parts and the chapters vary in length. At San Diego State University we use these materials in four one-semester courses. For two- or three-semester or quarter programs, topics would need to be judiciously selected. We provide timelines for each part that can assist instructors in making decisions about topics to include. The actual choices will probably depend on the syllabi for individual institutions, which vary substantially.

If you offer only one course, we suggest that you provide enough depth on a few topics to convince future teachers that they must know this content well. Just touching on several topics is unlikely to have much impact on their knowledge. Place value and fractions are the major foci of elementary school mathematics, and so Chapters 2 (on place value), 6, and 7 (on fractions) should be included, at least. We also suggest Chapter 3 on the meanings of operations, Chapter 5 on using numbers in sensible ways, and Chapter 9 on ratio, proportion, and percent. Chapters 23,

24, and 25 all deal with measurement, and these chapters will provide some review of shapes. You will need to be judicious in assigning Learning Exercises because some of them assume knowledge in previous chapters. Issues for Learning should be carefully selected. You may want to include all Issues for Learning that deal with the NCTM *Principles and Standards for School Mathematics*, which can be found in 8.3, 12.4, 18.3, 25.3, and 27.5.

If you offer two courses, we suggest that the bulk of Parts I and III be the focus of your coursework, with some chapters and sections skipped over (such as 5.4, 10.3, and 11.2–4, Chapters 19, 21, 22, and 26). Chapter 12 would provide an overview of algebra in the curriculum and could stand alone from Part II. Chapters 27 and 29 could be selected from Part IV. Some universities offer topics from Part I for the first course, then half of the second course focuses on geometry (topics from Part III) and half on probability and statistics (topics from Part IV). Again, select those Issues for Learning sections that are relevant to what you teach.

Many universities now offer three courses for elementary teachers, and use different arrangements of content. Topics for Part I always appear. A second semester could be devoted to geometry (Part II), and the third course focuses on selected chapters on algebra (Part II) and statistics and probability (Part IV). Some institutions combine chapters from Parts II and III in one semester and devote a full semester to Part IV. Only with four courses can all of the four parts be reasonably included.

All middle school teachers should have the opportunity to learn the content of these chapters, and *more*, according to recommendations from *The Mathematical Preparation of Teachers*. Many of the chapters here may not make it onto your syllabi, but would be very appropriate for a course for middle school teachers.

References for the Introduction

Conference Board of Mathematical Sciences. (2001). *The mathematical preparation of teachers.* Washington, DC: Mathematical Association of America.

Committee on the Undergraduate Program in Mathematics. The Mathematical Association of America. (2004). *Undergraduate programs and courses in the mathematical sciences: CUPM curriculum guide.* Washington, DC: Author.

National Council of Teachers of Mathematics. (1989). *Curriculum and evaluation standards for school mathematics.* Reston, VA: Author.

National Council of Teachers of Mathematics. (2000). *Principles and standards for school mathematics.* Reston, VA: Author.

National Governors Association Center for Best Practices, Council of Chief State School Officers (2010). *Common core state standards for mathematics.* Washington, DC: Author.

National Research Council. (1989). *Everybody counts: A report to the nation on the future of mathematics education.* Washington, DC: National Academy Press.

National Research Council, Mathematics Learning Study Committee (2001). *Adding it up: Helping children learn mathematics.* Washington DC: National Academy Press.

O'Brien, T. C., with C. Wallach and C. Mash-Duncan. Problem-Based Learning in Mathematics. Unpublished paper.

National Research Council, Committee on Science and Mathematics Teacher Preparation. (2001). *Educating teachers of science, mathematics, and technology: New practices for the new millennium.* Washington, DC: National Academy Press.

Matthews, P., & Rittle-Johnson, B. (2009). In pursuit of knowledge: Comparing self-explanations, concepts, and procedures as pedagogical tools. *Journal of Experimental Child Psychology, 104,* 1-21.

Rowe, M. B. (1987). Wait time: Slowing down may be a way of speeding up. *American Educator, 11* (Spring 1987): 38–43, 47.

Schoenfeld, A. (1988). When good teaching leads to bad results: The disasters of "well taught" mathematics classes. *Educational Psychologist, 23,* 145–166.

Stigler, J. W., & Hiebert, J. (1999). *The teaching gap.* New York, NY: The Free Press.

Facilitating Small Group Discussions

If, as a mathematics teacher educator, you have chosen to use these materials to teach mathematics, you likely have a vision of instructing with a focus on reasoning and making sense of mathematics. You may believe, as we do, that students should be challenged to solve problems that require a significant amount of effort with the opportunity to reflect on their thinking. We also believe that students should understand the mathematics deeply enough to participate in, even lead, conversations about mathematics. Certainly, the ability to participate in mathematical conversations is important, but we also know these conversations can support their learning. Therefore, explanation is an essential aspect of our classes. With these goals in mind, it can be very beneficial to organize students for problem solving and discussion in small groups. We hope our suggestions will help you in your facilitation of small group discussions.

Why organize in small groups?

We have found a number of benefits of small group work. Some of your students will confidently approach these problems and others will find the small group context more comfortable. Small group settings of two to five students can provide more opportunities than the whole class setting for student engagement and for a student to articulate what he or she knows. Research in cognitive psychology has found that those who provide elaborate explanations to others learn from this elaboration. The activity of summarizing and highlighting requires the student to cognitively reorganize and structure the material (Slavin, 1995). Further, the small groups provide a "window" into student thinking as the students work and discuss ideas. You can use the insights gleaned from listening to lead your own mathematical conversations in whole class summaries. Finally, instructors should model the teaching strategies that prospective teachers will be expected to use in their classrooms; prospective teachers are unlikely to employ interactive styles of teaching unless they have experienced this teaching themselves.

Some general guidelines

Just putting students into groups does not mean that students will work collaboratively and have rich discussions about mathematics. You'll want to give clear directions and explicit support for collaboration in small groups (more on this in the following section). First, we suggest some general guidelines.

Both in whole class discussions and in small group settings, instructors must help create an environment that is conducive to sharing ideas and asking questions. Foster encouragement, listen carefully, and accept expressions of tentative mathematical ideas.

In our classes, small groups typically:
- Look for solutions to problems and provide accompanying justification
- Reach consensus on a conjecture
- Provide data or justification for a conjecture
- Define a term or derive a formula

The focus of these activities and your questions should always remain on helping students make sense of what they are learning and make connections. As you circulate to listen to student discussions, observe the pace at which they are working. If someone in a group is struggling, delay an immediate explanation. Instead, ask the students to tell you what they *do* know. In small groups and whole class conversations, talk about problem- solving strategies; make these strategies an explicit focus of conversation so they can come to be recognized as powerful tools.

Directions for structuring group work

Before asking students to work in small groups, provide them with explicit instructions about the work they are to do and why they are doing it. It is helpful to provide these instructions in written form for them to refer to as they work (on the board, on a distributed sheet, or projected). Carefully explain the goals of the work—create a table or organize a sheet to show what the expected result should be. It would be appropriate in these classes to remind the students frequently that we are interested in "Why?" Be clear about your expectations for sharing with the whole class. For example, work will be better organized if students are alerted to the fact that you'll want to display what they've done on a document camera.

When you give groups a task, tell them how much time they will have to do it. Anticipate that the groups will not finish simultaneously. Therefore, give them specific directions for what to do when they are finished. The directions for early finishers will vary according to the task and topic; for example, those students can be encouraged to come up with another approach to a problem, make another problem like the one they solved, share with another group, or do another challenge problem you have provided. As you monitor the pace, you may realize you need to allow less time for a task.

To sum up, prior to beginning small group work, give explicit instructions about the goals, the expected outcome, the allotted time, the means of organizing and sharing student work, and what students should do when they are finished. Make sure you follow up on small group work. It's very important that students get a sense of the work's importance. If students sense purpose, they will be more likely to engage in small group activity in the future.

Supporting collaboration within small groups

Within small groups, the expectation is that students work collaboratively, debate ideas, and construct knowledge. Students often need direction on what their activity should look like; much of this direction will be modeled by what you do.

Students in small groups have a responsibility to:
- focus talk on promoting understanding
- ensure everyone in the group has the opportunity to participate and understand
- exchange explanations and questions—not just answers
- listen respectfully and try to understand alternative perspectives and solutions
- debate and critique ideas, not people
- avoid rushing to explanation without first asking questions

Learning to ask questions

We find it helpful to have a few questions in mind and to teach students to ask these questions of each other. You may want to post some of the questions for their reference as they work.

Here are some we have found useful to share with students.
- Can you tell me what you know so far?
- Does anyone have another idea?
- Are we all convinced? Can someone play the role of skeptic and ask questions?
- Why choose [addition, subtraction, multiplication, division]?
- Have we considered all cases in an orderly fashion? How can we be sure we've considered them all?
- Can we work together through some examples?
- Can we think of any counterexamples, where the defined item meets some criteria but not all? Is there any item that fits our definition that is not a_____?
- Is there a pattern?
- How can we check our [formula or equation]?
- What is the meaning of the symbols we are using?
- How does your representation help you communicate?
- How does this [story] relate to [division] or a particular conception of [division]?

In problem-solving situations, remind students to ask quantitative reasoning questions:
- Can we imagine the situation?
- What is the quantity of interest?
- What do we know about the nature of the quantities? Are they changing? Staying constant?
- Would drawing a diagram help reveal relationships?

We have focused here on general suggestions that we hope support your efforts to facilitate effective collaboration among students in small groups. Consult the bibliography and other references when you are ready to delve deeper.

Bibliography

Chapin, S. H., O'Conner, C., & Anderson, N. C. (2003). *Classroom discussions: Using math talk to help students learn (Grades 1–6)*. Sausalito, CA: Math Solutions Publications.

Johnson, D. W., & Johnson, R. T. (1987). *Learning together and alone: Cooperative, competitive, and individualistic learning*. Englewood Cliffs, New Jersey: Prentice Hall.

National Council of Teachers of Mathematics (2000). *Principles and standards for school mathematics*. Reston, VA: Author.

Reid, J. (2002). *Managing Small Group Learning*. Downloaded from http://www.eric.ed.gov:80/ERICDocs/data/ericdocs2sql/content_storage_01/0000019b/80/19/f3/51.pdf

Roseth, C. J., Garfield, J. B., & Ben-Zvi, D. (2008). Collaboration in learning and teaching statistics. *Journal of Statistics Education*. Downloaded from http://www.amstat.org/publications/jse/v16n1/roseth%20pdf.html

Slavin, R. E. (1995). *Cooperative learning: Theory, research, and practice*. Boston: Allyn and Bacon.

Instructor Notes

Overview of *Part I: Reasoning about Numbers and Quantities (RNQ)*

Goals Our primary goal for this course is that elementary and middle school teachers, whether prospective or practicing, develop a deep understanding of numbers and number operations. A second goal is to help them develop habits of reasoning quantitatively. "Story problems" have traditionally been given for practice in using a formula, such as distance = rate × time. Our approach is very different. We want those planning to teach to be able to *analyze* problems quantitatively without solely resorting to formulas or symbolic algebra, at least at this stage. Drawings should accompany a quantitative analysis of a problem.

Key Ideas Here are the key ideas presented in Part I: Reasoning about Numbers and Quantities, although not necessarily in this order.

Numbers

- Our numeration system can be understood only if the significant role of place value is recognized.

- There are different generic contexts that can be modeled by arithmetic operations. Hence, there are different ways of thinking about these operations.

- Standard algorithms are not the only ways to carry out arithmetic operations. Alternative algorithms can be valuable in developing understanding of the steps of a standard algorithm. Properties of operations undergird calculations.

- Different types of calculating skills are appropriate for different problematic situations. Mental computation, estimation, paper-and-pencil computation, and calculators all have their places in our daily lives.

- Understanding the different meanings and different representations of rational numbers, and facility in changing easily from one representation to another, are fundamental to having good number sense.

- The mathematics underlying the algorithms for operating on rational numbers can and should be understood.

Quantities

- Mathematical problem situations can be better understood when they are analyzed by recognizing the quantities involved and the relationships among these quantities.

- Understanding quantities includes understanding the values that the quantity can take on. Very large values and fractional values are the most difficult to understand and need special attention. Working with fractional values demands that we pay particular attention to the referent unit of a fraction.

- Quantities can be compared additively or multiplicatively, depending on the nature of the situation. Students should recognize whether a situation is additive or multiplicative in nature and know how to respond.

- A multiplicative comparison of two quantities results in a ratio, which is itself a quantity.

- A ratio can be thought of as a measure of some attribute.

- A rate is a ratio of quantities that change, but without changing the value of the ratio. Equal ratios represent the same rate.

This course includes work in conventional numerical mathematics but in slightly unconventional ways. There is a strong focus on number sense, on coming to understand numbers, and on being able to operate on them in nonstandard ways. Students (and teachers) who have taken this course report that they found the mental computation and estimation, the examination of children's work, the different approach to fractions and ratios, and the focus on quantitative reasoning to be extremely helpful.

Particular attention needs to be paid to the development of quantitative reasoning. Some students may at first be resistant to the focus but usually they come to see the advantages of what we call quantitative analysis. Students must be helped to understand how to identify the quantities within a situation and the relationships among the quantities. This is often best done through a diagram or drawing of some sort. Throughout this course you will see many drawings representing situations. It is not sufficient for the instructor to produce a diagram or drawing to help students make sense of a problem. Students must learn to do it themselves. In particular, students should be able to explain their drawings conceptually, not just as a report of the steps they did. Having students put their diagrams on the board for discussion by the class is often very useful, but of course must be done sensitively so that the students do not feel that their work is inadequate or is being ridiculed.

Your Students   This information may be useful to you if you have never taught preservice or practicing elementary teachers. Their mathematics backgrounds and confidence levels cover an enormous range. Some should be math majors; others are still struggling with fractions and decimal points. Some welcome any challenging problem; others feel that they should be expected only to imitate worked-out examples. As with most required mathematics classes, your toughest job will be to convince the "weaker" students that they can indeed succeed and to inspire the indifferent students to love and admire mathematics and mathematical thinking.

Sometimes students are expecting a methods-of-teaching course. Although there are indirect messages about teaching methods built into the materials—for example, some work in small groups, hands-on manipulatives, explanations as a part of mathematics—the concern here is building *understanding* of numbers and quantities, *not of how to teach* numbers and quantity topics. At the same time, we encourage you to model some of the pedagogy in which you hope your students will engage as teachers. It is difficult to enact a pedagogy that you have never experienced.

Prospective teachers too often feel that work with whole numbers, decimal numbers, and fractions is review for them. They will find, however, that there is much to learn here that is new and far more than review. Many of the ideas will be quite new and challenging for them. An underlying theme is to provide those who are teaching or who are preparing to teach opportunities to reconceptualize their notions about numbers, operations, and quantities.

Students with a fear of mathematics, particularly of work with fractions, will find that they can increase their mathematical comfort level by developing good number sense, particularly in Chapters 5 and 6. The instructor should emphasize reasoning and number sense throughout the text. One way to do this is invite students to compute mentally before using calculators and written algorithms. If you are comfortable facilitating this discussion, follow up by having them briefly share their mental computation strategies. It doesn't take much time and you then can allocate less time to this in Chapter 5 and subsequent chapters.

Assumed Background   Students are expected to have had prior courses at least through secondary-school algebra, and some skill in arithmetic operations on whole numbers, fractions, and decimals. This course is intended to build on this background. However, some of your students enter the course without this prior knowledge. If students have forgotten some of the arithmetic they should know, *Appendix A: A Review of Some Rules* can be referred to for review purposes. Because it is intended for review, it provides procedural knowledge that can be built upon in this course and helps students overcome some anxiety about not remembering arithmetic. Be sure to point this appendix out to your students.

Problem Solving   Both routine and nonroutine problems can be found throughout the text and the Learning Exercises. Problems beyond practice permeate the course. In particular, the ideas in *Reasoning with Numbers and Quantities* lay the groundwork for helping students to think more deeply about applied mathematical situations and to become effective in analyzing them and solving related problems. When approaching a new mathematical situation, good problem solvers will analyze the quantities and relationships between quantities that are embedded in the situation—even if only on a subconscious level. This focus on thinking about the quantities involved in a situation—what we call performing a "quantitative analysis"—is what allows one to identify the mathematical relationships in the situation and decide which quantities are relevant. Understanding a mathematical situation deeply is, in fact, understanding the quantitative relationships embedded in that situation. It is this understanding that allows one to reason further about a situation and, in the context of problem solving, determine the appropriate operations to perform.

Good problem solvers often come to understand a problem quantitatively without even realizing it, but analyzing the quantitative structure of an applied mathematical situation is a strategy that needs to be made explicit to many students because it is something that they are not accustomed to doing. Poor problem solvers have a tendency to worry about the *numerical values* that are given in the problem without paying attention to the quantities that these values are attached to and end up "searching" for operations to perform (often through the use of key words or by looking at the size and type of numbers in the problem). They do not really try to make sense of the problem, perhaps because they are not even aware that they should.

Thinking about the quantities and relationships between quantities in an applied mathematical situation is not only something that many students have difficulty with, but it is something that they frequently do not even try in the first place! Instructors are sometimes surprised at how much students struggle as they begin to try to really understand a mathematical situation quantitatively for the first time. The issues and ideas raised in the work with quantities will be quite new to them, and they often have a strong tendency to fall back into their old, comfortable patterns of focusing on numerical values and searching for operations. In this course, we try to provide the instructor with as much information as possible regarding the difficulties that students frequently encounter so that the instructor will be prepared to help them in their struggles.

Technology and Other Tools

Calculators   The use of calculators in schools and the role of traditional algorithms will likely come up. Prospective teachers sometimes have strong opinions about issues, but these opinions can often be uninformed and have an emotional component. It is important that any issues be discussed and that prospective teachers begin to reason through them. There are times when calculators are inappropriate, such as in the sections on estimation and mental computation. Instructors can help students understand when and when not to use a calculator. Calculator use in elementary school is discussed in the student (and instructor) text materials.

Video clips   We include a set of twelve video clips that were developed for the Integrating Mathematics and Pedagogy (IMAP) project at San Diego State University. Each is from an interview with one or more students doing mathematics. Viewers are often surprised and impressed with the variety of types of reasoning students use. We have found these clips to be highly motivational. *Appendix A* contains information, commentary, and discussion or reflection questions for these video clips. Together with the written examples of student thinking, they go a long way toward convincing prospective teachers that they must know mathematics well to be able to understand the reasoning of their students and to build on that understanding during instruction.

Software   We recommend that students visit various Web sites that are recommended in the exercises, particularly the applets from *Illuminations* (http://illuminations.nctm.org) and from the Virtual Library (http://nlvm.usu.edu/en/nav) for many activities and lessons relevant to this course. Particular applets from *Illuminations* are cited in the Learning Exercises.

Manipulatives   Concrete materials that help students visualize and understand mathematical concepts are used in most elementary schools. Prospective teachers also find them useful in building their own understandings. The primary ones used here are pattern blocks and multibase blocks. They can be ordered on many Web sites that cater to school mathematics: ETA Cuisenaire at http://www.etacuisenaire.com, Didax at http://www.didax.com, and EAI at http://www.eaieducation.com are but a few of such companies. Instructors find that having some pieces to display can be useful during instruction. In the back of the book there are masters for these manipulatives if you do not have commercial ones available.

Testing   Most instructors will use standard quizzes or tests as at least part of their evaluation of students. An assortment of items with answers, used by our instructors and colleagues at other universities, is included in the Test Bank. On tests, we try always to include at least one item, and preferably more, requiring that the student give an explanation.

Timeline   There is a great deal to learn in *Reasoning about Numbers and Quantities*. In some cases, it may not be possible to use all the sections. Here is a suggested timeline if these chapters are used in a 15-week course:

1   Reasoning about Quantities (1 week)

Spend only the first week on this chapter. There will be more work later on undertaking quantitative analysis. The section on the metric system is optional because it is treated in *Reasoning about Shapes and Measurement*. It appears here only because metric terms are used throughout Part I.

2   Numeration Systems (1 week)

CAUTION: Using bases other than 10 is new for some students, and they will want to spend more time on this chapter. However, the content here is not as important as content in future sections, and you should be sure to preserve time for that content. Assure the students that the purpose of work with different bases is to come to a better understanding of what a base system is, and a better understanding of our own base-ten system. In this case, we recommend that you test students only on very simple calculations in other bases and that they be told of this decision.

3   Understanding Whole Number Operations   (1.5 weeks)

This is a long chapter. Much of sections 3.2, 3.4, and 3.5 can be assigned as reading, but deserves class discussion. Sections 3.3 and 3.6 are particularly important. The work of elementary school students in these sections often amazes prospective teachers. By examining children's thinking, they often come to realize that knowing just one way to do things is not sufficient for teaching.

4   Some Conventional Ways of Computing   (0.5–1 week at most)

Make sure that your students understand the traditional algorithms for computing with whole number and decimals. They probably need to consider long forms of algorithms before they can understand our traditional abbreviated ways of computing. The same will be true for their own students.

5   Using Numbers in Sensible Ways (1 week)

Most students often have very little number sense, and this chapter will help them develop it further. The section on scientific notation is optional.

6   Meanings for Fractions and
7   Computing with Fractions (4 weeks)

Many of your students dread fractions because they don't understand them. These two chapters deserve time. It is vitally important that, as teachers, they understand fractions and how to use them.

8   Multiplicative Comparisons and Proportional Reasoning and
9   Ratios, Rates, Proportions, and Percents (2–3 weeks)

There is much that is new here, and it is crucial for teachers to understand the type of reasoning that is the backbone of these sections.

10 Expanding Our Number System   (0.5–1 week)

Sections 10.5 and 10.6 are not required of elementary teachers in most states. The other sections will require about two days: introducing big ideas of signed numbers, models, and adding and subtracting signed numbers. Don't neglect having the students read 10.2 and 10.7 regarding children's thinking. If time permits, spend one to two classes on the last two sections.

11 Number Theory (1–3 weeks)

Students need to know the terms in Section 1, prime factorization, GCF, and LCM at least.

Courses for middle school teachers should allow a quicker pace and the use of all parts of the chapters.

Instructor Notes for Chapter 1: Reasoning About Quantities

INSTRUCTOR NOTE 1: OVERVIEW OF CHAPTER 1

This first chapter introduces quantitative reasoning. The idea of quantities and their values is interwoven into the other chapters, some more explicitly than others. The following sections are included in this chapter.

1.1 *Ways of Thinking About Solving Story Problems.* In this section, we motivate a need to use more than key words to determine an operation for solving story problems. Rather, one needs to undertake some quantitative reasoning. A quantity is described as something that can be measured or counted. The value of a quantity is the count or measure of the quantity.

1.2 *Quantitative Analysis.* This is the heart of the work with quantities. Students must identify quantities and their relationships in problem situations before assigning values. They will then often know what to do with the values.

1.3 *Values of Quantities.* This section contains a discussion of how values can be expressed. Different systems of measurement are shown for this purpose.

1.4 *Issues for Learning.* Quantitative reasoning can be used to make sense of situations, and using drawings to represent situations is a fundamental aspect of this.

1.5 *Check Yourself.* This section, as with all Check Yourself sections at the end of chapters, provides a summary of the chapter.

Part of Section 1.3 deals with the metric system. There is a more thorough treatment of the metric system in *Reasoning about Shapes and Measurement.* We include a short discussion of metric units here to justify using these terms in Part I.

Students do not have answers provided for the activities and discussions, but the margin notes for instructors provide many of the answers or other useful information. If students are to learn from the activities and discussions, the instructor needs to bring closure to each class discussion and activity in some way. Most of the time, this can occur by asking groups to share their work. If time does not permit, you may want to display the answers with a projection system to show to students as the activity is ending.

INSTRUCTOR NOTE 1.1A *Discussion 2: Easy to Quantify?*

Students may interpret the phrase "easy to quantify" in different ways. For example, some students may feel that infant mortality rate is easy to quantify because it is not difficult to identify the quantities one would use to measure it (deaths per so many births). Others, however, might feel that it is difficult to quantify because collecting information about all infants may not be an easy task. Some may feel that human intelligence is easy to quantify because IQ tests can be administered rather easily, while others may feel that an IQ test (or any other test) is not a reliable measure of intelligence and that intelligence is therefore difficult to quantify. Some may say that the livability of a city is not quantifiable, but news media report the ten most livable cities using a number of quantities such as days of sunshine, low crime rate, cost of living, low unemployment, and other such quantities. You may want to discuss these different interpretations of the phrase "easy to quantify" as they arise in class discussion and then answer the question according to these different interpretations. The point is that one must be able to quantify an attribute or quality before it can be measured.

INSTRUCTOR NOTE 1.2A An instructional suggestion for beginning quantitative analyses

We have found that giving students a relatively simple word problem to work on for a few minutes before beginning Section 1.2 can be extremely useful. The hot dog problem in Activity 1 is used for this purpose. This problem may seem simple, even trivial, but we have found that some students take the numbers in the problem and start operating on them without really understanding the problem. With a drawing they are able to solve it. The drawing can be quite simple and can lead students to find the ratio of $2\frac{3}{4}$ and $4\frac{1}{4}$. At this point you may want to have students read Section 1.4, Issues for Learning, and then discuss what is said there about solving word problems and about how drawings help in understanding problems.

The sisters and brothers problem, introduced in Activity 2, is next considered.

> Two women, Alma and Beatrice, each had a brother, Alfred and Benito, respectively. The two women argued about which one stood taller over her brother. It turned out that Alma won the argument by a 17-centimeter difference. Alma was 186 cm tall. Alfred was 87 cm tall. Beatrice was 193 cm tall. How tall was Benito?

Give students five or ten minutes (either individually or in groups) to work on this activity before discussing the solution given in the text. Have a few students or groups share what they tried. Some may approach the problem with algebra, but algebra should be downplayed since the problems in this course require only understanding the relationships and *not* algebraic sophistication. Others may make very little progress at all. The idea is just for students to become familiar with the problem and to struggle for a bit before discussing the solution that is given in the text. Praise any attempts at making a drawing.

The goal is for students to learn to see quantitative analysis as the process of coming to a complete understanding of a mathematical situation. When students imagine what's going on in a problem and can describe the situation fully, they are in effect analyzing the problem quantitatively. This focus shifts the students' thinking away from simply searching for operations in order to get an answer.

To help students come to understand the quantities embedded in a situation and how they are related to each other, you may have them engage in a number of different activities, as illustrated here: making a list of the quantities involved, making appropriate drawings that clarify the problem situation, acting out the situation, or trying to describe one's understanding to another. As students engage in these activities, it is important that they do not undertake them merely as independent tasks; that is, they shouldn't just see them as a list of things they are supposed to do for their own sakes. These activities are all part of the process of coming to understand a situation deeply, and the focus should always be on how what is being done helps to improve that understanding. A drawing, for example, may reveal important relationships among the quantities. When one is able to develop a solid quantitative understanding of the situation, a path to the solution follows almost naturally.

These early sections provide a basis for much of the work that students will do throughout *Part I: Reasoning about Numbers and Quantities*. It is important to take sufficient time in class to discuss the value of gaining a thorough understanding of a problem. Students should realize that they are expected to make sense of the mathematics they are doing and that finding answers to problems follows naturally from that understanding.

INSTRUCTOR NOTE 1.2B The problem in *Down the Drain*

Note the assumption in Activity 3 that the tub will not spill over before the plug is pulled.

Make sure that students identify such implicit quantities as

- the volume of water in the tub (a varying quantity, increasing for 4 seconds, decreasing until empty),

- the initial amount of water in the tub (0 gal because the problem states that the tub is empty),

- the amount of water in the tub 4 minutes after the faucet is opened (4.5 gal/min × 4 min = 18 gal),

- the rate of change of the water in the tub after the 4 minutes of fill (6.3 gal/min – 4.5 gal/min = 1.8 gal/min),

- the amount of time it takes to fill the tub (can't know without knowing size of tub),

- the amount of time it takes to empty the tub (this could be the question to be solved here: 18 gal decreasing by 1.8 gal per minute would require 10 minutes, plus the 4 minutes before the drain was opened is 14 minutes),

Here are some additional discussion questions for this activity that you can use to help students think about and analyze the situation:

- Does the size of the tub matter?

- In what cases will the size of the tub matter?

- Does the water level matter?

- What if the rates of flow were the same for the problem?

- What if the time after which the drain is opened is increased? decreased?

- Etc. (Be creative!)

As you ask additional questions like the ones above (and thus alter the original problem), it may be useful for students to draw and compare the qualitative graphs of some of these new situations. A qualitative graph, like the one below, does not have numbers on the axis, only labels. Then a sketch of the situation is made to indicate what is happening, in this case, over time.

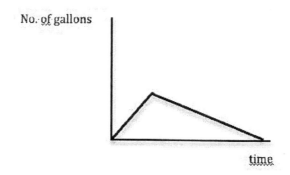

INSTRUCTOR NOTE 1.2C The triathlon problem (Learning Exercise 6)

The solution to this problem is in the Instructor Answers. Initially, students struggle with a number of issues when they try to list the relevant quantities in a situation:

- Some students may still be unclear on the difference between the value of a quantity and the quantity itself.

- Many students will not be specific in their labeling of quantities. For example, students will list things like "speed" as quantities without stating a specific speed, such as Bea's running speed. When students do this, it is possible that they are simply being sloppy with their language. However, it might also indicate that they do not yet understand the concept of a quantity and that they really do not have a specific speed in mind at all nor a notion of speed itself as a valid quantity.

- Students often have difficulty naming quantities for which values are not given, such as the time from the beginning of the triathlon to the time Bea catches up with Aña. Students also have a tendency to believe that if the value of a quantity is not given or not known, then that quantity is not important to the situation.

- Students frequently have difficulty dealing with quantities that vary over time, such as the distance between Aña and Bea. Not only do students have difficulty visualizing these quantities, but they also tend to not even recognize them as quantities in the first place because they think of a quantity as something with a fixed value.

This last point deserves some attention. A period of enlightenment often occurs for students when they are able to visualize in their minds the way in which a quantity changes over time. Take, for example, the following excerpt from a class discussion of the triathlon problem, after a student (John) raised the issue of the "distance between Aña and Bea" as a quantity:

Student: I think what [John's] conceptualization did for me…Before it was just, "Hey, when do they catch up and then I'm done!" But when he said it his way, I saw it as a problem in motion. I saw Aña catching up, and then I saw her passing. (As she says this, the student acts out the problem by holding up her right index finger and moving it slowly to the right and then holding up her left index finger and moving it faster to the right so that it "overtakes" her right index finger.) Then I saw the quantity decrease (now holding up her hands with palms facing each other and bringing them slowly together), then I saw it go up (now moving her hands slowly apart). I started seeing a curve in here that I didn't see in my mind until he said his question...

Observer: That's fascinating that the introduction of this quantity changed the way that you actually viewed the whole situation.

Student: Yeah, I could visualize it.

This student's conceptualization of the problem changed as she began to think about varying quantities. The problem became "active" to her as she thought about "distance between Aña and Bea" as a valid quantity. There are different ways for students to practice visualizing varying quantities: making a qualitative graph in which the axes are labeled but there is no detailed numerical scale, drawing a picture, enacting the situation by having students play the roles of Aña and Bea, or having students describe their thinking. You may want to include some of these activities in the class discussion.

Some students may solve this problem algebraically by saying that when the distance between the two girls is 0, then $225t = 600 + 200t$ and solving gives $t = 24$ seconds, which can be used to answer the questions. Although this solution is not wrong, try to avoid algebraic solutions because these problems can be solved without algebra, and when they are, they indicate a solid understanding of the problem, the type of understanding needed for teaching. (The triathlon problem is revisited algebraically in Section 14.2.)

INSTRUCTOR NOTE 1.3A   Measurement units

This section touches briefly on ideas of measurement, namely, that the value of a given quantity depends on the unit that we use to measure that quantity, and that we have reasons for choosing the units of measurement that we do (even if the reason is just for convenience). These points may seem obvious, but to many students they are not. However, we suggest that you should not spend much time on this section. A discussion in one class is all the time that can be afforded in the usual course. (A fuller treatment of measurement is in *Part III: Reasoning about Shapes and Measurement*.) We suggest that you not test students on metric units and that they be told that. We will refer to metric units throughout the course, and students should have an awareness of what they mean. It was our intention to include only enough information about measurement to justify our use of metric measurement terms throughout. If you feel that this treatment is not necessary for your students, you can omit this section.

Instructor Notes for Chapter 2: Numeration Systems

INSTRUCTOR NOTE 2: OVERVIEW OF CHAPTER 2

The following sections are included in this chapter.

2.1 *Ways of Expressing Values of Quantities.* This brief introductory section provides some background on historical ways of recording counting, setting the stage for our Hindu-Arabic place-value system of symbolizing numbers.

2.2 *Place Value.* Place value is a "big idea" in the elementary school curriculum. All operational procedures with whole numbers and decimal numbers are based on place value. This section introduces place value, a topic that will continue through several chapters.

2.3 *Bases Other Than Ten.* Work in different bases appears here because exposure to other bases clarifies the meaning of place value, which until now is so intricately intertwined in students' minds with our base-ten system that they cannot distinguish between base ten and the broader idea of place value.

2.4 *Operations in Different Bases.* A little of this goes a long way. Again, the point is to understand the role of place value in the algorithms we use for arithmetic operations. There is no need to develop efficiency using bases other than ten, so doing more than a few problems is unnecessary.

2.5 *Issues for Learning: Understanding Place Value.* As with all Issues for Learning sections, this section offers a chance to reflect on topics from the chapter.

2.6 *Check Yourself.*

The work in this chapter is crucial for developing a deep understanding of *place value* and the manner in which place value depends on the ability to use *units* (or *ones*) when writing numbers, particularly, how units are grouped in order to write numbers and calculate. Using bases other than ten can help teachers understand the role of grouping units when writing numbers and when calculating. In base ten, we say that 532 represents 5 groups of one hundred (or 10^2), 3 groups of ten, and 2 ones. But this same number, in base eight, would mean 5 groups of sixty-four (or 8^2), 3 groups of eight, and 2 ones. (Actually, in base eight we could use 10 to represent eight, so there would be 5 groups of 10^2, where the symbol 10 represents one eight and 10^2 represents eight^2).

In an interesting article, the mathematician Ron Ahroni, who took time off to teach in an elementary school, tells about what he learned from this experience. Some excerpts from his 2005 article titled "Helping Children Learn Mathematics" are below.

> But what surprised me most was that I learned mathematics. Actually, a lot of it. This would not be the case had I gone to teach in a high school. The mathematical concepts there are known to a professional mathematician. In elementary school, it's the teaching of the most basic principles

that counts—the nature of numbers, the meaning of the arithmetical operations, the principles of the decimal system. About these, it is rare for a mathematician to stop and think.

Elementary mathematics is structured in the same way as high-level mathematics. Namely, it is layered. Each layer is built on top of the previous one. Just as in a complicated proof, the order in which the components are put together is important.

The difference is that the layers in elementary school are those at the bottom of the tower. The structures that are built are not tall. But, as if to compensate, there can be difficulties. They are often hidden, as if they were built under water, meaning that it is not always easy to realize what they are. Elementary mathematics is usually not sophisticated, but it is deep.

The meaning of an operation is the link between it and reality, the real world operation corresponding to it. The calculation is finding the result. But again, there is something that is not often realized: It is not really finding the result. It is finding the *decimal representation* of the result. Ancient man, when adding eight and four, drew eight lines beside four lines, and represented the result by twelve lines—there is no "calculation" here, and ancient man did not have to send his children to school to learn this. In "8 + 4 = 12," on the other hand, there is calculation, and an invisible operation is performed: that of collecting ten units into one "10." *And of course there is also the "place value" writing of the number, another non-trivial principle. Thus, understanding the algorithms for calculation is tantamount to deep understanding of the decimal system.* (Italics not in the original.) (See http://www.aft.org/pubs-reports/american_educator/issues/fall2005/aharoni.htm for the entire article.)

Our base-ten system of expressing numbers is our *decimal* system. "Deci" comes from the Latin word for "ten." Of course, teachers must have a deep understanding of our place-value system before they can teach it well. For most, this understanding develops when it is generalized to other place-value systems, the topic of this chapter.

We assume in this chapter that students know how to read and write numbers, but there may be some who do not. One way to check on this is to ask them to write the number corresponding to 3.6 million dollars. Some will write $3,000,000.6 rather than $3,600,000. Also, note that Roman numerals are introduced only in the Learning Exercises of Section 2.1.

INSTRUCTOR NOTE 2.1A Working with bases other than ten

This section provides an introduction to working with bases other than 10 (or ten, as the notes have it, since the symbol "10" does not mean this many: x x x x x x x x x x, in other bases). Other than references to the difficulty of calculating in some old numeration systems, there is no computation in nonbasimal numbers in this section. Point out the conventional nature of this material (and how we express number ideas), just as what measurement units we use is a convention.

More historical information on numeration systems is provided. Emphasize again that *how* we write numbers is a convention. The distinction between *number* (an idea) and *numeral* (a written sign for the idea) is not emphasized here, but you may want to point it out. The idea of two-ness stays the same, but what written marks we make, or what words we say, to communicate the idea of two are conventions that have changed over the years and from society to society.

INSTRUCTOR NOTE 2.1B An example of numbers without a base system

The reference to the Papua New Guineans is from Saxe, 1981 (see the references at the end of the chapter). For his research study he visited a tribe that had only recently been discovered by the outside world and whose members were unfamiliar with modern ways of living, including present-day ways of expressing and operating on numbers. Their counting system, dependent on pointing to body parts, extended only as far as twenty-two (but of course they did not use this name). When a small trading store was set up in their village, some found that their counting system was not large enough to accommodate buying and selling, and people developed innovative ways of extending their number system. A question such as "In general, what influence does cross-cultural commerce have on expressing values of quantities?" might be worth asking.

INSTRUCTOR NOTE 2.1C The history of numeration

One follow-up to this section, for possible additional credit, could be based on a student pursuing one or more of the old numeration systems. This could range from a relatively short encyclopedia exercise to a longer project. Some history of mathematics books are organized so that it is relatively easy to find material on numeration systems, and some books devoted largely to the history of numeration are Menninger, Karl. (1969). *Number Words and Number Systems.* Cambridge, MA: MIT Press; and Cajori, Florian. (1974). *A History of Mathematical Notations.* LaSalle, IL: Open Court.

INSTRUCTOR NOTE 2.2A A misconception dealing with the decimal point

This paragraph is extremely important because it addresses the serious misconception that a decimal point, rather than the ones place, is the "focus" of a decimal number. Using coins helps students understand how we can name the same number in different ways. Thus, the number of dollars, $34.56 can be thought of in terms of dollars, in terms of the number of "ten dollars" in this amount, the number of dimes, and the number of pennies: 3.456 tens, 34.56 ones, 345.6 tenths (dimes), and 3456 hundredths (pennies). Thinking about numbers in this way is unusual, but understanding this way of thinking about numbers is essential to understanding place value.

INSTRUCTOR NOTES 2.3A Teaching *Bases Other Than Ten*

This section and the next section introduce content that is very new to most prospective and practicing teachers. Work with different bases is motivated by the fact that few people have a good understanding of our base-ten system, and the manner in which we use it in calculating. This is true, too, of prospective teachers, and sometimes of practicing teachers (c.f., Thanheiser, 2009, in the *Journal for Research in Mathematics Education*). Some of your students will struggle in coming to understand work with different bases, but the struggle is worthwhile if they begin to understand, in a deeper way, what a place-value system has to offer. Because base ten is taken for granted, we find that using different bases forces an awareness of how a base system works. Most computational errors made with whole numbers and decimal numbers on the part of elementary students is due to a lack of understanding of base ten. If teachers have a solid grounding in working with base systems, they are more apt to understand and be able to correct these errors.

However, care should be taken in allocating time to working with base systems other than ten. Students will want to spend more time on this topic because it is so unfamiliar. Remind them that the point is *not* to become fluent in another base, *but to help them understand the importance of our own base-ten system and why children struggle to understand it.* Only base ten is taught in the vast majority of elementary schools. Again, too much time spent here will mean too little time to spend later on topics they will actually be teaching.

Some applets from the *Illuminations* Web site are recommended in this section, and students will benefit from using them.

INSTRUCTOR NOTE 2.3B Multibase Blocks

Multibase blocks were first made of wood and were quite expensive. They are available in base 4, base 5, base 6, and base 10. Base-ten blocks are now more readily available in plastic and even in cardboard. They are useful in coming to understand standard algorithms. Before using the sketches, discuss what each block looks like: one small cube or block; 10 cubes or blocks glued together make one "long," 10 longs glued together make a "flat," and 10 flats glued together make a "large block." Discuss with students what these blocks would look like using bases other than 10. In the instructional materials in Appendix D, you will find templates for cutting out two-dimensional "blocks" in bases two, four, five, and ten.

INSTRUCTOR NOTE 2.3C A place-value game

A popular activity in the primary grades is called Race for a Flat. Using base-ten materials, children take turns throwing a die or two, noting the dots on top, taking that many units, and then trading for longs (tens) if they can. The winner is the student who can first trade ten longs for a flat (a hundred). Unless a recording, or at least oral statements, of numerals or words (e.g., had 29, rolled 3, then had 29 + 3, or 32) accompany the play, there may be no link to work with numerals or number words. Notice that this game can be revealing to an observant teacher: If ten dots are rolled, are the child who takes a long and the child who counts out ten ones at the same level of understanding? You may want to try the game with your class.

INSTRUCTOR NOTE 2.4A Modeling a subtraction problem using drawings of blocks

In this section, we introduce operations in different bases. The multibase blocks can be used to clarify the place-value basis for the algorithms. Drawings can also be used to represent the operations. At least one problem should be modeled for the students. It is *very* important to show what is happening with the traditional algorithm at each step along the way. For example, you could model 124 − 65 by following these steps, presented here via a drawing, using the small block to represent one unit.

Make sure you always define the unit. Consider this problem in base seven also. Step 1 represents the problem.

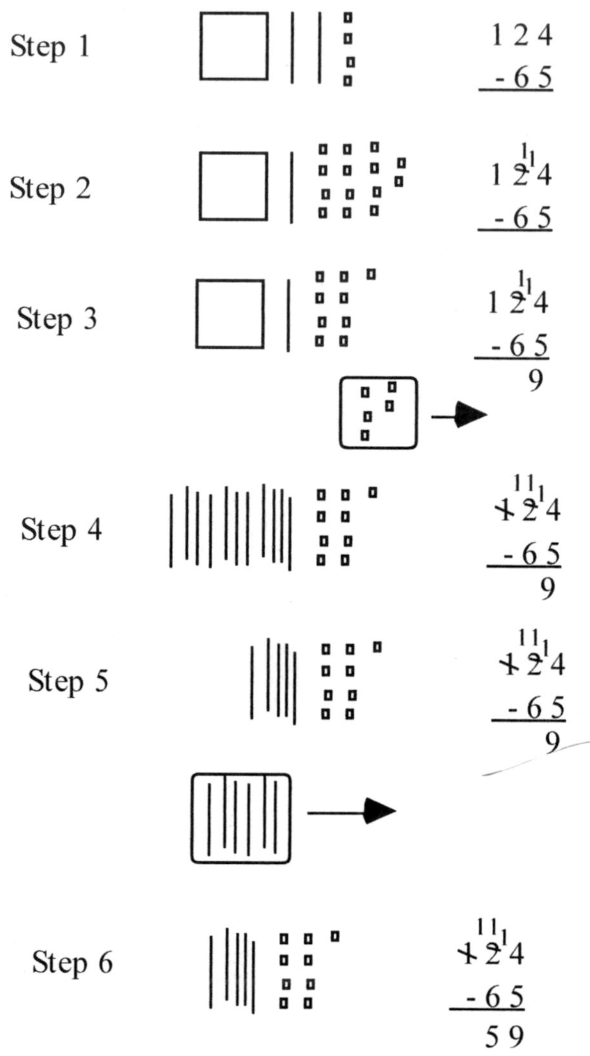

Step 1

$$1\ 2\ 4$$
$$-\ 6\ 5$$

Step 2

$$1\ \overset{1}{\cancel{2}}\ 4$$
$$-\ 6\ 5$$

Step 3

$$1\ \overset{1}{\cancel{2}}\ 4$$
$$-\ 6\ 5$$
$$9$$

Step 4

$$\overset{1\ 1}{\cancel{1}\ \cancel{2}}\ 4$$
$$-\ 6\ 5$$
$$9$$

Step 5

$$\overset{1\ 1}{\cancel{1}\ \cancel{2}}\ 4$$
$$-\ 6\ 5$$
$$9$$

Step 6

$$\overset{1\ 1}{\cancel{1}\ \cancel{2}}\ 4$$
$$-\ 6\ 5$$
$$5\ 9$$

What would change if this problem was in base seven rather than base ten?

Step 1, in which the 124 is represented, is the same in both base ten and base seven. Note that in neither case can 5 be subtracted from 4 (without using negative numbers).

In Step 2, exchange one long for units. In base seven, there would be seven additional ones rather than the ten additional ones shown here.

In Step 3, five ones would be removed, leaving nine ones in base ten. In base seven, six ones would remain.

In Step 4, the flat is replaced by ten longs to make it possible to remove six longs. In base

Instructor Notes for Chapter 3: Understanding Whole Number Operations

INSTRUCTOR NOTE 3: OVERVIEW OF CHAPTER 3

This is a rather long chapter, consisting of eight sections. All sections provide important background for elementary teachers. The study of quite sophisticated children's thinking in some sections surprises many and can be motivating as prospective teachers begin to realize how much more they need to know to teach mathematics well. None of it should be omitted.

The sections in this chapter include:

3.1 *Additive Combinations and Comparisons.* Quantitative reasoning ideas are used to introduce additive combinations and comparisons.

3.2 *Ways of Thinking about Addition and Subtraction.* Different types of situations (take away, comparison, missing addend) that call for addition or subtraction are described with examples given.

3.3 *Children's Ways of Adding and Subtracting.* The examples here of students reasoning about addition and subtraction is an eye-opener for many prospective and even practicing teachers.

3.4 *Ways of Thinking about Multiplication.* Situations calling for multiplication (repeated addition, array, part of amount, fundamental counting principle) are described, with examples.

3.5 *Ways of Thinking about Division.* Situations calling for division (repeated subtraction, sharing equally, missing factor) are described, with examples.

3.6 *Children Find Products and Quotients.* More examples of children's reasoning are displayed and discussed, this time dealing with ways of multiplying and dividing before formal instruction on algorithms.

3.7 *Issues for Learning: Developing Number Sense.*

3.8 *Check Yourself.*

INSTRUCTOR NOTE 3.1A Additive combinations and additive comparisons

The terms introduced in this section, "additive combinations" and "additive comparisons," are used very deliberately so that they can be contrasted in later sections with multiplicative combinations and comparisons. As a preview of what is to come, the distinctions are as follows: When quantities are *combined additively*, they are joined together, so the appropriate arithmetic operation is usually addition. When two quantities are *compared additively*, we are often interested in finding the difference of their values, and so the appropriate arithmetic operation is usually subtraction. But when two quantities are *compared multiplicatively*, we look at the ratio of their values. Quantities are *combined multiplicatively* in situations where we develop compound units such as person-hours, or when the situation calls for the fundamental counting principle to be used.

Recognizing a situation as multiplicative rather than additive and then reasoning about the situation multiplicatively rather than additively does not usually happen until children are in the middle grades, and even then there is a gradual development of understanding the difference between additive and multiplicative reasoning. The transition from reasoning additively in all situations to reasoning multiplicatively when that is appropriate is at the heart of the development of proportional reasoning, the "big idea" of the middle grades.

Focusing on what is happening with the quantities—that is, reasoning quantitatively—is much different from focusing on the *values* of the quantities, a focus that is arithmetic in nature. Reasoning quantitatively makes a meaning-based transition from arithmetic to algebra possible because the quantitative analysis of algebraic story problems becomes simply an extension of the quantitative analysis of arithmetic story problems.

The drawing could look like this, and the solution is at the side.

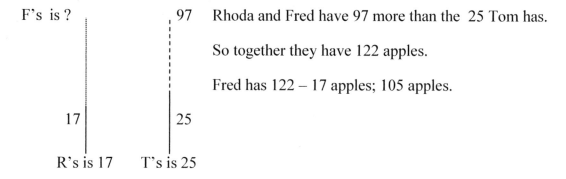

F's is ?   97   Rhoda and Fred have 97 more than the 25 Tom has.

So together they have 122 apples.

Fred has 122 – 17 apples; 105 apples.

17   25

R's is 17   T's is 25

INSTRUCTOR NOTE 3.1B Ways to think about *Activity 2: It's Just a Game*

The purpose of this section is to provide practice in analyzing the quantitative structure of complex additive situations. The situations are complex not because of the operations needed to solve them, but because of the number of quantities and quantitative relationships they contain. Situations with simple quantitative structures do not sustain the level of discussion that is needed to become skillful at analyzing problems, thus the choice of complex situations and sometimes unrealistic numbers is deliberate.

For example, in the activity *It's Just a Game*, several quantities and relationships need to be kept track of. Students need to see that there are three differences in the situation that are relevant quantities: (1) the difference between Team A's and Opponent A's scores; (2) the difference between Team B's and Opponent B's scores; and (3) the difference between these two differences (which is what the 8 points refer to). Drawing diagrams like the one below can be a powerful way to help students understand the quantitative structure of a complex situation like *It's Just a Game*.

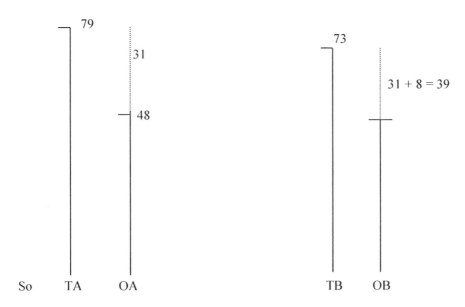

Thus Opponent B scored 73 − 39 = 34 points.

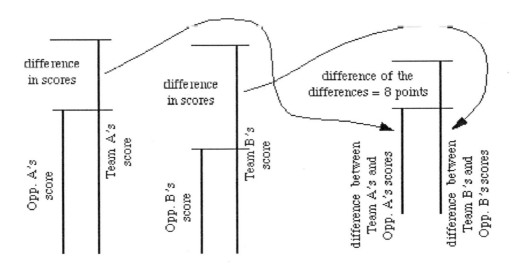

Try to encourage your students to draw diagrams when they are having trouble making sense of a situation. It is doubtful that they will be able to draw diagrams like this one right away. Let them struggle with it for a bit. After discussing some of the diagrams that they have come up with, you may want to present a diagram like this one for discussion.

INSTRUCTOR NOTE 3.1C Notes on Learning Exercises for Section 3.1

Some students may find Problems 1 and 2 strange because they are not "real" problems. The items ask students to describe how they *would* calculate the value of a specific quantity if they knew the values of two other related quantities. Students for whom mathematics consists only of calculations will find these items different and perhaps puzzling. Try not to volunteer too much help. If students ask, encourage them to read and interpret the directions carefully. To generalize 1b: If we know the size of the difference between two quantities and the value of the smaller quantity and we want to know the value of the larger quantity, we have to add the known difference to the smaller quantity.

Encourage students to draw diagrams showing the quantitative relationships in the situations presented in these learning exercises, even if they do not need the diagrams to reason through the problem. Make sure they understand that they should be able to produce the types of diagrams that could be used to help children understand the quantitative structure of these situations.

INSTRUCTOR NOTE 3.2A Rationale for considering children's ways of thinking in a content course

Although these materials are designed for content courses rather than methods courses, we have found that students often ask the question, "What does this have to do with teaching?" Of course, one answer to this question is that in order to teach mathematics, one must first understand the material at a deep level. However, effective teachers must also have some knowledge about the type of reasoning that their students are likely to exhibit. We have found that students often find these sections very motivational because it helps them to see the educational relevance of the mathematics they are learning, and leads them to understand that they must have a better knowledge of what might seem to be so simple: adding and subtracting.

INSTRUCTOR NOTE 3.3A Examples of children's ways of subtracting

Instructors have frequently reported that this section, and other sections or film clips that demonstrate the power of children's reasoning (particularly those who understand place value and operations), have changed the nature of the discourse in the class. All of the methods shown here were actually used, usually by children interviewed in research studies.

This activity will take some preparation. The nine students are second-graders, doing a calculation that is advanced for children in the usual second-grade class. Encourage your students to keep base-ten blocks in mind as they study the children's work. Students 1, 6, and 7 almost certainly understand and have produced their own methods for subtracting: Student 1 by using negative numbers (known probably from playing around on a calculator), Student 6 by taking the numbers apart and using place value understanding, and Student 7 by using the fact that $a - b$ is the same as $(a + c) - (b + c)$, probably discovered (but not symbolized in this way) by playing around with numbers. Students 8 and 9 likely do understand because their algorithms (which are very similar) would not have been formally taught. Basically, they have worked from left to right rather than the traditional right to left and dealt with the numbers rather than just columns of digits. Students 3 and 4 might understand but are more likely to have memorized these methods in school. Student 5 might or might not understand—it is not clear whether the mistake was due to carelessness or lack of understanding. Student 2 clearly does not understand what is taking place and is trying to use a poorly remembered algorithm.

INSTRUCTOR NOTE 3.3B The equal additions method of subtraction

See Activity 6, Question 3. The Equal Addition method used by Student 4 is commonly taught in other countries. If you have a diverse group of students, ask if any have seen or used this method. Someone probably has. The thinking is this: "I can't take 9 from 4, so I will add 10 to both numbers, but in the first number I will add the 10 in the units column, and in the second number I will add the 10 in the tens column. Now I have 14 ones, remove 9 ones, and 5 ones are left. Now I want to take 8 tens from 6 tens, but I can't, so I will add 100 (ten tens) to each number. In the first number I will add it to the tens column, so I have 16 tens. In the second number I will add it to the hundreds column, so I have 1 hundred. Now subtract 8 tens from 16 tens, leaving 8 tens, and subtract 1 hundred from 3 hundreds, leaving 2 hundreds. So 2 hundreds, 8 tens, and 5 ones are left, or 285."

INSTRUCTOR NOTE 3.3C Using children's ways.

Activity 7 asks for the following answers:

1.	8.	9.
438	438	438
− 159	− 159	− 159
− 1	~~300~~	300
− 20	~~280~~	− 20
300	279	280
279		− 1
		279

6. First I take the 100 away from the 400 and that's 300. Then I put the 38 back in and it's 338 − 59. I take the 50 away from the 330, first 30 to 300 then 20 to 280. Then I put the 8 back in and it's 288. Now I take the 9 away, 8 first to 280 then 1 more to 279.

7. It's the same as $439 − 160$ and thats the same as $479 − 200$ and that's 279.

INSTRUCTOR NOTE 3.4A A drawing for a story problem

Here is a drawing, although not to scale, for this *Think about*:

1	1	1	1/2
1	1	1	1/2
1/4	1/4	1/4	1/8

By counting:

$$6 + 2(\tfrac{1}{2}) + 3(\tfrac{1}{4}) + \tfrac{1}{8} = 7\tfrac{7}{8}$$

By multiplying:

$$2\tfrac{1}{4} \times 3\tfrac{1}{2} = \tfrac{63}{8} = 7\tfrac{7}{8}$$

INSTRUCTOR NOTE 3.4B Drawing for a *Think about*

$6 \times \frac{1}{2}$ is 6 halves is 3 $\frac{1}{2}$ of 6 is 3

INSTRUCTOR NOTE 3.4C Multiplication using both repeated addition and part-of-a-quantity

Buying 5.3 pounds of something costing $4.20 per pound can be thought of as buying 5 pounds and then 0.3 pound, so repeated-addition multiplication describes the cost of the 5 pounds (5×4.2) and part-of-an-amount multiplication describes the cost of the 0.3 pound (0.3×4.2). Hence, a multiplication with a mixed-number type as first factor, like the 5.3 in 5.3×4.2, can be interpreted as a mix of repeated-addition and part-of-an-amount multiplications. (The distributive property of multiplication over addition contains this explanation nicely on a purely mathematical basis: $5.3 \times 4.2 = (5 + 0.3) \times 4.2 = (5 \times 4.2) + (0.3 \times 4.2)$.)

Instructor Notes for Chapter 4: Some Conventional Ways of Computing

INSTRUCTOR NOTE 4: OVERVIEW OF CHAPTER 4

This is a short chapter with just three sections:

4.1 *Operating on Whole Numbers and Decimal Numbers.* This section provides students with an opportunity to come to understand the standard algorithms they probably all use.

4.2 *Issues for Learning: The Role of Algorithms.*

4.3 *Check Yourself.*

The chapter begins with a review of conventional algorithms for computing with whole numbers and decimal numbers, but with an emphasis on understanding the algorithms by focusing on place value through the use of place-value materials or drawings. We then, in Section 4.2, discuss the role of standard algorithms in the curriculum. The question of when, or even whether, to teach standard algorithms has been a controversial one. Some educators propose delaying instruction on standard algorithms until after children show their understanding of the operations by using algorithms that are transparent and can eventually lead to understanding standard algorithms. Others believe that time should not be spent on nonstandard algorithms. Knowing the standard algorithms and being able to use them efficiently constitutes the better part of the basic skills children must learn in elementary school. We attempt to open up that discussion of how standard algorithms could be taught.

INSTRUCTOR NOTE 4.1 All of these algorithms generate a quotient of 12.

$$
\begin{array}{r}
15\overline{)180} \\
\underline{75} \quad 5 \\
105 \\
\underline{75} \quad 5 \\
30 \\
\underline{15} \quad 1 \\
15 \\
\underline{15} \quad 1 \\
0 \quad 12
\end{array}
\qquad
\begin{array}{r}
15\overline{)180} \\
\underline{150} \quad 10 \\
30 \\
\underline{30} \quad 2 \\
0 \quad 12
\end{array}
\qquad
\begin{array}{r}
12 \\
15\overline{)180} \\
\underline{180} \\
0
\end{array}
$$

Instructor Notes for Chapter 5: Using Numbers in Sensible Ways

INSTRUCTOR NOTE 5: OVERVIEW OF CHAPTER 5

This chapter focuses on developing number sense. Our premise is that children will not develop good number sense and the ability to use it if it is not modeled in classrooms. This chapter includes these sections:

5.1 *Mental Computation.* Mental computation allows students to become facile with numbers and to develop new realizations about numbers and how they are related to one another. They see that there are many ways at arriving at a correct solution and that which way is better (perhaps better said as "ways are better") depends on the problem itself.

5.2 *Computational Estimation.* Students at first feel uncomfortable with estimation, but with some practice find that it is really not that difficult, and that it is a very handy skill to have. This section helps future teachers realize that there is not just one way to arrive at an answer and that there is not just one correct answer to a problem calling for an estimate.

5.3 *Estimating Values of Quantities.* Estimating counts and measures is a skill worth developing. To begin, one must have some benchmarks that can be applied, such as that the width of a classroom door is usually about 1 meter.

5.4 *Using Scientific Notation for Estimating Values of Very Large and Very Small Quantities.* Describing the size of very large quantities (such as the distance to the sun) can be unwieldy (an understatement) unless scientific notation is used. If you have time constraints, you may wish to skip over this section.

5.5 *Issues for Learning: Mental Computation.*

5.6 *Check Yourself.*

Note: Chapter 6.4 also includes estimation and mental computation using fractions.

Some prospective teachers find this chapter difficult. Many say, "I can't work math in my head—I need a pencil and paper," or they resist estimating because they have spent at least 12 years getting the exact answer using paper and pencil. But we have found with many that when they spend time with mental computation and computational estimation they gain skills that result in renewed confidence in their mathematics.

INSTRUCTOR NOTE 5.1A Becoming good at mental computation

Ask students to do each of these mental calculations in as many ways as possible. Many will try to mentally use the standard algorithm. Even though these are mental exercises, you may wish to record stepwise some of the solutions, so students can study them later. For each, ask if there is an easier way or another way to do the computation mentally. Try to have students introduce many ways themselves. If some good strategies do not arise, tell them you have had other students do them in these ways. For example:

For 152 – 47: subtract 40 to get 112, then subtract 7 to get 105

OR add 3 to each number: 155 – 50 is 105;

OR add 3 to 47 to get to 50, then 100 to get to 150, then 2, for a total of 105 (a missing addend approach to subtraction);

OR any other method you find useful.

For 1000 – 729, note that counting up is much easier than the standard algorithm, even if pencil and paper is available: + 1 to 730, + 70 to 800, + 200 to 1000, so 271.

For 25 × 24, think of 25 as 100/4, so on dividing 24 by 4, get 100 × 6; OR 25 × 4 × 6 is 100 × 6. For 15% of 240, first find 10%, then halve that, and then add the two results.

Mental calculation can at times take advantage of some writing down of numbers, just to keep track of the calculations being done mentally. Mental computation does *not* mean that paper and pencil are not allowed.

This section is a good place to review properties of operations. Many opportunities will occur in the exercises. Help students think more flexibly about numbers and operations. If needed, refer students to *Appendix F: A Review of Some Rules*, to the section on properties of operations.

Properties of operations are considered more formally in Chapter 10 but should be referenced wherever appropriate.

INSTRUCTOR NOTE 5.1B *Discussion 1: Becoming Good at Mental Computation*

Several of these problems in *Becoming Good at Mental Computation* should be discussed by the class. For #2, some students will say this is the same as 20 × 20, but obviously the last digit is 9, not 0. One way is to think of this as 19 × 20 +19 × 1, or 380 + 19, or 399. Be alert to whether students treat this in the conventional U.S. way as nineteen 21s, or as twenty-one 19s (21 × 19). Point out that commutativity of multiplication allows either way, providing another degree of flexibility.

For #3, you are apt to see solutions that beg this question: "Why can you just delete the same number of zeros?"

For #4, students begin the computation without looking carefully at the numbers first. Note the 3476 – 1476.

#5: One way this can be done is to take 100 × 340, then divide by 2, for 17,000.

#6 yields to a distributive property; here are other such exercises if you wish to use them: 17 × 89 + 83 × 89; 88 × 23 + 12 × 23.

INSTRUCTOR NOTE 5.2 Ways that children estimate

Jack's way is easy, efficient, and gives a better estimate than Shawn's way (unless the context calls for an overestimate).
Maria uses a safe, reliable method of rounding one factor up and the other down.
Jimmy shows good number sense that helps him compensate to get close to the exact answer.
Deb shows what Shawn should have done—compensate for his rounding.
Sam's way is mathematically appealing—he is thinking outside the box.

Instructor Notes for Chapter 6: Meanings for Fractions

INSTRUCTOR NOTE 6: OVERVIEW OF CHAPTER 6

We consider here the different ways that fractions are used in the school context. This chapter includes the following sections:

6.1 *Understanding the Meanings of $\frac{a}{b}$.* The fraction $\frac{a}{b}$ is presented as part of a whole and as representing division.

6.2 *Equivalent (Equal) Fractions.* Recognizing when two fractions are equivalent is fundamental to understanding and operating on fractions.

6.3 *Relating Fractions, Decimals, and Percents.* It is relatively easy to write a fraction as a decimal; simply divide the numerator by the denominator. However, writing decimals as fractions is considerably more difficult, and ways of doing so are discussed here. Writing fractions and decimals as percents and vice versa is reviewed.

6.4 *Estimating Fractional Values.* Estimating fractional quantities requires fractional number sense. This section may appear to be a review of sorts, but you may be surprised at how much difficulty many students have with this section. Be sure students spend some time using the fraction applet if it is available to you.

6.5 *Issues for Learning: Understanding Fractions and Decimals.*

6.6 *Check Yourself.*

In the first section, we review the part-whole interpretation for fractions and then briefly discuss the division interpretation. (Ratios are treated in Chapters 8 and 9.) Especially important is the notion of equivalent or equal fractions and using this knowledge to compare nonequivalent forms. The interrelationships among forms of rational numbers—fractions and decimals—are then discussed.

The jury is out on how well students understand even the part-whole interpretation of fractions; if they do, it is often restricted to parts of a pie shape. There is an advantage to using circles rather than rectangles because students often "add on" to a rectangle to arrive at an answer, something that cannot be done with a circle. Both should be used at various times.

Also, there is evidence that shows that many students do not realize that $\frac{a}{b}$ and $a \div b$ are interchangeable. In discussing the part-whole interpretation, be sure to include fractions greater than 1.

These sections are relatively brief, but with long exercise sections. Much of what is to be learned in this chapter is developed through the exercises.

INSTRUCTOR NOTE 6.2A

Prospective teachers can usually identify equivalent fractions but cannot *explain* why two fractions are equivalent. Drawings of both discrete and continuous situations are used to show equivalence. Some elementary teachers like to use paper folding to show equivalence of fractions. One "trick" for folding in thirds, invented by third-grade students (Kieran, 1995), is to fold one side over until you "see halves" at which time the fold is at the one-third mark. Then fold the other side over where the half is seen and that fold will be at the other third mark. They went on to refine this method to fold fifths, by folding both sheets of paper over toward the center until they could "see thirds" and then continued folding at the places where the ends of the sheets met.

In this section, we also consider nonequivalent fractions, and students are asked in the exercises to compare fractions by their size. Using the part-whole notion of fractions, they should be able to compare unit fractions and then use that information to compare fractions that are multiples of unit fractions. Encourage students to compare fractions using their "close to" and part-whole knowledge because that will lead to more sense-making with fractions. "Number Neighbors" in Section 6.4 could be used in Section 6.2. Using a common denominator or decimal approach can lead to a very rote application of rules without increasing one's fraction sense.

Pattern blocks are excellent for showing equivalence (for carefully chosen examples).

INSTRUCTOR NOTE 6.3A

There are three main ideas to this section:

1. The decimal equivalent of every fraction ($\frac{\text{whole number}}{\text{whole number} \circ 0}$) is either a terminating or a repeating decimal. The decimal equivalents terminate when equivalent fractions can be formed such that the denominator is a power of 10, that is, the factors are 2s and 5s. For example, consider $\frac{17}{800}$. 800 factors to $2 \times 2 \times 2 \times 2 \times 2 \times 5 \times 5$. When the numerator and denominator are both multiplied by $5 \times 5 \times 5$, the new denominator is $(2 \times 5)^3$, or 100,000. Consider $\frac{3}{12}$: although 12 has a factor of 3, it matches with the 3 in the numerator, leaving $\frac{1}{4}$, or $\frac{25}{100}$, which is 0.25.

2. When a whole number is divided by 7, the only possible remainders are 0, 1, 2, 3, 4, 5, and 6. But 0 cannot be a remainder, because if it were, the decimal would terminate, contrary to Point 1. Therefore, for $\frac{1}{7}$, or $1 \div 7$, after six (or fewer) places the digits in the quotient must start repeating. For $\frac{3}{11}$, there will be 10 or fewer places before repeating must begin. Such is the case for any fraction in simplest form for which the denominator has factors other than 2 and 5.

3. Every repeating or terminating decimal can be expressed as a fraction, but nonrepeating, nonterminating decimals cannot. For a terminating decimal, simply write the fraction as the decimal is read: 0.3 is three-tenths is $\frac{3}{10}$. A procedure is provided for changing repeating decimals to fractions.

Rational numbers (positive and zero) can then be defined to include either repeating or terminating decimal numbers or fractions in which the numerator and denominator are whole numbers and the denominator is not zero. (Negative rationals are introduced in Chapter 10.) Irrational numbers are defined as nonrepeating, nonterminating decimal numbers.

INSTRUCTOR NOTE 6.3B Finding the fraction for a repeating decimal

The method given in Section 6.3 for finding the fraction for a repeating decimal builds on students' likely knowledge that $0.\overline{3} = \frac{1}{3}$. Another commonly used method is illustrated here, but not in the text, in case you are familiar with it and would like to present it.

Think of $0.\overline{5} = 0.55555...$ and multiply by 10:

$$10 \times 0.\overline{5} \quad = \quad 5.5555... \text{ Then}$$

$$
\begin{aligned}
10 \times 0.\overline{5} &= 5.5555... \\
\underline{1 \times 0.\overline{5}} &= \underline{0.5555...} \quad \text{Subtracting gives} \\
9 \times 0.\overline{5} &= 5 \quad \text{and, on dividing both sides by 9,} \\
0.\overline{5} &= \tfrac{5}{9}
\end{aligned}
$$

This technique works with repeating decimals that have one digit repeating endlessly because multiplying by 10 affects the place value of each digit by 10. The result in effect "moves" the digits one place value to the left and keeps the endless part set up so that the subtraction gives a difference with only a finite number of nonzero digits.

$$
\begin{aligned}
10 \times 18.\overline{2} &= 182.222222222222... \text{ (forever)} \\
\underline{1 \times 18.\overline{2}} &= \underline{18.222222222222... \text{ (forever)}} \\
9 \times 18.\overline{2} &= 164 \quad \text{and on dividing both sides by 9} \\
18.\overline{2} &= \frac{164}{9}
\end{aligned}
$$

Suppose that the repeating block of digits has more than one digit, as in $7.3\overline{456}$:

$$7.3\overline{456} = 7.345656565656... \text{ (forever)}$$
$$10 \times 7.3\overline{456} = 73.456565656565... \text{ (forever)}$$

Multiplying by 10 does not adjust the digits so that the endless parts disappear on subtraction. We need to move the digits *two* place-values:

$$100 \times 7.3\overline{456} = 734.565656565656... \text{ (forever)}$$
$$1 \times 7.3\overline{456} = 7.345656565656... \text{ (forever)}$$

Subtracting gives $99 \times 7.34\overline{56} = 727.22$, or $7.34\overline{56} = \frac{727.22}{99}$. To get the result in the usual $\frac{\text{whole number}}{\text{nonzero whole number}}$ form, $7.34\overline{56} = \frac{727.22 \times 100}{99 \times 100} = \frac{72722}{9900}$.

In general, if the repeating block is n digits long, multiplying the number by 10^n and then subtracting the number will get rid of the infinite part and leave an easily solved equation. Some adjustment, as in the last example, may be necessary to get the result in $\frac{\text{whole number}}{\text{nonzero whole number}}$ form.

INSTRUCTOR NOTE 6.4A Formalizing "close to"

Many students have never been exposed to the type of thinking needed for this activity and do not know how to tell when a fraction is close to 0, $\frac{1}{2}$, or 1. Student-invented "rules" need to be discussed as a class before the exercises are assigned. Examples of responses you should expect from your students: close to 0—when the numerator is a small number; and close to 1—when the numerator and denominator are close to each other. Such responses should be praised, but you also want to make sure that students are not reasoning additively in their responses. For example, most people would agree that $\frac{7}{8}$ is close to 1 but $\frac{2}{3}$ is not close to 1, even though the numerator and denominator differ only by 1 in both cases. (In the video clip of Ally, this type of error is made.) Make sure that students are precise in their answers. For example: close to 0—when the numerator is very small *relative to the denominator*; and close to $\frac{1}{2}$—when the denominator is about twice as large as the numerator or the numerator is about one-half the denominator, etc.

Instructor Notes for Chapter 7: Computing with Fractions

INSTRUCTOR NOTE 7: OVERVIEW OF CHAPTER 7

Computing with fractions is, for many teachers, perhaps the most dreaded part of elementary school instruction. Once again, we try to make sense of the algorithms we use for operating on fractions. The sections in this chapter include the following:

7.1 *Adding and Subtracting Fractions.* An understanding of a fraction as a number, an understanding of equivalent fractions, and an understanding of common denominators are fundamental to addition and subtraction of fractions.

7.2 *Multiplying by a Fraction.* The problem of referent units is crucial to understanding multiplication of fractions, and time is spent exploring this fact.

7.3 *Dividing by a Fraction.* Once again, the role of referent units is explored, building on the repeated-subtraction view of division.

7.4 *Issues for Learning: Teaching Calculation with Fractions.*

7.5 *Check Yourself.*

Some of the students will express surprise at learning that the algorithms for operating on fractions can be understood, particularly the division algorithm. One "secret" to understanding operations on fractions is to keep always in mind the importance of identifying the unit(s) for the fractions being operated on. Students will be reminded of this point repeatedly, but it is also important for the instructor to emphasize it. Be sure to spend class time discussing the exercises, where much of the learning in this chapter will take place.

INSTRUCTOR NOTE 7.1A A historical problem

Problem 5, borrowed from Streefland (1991 in the references for Chapter 7), relates ratios and fractions. 8 loaves: 10 men is 4 loaves: 5 men is $\frac{4}{5}$ loaf: 1 man. Some students will need to draw these out, perhaps using trial and error until a solution is found and until they can adequately answer 5c: the sum of the fractions, changed to an equivalent fraction with 8 in the numerator, provides the number of men in the denominator. The problems are of historical interest, but you may want to skip them due to time constraints.

INSTRUCTOR NOTE 7.2 A common error and the issue of referent units

Some textbooks for prospective teachers say that to illustrate multiplication of fractions, such as $\frac{2}{3} \times \frac{3}{4}$, first draw a rectangle. Divide it into thirds in one direction and crosshatch two of the three parts. Divide it into fourths in the other direction and crosshatch (in a different direction) three of the four parts. The number of sections with double crosshatching (6 in this case) is the numerator of the product, while the total number of parts is the denominator (12 in this case). You may find that some of your students use this method. It is not productive because it simply becomes another algorithm, and students don't understand why it works. In fact, by using this method students will not even notice that the $\frac{3}{4}$ is already partitioned into three parts so that we simply need to take two of those parts to obtain $\frac{2}{3}$ of $\frac{3}{4}$. We try to modify this method to make it understandable here.

Another issue that needs discussion is that of the referent units. That is, when we say that $\frac{2}{3}$ of $\frac{3}{4}$ is $\frac{1}{2}$, we are referring to some whole, and taking $\frac{3}{4}$ of that whole, or $\frac{3}{4}$ of 1. The whole is the *referent unit* for the $\frac{3}{4}$. But the referent unit for the $\frac{2}{3}$ *is* the $\frac{3}{4}$ piece because we are finding $\frac{2}{3}$ of $\frac{3}{4}$. Finally, the $\frac{1}{2}$ refers back again to the original whole; the product is $\frac{1}{2}$ of the original whole. Once students understand this, they have a much deeper understanding of what multiplication of fractions is all about. In fact, you may prefer to say, find $\frac{2}{3}$ *of* $\frac{3}{4}$ *of* 1.

INSTRUCTOR NOTE 7.3A Understanding division of fractions

Fraction division is easy to undertake but the most difficult to understand of the operations. We find that when prospective (and practicing) teachers understand division by a fraction, they have a much deeper understanding of what division is all about and what fractions are. This is a challenging lesson, and your students may struggle with it. The repeated-subtraction interpretation of division lends itself nicely to division of fractions and is the primary focus of this section. Working through all of the exercises is very important to attain understanding of division of fractions.

INSTRUCTOR NOTE 7.3B Using the partitive model when dividing fractions

A partitive model can also be used to make sense of division of fractions. In her book *Knowing and Teaching Elementary Mathematics* (1999, published by Erlbaum), Liping Ma noted that the fractional version of the partitive model is to find a number when part of it is known and provided this example from the work of Chinese teachers:

"The mom bought a box of candy. She gave $\frac{1}{2}$ of it, which weighed $1\frac{3}{4}$ kg, to the grandma. How much did the box of candy originally weigh?" We need to find the number such that $\frac{1}{2}$ of it is $1\frac{3}{4}$. Then the whole is twice $1\frac{3}{4}$, which is $3\frac{1}{2}$.

Instructor Notes for Chapter 8: Multiplicative Comparisons and Multiplicative Reasoning

INSTRUCTOR NOTE 8: OVERVIEW OF CHAPTER 8

The sections in this chapter include:

8.1 *Quantitative Analysis of Multiplicative Situations.* This section continues the discussion of quantitative analyses of problem situations, but this time in the context of multiplicative situations rather than additive ones.

8.2 *Fractions in Multiplicative Comparisons.* The relation between fractions and ratios are explored in this section.

8.3 *Issues for Learning: Standards for Learning.*

8.4 *Check Yourself.*

To introduce this section, consider the following problem, which involves both multiplicative and additive reasoning. Point out each as you develop the problem.

> Dieter A: "I lost $\frac{1}{8}$ of my weight. I lost 19 pounds."
>
> Dieter B: "I lost $\frac{1}{6}$ of my weight and now you weigh 2 pounds less than I do."
>
> How much weight did Dieter B lose?

First, make a list of the relevant quantities; second, fill in the values that you know:

Dieter A's weight before the diet	
Dieter A's weight after the diet	
Dieter B's weight before the diet	
Dieter B's weight after the diet	
The fraction of weight lost by Dieter A	$\frac{1}{8}$
The fraction of weight lost by Dieter B	$\frac{1}{6}$
The amount of weight lost by Dieter A	19 pounds
The amount of weight lost by Dieter B	
The difference in their weights before the diets	
The difference in their weights after the diets	2 pounds (A is 2 pounds less than B)

Then help students see how these quantities are related to each other by drawing a diagram such as the following, which shows the relationships between quantities in the situation.

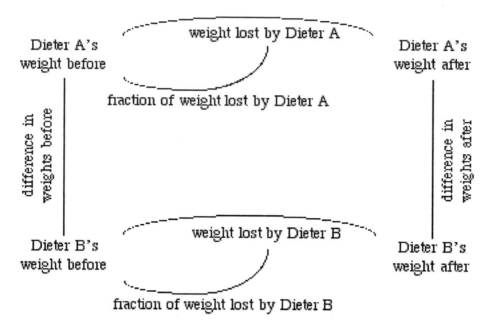

Here are the key points to bring out:

- This diagram involves only quantities, but no actual values.

- Understanding the relationships in this diagram *is* understanding the problem.

- It doesn't really matter what values are given in the problem because once we understand the diagram, we can use the relationships between quantities to find the values that we need. Understanding the problem is independent of the values that are given in the problem.

A key to understanding the Dieter's Problem is to realize that there are two different ways to compare the weights before and after the diet. You can either look at the difference (the weight lost) or the ratio (the fraction of the weight lost). Given the fraction of weight lost and the original weight, many students can find the new weight. However, students have difficulty trying to find the original weight, given the fraction lost and the new weight (which is what they must do in this problem). To help students see the relationships between these quantities, the following diagram may be helpful:

Dieter A's original weight (before diet)

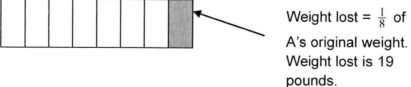

Weight lost = $\frac{1}{8}$ of A's original weight. Weight lost is 19 pounds.

Thus, 19 × 8 is 152, which is A's weight before the diet.

152 – 19 = 133, which is A's weight after the diet. (take-away subtraction)

133 + 2 = 135 is B's weight after the diet. (additive comparison)

135 is $\frac{5}{6}$ of B's weight before the diet so B weighed 162 pounds.

B lost 162 – 135 = 27 pounds.

INSTRUCTOR NOTE 8.1A Defining ratio

Thinking of a ratio as the result of comparing two quantities multiplicatively is a departure from the usual definition of a ratio as an ordered pair of numbers or as a quotient, but the two ways of thinking about ratio are not antithetical. The usual treatment of ratio begins by defining equivalent ratios and proportions and then follows with problems of solving proportions. In contrast, we linger awhile on the difference between comparing quantities additively and multiplicatively, and when each is appropriate. We analyze the structure of multiplicative situations in which ratios play a role. We do problems in which both fractions and ratios appear and in which their roles are contrasted. (We also prepare students for considering situations in which ratio can be used as a measure, as in Section 9.1. Using ratio as a measure calls for a different way of thinking about ratio—much different from the usual comparing of the numerosities of two sets or the comparing of two measurements.) We view reasoning proportionally as more than setting up and solving proportion equations, as is illustrated in *Appendix F: A Review of Some Rules*. Rather, we present reasoning proportionally as recognizing and dealing with proportional situations conceptually, rather than just as a skill. Certainly, understanding proportional situations could lead to solving proportions of the form $\frac{x}{a} = \frac{b}{c}$, but our students should have other, more meaning-centered ways at their disposal.

INSTRUCTOR NOTE 8.1B The inheritance problem

Students have quite a bit of difficulty with this problem because the relationships given relate parts of the whole to other parts of the whole (each relative's inheritance), rather than parts of the whole to the whole itself. That is, the problem deals with a part-part situation rather than a part-whole situation. (Part-part versus part-whole situations are further discussed in Section 8.2.) Students are likely to start with the entire estate and try to divide it so that everything works out. Many will try to use either algebra ($x + 2x + x + 2x = 140{,}000$, or something similar) or trial and error.

To help students *see* the relationships between the quantities in this situation, have them start by drawing a diagram of the children's inheritance and the grandchildren's inheritance:

child 1

child 2

grandchild 1

grandchild 2

Since all of these parts together constitute the entire estate, we can think of the estate as cut up into six equal parts ($140,000 ÷ 6), with each child getting two parts and each grandchild getting one.

INSTRUCTOR NOTE 8.1C Multiplicative reasoning situations

Practice with reasoning in these types of situations is essential for students to develop multiplicative reasoning. You are encouraged to create similar types of situations to present to your students on a regular basis. Also, capitalize on any future opportunity these materials may offer to emphasize the relationship between ratios and fractions as illustrated by these situations. Look out for the students who will seek a "rule of thumb" for getting answers mechanistically, bypassing any reasoning. Insist that they draw diagrams and show the relationships between the relevant quantities.

INSTRUCTOR NOTE 8.2A The relationship between ratios and fractions

Students are likely to have difficulty with these tasks, yet they are essential to understanding multiplicative comparisons and the relationship between ratios and fractions. We suggest you make up more tasks similar to these, as your students will need additional practice with this kind of thinking.

To help students understand the relationship between the parts of the candy bar, a diagram of the two parts A and B should be made first, separately from the original whole bar. Here is some work for #3:

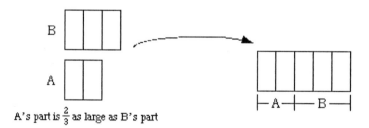

A's part is $\frac{2}{3}$ as large as B's part

Doing this makes more explicit the fact that we are comparing one part to the other part. Many students have difficulty distinguishing between comparing two parts and comparing a part to the whole—that is, part-part comparisons versus part-whole comparisons. Students tend to want to do the latter because they are used to thinking of fractions in terms of parts of a whole. For example, in Problem 3 where A's part is $\frac{2}{3}$ as large as B's part, many students will want to cut the entire bar into three pieces and shade two.

As students begin to feel more comfortable with part-part comparisons and working through the activity, some may identify a pattern for cutting up the candy bar correctly (e.g., add the numerator and denominator of the fraction to decide how many pieces to cut the bar up into). Praise any such suggestions, recognizing the fact that mathematics often involves finding patterns in situations. However, be sure to insist that students continue to make sense of the diagrams that they draw—that is, that the diagram does not simply become a procedure that they use to find the answer. We have found that some students are able to learn the procedure for drawing effective diagrams and successfully solve problems using this procedure, but when they are asked to explain a diagram, they are unable to describe how it relates mathematically to the problem.

To help encourage students to pay attention to the meanings of their diagrams, a good idea is to give your students problems that are similar to but not the same as the problems given here. For example, a candy bar could be divided up between three people, with various ratios given. (See the pizza problem in Example 5.) This prevents students from falling back on any "formulas" they have developed for figuring out the answer.

INSTRUCTOR NOTE 8.2B Notes on Learning Exercises for 8.2

"Unrealistic" numbers are used here to *force* thinking about the meanings of the values and their relationships. For that reason, make sure that students do not simply fall back on their use of algebra to solve these problems. In Exercise 1, for example, some students may come up with the equation $\frac{3}{8}x = 2$, and be able to solve it for x (although many will not). Acknowledge such efforts, but point out that the purpose of these exercises is to think about the multiplicative relationships between quantities, and encourage students to solve the problems using diagrams. For Exercise 2, have students draw two spools. Then ask them: "How can the drawing be completed so that the two spools represent $\frac{3}{8}$ of something? What is that something?" Students may struggle with this because two spools are not easily divided into three parts.

In Exercise 3, students may immediately want to divide the 10 by the $2\frac{3}{8}$. Make sure they can explain why division is the appropriate operation, using ratio terminology. For example, "The ratio of the number of sticks of butter Les used to the number of sticks of butter called for in the recipe is $10 : 2\frac{3}{8}$, which means that the number of sticks of butter Les used is $\frac{10}{2\frac{3}{8}}$ times as much as the number of sticks of butter called for in the recipe."

To help students see the relationship between these two quantities, you may want to have them draw the following diagram:

Sticks of butter used by Les

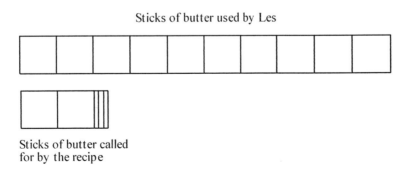

Sticks of butter called
for by the recipe

Students will probably realize that they need to figure out how many times the $2\frac{3}{8}$ sticks of butter will "fit into" the 10 sticks of butter (hence their desire to divide). Their difficulty will come once they have fit the $2\frac{3}{8}$ sticks in 4 times and have $\frac{1}{2}$ stick left because they will be unsure what to do with the $\frac{1}{2}$. It will take some discussion for them to realize that they need to figure out how much of a recipe the $\frac{1}{2}$ stick of butter is, and the way to do that is to compare it to the $2\frac{3}{8}$ sticks that the recipe calls for. Thus, Les uses four plus $\frac{\frac{1}{2}}{2\frac{3}{8}}$ times as much butter as the recipe calls for. Of course, this simplifies to $4\frac{4}{19}$, but this simplification tends to obscure the reasoning.

This is just one direction in which the discussion can go. The idea is that students become comfortable with comparing two quantities multiplicatively through the use of a ratio, and that they learn to draw diagrams that can help them reason through such situations.

Instructor Notes for Chapter 9: Ratios, Rates, Proportions, and Percents

INSTRUCTOR NOTE 9: OVERVIEW OF CHAPTER 9

This chapter contains the following sections:

9.1 *Ratio as a Measure.* Ratio can be used as a unit of measure in order to make a comparison. This section builds on the treatment of ratio in Chapter 8.

9.2 *Comparing Ratios.* Proportions are considered as a whole, not as cases. Situations that can be solved by using proportional reasoning are explored.

9.3 *Percents in Comparisons and Changes.* The treatment of percents here builds on the earlier work estimating with percent. This section contains some rather difficult topics—ones widely misunderstood and misused.

9.4 *Issues for Learning: Developing Proportional Reasoning.*

9.5 *Check Yourself.*

This chapter builds on ideas introduced in Chapters 1 and 8. The exercise sets are long and you may find you need to devote class time to many of the exercises.

INSTRUCTOR NOTE 9.1   When does ratio act as a measure?

Traditional instruction on ratio and proportion typically focuses on writing ratios (as in, "Write a ratio that expresses the number of boys to the number of girls in this classroom") or on finding the missing term in a proportion (with a procedural emphasis). In contrast, the "squareness" problem and the ski-slope problem in this section are intended to allow students to come up with ratio as a way of quantifying certain attributes of objects, namely the squareness of a rectangle and the steepness of a ski slope. Students use ratios to quantify things in the real world (speed, for example), yet they are often unaware of how and when ratios are being used and do not recognize when using a ratio to measure the value of a quantity is appropriate. In the squareness problem, for example, it is not at all obvious to some students that one should look at the ratio of the two sides. These students may suggest measuring "squareness" by taking the difference between the two dimensions—an additive comparison. The smaller the difference, the closer the rectangle is to being a square. Realizing when the value of a quantity must be found by looking at a multiplicative comparison between two other quantities (i.e., a ratio) is an important step for students.

Instructional Suggestions: It is not at all obvious to many students how this comparison should be made, and discussion will take time, but it is worth the time spent on it. If you want background reading for your own knowledge, see Simon and Blume (*Journal of Mathematical Behavior, 13*, 1994, 183–197).

That ratio is the appropriate measure for the attributes of "squareness" and "steepness" should become obvious to the students through discussion and examination of cases. It is *extremely important* that you do not simply tell students to use a ratio in each case. Let the students take the lead in this discussion, particularly in coming up with examples to "test" ideas. You should be prepared with carefully chosen counterexamples, however, to challenge suggestions from the students—in particular, suggestions involving the difference between length and width in the case of squareness, or between height and length in the case of steepness. Presenting cases like the ones below may help students to see that additive comparisons are not good measures of "squareness" or "steepness" and that another approach is required:

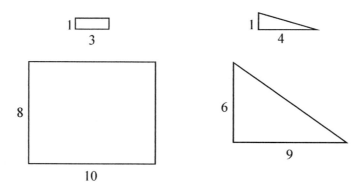

Acknowledge any rise-over-run contributions, but don't pursue those first. Although fairly accurate sketches will be useful in proving or disproving conjectures, make it clear that what is needed is a method that could be communicated by words (such as in a telephone conversation). Students will have difficulty in dealing with different ideas that involve reciprocals (e.g., height/length and length/height) as well as ideas that might involve contrasting arguments based on $1{:}x$ values with arguments based on $a{:}1$ values. Be prepared for the unexpected—one of our students suggested the ratio of the area to the difference of the sides!

INSTRUCTOR NOTE 9.2A

It is important that students be given some time to think about this discussion question. You might even want to assign the question as homework. Don't be too eager to help, even when students take a long time to respond. Giving them more examples will not advance their understanding as much as coming up with examples on their own. Also, students' responses to this question will tell you where they are and what you will need to do to help them understand the usefulness of ratios, so listen carefully to their thinking. Allow time for students to share their examples and have the class judge their appropriateness. After examples are shared, you might want to remind students about the discussion of the example in Section 8.1 where the population grew by 1000 people in two towns: one where the original population was 1000 people and another where the original population was 100,000 people. What quantity would best assess the impact of the growth on the town? Clearly, the actual growth must be compared (multiplicatively) to the original population. The ratio or percent of growth to total population is a better measure of the impact than additive reasoning in which one simply considers the number of extra people, which is the same in both cases. Another example could be: Berta made 11 free throws out of 19 attempted, and Lisa made 17 out of 35. Who has been more effective in making free throws? Although Lisa made 6 more free throws than Berta, most students will agree that Berta is the more effective of the two. One must consider the number of free throws *relative* to the number of attempts.

INSTRUCTOR NOTE 9.2B Solution using a three-column table

One way:

People	Time	Notes
600	15 min	given
2400	1 hour	× 4
1200	.5 hour	÷ 2
3600	1.5 hours	× 3

INSTRUCTOR NOTE 9.2C Seating arrangements problem

Streefland (1991, reference in Chapter 7) used seating arrangements and distributing pizza as "the breeding ground in which a process of vertical mathematization takes root and in which ratios and fractions are both distinguished from and connected to each other" (p. 51).

For Question 1, the alternate ways might lead to spontaneous construction of many sorts of elaborate graphs, such as:

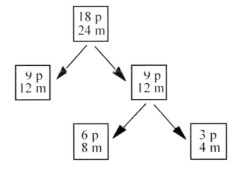

For Question 2a, it is certainly possible to compare the two ratios through some rote procedure, such as obtaining a common denominator. However, explaining the problem further, as one would for a child, is useful. As above, we could show that $\dfrac{10p}{14m}$ is equivalent to $\dfrac{5p}{7m}$ and $\dfrac{8p}{10m}$ is equivalent to $\dfrac{4p}{5m}$. Then we could draw out how much each member would get. For example, for $\dfrac{5p}{7m}$ we could count off the pieces each person gets in several ways, two of which are:

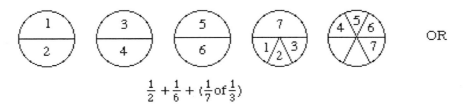

$$\frac{1}{2} + \frac{1}{6} + (\frac{1}{7} \text{ of } \frac{1}{3})$$

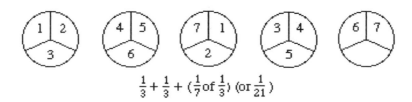

$$\frac{1}{3} + \frac{1}{3} + (\frac{1}{7} \text{of} \frac{1}{3}) \text{ (or} \frac{1}{21})$$

Of course, there are many different ways of cutting and sharing the pizzas, but once this is done, it is easy to compare the two situations.

INSTRUCTOR NOTE 9.2D   The orange juice problem

This problem is worth spending some time on. There are more correct answers given for (1) than for (2) for at least two reasons. One reason is that some students are able to convert the ratio of $\frac{3}{4}$ to its equivalent $\frac{6}{8}$ more easily, and thus the comparison to the ratio $\frac{5}{8}$ is easy. These same students may have difficulty converting the ratio $\frac{3}{5}$ to one that can be easily compared to $\frac{5}{8}$. The other reason is that some students may reason about the problem additively in both cases. In (1), although the reasoning is inappropriate, they would answer correctly. Yet in (2), reasoning additively will not lead them to the correct answer. Because students are generally more inclined to reason additively than multiplicatively, this accounts for the greater number of correct responses in (1) than in (2). Keep this point in mind when you develop test questions.

INSTRUCTOR NOTE 9.3A   The *Fair or Not?* problem from Activity 5

Students usually try an example to decide. If they don't, you may suggest an original wage of $10/hour and an article priced at $100 before the sale.

When students see that there is a difference in Problem 1, ask whether it depends on the pay rate. The general argument may or may not be convincing: After the cut, the employee was getting 90% of the original pay, but with the raise, he/she is back to only 99% of the original pay.

That there is no difference in the two methods in 2 will be apparent in an example, of course, but whether it depends on the price of the article might not be clear to any who do not see proportionality involved through the percents. A general argument might go: "With your idea, you would be paying the 8% tax on 80% of the original price, or 108% of 80% of the price. With the clerk's way, you would be paying 80% of the after-tax price, or 80% of 108% of the original price. 108% of 80% is the same value as 80% of 108%. In symbols, if P is the original price, you are comparing 1.08 x (0.80 x P) and 0.80 x (1.08 x P). In either case, you are multiplying P by the same two factors: 1.08 x (0.80 x P) = 0.80 x (1.08 x P)." Check to see whether students think that different discount percents or sales tax rates might give results that do differ.

One instructor had his students interview others outside the class about the second setting:

> "If you buy something in a store on which you have to pay tax and there is a percentage discount on
> the item, does it make a difference to what you have to pay if they add the tax first and then take off

the discount or take the discount off first and then add the tax?" Without trying an example, fewer than 20% of those interviewed (all adults) gave a correct response. (Mukhopadhyay & Greer, 2002, Six characters in search of an answer. In A. Cockburn and E. Nardi (Eds), *Proceedings of the 26th Annual Conference of the International Group for the Psychology of Mathematics Education,* Norwich, England: University of East Anglia, p. 303.)

Instructor Notes for Chapter 10: Integers and Other Number Systems

INSTRUCTOR NOTE 10: OVERVIEW OF CHAPTER 10

This chapter contains the following sections:

10.1 *Big Ideas About Signed Numbers.* The number line is used here to introduce signed numbers and additive inverses.

10.2 *Children's Ways of Reasoning About Signed Numbers.* We highlight here some very recent research on elementary ideas about negative numbers as they are used to solve a variety of problems.

10.3 *Other Models for Signed Numbers.* Everyday usage of signed numbers is explored. The colored chip model is also examined.

10.4 *Operations with Signed Numbers.* The colored chip model and the number lines are both used to add and subtract signed numbers.

10.5 *Multiplying and Dividing Signed Numbers.* Making sense of these operations is the focus of this section. This topic may be the first one introduced in middle grades that cannot be understood intuitively and is thus difficult to teach. Future teachers should be prepared with explanations.

10.6 *Number Systems.* The real numbers and the density property are introduced. The field properties are extended to real numbers.

10.5 *Issues for Learning: Open Number Sentence.*

10.6 *Check Yourself.*

It is well known that negative numbers can cause great conceptual difficulties for children and sometimes for adults. This fact should not be surprising because many mathematicians little more than a century ago looked upon negative numbers with suspicion. The following notes come from an article on negative numbers by Streefland (1996).

> The resistance to negative numbers was at least in part due to the lack of the ability to make sense of negative numbers. Lazare Carnot (1753–1823) is quoted as saying: "A multitude of paradoxes and relative absurdities result from the same notion; for instance, that -3 would be smaller than -2; nevertheless $(-3)^2$ would be greater than $(-2)^2$, that is to say that, considering two unequal quantities, the square of the greater would be smaller than the square of the smaller. This shocks every clear idea which one may get referring to the notion of quantity" (p. 60). Finally, the German mathematician Hankel solved the problem of how to think about negative numbers when he published his *Theory of Complex Numbers* in 1867. In this work he established the "principle of permanence" of formal laws, which expresses the preservation of formal algebraic laws, for instance when shifting from positive whole numbers to integers. This work gave a formal mathematical foundation for work with negative

numbers. (Streefland, L. (1996). Negative numbers: Reflections of a learning researcher. *The Journal of Mathematical Behavior, 15,* 57–77.)

In this chapter, we recognize that our students have already been exposed to rules for operating on integers. But even if they remember the rules, it is highly doubtful that they have ways of explaining these rules to children when they begin to teach.

The increased emphasis on the number line in this chapter reflects the increased emphasis on the number line in the Common Core State Standards.

Depending on the time you have remaining in a course focusing on K–6, you may want to omit Section 10.5 on multiplication and division with signed numbers. State frameworks and textbooks may (but not always) delay multiplication and division until seventh grade.

This chapter also provides an opportunity to review the properties of operations. Although students do not know these properties as *field* properties, they will have some familiarity with the properties and their names from previous chapters and perhaps from Appendix F.

INSTRUCTOR NOTE 10.4A Adding and subtracting integers

There are other concrete ways of thinking about addition and subtraction of integers, for example, by using temperature changes or by using credits and debits. Many teachers like to use "letter carrier" stories, in which paychecks or bills are delivered. (See Instructor Note 10.5B for the use of this interpretation in multiplication.) The chip method we introduce here has also been used successfully by many teachers to teach addition and subtraction of integers. It does have some historical precedence (see the beginning of Chapter 10.5 on how the Chinese denoted positive and negative values in 200 BC).

The use of the chips as a model for thinking about addition and subtraction does work out well, and the chips could be interpreted as $1 in pay or $1 owed, imitating the Chinese method. (In passing, note that the chips could be interpreted as atomic charges or "point won" and "point lost" in a game setting.) Even for the conceptually difficult $3 - 5$ or $3 - {}^-5$, with a clever choice for showing the minuend (the 3), the chip model gives answers. As importantly, when one notices after the take-away step that the original subtraction has turned into what could be viewed as an addition, the rule is perhaps less arbitrary (although language like "removing a debt can be accomplished by gaining the same amount" may bolster the argument). The approach builds in an essential way on $n + {}^-n = 0$, the crucial property of additive inverses.

Here is how one might proceed in showing $3 - 5$ with the chips.

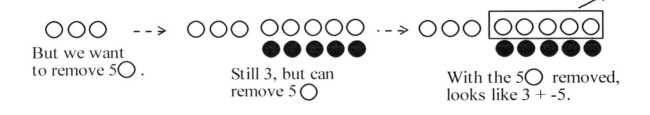

But we want to remove 5◯.

Still 3, but can remove 5 ◯

With the 5◯ removed, looks like 3 + -5.

Finally, we can match three gray chips and three blue chips to obtain just 2 gray chips, or $^-2$. (Note that adding 2 gray chips and 2 blue chips could also work because then 5 blue chips could be removed, leaving 2 gray chips. This way is discussed in the text just after Discussion 3.)

For a different subtraction, $3 - {}^-5$, after removing the 5 gray chips, one can interpret the chips as $3 + {}^+5$, also an exact support of the usual rule.

INSTRUCTOR NOTE 10.5A   Multiplying and dividing integers

The fact that the product of two negative numbers is positive is an intellectually challenging idea to grasp. Those students who have difficulties with the rules for multiplication of signed numbers may even be those students who try to make sense of mathematics. Multiplication involving negative numbers may be the first time these students have met any mathematics that was not intuitively clear and that does not make sense to them. Alternately, those who seem *not* to find this topic difficult may be those students who believe that mathematics is simply a set of rules and that these rules are no different than any others in terms of difficulty.

This section offers three arguments for the product of two negatives being positive. The first builds on patterns, the second on a continuation of the properties of multiplication, and the third uses the chips but introduces a new way of thinking about multiplication (when the first factor is negative). The model extends the use of chips from Section 10.3, even though we know no elementary- or middle-school textbook that uses this method. (Most seem to rely on the pattern argument.) Whether or not you spend time on the chip model could depend on the time spent with chips in Sections 10.3 and 10.4.

You will note that the story problems in the Learning Exercises (#5 and #6) are somewhat artificial. More advanced work in science would allow richer problems, but that background cannot be assumed. Students sometimes regard the story problems for addition and subtraction (in 10.4) as especially contrived because the questions can be answered without the use of signed numbers.

INSTRUCTOR NOTE 10.5B Division *and* multiplication as repeated subtraction?

Although it is tempting to interpret $^-2 \times 4$ using "repeated subtraction" language, repeated subtraction is language often used solely and more conventionally for one view of division. If you choose to use such language, the fuller "repeated subtraction division" or "repeated subtraction multiplication" might be necessary. An alternative is to build on the letter-carrier interpretation mentioned earlier (positive: paycheck; negative: bill to pay). Addition would mean that the letter carrier brings more than one item, and subtraction would mean that the letter carrier would take back an item delivered by error. In each case, the answer is the extent to which one's financial situation has changed. For multiplication, $^-2 \times 4$ would mean that the letter carrier takes back two paychecks, each of $4, giving an influence of $^-\$8$ on one's financial situation. $^-2 \times {}^-4$ would mean the taking back of 2 bills for $4 each, thus giving a $+\$8$ change to the finances.

INSTRUCTOR NOTE 10.6A Field properties

Activity 11 Do the Field Properties Hold in Clock Arithmetic?
Be sure students find that all 11 properties hold. It will be easier to talk about once the table is
filled in, as it is here.

+	0	1	2	3	4
0	0	1	2	3	4
1	1	2	3	4	0
2	2	3	4	0	1
3	3	4	0	1	2
4	4	0	1	2	3

×	0	1	2	3	4
0	0	0	0	0	0
1	0	1	2	3	4
2	0	2	4	1	3
3	0	3	1	4	2
4	0	4	3	2	1

As you probably remember, modular systems give fields only when the modulus is a prime
number. By studying several systems and noting when the systems with a composite number of
elements break down as fields (no multiplicative inverses for some nonzero numbers), students
might be able to conjecture the correct result (as prompted in Learning Exercise 6).

INSTRUCTOR NOTE 10.6B Just for you. Excerpted from a long conversation in *Smilla's Sense
of Snow*, a novel by Peter Hoeg, pp. 121–122.

> Do you know what the foundation of mathematics is? The foundation of mathematics is numbers.
> If anyone asked me what makes me truly happy, I would say: numbers. And do you know why?
> Because the number system is like life. First you have the natural numbers. The ones that are
> whole and positive. The numbers of a small child. But human consciousness expands. The child
> discovers a sense of longing, and do you know what the mathematical expression is for longing?
> The negative numbers. The formalization of the feeling that you are missing something. And
> human consciousness expands and grows even more, and the child discovers the in-between
> spaces. Between stones, between pieces of moss on the stones, between people. And between
> numbers. And do you know what that leads to? It leads to fractions. Whole numbers plus
> fractions produce rational numbers. And human consciousness doesn't stop there. It wants to go
> beyond reason. It adds an operation as absurd as the extraction of roots. And produces irrational
> numbers. It's a form of madness. Because the irrational numbers are infinite. They can't be
> written down. They force human consciousness out beyond the limits. And by adding irrational
> numbers to rational numbers, you get real numbers. It doesn't stop. It never stops. Because now,
> on the spot, we expand the real numbers with imaginary square roots of negative numbers. These
> are numbers we can't picture, numbers that normal human consciousness cannot comprehend.
> And when we add the imaginary numbers to the real numbers, we have the complex number
> system. The first number system in which it's possible to explain satisfactorily the crystal
> formation of ice.

Instructor Notes for Chapter 11: Number Theory

INSTRUCTOR NOTE 11.0

The following sections are in this chapter:

> 11.1 *Factors and Multiples, Primes and Composites.* The ideas in this section are not new, but students may need practice with vocabulary.

> 11.2 *Prime Factorization.* The prime factorization theorem is introduced and used. As is shown in 11.5, the ideas here are not trivial for these students.

> 11.3 *Divisibility Tests to Determine Whether a Number Is Prime.* The tests for 2, 3, 4, 5, 6, 8, 9, 10, and 12 are considered, and then some tests for some other composite numbers are explored.

> 11.4 *Greatest Common Factor, Least Common Multiple.* These topics arose in earlier chapters, but here methods for finding them are provided.

> 11.5 *Issues for Learning: Understanding the Unique Factorization Theorem.*

> 11.6 *Check Yourself.*

"The problem of distinguishing prime numbers from composite numbers and of resolving the latter into their prime factors is known to be one of the most important and useful in arithmetic. It has engaged the industry and wisdom of ancient and modern geometers to such an extent that it would be superfluous to discuss the problem at length....Further, the dignity of the science itself seems to require that every possible means be explored for the solution of a problem so elegant and so celebrated." (Carl Friedrich Gauss, *Disquisitiones Arithmeticae*, 1801)

The ideas in this chapter may appear to be simple, but many of them are subtle and at first not easily understood. The studies referenced in the *Issues for Learning* section highlight the difficulty of applying the prime factorization theorem. The activities and exercises are designed to help the students think through the major ideas in this unit. Reasoning and problem solving are required on the part of the students.

In elementary school textbooks, some number theory usually precedes the work with fractions so as to allow the use of least common multiples for adding and subtracting fractions and the identification of common factors for simplifying fractions. However, there is much more to number theory, and we devote this chapter to that study, having reviewed necessary topics such as least common multiple as needed in earlier chapters (Chapters 6 and 7).

You might also want to refer students to the following Web sites, as well as asking them to Google "prime number":

> http://www.claymath.org/posters/primes/ for a look at prime numbers and their usefulness, and

Beckham in His Prime Number by Marcus du Sautoy for *+Plus Magazine* at
http://plus.maths.org/issue26/features/sautoy/

INSTRUCTOR NOTE 11.2

We prefer the label Unique Factorization Theorem, or Prime Factorization Theorem over the
Fundamental Theorem of Arithmetic because the UFT is a more transparent term. The FTA is,
however, mentioned several times. The UFT might seem simple to you, but it does cause
students problems, as can be seen in Section 11.5, *Issues for Learning*, which you might want to
read at this juncture.

If your sense of theatrics allows it, you may wish to pretend to be a mind reader, along the lines
of this script:

> "When you work with math long enough, you develop the ability to read minds about math things. I
> will demonstrate. Write down a number of the form abc,abc, like 727,727. (Write 727,727 on the
> board.) You do not have to repeat any digits, but follow the abc,abc form. Do not let me see your
> number." Then call on someone, stare at him/her intently, perhaps close your eyes as though
> concentrating, and then say, "77 is a factor of your number." (Other choices are 7, 11, 13, 91, and
> 143.) Have the person confirm that you are correct, probably with a calculator to speed things up.
> Repeat with another student or two, using a different factor from the 7, 11, 13, 77, 91, 143 list each
> time. With any luck, students will wonder how you are "reading their minds." You may wish to
> give them the hint, abc,abc = 1001 × abc. Whether you tell them that $1001 = 7 \times 11 \times 13$ may
> depend on what you have covered, or plan to cover.

INSTRUCTOR NOTE 11.3

In this section, we examine ways to check for divisibility and to check whether or not a number
is prime. The fact that when we are testing for primeness of a number, we need only check for
divisibility by primes not more than the square root of that number is a difficult one for students
to understand. The activities and exercises are designed to help the students think through the
major ideas in this section. Reasoning and problem solving are required on the part of the
students. It is helpful for them to be able to discuss these ideas in pairs, in groups, or as a class.

The divisibility tests for 2 and for 5 and for 10 are well known. Of course, one general "test" that
can always be used to see if n is a factor of q is to divide q by n, and if the remainder is 0, then n
is a factor of q. There are many less well-known tests. We provide tests for 3 and 6 and 9 to
students in this section, but you may want to introduce other tests and the rationales (or quasi-
proofs) of the tests.

The test for 9 is as follows: 9 is a factor of n if and only if 9 is a factor of the sum of the digits of
n. The rationale is very similar to that for divisibility for 3.

The divisibility test for 4 is as follows: 4 is a factor of n if and only if the number formed from
the last two digits of n is divisible by 4. For example, the last two digits of 8752 form the number
52. 8752 is divisible by 4 if and only if 52 is divisible by 4. To show this, first expand 8752:
$8(1000) + 7(100) + 5(10) + 2 = 8 \cdot 4 \cdot 250 + 7 \cdot 4 \cdot 25 + 5 \cdot 10 + 2 = 4 \cdot (8 \cdot 250 + 7 \cdot 25) + 52$. Then
use an argument similar to that above.

The test for 8 is as follows: 8 is a factor of n if and only if the number formed from the last three digits of n is divisible by 8. A rationale can be given similar to that for divisibility by 4.

The divisibility test for 6 is that 6 is a factor of n if and only if both 2 and 3 are factors of n. (Note that 2 and 3 are relatively prime.) Similar tests can be developed for 12, 15, 18, and so on.

The divisibility test for 11 is somewhat similar to that for 3 and for 9, but slightly more difficult. If you wish to demonstrate it, here is one way to do so: 11 is a factor of n if and only if 11 is a factor of the difference of the sum of every other digit and the sum of the other digits. For example, to check whether or not 11 divides 273,845, check that $2 + 3 + 4 = 9$, $7 + 8 + 5 = 20$, and $20 - 9 = 11$, which is a multiple of 11, so 11 is a factor of 273,944. Or 324 is not divisible by 11 because $3 + 4 = 7$ and $7 - 2 = 5$, and 5 not a multiple of 11. Consider 4653: $4 + 5 = 9$ and $6 + 3 = 9$: $9 - 9 = 0$, which is a multiple of 11. (0 is a multiple of every whole number.)

Note that $100000 = 100001 - 1$; $10000 = 9999 + 1$; $1000 = 1001 - 1$; $100 = 99 + 1$; $10 = 9 + 1$ and that 100001, 9999, 1001, and 99 are all divisible by 11; that is: $10^{2n} - 1$ is divisible by 11 and $10^{2n+1} + 1$ is divisible by 11 (where $2n$ is any even number and $2n - 1$ is any odd number).

Consider the number 4653, which by the "rule" above is divisible by 11. (It is 11×423.)

$$4653 = 4(1000) + 6(100) + 5(10) + 3 =$$

$$4(1001 - 1) + 6(99 + 1) + 5(11 - 1) + 3 =$$

$$4(1001) - 4(1) + 6(99) + 6(1) + 5(11) - 5(1) + 3 =$$

$$[4(1001) + 6(99) + 5(11)] + [(-4) + 6 + (-5) + 3]$$

We know that $[4(1001) + 6(99) + 5(11)]$ is divisible by 11.

Therefore, 4653 is divisible by 11 if and only if $[(-4) + 6 + (-5) + 3] = 0$ is divisible by 11, which it is.

Once divisibility tests for 2, 3, 4, 5, 6, 8, 9, 10, and possibly 11 are set, students may naturally ask about one for 7. Below is one that we have used with the students (but not tested on), with the warning, "It's probably easier just to divide by 7." We do not usually give any sort of rationale for the test, or hypothesize how someone thought of it, for this audience.

Divisibility test for 7: Take the last digit, double it, and subtract that from the number given by the other digits. 7 is a factor of the original number if and only if 7 is a factor of that difference. The process may be repeated until it is easy to see whether 7 is a factor.

Example: Is 7 a factor of 16,576?

Think of 16,576 with the last digit separate: 1657|6. Cut off the ones digit, 6, and double it, getting 12. Subtract 12 from the 1657, getting 1645 (next thought of as 164|5).

Double 5, subtract that 10 from 164: 154, or 15|4   Double 4 to get 8, subtract 8 from 15, getting 7. 7 is a factor of 7, so 7 is a factor of the original 16576.

Example: Is 7 a factor of 8123?

812|3. $812 - (2 \times 3) = 806$. 80|6. $80 - (2 \times 6) = 68$. 7 is not a factor of 68, so 7 is not a factor of 8123.

A rationale for the "if" part is suggested as follows. Suppose the number can be written *Khtu*, and the divisibility test works. Then for some x,

$100K + 10h + t - 2u = 7x$, or

$100K + 10h + t = 7x + 2u$. But then, multiplying by 10,

$1000K + 100h + 10t = 70x + 20u$. Adding u to each side gives

$1000K + 100h + 10t + u = 70x + 21u = 7(10x + 3u)$, so 7 is a factor of the left-hand side, or *Khtu*.

References

Rowe, Mary Budd. (1987) Wait time: Slowing down may be a way of speeding up. *American Educator, 11* (Spring 1987): 38–43, 47.

Overview of *Part II: Reasoning About Algebra and Change (RAC)*

Goal   Our primary goal for this course is that prospective or practicing elementary and middle school teachers come to view algebra as a powerful tool for representing, analyzing, and solving problems. The study of change is a tool leading to this realization.

Key Ideas   Here are the key ideas presented in Part II, *Reasoning about Algebra and Change,* although not necessarily in this order:

- Algebra can be thought of as a language, as generalized quantitative reasoning, as generalized arithmetic, and as a tool for solving problems.

- Symbols are used in algebra to help us represent values of quantities and to describe and generalize patterns.

- The study of patterns leads naturally to the study of functions, a central idea throughout mathematics.

- Quantitative reasoning about problem situations with numbers translates readily into quantitative reasoning about problem situations in which algebraic symbols are used in place of numbers.

- Tables, graphs, and equations are three fundamental ways of exhibiting information about things that change, and one should be able to move effortlessly from one to another.

- The slope of a straight line provides information about rate of change.

- Graphs without numbers, sometimes called qualitative graphs, are useful in coming to understand how to interpret graphs.

Reasoning about Algebra and Change is not intended to be a review of high school algebra and the symbolic manipulations that often drive such a course. Rather, *RAC* is intended to help students better understand the power of algebra as a set of tools for representing and solving problems.

Assumed Background of Students   Students are expected to have had courses at least through secondary school algebra. Your students may or may not have many algebraic skills. Some review is provided in Chapters 12 and 15, but the concern here is building prospective teachers' understanding of concepts underlying algebra and change, not of how to teach algebra and change topics, nor of how to carry out algebraic manipulations. You may need to remind them of this focus.

We also recommend some acquaintance with many of the topics found in Part I, *Reasoning about Numbers and Quantities,* including rational numbers and quantitative reasoning. Appendix A reviews topics in arithmetic for those who need such a review.

Problem Solving   We return to ideas introduced in Part I, *Reasoning about Numbers and Quantities,* to identify the quantities and their values in problem situations, and then use that knowledge to solve algebraic problems quantitatively. Beginning with the first chapter, there is a focus on patterns and how patterns can be generalized and often expressed as functions. Problems dealing with the interrelationships among tables, graphs, and algebraic equations as representations of quantitative situations are a central concern of *RAC*. Change is studied in the context of distance/time/speed settings, with problems relating these quantities. The ability to draw and interpret graphs is developed through problems that call for graphing without numbers or interpreting such graphs. Problems dealing with the difficult notion of average speed lead into other weighted-mean problems.

Technology   We recommend but do not require the use of motion detectors to help students understand how to read and draw graphs. We have found that even a short class using the motion detector can later lead students, when graphing, to say to one another: "This can't be right because if we used a motion detector to represent this, the graph would look like..."

We also recommend the use of the (supplied) Over and Back program. This software has been redesigned, based on an earlier Mac-only version that has, over the years we have used it, proved to be a powerful means of studying average rate of change.

Timeline   We provide a rough guide to time allotments for *Reasoning about Algebra and Change.*

12   What is Algebra?   (~ 2 weeks)

This chapter explores the many ways of thinking about algebra, as a symbolic language, as generalized arithmetic, as a study of patterns and of functions, as reasoning about quantities, and as a powerful tool for solving problems. It extends what was learned in Part I about quantitative reasoning. Once again, problems are analyzed quantitatively. It is possible to teach this chapter without having had the quantitative reasoning chapters in Part I, but if so, it will probably take longer than indicated. As you discuss solutions to problems, it is important to connect symbols, properties, and representations. Encourage your students to notice and describe patterns, structure, and regularities in arithmetic operations. Some instructors like to take more time with this chapter and incorporate other work with patterns and functions from other sections, thus the time will vary.

13   A Quantitative Approach to Algebra and Graphing   (~ 3 weeks)

Graphs and algebra are used to represent quantitative relationships. Connections among quantitative situations, graphs, and algebraic equations are studied, with a focus on understanding slope of linear functions. Proportional relationships are represented by linear functions. Finally, a few nonlinear functions are studied. Depending on time constraints, you may want to exclude Section 13.4 on nonlinear functions.

14   Understanding Change: Relationships among Time, Distance, and Rate   (2–4 weeks)

In this chapter, the movements of a cartoon character are used to graph time and distance. With this character we can focus on movements without considering time needed to speed up or slow down. Rate is considered here to be interchangeable with speed. There is an emphasis on graph interpretation, which many students enjoy because it clarifies ideas for them about what graphs tell us. The use of a motion detector is recommended for this chapter. Some students may require more time with this chapter than others will.

15 Using Algebra to Solve More Problems (2–4 weeks)

Students use one point and the slope, or two points, to determine and graph linear functions. Cases using two linear functions to solve problems are also presented. Problems are solved numerically, graphically, and algebraically, and these types of solutions are compared. Average speed and weighted averages are included, and average speed is studied with the help of the Over and Back applet.

For courses with very limited time for algebra topics, Chapters 12 may be the only chapter you use. If so, we recommend that you replace Section 12.6 on NAEP testing and include instead Section 13.5 dealing with algebra topics from the NCTM *Principles and Standards for Mathematics* and the Common Core State Standards.

Chapters 13 and 14 fit well together. Proportional reasoning is a topic found in all parts of the text materials and is here discussed in terms of linear functions that represent proportions.

For a half-semester course, you may need to exclude Section 13.4 (although students should know that not all functions are linear) and all of Chapter 15. A course for prospective middle school teachers should include all chapters and sections here.

We also note that Part IV, *Reasoning about Chance and Data,* assumes an understanding of slope, which is addressed in Chapter 13, Section 2.

References in Part II can be found at the end of the Instructor Notes for Part II.

Instructor Notes for Chapter 12: What Is Algebra?

INSTRUCTOR NOTE 12: Overview of Chapter 12

This first chapter is intended to provide a broad overview of algebra, building on and extending students' work with numbers and with quantitative reasoning. We assume that students have had the chapters from Part I dealing with number, or their equivalent. While it is possible to teach this chapter without having had the quantitative reasoning chapters in Part I, that earlier work does provide a foundation for some of the work in Part II. If students have not had this foundation, some sections may require more time.

Here are the sections for Chapter 12:

12.1 *Algebra as a Symbolic Language.* Different uses of algebraic symbols are discussed, in particular the use of a symbol as a variable. Properties of operations are reviewed and used to solve algebraic equations. CCSS emphasize students' understanding of properties and engagement in mathematical practices. Connections are among children's mental and written computations, properties and models.

12.2 *Algebra as Generalized Arithmetic.* Operations on algebraic expressions are shown to be generalizations of operations on numbers.

12.3 *Numerical Patterns and Algebra.* Recognizing, describing, generalizing, and extending patterns, including arithmetic and geometric patterns, are the focus of this chapter.

12.4 *Functions and Algebra.* Work with generalizing patterns leads naturally to the study of functions.

12.5 *Algebraic Reasoning About Quantities.* Reviewing and building on chapters on quantitative reasoning from Part I, *Reasoning about Numbers and Quantities*, work here provides a sound basis for approaching and solving "story problems," using quantitative reasoning.

12.6 *Issues for Learning.* Findings on fourth-grade and eighth-grade achievement in algebra, from the National Assessment of Educational Progress, are summarized.

12.7 *Check Yourself.* This section, as with all *Check Yourself* sections at the end of chapters, provides a summary of the chapter.

A review of the research on the difficulties that students have that affects the learning of algebra shows that some students:

1. "believe that the equals sign represents a unidirectional operator that produces an output on the right side of the input from the left (e.g. it is appropriate to write $3 + 5 = 8$, but not $8 = 3 + 5$);
2. focus on finding particular answers;

3. do not recognize the commutative and distributive properties;
4. do not use mathematical symbols to express relationships among quantities;
5. do not comprehend the use of letters as generalized numbers or as variables;
6. have great difficulty operating on unknowns; and
7. fail to understand that equivalent transformations on both sides of an equation do not alter its truth value" (Carraher & Schliemann, p. 270).

The topics in Chapter 12 address all of these issues with the exception of the first. You may find it interesting to check this belief with your own students. Also, the work here with symbols can be confusing, as noted by Usiskin (1988), who presented five equations (in the sense of having an equation sign in them) involving such symbols. His purpose was to illustrate a psychological rather than a logical complexity faced by students and teachers. Consider the following:

1. $A = LW$
2. $40 = 5x$
3. $\sin x = \cos x \cdot \tan x$
4. $1 = n \cdot \frac{1}{n}$
5. $y = kx$

Each of these equations uses letters in a different way. As Usiskin observed, "We usually call (1) a formula, (2) an equation (or open sentence) to solve, (3) an identity, (4) a property, and (5) an equation of a function of direct variation.... Only in (5) is there the feel of "variability" from which the term *variable* arose" (p. 9). These multiple uses of symbols are something to keep in mind in this chapter and future chapters.

INSTRUCTOR NOTE 12.1A What students should already know

As part of Chapter 10 of Part I, we focused on properties of real number operations and defined a field as a set of numbers having the standard eleven properties of operations. Students should have this knowledge but we know many do not, and we repeat this content here because it is crucial to the study of algebraic reasoning. If your students have studied these properties in a previous course, you may be able to skip over some of this chapter. However, there is value in connecting these properties to student thinking (as in Activity 1) and t models (as in Examples 5 and 6). We also note that Appendix F contains a review of basic arithmetic, including a review of signed numbers and of properties of addition and multiplication.

INSTRUCTOR NOTE 12.1B Using properties in mental computation

If you have the time, you will find that spending more time on mental computation, using examples and Learning Exercises from Chapter 5, is worthwhile. Properties of operations and other properties, such as what happens when a number is multiplied or divided by some power of 10, can be reviewed as they are used. We have seen a fourth-grade teacher undertake mental computation in her class by asking a series of questions such as: What is 8×7? What is 80×7? What is 800×7? What is 800×70? What is 801×70? (which makes use of the distributive property) and so on, in each case asking her students for the name of the property used to get from one step to the next. Students may first be asked to make statements about how the product is affected by a change in the factors (e.g., when a factor is multiplied by 10, the product is multiplied by 10).

INSTRUCTOR NOTE 12.2A Connecting algebra and arithmetic

In this section, we review arithmetic operations on whole numbers and fractions. Students are often surprised when they can now make sense of the "rules" for operating on algebraic expressions because they are the same rules used when operating on numbers. Teachers who understand this transfer effect can make algebra much easier to learn than it now is for many students. You may want to provide additional exercises from an algebra textbook and ask students how those problems relate to arithmetic exercises.

INSTRUCTOR NOTE 12.3A   A justification

An algebraic justification follows from calculating $(10n + 5)^2$, where n is the number of tens. Once the shortcut is found, follow-up with questions such as asking whether the shortcut can be applied to squaring three-digit numbers like 105 or whether it can be used with, say, 4.5^2 or $(6\frac{1}{2})^2$ or 155^2.

INSTRUCTOR NOTE 12.4A The principle of parsimony

When there is more than one rule that describes a set of data, the guide we rely on is called Occam's razor, or the principle of parsimony: *The simplest explanation is the best one.* So if there is no way to check further, $y = x + 50$ would naturally be the one used (but tentatively). As mentioned in the text, at some stage, children (and their teachers) should know that trusting a generalization based on a pattern is risky, even though most work in the schools proceeds as though the simplest rule is the only one possible.

You may wonder how a "razor" enters in. This excerpt, "Occam's Razor" from http://pespmc1.vub.ac.be/OCCAMRAZ.html, gives an explanation:

> Occam's razor is a logical principle attributed to the mediaeval philosopher William of Occam (or Ockham). The principle states that one should not make more assumptions than the minimum needed. This principle is often called the principle of parsimony. It underlies all scientific modeling and theory building. It admonishes us to choose from a set of otherwise equivalent models of a given phenomenon the simplest one. In any given model, Occam's razor helps us to "shave off" those concepts, variables or constructs that are not really needed to explain the phenomenon. By doing that, developing the model will become much easier, and there is less chance of introducing inconsistencies, ambiguities and redundancies.

You may also wonder about two topics that are missing at this point. We rarely have had time to pursue the following one. But the technique might help to cast a bit more doubt on conclusions based on patterns, or it may be useful in case a student doubts that any other function is possible. The pattern in the table below would certainly suggest that for $x = 4$, y must be 12. But independent of some real-life source for the data (which could then be checked for the $x = 4$ case), *any* value could be put for y, for the $x = 4$ case! Say you want a rule that would give 52 or some mixed or irrational number. Study the equation to the right of the table to get the idea of how to generate such a rule.

x	y
1	9
2	10
3	11
4	? (52?)

$$y = 9 \cdot \frac{(x-2)(x-3)(x-4)}{(1-2)(1-3)(1-4)} +$$
$$10 \cdot \frac{(x-1)(x-3)(x-4)}{(2-1)(2-3)(2-4)} +$$
$$11 \cdot \frac{(x-1)(x-2)(x-4)}{(3-1)(3-2)(3-4)} +$$
$$52 \cdot \frac{(x-1)(x-2)(x-3)}{(4-1)(4-2)(4-3)}$$

A second topic omitted at this point is the "differencing" technique that enables one to predict some function rules (quadratic, cubic,…, as well as linear). The technique is introduced in Section 15.5, although it may partially arise naturally in Chapter 13 when rates of change for nonlinear situations can be examined.

INSTRUCTOR NOTE 12.5A   An example of quantitative reasoning

Students who did not study quantitative reasoning in Part I, *Reasoning about Numbers and Quantities*, may need some additional examples from you, the instructor. We discuss one here, called the dieter's problem, which was provided in the instructor notes from Part I. There is an extra element to this problem that you will also want to discuss, and that is the difference between additive reasoning and multiplicative reasoning. In a nutshell, additive reasoning is used to compare quantities by subtraction, whereas multiplicative reasoning is used to compare quantities using a ratio. For example, if a puppy weighs 7 pounds when purchased and 21 pounds six months later, we could compare these two quantities additively by subtracting 7 from 21 and saying the dog weighs 14 pounds more. But we could also apply multiplicative reasoning using a ratio of 21 to 7 and say the dog has tripled its weight. Multiplicative reasoning is a form of proportional reasoning, an extremely important "big idea" of upper elementary- and middle-school grades.

We basically use the following steps when using quantitative reasoning to solve a word problem. First, identify the quantities, some of which are not stated. (Thus, we might talk about the puppy's weight when purchased, which is stated. We could talk about how much weight the puppy gained, which is not stated.) Second, we identify the values for each quantity. (The puppy's weight when purchased was 7 pounds.) Some of the values are unknown. Third, we identify the relationships among the quantities. This is often best done using drawings. And fourth, only now do we actually carry out any operations to find the answer. *What is crucially important is that these steps prevent students from doing what they usually do: noting the numbers then guessing which operations will lead to the answer.*

Here is the dieter's problem, solved using these four steps. This problem involves both multiplicative and additive reasoning.

  Dieter A: "I lost $\frac{1}{8}$ of my weight. I lost 19 pounds."

  Dieter B: "I lost $\frac{1}{6}$ of my weight, and now you weigh 2 pounds less than I do"

How much weight did Dieter B lose? ♦

First: Make a list of the relevant quantities, and only then fill in the values that you know:
Dieter A's weight before the diet
Dieter A's weight after the diet
Dieter B's weight before the diet
Dieter B's weight after the diet
The fraction of weight lost by Dieter A $\frac{1}{8}$

The fraction of weight lost by Dieter B $\frac{1}{6}$

The amount of weight lost by Dieter A 19 pounds
The amount of weight lost by Dieter B
The difference in their weights before the diets
The difference in their weights after the diets 2 pounds (A is 2 pounds less than B)

You can help students see how these quantities are related to each other by drawing a diagram such as the following that shows the relationships between quantities in the situation.

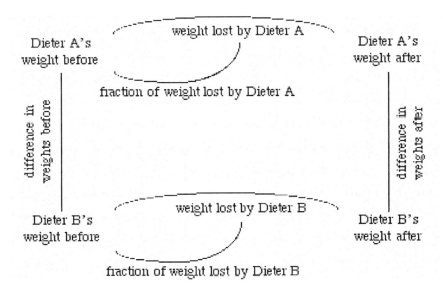

Here are the key points to bring out:

- This diagram involves only quantities, but no actual values.

- Understanding the relationships in this diagram *is* understanding the problem.

- It doesn't really matter what values are given in the problem because once we understand the diagram we can use the relationships between quantities to find the values that we need. Understanding the problem is independent of the values that are given in the problem.

A key to understanding the Dieter's Problem is to realize that there are two different ways to compare the weights before and after the diet. You can either look at the difference (the weight lost) or the ratio (the fraction of the weight lost). Given the fraction of weight lost and the original weight, many students can find the new weight. However, students have difficulty trying to find the original weight, given the fraction lost and the new weight (which is what they must do in this problem). To help students see the relationships between these quantities, the following diagram may be helpful:

Dieter A's original weight (before diet)

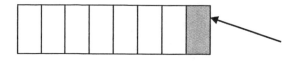

Weight lost = $\frac{1}{8}$ of A's original weight. Weight lost is 19 pounds.

Thus, 19×8 is 152, which is A's weight before the diet.

$152 - 19 = 133$, which is A's weight after the diet. (take-away subtraction)

$133 + 2 = 135$ is B's weight after the diet. (additive comparison)

135 is $\frac{5}{6}$ of B's weight before the diet, so B weighed 162 pounds.

B lost $162 - 135 = 27$ pounds.

INSTRUCTOR NOTE 12.5B Helping students reason quantitatively

First, list quantities, *then* values. You may want first to distinguish between relevant quantities and irrelevant quantities (the first six are irrelevant, the last four are relevant).

Quantities	Values
Tom's age	16
Dick's age	14
Harry's age	9
Amount Tom paid	$4
Amount Dick paid	$2
Amount Harry paid	$3
Size of the pie	1 (whole)
Amount eaten by Tom	?
Amount eaten by Dick	?
Amount eaten by Harry	?

Then, a drawing helps visualize the relationships and leads to the answer (without algebra needed).

Tom

Harry

Dick

These are multiplicative comparisons because we use ratios to compare amounts: Comparing Toms and Harry's amounts is a 2:1 ratio. Comparing Dick's and Harry's amounts is a $1\frac{1}{2}$: 1 ratio. Comparing Tom's and Dick's amounts is a $2:1\frac{1}{2}$ ratio.

Putting all the parts together, using halves of what Harry had, yields 9 equal parts of which Tom ate 4, Harry ate 2, and Dick ate 3.

Total

Thus, Tom ate $\frac{4}{9}$ of the pie, Harry ate $\frac{2}{9}$ of the pie, and Dick ate $\frac{3}{9}$ of the pie.

Instructor Notes for Chapter 13: A Quantitative Approach to Algebra and Graphing

INSTRUCTOR NOTE 13: OVERVIEW OF CHAPTER 13

Here are the sections in this chapter and a sketch of their contents:

13.1 *Using Graphs and Algebra to Show Quantitative Relationships.* Students make graphs and write equations that exemplify an algebraic situation.

13.2 *Understanding Slope: Making Connections Across Quantitative Situations, Graphs, and Algebraic Equations.* Situations with a constant rate of change lead to a line of the form $y = mx + b$, where m is the slope and b the y-intercept.

13.3 *Linear Functions and Proportional Relationships.* A linear function yielding a line that passes through the origin is shown to represent a proportion.

13.4 *Nonlinear Functions.* This section contains a brief treatment of parabolic, absolute value, and exponential functions.

13.5 *Issues for Learning: Algebra in the Elementary Grades.* Algebraic ideas suitable for instruction in the elementary school are outlined, based on the *Principles and Standards for School Mathematics,* a publication of the National Council of Teachers of Mathematics.

13.6 *Check Yourself.* This section, as with all *Check Yourself* sections at the end of chapters, provides a summary of the chapter.

Many researchers and other educators have advocated a quantitative approach to algebra (e.g., Conference Board of Mathematical Sciences, 2000; Carraher & Schliemann, 2007; Lacampagne, Blair, & Kaput, 1995; Smith & Thompson, 2007). Thompson and Thompson (1995) outlined an approach in which students first identified quantities, explored how the quantities were related, and then used algebra as a language to represent the quantitative relationship. This approach addresses the lack of attention in traditional instruction on the use of algebraic symbols as varying quantities as opposed to unknowns (Philipp, 1992). You may wish to look at Kieran (1993, pp. 192–93) for a history of the quantitative approach to functions.

INSTRUCTOR NOTE 13.1A Student graphs for Activity 2

It is important to leave this activity as open as possible. Let students decide what their graphs should look like and what should go on each axis. It is important *not* to tell them to put time on the horizontal axis. If students are confused, tell them to graph the situation any way they can. Don't be surprised if the graphs differ across groups. The figure below contains rough sketches of six groups' graphs that were taken from the same classroom.

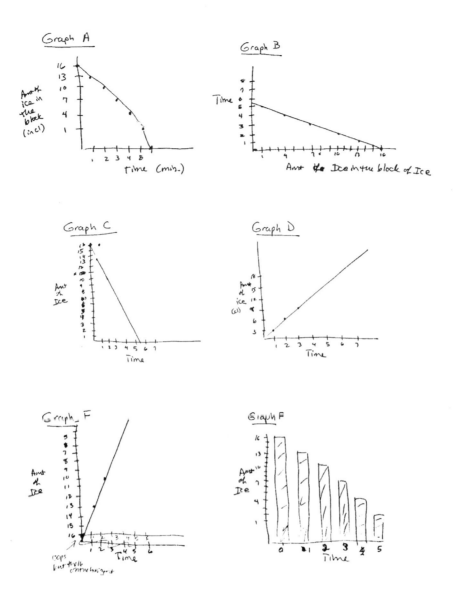

Figure: Examples of Graphs for "A Picture Is Worth 1000 Words."

The first goal of a follow-up discussion should be to figure out whether or not all the graphs capture the right information. For example, Graph D (see figure) is incorrect because the group wrote the correct quantity on the *y*-axis but actually graphed the amount of water that had melted, not the amount of water left in the block of ice. Graph A is also incorrect toward the end.

Discussing the notion of convention here is also important. Notice that Graphs B and C illustrate this situation by switching the quantities on the axes. Some students may say that "you're supposed to put time on the *x*-axis because it's the independent variable," but they don't know why. A discussion leading to reason that both graphs represent the same information and that neither graph is "wrong" is helpful here. However, Graph C is more conventional. To see why we typically use Graph C, ask students to tell you about the block of ice situation using each graph. In Graph C, it is fairly easy for students to read the graph from left to right and say that as time is passing, the block of ice is getting smaller. It is more difficult to read Graph B by reading from left to right.

Students soon catch on that they want the graph to fall from the left to the right to show that something is decreasing. Notice that both Graphs B and C fall from left to right (i.e., have a negative slope). However, if we allow the reverse ordering of numbers on Graph E, the graph looks completely different—it rises from left to right. Some students will think Graph E is too confusing for this reason, and also because they are accustomed to seeing 0 at the bottom (not 16). Other students might think Graph E is okay.

When discussing Graph F, ask your students: What information can be determined from Graphs B or C but not from F? How much ice is left in the block after 2.5 minutes?

INSTRUCTOR NOTE 13.2A Misconceptions about slope

Activity 5 in this section introduces the concept of slope and addresses some misconceptions that are often held. Students can usually remember the slope formula ("rise over run"), but the value of the slope often holds little meaning for them. Many do not see the slope as measuring how one quantity in the situation changes with respect to the other.

Sometimes when operations on the numbers are easy (e.g., when the calculation results in a whole number), students can interpret the meaning of slope. For example, in 2a of the activity many students will be able to say that the 20 means "20 miles per gallon." However, many students will have difficulty interpreting the slope in 1a, even if they are able to correctly compute this slope as $\frac{1}{20}$. They often want to read this as "1 to 20" or even "20 miles per gallon," rather than "$\frac{1}{20}$ of a gallon per mile." (In fact, many students think that the slopes in parts 1a and 2a are the same.) Asking students what the $\frac{1}{20}$ means as a *value* helps them think about this slope as the amount of fuel that is used per *one* mile traveled.

Another common misconception is to think that slope is a measure of the steepness of a line, without thinking about the scale that is used. It is not until you change the scale (in Activity 7) that this difference becomes evident. This is an important point to discuss. Students will often look at two different graphs and automatically say that the one that looks "steeper" has the larger slope, even though the scales on the two graphs may be quite different. Students also tend to equate "less steep" with small values of slope and "more steep" with large values of slope.

INSTRUCTOR NOTE 13.3A

Proportional reasoning runs through all parts of this textbook. In Part I, *Reasoning about Numbers and Quantities,* students considered ratios and proportions as a part of their study of multiplicative reasoning. Ratios were used to compare quantities multiplicatively. In Part II, *Reasoning about Algebra and Change,* students learn that relationships between quantities that are linear and pass through the origin are proportional in nature.

You may want to take more problems from Part I for practice. See Chapter 9 in particular.

INSTRUCTOR NOTE 13.3B Input and output of the soda machine

Here are some sample answers for *The Soda Machine* activity.

1. How many cups does one container of fluid hold? Explain.
   The 8 containers together contain the same amount of fluid as the 6 cups together. The amount of fluid in 1 container is $\frac{1}{8}$ of the fluid in the 8 containers. One-eighth of the fluid in the 8 containers is also the same amount as $\frac{1}{8}$ of the fluid in 6 cups. But $\frac{1}{8}$ of 6 is $\frac{6}{8}$.
   So, 1 container holds $\frac{6}{8}$ cups of fluid.

2. How many containers of fluid does one cup hold? Explain.
   The 8 containers together contain the same amount of fluid as the 6 cups together. The amount of fluid in 1 cup is $\frac{1}{6}$ of the fluid in the 6 cups; $\frac{1}{6}$ of the fluid in the 6 cups is also the same amount as $\frac{1}{6}$ of the fluid in 8 containers; $\frac{1}{6}$ of 8 is $\frac{8}{6}$. So, 1 cup holds $\frac{8}{6}$ containers of fluid.

3. What fraction of each cup is made up of Secret Formula? Explain.
   Since every 8 containers contain 3 containers of Secret Formula, every fraction of 8 containers will contain that same fraction of 3 containers Secret Formula. It's like saying any amount of soda pop is always $\frac{3}{8}$ (37.5%) Secret Formula. Since any amount of soda pop is 37.5% secret formula, then 1 cup is 37.5% Secret Formula.

4. What fraction of each cup is made up of water? Explain.
   A cup of soda pop is $\frac{3}{8}$ secret formula. Since soda pop is made completely of secret formula and water, what is not secret formula must be water. So a cup of soda pop is $\frac{5}{8}$ (i.e., $1\frac{3}{8}$) water.

5. Complete this table (orientation is different than the table in the text):

Containers of Sec. Form.	Containers of Water	Cups of Soda Pop
3	5	6
$3 \times \frac{8}{5}$ There are 8 cups of water, so there is $\frac{8}{5}$ times as much water as the first row. So there is $\frac{8}{5}$ times as much Secret Formula as in the first row.	8	$6 \times \frac{8}{5}$ There are 8 cups of water, so there is $\frac{8}{5}$ times as much water as the first row. So there is $\frac{8}{5}$ times as much soda pop as in the first row.
4	$5 \times \frac{4}{3}$ There are 4 cups of Secret Formula, so there is $\frac{4}{3}$ times as much Secret Formula as in the first row. So there is $\frac{4}{3}$ times as much water as in the first row.	$6 \times \frac{4}{3}$ There are 4 cups of Secret Formula, so there is $\frac{4}{3}$ times as much Secret Formula as in the first row. So there is $\frac{4}{3}$ times as much soda pop as in the first row.
$3 \times \frac{9}{6}$	$5 \times \frac{9}{6}$	9

There are 9 cups of soda pop, so there is $\frac{9}{6}$ times as much soda pop as in the first row. So there is $\frac{9}{6}$ times as much Secret Formula as in the first row.	There are 9 cups of soda pop, so there is $\frac{9}{6}$ times as much soda pop as in the first row. So there is $\frac{9}{6}$ times as much water as in the first row.	
7	$5 \times \frac{7}{3}$	$6 \times \frac{7}{3}$
$3 \times \frac{18}{5}$	**18**	$6 \times \frac{18}{5}$
n	$5 \times \frac{n}{3}$ There are n cups of Secret Formula, so there is $\frac{n}{3}$ times as much Secret Formula as in the first row. So there is $\frac{n}{3}$ times as much water as in the first row.	$6 \times \frac{n}{3}$ There are n cups of Secret Formula, so there is $\frac{n}{3}$ times as much Secret Formula as in the first row. So there is $\frac{n}{3}$ times as much soda pop as in the first row.
$3 \times \frac{k}{5}$ There are k cups of water, so there is $\frac{k}{5}$ times as much water as in the first row. So there is $\frac{k}{5}$ times as much Secret Formula as in the first row.	**k**	$6 \times \frac{k}{5}$ There are k cups of water, so there is $\frac{k}{5}$ times as much water as in the first row. So there is $\frac{k}{5}$ times as much soda pop as in the first row.
$3 \times \frac{h}{6}$ There are h cups of soda pop, so there is $\frac{h}{6}$ times as much soda pop as in the first row. So there is $\frac{h}{6}$ times as much secret formula as in the first row.	$5 \times \frac{h}{6}$ There are h cups of soda pop, so there is $\frac{h}{6}$ times as much soda pop as in the first row. So there is $\frac{h}{6}$ times as much water as in the first row.	**h**

Instructor Notes for Chapter 14: Understanding Change: Relationships Among Time, Distance, and Rate

INSTRUCTOR NOTE 14: OVERVIEW OF CHAPTER 14

Here are the sections in Chapter 14:

14.1 *Distance-Time and Position-Time Graphs.* Cartoon settings are represented with qualitative graphs.

14.2 *Using Motion Detectors.* This is an optional section, but some are doable exercises without motion detectors. We recommend including it if you have access to at least one motion detector.

14.3 *Graphs of Speed Against Time.* Speed-time graphs are shown to be related to distance-time graphs.

14.4 *Interpreting Graphs.* Stories are created for qualitative graphs and vice versa.

14.5 *Issues for Learning: Common Graphing Errors.* Errors from not knowing graphing conventions are discussed, including the "graph as picture" misconception.

14.6 *Check Yourself.*

Students often have a great deal of difficulty thinking simultaneously of distance, time, and rate (speed) as three related quantities, even when they can manipulate $d = rt$ equations with some facility. Hence, the focus at this time is on those quantities *as* quantities, on their relationships, and on graphs, with equation-writing building on that focus.

We use the term *speed* rather than *velocity* because speed is most likely the term elementary teachers will use with their students. Keep in mind, however, that the term velocity could be used instead. (In fact, the distinction between the conventional uses of these terms is discussed later in association with negative velocity, but only in a positive/negative sense, not the sense of velocity as a vector.)

We have found that it can be very powerful to begin the chapter (or the algebraic reasoning unit of a class) with a motion detector activity. With only one motion detector, a student in front of the room can be asked (through directions on an index card) to walk in a particular way (e.g., start a distance away from the motion detector and walk slowly toward it, at a constant speed). Students can then discuss what is being represented on the projected graph and why the graph looks as it does. See 14.2A.

INSTRUCTOR NOTE 14.1A: Relationships among quantities

The purpose of this example is to help students understand the relationships among the quantities *before* they try to graph them. You might help them produce a chart such as the following as you progress through Activities 1, 2, and 4 (Activity 4 is in Section 14.3).

Quantities	Segment 1 of story	Segment 2 of story	Segment 3 of story
Distance & Time (Focus of Activity 1)	Distance increases as time increases.	Distance stays the same as time passes.	Distance continues to increase again as time passes.
Distance from the Cave & Time (Focus of Activity 2; the final segment would differ)	Distance from cave increases as time increases.	Distance from cave stays the same as time passes.	Distance from cave decreases as time passes.
Speed & Time (Focus of Activity 4)	Speed is slow yet constant—it does not increase or decrease as time passes.	Speed doesn't change (it's 0) as time passes.	Speed is faster than in Segment 1 but doesn't increase or decrease during Segment 3, as time passes.

Of course, you don't physically have to produce this chart. The point is for students to be able to use this type of language to describe the relationships between quantities for the various segments of time.

INSTRUCTOR NOTE 14.1B Sample graphs for Example 1 and Activity 2

Here are sample graphs for Example 1 and Activity 2, leading up to where (total) distance-time and position-time graphs are contrasted.

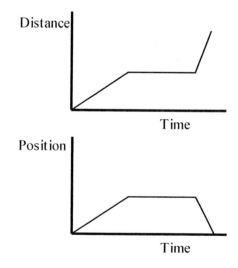

INSTRUCTOR NOTE 14.2A Where to find motion detectors

If you have the resources, we highly recommend using a motion detector, at least for demonstration, either with a computer or with a calculator (see http://www.vernier.com). Nothing else seems to bring home to students what graphs of motion really look like. Students often refer back to motion detector graphs as they work problems in the later units.

Information about Motion Detector Set Ups   Sources of equipment include http://www.vernier.com/. Motion detectors may be connected to computers or to some Texas Instrument calculators (http://education.ti.com, and its CBR). A display mechanism, such as a document camera, facilitates class discussions of graphs made by walks.

In Section 14.3, students explore velocity versus time graphs. Some motion detector software can also display velocity versus time graphs (as well as acceleration versus time graphs, and force versus time graphs).

INSTRUCTOR NOTE 14.2B Common misconceptions about graphs

The *Take a Hike* activity can reveal two general misconceptions about graphs of motion:

1. Graph as Line Segment Misconception

Students with this misconception, which was identified by Thompson (1994), often view graphs of functions (and linear relations in particular) as complete objects that can be bent much as physical wires. Thompson contrasted this view with a pointwise interpretation of graphs as sets of points. In a pointwise view, one cannot simply pick up or bend a graph without changing the underlying relationships.

Here is one example of how the graph-as-line-segment misconception can lead to some confusion. The students are trying to make a graph with a steep negative slope. After the walker creates one graph, another student suggests that, in order to make a steeper slope, he should stand farther back. Thus, for her, the graph would be steeper if one could slant it up more by raising the *y*-intercept. The motion detector enables her to test out her theory empirically and then revise her thinking. At the end of the segment, she concludes that if she walks faster, she can cover the same amount of distance in less time. She then draws a graph in which she starts at the same location but finishes sooner and hence creates a graph with a steeper slope.

2. Graph as Path Misconception

The graph-as-path view has been well documented in the literature (cf. Bell & Janvier, 1981; Leinhardt, Zaslavsky, & Stein, 1990; Monk, 1992) and often arises in this exercise. When students are asked, for example, to create a graph of a line with a negative slope, they may walk on a diagonal path. What they soon notice is that the motion detector cannot follow them; this realization leads to a better understanding of the fact that the graph is measuring motion in only one dimension. It is interesting to note that even after students have rectified their understandings when trying to create a line graph, some may return to the graph-as-path view and walk in a parabolic or circular path when completing Part 3 of Activity 3.

Graph 4c in the *Take a Hike* activity can form the basis of a rich discussion of continuity. Although it is technically impossible (except in cartoons) to instantaneously jump from one place to another, the graphs we draw as mathematical models need not always reflect physical possibilities. Similarly, Graphs 4f and 4g can support conversations about being in two places at once. Students interpreting Graph 4g may suggest that the walker is "going back in time." This interpretation may once again reflect a graph-as-path view rather than a pointwise interpretation.

See also Section 14.5.

INSTRUCTOR NOTE 14.3A   Problems relating speed and time

In this section, we discuss the relationship between speed and time and can again relate speed to the slope of the distance-time graph. Students often have difficulty graphing speed against time, especially when they are asked to go back and forth between speed-time and distance-time graphs. For example, many students want to draw constant speed in a speed-time graph as a "slanted" line (as in a distance-time graph), not as a horizontal line.

When reasoning about speed, try not to let students simply talk about the "steepness" of a line or curve in the distance-time graph. Force them to use the quantities of distance and time in their explanations. For example, the second version is more precise than the first one is:

> "Jack's speed is faster than the Karen's speed because the graph for Jack's trip is steeper than the graph for Karen's trip."

versus

> "Jack's speed is faster than Karen's speed because, in the same amount of time, Jack travels a larger distance than Karen does."

INSTRUCTOR NOTE 14.3B   Negative velocity

Part 4 of Activity 4 provides an opportunity to discuss the notion of negative velocity, and the distinction between velocity and speed. This topic is worth some discussion, as students frequently do not understand the concept of negative velocity. For many of them, speed and velocity are identical—they both measure "how fast." Because negative numbers are less than 0, students often reason that a negative speed must be "less fast" than a speed of 0 (which is, of course, impossible). Thus, the notion of negative velocity does not hold any meaning to these students. Again, only positive/negative velocity come up in the module, not the full-fledged vector treatment of velocity that you may know.

One way to help students understand negative velocities within the context of the Wile E. Coyote activity is to return to the graphs of total distance and distance from the cave and think about Wile E.'s speed (velocity) in each case. For the third segment of the journey, the total-distance graph has positive slope while the distance-from-the-cave graph has negative slope. Although students feel comfortable with this situation, they are often unwilling to make the next leap and say that Wile E.'s velocity is positive on the total distance graph and *negative* on the distance-from-the-cave graph. The key here is to think about speed as not just "how fast" but as a rate that measures how two quantities change in relation to each other. During Segment 3, the total distance traveled is increasing every second, but the distance from the cave is decreasing every second. You may want to equate this with another context such as withdrawing money from an account at regular intervals. Students will likely accept this as a situation involving a negative rate of change. If they think about distance decreasing over time as a similar situation, they may be more willing to accept the notion of negative velocity.

INSTRUCTOR NOTE 14.3C When endpoints have open or closed circles

The diagram in Part 4 of Activity 4 uses open and closed circles. This may need to be discussed with students. Often they will want to connect line segments so that the graph is continuous, sometimes by drawing a vertical line. Discuss why it doesn't make sense to do this (that is, you can't be going more than one speed at a specific point in time). Also remind students that this is the cartoon world, so it is possible to change speeds instantly.

INSTRUCTOR NOTE 14.4A Story from a student

Here is one story written by a student:

A man is driving down a hill, accelerating at a constant rate as he travels. At the bottom of the hill, he immediately starts up another hill, slowing down at a steady rate and just making it to the top of the hill. At the top of the hill, he stops and looks at the view. He then accelerates at a steady rate until he reaches a reasonable speed. Then he travels for a while at that speed.

INSTRUCTOR NOTE 14.4B The topic of *change* in the elementary curriculum

As you probably have noticed, the mathematical experiences of many students lead them to focus primarily on generating numerical answers, so they are sometimes reluctant to give a prose answer to a question. We have had some luck in convincing these prospective teachers that, as noted in the text, giving explanations is what they will be doing when they teach, so giving explanations here is good practice, even though some of the ideas are more advanced than those they will be teaching. Good explanations tell *why* something might have happened and are not just reports of *what* happened; good explanations should use technical language correctly and not mix up different ideas (e.g., use "height" when "rate" is intended, or vice versa).

One curriculum project developed with funding from the National Science Foundation is TERC's *Investigations in Number, Data, and Space* curriculum for Grades K–5. If you have access to the Grade 4 material, you will find a very nice unit on graphing called "Changes over Time." The approach to graphing is very similar to the quantitative approach you have seen in this unit. In one investigation, students first collect height data over time for some seeds that they plant. Some pages from the *Investigations* unit show how to help young students make connections between the plant situation and graphs. It is good for prospective teachers to make a connection between what they are doing in this class and how it relates to elementary school textbooks. If you can make overhead transparencies of these pages, have your students work each problem. We have used these pages with the following activity:

Activity: Grade each of the following *explanations* (written by former prospective elementary teachers) on a 0–5-point scale. The problem that the students were working on follows. It is from TERC's elementary school curriculum, *Investigations in Number, Data, and Space* (in *Changes over Time*, p. 94).

Problem: Which plant is growing faster during the time shown on the graph, plant E or plant F? Tell how you decided.

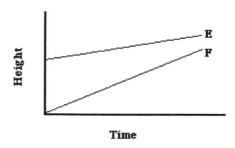

1. Plant F is growing more quickly. Over time, Plant E's height is beginning to decrease. Its height was increasing more at the beginning of time. Plant F over time is continually steadily increasing its height.

2. Plant F is growing faster because in the same amount of time, plant F's height is greater.

3. Plant F is growing faster because the distance where Plant F began growing to the time it stopped it looks as if it has grown about twice the height of Plant E.

4. Line F had a greater vertical gain than Line E in an equal time. That means Plant F grew more in the same time as Plant E. So Plant F grew faster than Plant E.

5. Plant F. In the same allotted time, Plant E and F have the same size. But it seems that Plant E had an advantage in size when Plant E and F were compared. Consequently, Plant F has grown faster.

6. Plant F is growing faster because the angle of the line is steeper than Plant E.

Then discuss:

1. What are some characteristics of a good explanation?

2. Characterize some common difficulties writing explanations.

3. Middle school (and high school) students often confuse steepness with height. For example, a common incorrect response to the original plant question is that Plant E is growing faster because it is "higher" than Plant F (because the line for Plant E is "above" the line for Plant F). How could you help a student who responded this way? Would saying that the line for Plant F is steeper than the line for Plant E help? Why or why not?

Note that we have a page from the TERC materials for Grade 4 included in this chapter.

Instructor Notes for Chapter 15: Further Topics in Algebra and Change

INSTRUCTOR NOTE 15: OVERVIEW OF CHAPTER 15

Sections in Chapter 15 are as follows:

15.1 *Finding Linear Equations.* The focus here is on writing equations of a line, using a point-slope form and the two-point form.

15.2 *Solving Two Linear Equations in Two Variables.* Problems sometimes lead to two equations in two variables. How are these problems solved?

15.3 *Different Approaches to Problems.* Numerical, graphical and algebraic approaches are explored.

15.4 *Average Speed and Weighted Averages.* An applet is used to allow students to deal with average speed. Weighted averages in other situations are also studied.

15.5 *More about Functions.* Functions in nonnumerical settings, composition of functions, and the differencing technique are explored.

15.6 *Issues for Learning: Topics in Algebra.* Research on the learning and teaching of algebra is presented.

15.7 *Check Yourself.*

The topics in this chapter bring together and build on topics in Chapters 12, 13, and 14. Sections 15.1 and 15.2 provide additional information for, and review of, linear equations and lessons here are more traditional in format. Sections 15.3 and 15.4 form the heart of this chapter and, depending on time constraints, may be the only two sections you choose from this chapter; Section 15.3 is more dependent on the previous two sections, however, so you would need to provide some supplementation if you skip the first two sections and begin with Section 15.3. We strongly urge you to include Section 15.4 if you have time for only one section. Section 15.5 considers topics that are useful but not as important for elementary teachers as previous sections. Section 15.6 considers difficulties students (including prospective teachers) have with this content, based on research.

INSTRUCTOR NOTE 15.3A Electronic games

1. Solving by arithmetic, we see that costs are the same with the purchase of 6 games.

Pretendo		Sega-Nemesis	
Games	Cost in $	Games	Cost in $
0	180	0	120
1	220	1	170
2	260	2	220
3	300	3	270
4	340	4	320
5	380	5	370
6	420	6	420
7	460	7	470

2. The lines will have equations $P(g) = 180 + 40g$ and $S(g) = 120 + 50g$ and will intersect at (6, 420).
3. $180 + 40g = 120 + 50g$, $10g = 60$, $g = 6$ The cost is the same if 6 games are purchased.
4. Pretendo begins at $180 and Sega-Nemesis begins at $120, so Sega-Nemesis has to make up a difference of $60. For each game bought, it makes up $10, so it will take 6 games to make up the difference of $60.

INSTRUCTOR NOTE 15.4A The big ideas associated with weighted averages

Three major ideas are addressed here: (1) the notion of rate as a proportional quantity (see Section 9.2); (2) the notion of using constant speed to model a trip composed of different speeds; and (3) the concept of average speed and weighted averages. The activities are designed to support the development of increasingly sophisticated concepts of speed ranging from speed as distance to speed as ratio to the concept of speed as a rate. According to Thompson (1994), students conceptualizing speed as rate experience the situations described here as involving covarying accumulations of the quantities of distance and time. The concept of average speed is developed in the first activity by exploring the constant speed at which a character would have to run in order to tie another character with more sporadic speeds. The concept of using constant speed as a way to model varying patterns is designed to provide students with a tool for further exploration of average rate. Although students know that it is unrealistic to travel at a constant speed for any given period of time, it is very handy to think about constant speed as a theoretical tool for modeling a trip in which a character travels a given distance in a given period of time at different speeds.

Similarly, many students will not know how to work with weighted averages. You will find that many students have no idea how grade-point averages are calculated, for example.

One instructor has used Simpson's paradox to motivate the idea of weighted averages. The paradox involves situations in which a piecemeal superiority nonetheless gives a cumulative inferiority! Sorting out what is incorrect is a bit involved, so we did not include a sample for the students. But if you choose to include the topic, here is an example.

Example involving Simpson's paradox: Two baseball players, A and B, have a friendly competition about who is the better batter. So they keep track for two weeks. During week 1, A gets 1 hit out of 5 at-bats (20% or 0.200), and B gets 5 hits out of 20 at-bats (25% or 0.250). During week 2, A gets 14 hits out of 25 at-bats (56% or 0.560), and B gets 7 hits out of 10 at-bats (70% or 0.700). So each week, player B's average is better than player A's: 25% versus 20% and 70% versus 56%. On looking at the total performance for the two weeks, however, player A got 15 hits in 30 at-bats (50% or 0.500) and player B got 12 hits in 30 at-bats (only 40% or 0.400).

Explanation: The apparent paradox shows the importance of weighting averages on partial performances. Player A's performances were based during week 1 on only 1/6 of the total, but during week 2, on 5/6 of the total. So naturally the week-2 performance dominates. Player B, on the other hand, during week 1 batted 2/3 of the total at-bats, and only 1/3 during week 2, so the week-1 performance dominates. Weighting the weekly performances by their overall significance gives the following calculations.

Player A: $\frac{1}{6} \times 0.2 + \frac{5}{6} \times 0.56 = 0.5$, and

Player B: $\frac{2}{3} \times 0.25 + \frac{1}{3} \times 0.7 = 0.4$.

Wikipedia (http://en.wikipedia.org) gives other examples of Simpson's paradox.

INSTRUCTOR NOTE 15.4B

The (0, 0) and (150, 800) points are the easiest ones to use to calculate the slope of the dashed line in the figure that follows, of course. The earlier work with constant speeds should help students understand that the slope of the dashed line gives a constant speed that would cover the same distance for the whole trip in the same time, that is, the average speed for the trip.

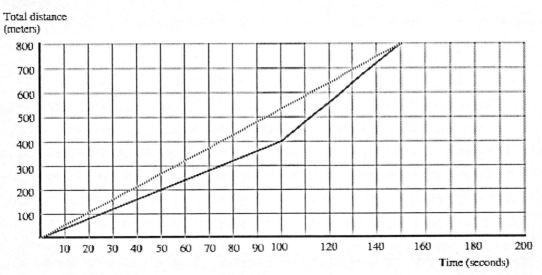

INSTRUCTOR NOTE 15.4C

Over and Back (supplied) is a Java program than can be accessed from the Internet at the site given in Activity 10. *Over and Back* can be used in a variety of ways, depending on your computer facilities (and time constraints): demonstration in class; a class held in a computer lab, with two or three students per computer; or as an out-of-class assignment after an in-class demonstration. The scale on the distance line can be changed, as can the speeds. This program was designed by Janet Bowers and builds on an earlier program designed by Pat Thompson.

INSTRUCTOR NOTE 15.5A

The *Painted Cubes* activity is also described in the 1989 NCTM *Curriculum and Evaluation Standards for School Mathematics* (p. 99), which might be more readily available than the Phillips booklet is. Following are some answers for the general case; students might need some hints (for example, "for the 2-squares-painted cases, write them as multiples of 12: $0 = 0 \times 12$, $12 = 1 \times 12$, $24 = 2 \times 12$, $36 = 3 \times 12$"), although an insightful approach might give the generalization (see the parenthetical notes with the answers).

> For a cube n on each edge,
> 3 squares painted: 8, for any n (the 8 corner cubes)
> 2 squares painted: $12(n-2)$ (the cubes not in corners but along the 12 edges)
> 1 square painted: $6(n-2)^2$ (the cubes with just one face showing; there are 6 faces)
> 0 squares painted: $(n-2)^3$ (the cubes inside).

The activity itself does not call for a graph, but as time permits, you might show graphs or ask for graphs so that students are reminded that graphs may not involve collinear points.

Here is the table with entries:

Size of cube	Paint on 3 squares	Paint on 2 squares	Paint on 1 square	Paint on 0 squares	Totals	Notes
2 by 2 by 2	8	0	0	0	8	2^3
3 by 3 by 3	8	12	6	1	27	3^3
4 by 4 by 4	8	24	24	8	64	4^3
5 by 5 by 5	8	36	54	64	125	5^3

References

Bell, A., & Janvier, C. (1981). The interpretation of graphs representing situations. *For the Learning of Mathematics, 2*(1), 34–42.

Carraher, D. W., & Schliemann, A. D. (2007). Early Algebra and Algebraic Reasoning. In F. Lester (Ed.) *Second Handbook of Research on Mathematics Teaching and Learning* (pp. 669–705). Reston, VA: National Council of Teachers of Mathematics & Charlotte, NC: Information Age Publishing.

Conference Board of the Mathematical Sciences (2000) *The Mathematical Education of Teachers.* Providence, RI: American Mathematical Society.

Kaput, J. (1995). Long-term algebra reform: Democratizing access to big ideas. In C. B. Lacampagne, W. Blair, & J. Kaput (Eds.), *The Algebra Initiative Colloquium* (pp. 33–52). Washington, DC: U.S. Government Printing Office.

Kaput, J. J., & Roschelle, J. (1997). Deepening the impact of technology beyond assistance with traditional formalism in order to democratize access to ideas underlying calculus. In E. Pehkonen (Ed.), *Proceedings of the 21st Conference of the International Group for the Psychology of Mathematics Education.* Lahti, Finland: University of Helsinki.

Kieran, C. (1993). Functions, graphing, and technology: Integrating research on learning and instruction. In T. A. Romberg, E. Fennema, & T. P. Carpenter (Eds.), *Integrating Research on the Graphical Representations of Functions* (pp. 189–238). Hillsdale, NJ: Erlbaum.

Lacampagne, C. B., Blair, W., & Kaput, J. (Eds.) (1995). *The Algebra Initiative Colloquium.* Washington, DC: U.S. Government Printing Office.

Leinhardt, G., Zaslavsky, O., & Stein, M. K. (1990). Functions, graphs, and graphing: Tasks, learning and teaching. *Review of Educational Research, 50*(1), 1–64.

Monk, S. (1992). Students' understanding of a function given by a physical model. In E. Dubinsky & G. Harel (Eds.), *The Concept of Function: Aspects of Epistemology and Pedagogy* (pp. 175–194). Washington, DC: Mathematical Association of America.

National Council of Teachers of Mathematics. (1989). *Curriculum and Evaluation Standards for School Mathematics.* Reston, VA: Author.

Occam's Razor. http://pespmc1.vub.ac.be/OCCAMRAZ.html, 30 July 2005.

Philipp, R. A. (1992). The many uses of algebraic variables. *Mathematics Teacher*, 85, 557–561.

Phillips, E. (1991). Patterns and Functions, from the *Addendum Series*, Grades 5–8. Reston, VA: National Council of Teachers of Mathematics.

Smith, J., & Thompson, P. (2007). Quantitative reasoning and the development of algebraic reasoning. In J. J. Kaput, D. W. Carreher, & M. L. Blanton (Eds.), Algebra in the early grades (pp. 95–132). New York: Erlbaum.

TERC. (1998). Investigations in number, data, and space. Specifically, C. Tierney, R. Nemirovsky, & A. Weinberg, *Changes over Time*, p. 94. Menlo Park, CA: Dale Seymour Publications.

Thompson, A. G., & Thompson, P. W. (1995). A cognitive perspective on the mathematical preparation of teachers: The case of algebra. In C. B. Lacampagne, W. Blair, & J. Kaput (Eds.), *The Algebra Initiative Colloquium* (pp. 95–116). Washington, DC: U.S. Government Printing Office.

Thompson, A. G., & Thompson, P. W. (1996). Talking about rates conceptually, Part II: Mathematical knowledge for teaching. *Journal for Research in Mathematics Education, 27*, 2–24.

Thompson, P. W. (1994). Students, functions, and the undergraduate curriculum. CBMS *Issues in Mathematics Education*. Washington DC: Conference Board of Mathematical Sciences.

Usiskin, Z. (1988). Conceptions of school algebra and uses of variables. In A. F. Coxford & A. P. Schulte (Eds.), *The Ideas of Algebra* (1988 Yearbook, pp. 9–19). Reston, VA: National Council of Teachers of Mathematics.

Overview of *Part III: Reasoning About Shapes and Measurement*

Goals. Our primary goal is that elementary (and middle) school teachers become comfortable enough with a variety of geometrical shapes and their allied numerical measurements so that they are prepared to teach this content. Teachers should also attain a certain level of spatial reasoning.

Key Ideas. Here are the key ideas presented in *Part III: Reasoning about Shapes and Measurement*, although not necessarily in this order:

Shapes

- Shapes can be classified, giving rise to hierarchies based on the properties of individual shapes. Students must understand and appreciate definitions for these shapes and know their conventional names.

- The study of three-dimensional shapes provides an entrance (for most students) into unfamiliar shapes.

- Exploring three-dimensional shapes allows opportunities to learn about and put into practice spatial visualization. Having a self-constructed set of polyhedra provides students with ways to explore three-dimensional shapes.

- Size changes of planar and space figures require understanding similarity (based on proportional reasoning). The use of a scale factor in determining similarity leads to viewing a similarity as a function.

- Shapes, both two- and three-dimensional, may have symmetries of different types.

- Rigid motions (isometries) include translations, reflections, rotations, and glide reflections. The figure that results from a rigid motion is congruent to the original figure.

Measurement

- Direct measurement of a characteristic of an object involves matching the object with a unit, or copies of a unit, having that characteristic. The matching should be based on the characteristic. The number of units, along with the unit, gives the measurement, or the value, of the quantity associated with the characteristic.

- Standard units are used since they are relatively permanent and enable communication over time and distance. Nonstandard units may be used in schools to allow a focus on the process of measurement.

- Measurements are approximate, unless one includes counts as measurements; counts can be exact.

- A quantity may be measured by thinking of the object being measured as "cut" into a number of pieces, measuring the quantity in each piece, and then adding up to those values.

- Measurement formulas can be justified and applied meaningfully.

- Estimation of measurements is a practical skill that deserves attention in the curriculum.

- The Pythagorean theorem is a valuable tool in working with a variety of shapes and formulas.

Because we did not intend a rigorous, proof-oriented course and because the students are assumed to have some familiarity with geometry, the gradual build-up from points, lines, and planes is not essential. One can even deal with the relatively unfamiliar 3D shapes early, building in any review of terms necessary.

One theory that has shaped how some topics in these chapters are treated is that of the van Hieles, Dutch educators who studied geometry learning and teaching extensively. Two of their main points are that the understanding of a topic exists in *levels* of understanding, and that teaching the topic should recognize these levels. For example, to expect students to prove results about rhombuses when they can scarcely recognize a rhombus is not apt to be fruitful. At a first level, students might recognize a shape as a rhombus *solely on its global appearance*, without attention to particular features or relationships that make the shape a rhombus. Instruction that leads the students to focus on the pertinent features or relationships in a rhombus could then result in a higher level of understanding. Eventually, students can recognize hierarchical relationships—for example, a rhombus is a special parallelogram, and a square is a special rhombus—and perhaps deductively establish results for rhombuses, such as the area of a rhombus is half the product of the lengths of its diagonals. Occasionally in *RSM*, you will notice a sequence showing a van Hiele influence: gross recognition, then focus on features, then perhaps some sort of reasoning that should lead to a result.

Some students' preconceptions about geometry are negative, often influenced by a secondary school course in which they had poor or mysterious experiences with proof. Although *RSM* is concerned with justifications of results, the level of those justifications is not that of a rigorous mathematics course for majors. Indeed, the usual apparatus for proofs based on triangle congruence does not receive a significant amount of attention, and arguments utilizing symmetry will be acceptable even without a careful definition of symmetry. There are activities aimed toward making clear that although patterns and drawings are excellent sources of conjectures, they are not safe grounds for general conclusions.

Assumed Background. The assumptions are that the students did have a course in geometry in secondary school but that they may remember only a little from that course. Some of the early work is intended to reveal how much vocabulary is remembered. Ideally, Section 16.1, a review of some planar vocabulary, could be skipped. Most students can name some shapes (e.g., square, rectangle, triangle, circle), and many remember $A = lw$ and $V = lwh$. However, most often they do not spontaneously regard a square as a special rectangle, and they might be willing to use formulas in inappropriate places. We have assumed that the students can read and use a ruler and a protractor, although for an occasional student the protractor is a new tool. Appendix G, available via the book companion website, may help those who have never worked with a protractor. We also assume a minimal level of algebraic skill, but we have found that some students have little or no familiarity with square roots, beyond pressing a calculator button.

Some "Nonroutine" Problems. There is much to praise in a problem-based curriculum. Although there are some "meaty" problems in the Activities, Discussions and Learning Exercises of *Reasoning About Shapes and Measurement*, the materials are not set up to build on nonroutine problems. On the other hand, we have used some problems that do involve some explanation and longer write-ups by students. We recommend them to users, who may have favorite additional and/or alternative ones. Pages for use with the students are included in the textbook's companion website at www.whfreeman.com/reconceptmath2e. Here are the times we have used some of them.

16.1 Review of Polygon Vocabulary
Star Polygons. This problem allows the extensive gathering of data. Its solution does require some sensitivity to factors of numbers because the pairs of numbers that are relatively prime do give star polygons. We have used this problem even with students who have not had a recent treatment of number theory.

17.2 Introduction to Polyhedra
Polyhedra from Polygon Regions. This activity is mentioned in the Instructor's Notes for Section 17.2. Although no write-up is required, it gives an opportunity for a relatively nondirected exploration. This activity does require access to polygonal regions that can be connected to make polyhedra.

19.1 Tessellating the Plane
There is no supplementary instruction sheet here, but several instructors have had their students make a tessellation, perhaps with more than one modification of some basic shape involved. Some students can be quite imaginative, and the colorful nature of most of the products plants some seeds.

20.1 Similarity and Dilations in Planar Figures
A Puzzle about a Puzzle. This activity is included in the student materials as an opener to the work on similarity, primarily to help identify additive thinkers and to communicate to them that their additive thinking does not work in this context.

22.1 Some Types of Rigid Motions
Shapes from Four Triangles. This activity calls for careful attention to Exercise 7 in Section 22.1. Again, the problem shows the value of some sort of systematic approach. The idea is from Marilyn Burns, who uses two triangles of two colors each, a more complicated setup.

24.1 Area and Surface Area
Edges and Insides. As you may know, students sometimes have trouble keeping perimeter and area straight, or assume that shapes with the same perimeter will have the same area, and vice versa. Although these points come up in scattered exercises, both are combated here. This bare-bones activity can be put into a context, as it was in a student activity by the NCTM: The square regions can be thought of as tiles, and there is a concern not only for the number of tiles but also for the length of edging that would be needed.

24.2 Volume, or 25.2 Volume Formulas
Box Dimensions. We have used this assignment for review purposes and to have the students write, but the problem could be used with Chapter 24 or 25. The intent is that students will see the value and even the necessity of some sort of systematic approach.

Technology. To maximize its usability, *Reasoning about Shapes and Measurement* does not *require* any computer work. Such work is, however, highly recommended. We include a short set of optional lessons on using Geometer's Sketchpad (GSP), designed for us by Janet Bowers and outlined in Appendix C. The lessons serve as an introduction to this powerful software program and perhaps a motivation to learn more about Sketchpad. They can be found at http://crmse.sdsu.edu/nickerson. The four lesson sets (Special Triangles, Special Quadrilaterals [containing constructions by side lengths and by diagonals], Transformation Geometry, and Sum of Interior Angles of a Polygon) can be aligned with various sections of the chapters where these shapes and properties are learned. Instructor side notes will point to these places. Each set of lessons contains interactive java applets with reflection questions and answers, video tutorials showing how to create the sketch using GSP, and step-by-step construction directions that can be downloaded. This introduction provides sufficient information for students to begin experimenting with Sketchpad. If you choose, you can of course provide further instruction for the students. These lessons are particularly useful when these materials are used in a course for middle school teachers.

Several websites also produce excellent activities relevant to *Reasoning about Shapes and Measurement* that show, for example, rotations of polyhedra (good for spatial visualization), creation of planar tessellations, and work with transformation geometry. We particularly recommend the lessons and activities on the *Illuminations* web site (http://illuminations.nctm.org), and we reference that site in the text. The National Library of Virtual Manipulatives is another excellent source of activities (http://nlvm.usu.edu).

Some of the drawings in the Auxiliary Materials folder come from the Geometer's Sketchpad and are included for your adaptation if you are conversant with GSP. A Triangle Solutions spreadsheet in Excel is in the Auxiliary Materials folder; this spreadsheet allows you to create triangles that have, say, integral sides for ease of computation with similar or right triangles, but without faking the angle sizes. The spreadsheet allows SSS or SAS or ASA information to be entered, with the measurements of the other parts then calculated.

Manipulatives. In the early going we hoped to make the material maximally usable by avoiding any special equipment that a department might neither own nor have access to. (Colleagues in departments of education are, however, often a source of manipulatives). Of course, exposing the students to any materials that they might see in the schools is certainly desirable and, to use the same argument as the one for use with younger students, might lead to better learning on the part of the college students. The kit of 3D shapes the students assemble for Section 17.2 is vital, and these shapes involve only a small cost. Dot paper could be used instead of geoboards (and a master is included in the back of the text and on the textbook's companion website: www.whfreeman.com/reconceptmath2e). Chalkboard or whiteboard drawings, though static, might serve in the absence of flexible linkages or computer sketches.

Students should be required to have these items: (inexpensive) compass, ruler (metric and English), protractor, scissors, and transparent tape. Scissors and tape are required to make the kit from the nets found in the second chapter. We have occasionally asked the students to buy a set of 100 interlocking snap cubes that can be purchased by the campus bookstore from www.eaieducation.com (or other sites). Students should also use the square dot paper and the isometric dot paper in their materials as masters and make several copies of each.

If finances permit, we recommend that you, the teacher, have on hand:

- *Polydrons*, a commercial kit of interlocking plastic regions that are extremely useful for explorations and teacher demonstrations.
- *Interlocking snap cubes*, usually 2 cm by 2 cm by 2 cm (with contrasting colors, even this size is large enough to be fairly serviceable for an in-class demonstration).
- *Other 3D shapes*. Many departments have commercial kits, but candy, cosmetics, light bulbs, cans, and so on, sometimes come in unusually shaped containers.

- *Pentominoes* are mentioned in an exercise in Section 17.3; we mention them here only because there are commercial versions available that your students may see in schools.
- A *transparent cube* (nice but not essential for seeing different shapes in cross-sections of a cube). Instructors have also used clay, Play-Doh, and even cheese, to be cut with knives, putty knives, or dental floss.
- *Cardboard templates* for difficult-to-sketch regions (for example, regular polygons) are useful to the instructor for chalkboard drawings. *Caution*: Students need practice making freehand sketches, and sometimes when an instructor just holds up a region they do not make any drawings.
- *Pattern blocks*. We include masters for the pattern blocks and recommend that students run them on cardstock. We also recommend that the instructor have a plastic transparent set for use on an overhead projector.
- A chalkboard *protractor*, or a transparent one for use with an overhead projector, is useful on occasion, but particularly if you have to instruct on how to use a protractor.
- *Thin paper* for paper-tracing (ideal: the paper used to separate meat patties, from a restaurant-supply store).
- *MIRAs* (plastic devices for use with reflections).

There are many sources from which you may purchase such materials. A few to try are from ETA at www.etacuisenaire.com, Didax at www.didax.com, and EAI at www.eaieducation.com.

Timeline. The content in Part III is unlikely to be taught in its entirety in one semester. You will need to make decisions along the way on what is essential to keep in the course. If your institution has the luxury of three or four courses, some of this content can be shifted to another course.

Thus, in a one-semester course for elementary teachers, we might omit Sections 17.4 and 17.5 on congruent polyhedra and special polyhedra; 22.2–22.5 on Transformation Geometry (keeping only 22.1) and 26.2. We assume 3 hours of instruction per week. The following estimates are for a 15-week semester and are based on our own experiences in teaching this content. Additional time will be needed for review and for testing. *Note that measurement work requires a substantial amount of time*.

16 Polygons (1.5 weeks)

The first two sections, on vocabulary and the ordering of shapes, may be a review for some students yet new to others. The study of triangles and quadrilaterals leads to a hierarchical classification.

17 Polyhedra (2.5 weeks)

We *highly* recommend that students use the nets provided to build their own personal sets of polyhedral shapes to be used in this course. Many of the shapes and terms will be new to students. The section on representing and visualizing polyhedra is difficult for students with poor spatial visualization. If time is likely to be tight, skip the sections on congruent polyhedra and special polyhedra. In a course for middle school teachers, there should be time for these sections.

18 Symmetry (1 week)

The study of symmetry of shapes in a plane is essential for teachers because symmetry may arise in the primary grades. Symmetry of polyhedra could be deferred unless this class is for middle school teachers.

19 Tessellations (1 week)

Tessellating the plane is enjoyable and many students like to design figures that tessellate, but take care not to spend too much time here. Tessellating space could be deferred unless this class is for middle school teachers.

20 Similarity (1.5 to 2 weeks)

Chapter 20 is a very important chapter. Scale factors are used to transform figures into similar figures. The study of similarity continues our study of proportional reasoning from Parts I and II.

21 Curves, Construction, and Curved Surfaces (1 week)

Planar curves and curved surfaces are treated here. Standard ruler-compass constructions often are unfamiliar to students so they receive attention.

22 Transformation Geometry (1 day to 2 weeks)

An introduction to several types of rigid motions is necessary because they appear in elementary school textbooks. Finding images of rigid motions and compositions of rigid motions can be deferred unless this class is for middle school teachers.

23 Measurement Basics (0.5 weeks)

This chapter provides a foundation for the subsequent chapters dealing with measurement

24 Area, Surface Area, and Volume (1.5 weeks)

Students have many misconceptions about these topics and often do not understand the "covering" and "filling" with standard units necessary to find area and volume. Misconceptions also show up when they confuse area with perimeter.

25 Counting Units Fast: Measurement Formulas (1 week)

The standard circumference, area, and volume formulas are developed in this chapter, with attention to justifications.

26 Special Topics in Measurement (1 week)

Be sure to find time for the Pythagorean theorem in this chapter (Section 26.1), even if you can't cover all the chapter. The section could be covered earlier, with care in assigning Learning Exercises (many have to do with area and volume).

If your course is designed for middle school teachers, we think all of the chapters and sections should be included.

As the outline suggests, we have followed a "Cook's tour" approach to geometry, as opposed to a "less is more" treatment. A "less is more" course is certainly possible, using some of the sections here as starting points or reference materials. If you are not familiar with the distinction between the two approaches, Cook's tour is an informal description of a course covering many topics (the typical course), whereas a "less is more" course allows more attention to explorations, projects, and extended work on open-ended problems, but naturally does not cover every traditional topic. We hope that we have combated the "broad but shallow" criticism of a typical Cook's tour by attention to some central ideas and skills for the teacher. We have also chosen topics on a *need-to-know* (for the typical K−6/7 curriculum) criterion rather than a *nice-to-know* (because it is good knowledge) criterion.

Instructor Notes for Chapter 16: Polygons

Here are the section titles for Chapter 16:

16.1 *Review of Polygon Vocabulary.* Many words, but most "official" definitions for the polygons do not appear until 16.3. Some review of notations and angle adjectives.

16.2 *Organizing Shapes.* Introducing the idea of hierarchical classification.

16.3 *Triangles and Quadrilaterals.* Warnings about judgments based on drawings or numerical patterns. Conjectures about quadrilateral family. "Official" definitions and hierarchy.

16.4 *Issues for Learning: Some Research on Two-Dimensional Shapes.*

16.5 *Check Yourself.*

INSTRUCTOR NOTE 16.1A

Although we call this section a review of polygon vocabulary, some of this material may be new to several students. You may wish to assign the section as review and then assess students' understanding of the terms by asking them to show various shapes on a geoboard or on dot paper (square and/or triangular), with a loop of string and fingers as vertices (perhaps working with a partner) or just by sketches of examples. Some students have trouble with parallels and perpendiculars in freehand sketches, perhaps because they are unaware of the relationships. You may also want to show them a shape and ask them to name it. A loop of string (and fingers), a transparent geoboard, a geo-strip kit (plastic segments that can be joined), or a geo-rule (linked pieces of wood) is handy for showing a variety of polygons. Sometimes a chalkboard drawing of, say, a parallelogram doesn't do a good job of showing both pairs of parallel sides. Accordingly, a prepared supply of cardboard parallelograms, rhombuses, kites, and even square and rectangular regions can help make more accurate-looking drawings.

At this stage, some students may react solely on the basis of how a shape looks rather than on any relationships among its sides and/or angles. (cf. Section 16.4 or the Instructor Note 17.1A). Some of your questions should be aimed toward noticing these relationships ("What makes a rectangle a rectangle?" or "What seems to be true about the sides in any rhombus?"). Some of the exercises attempt to focus attention on these important relationships. Hierarchical relationships are pursued in the next section, with the official hierarchy given in Section 16.3 and also in the glossary, under "Polygon."

One alert may be in order: "Kite" may be regarded as a joke by some students, but it is in many curricula (and kites do have some interesting properties). We should also acknowledge that the U.S. usage of terms is not always shared around the world. Students from Great Britain may use *trapezium* for a U.S. *trapezoid*, for example.

There are many terms for the students to learn both in this section and in future sections. Encourage them to compile their own glossaries on 3 by 5 cards or in a computer file they can add to and print out. There is, however, a glossary toward the end of *Shapes and Measurement*.

INSTRUCTOR NOTE 16.1B

Although many books (and tradition) define a trapezoid as having exactly one pair of parallel sides, we are adopting the "at least one pair of parallel sides" definition. This allows a hierarchical connection between trapezoids and parallelograms. But parallelograms will not be regarded as special *isosceles* trapezoids, on the other hand, because the congruent diagonals feature of isosceles trapezoids is not true for parallelograms in general; isosceles trapezoids are then linked to rectangles. (See the hierarchy in the glossary, under "Polygon," or in Section 16.3.)

The designation of isosceles for some of these trapezoids in the drawn examples (the square and the rectangle) may puzzle some students and bring up the issue of exactly-one versus at-least-one. You should acknowledge that some books use the exactly-one definition because a student may bring in an elementary school textbook that uses the exactly-one version. An isosceles trapezoid for us will be a trapezoid for which the angles next to one of the parallel sides are the same size, to avoid parallelograms being isosceles trapezoids. Hierarchical relationships are discussed in the next section, where you may opt for the exactly-one-pair-of-parallel-sides definition for trapezoids. The more restrictive "exactly one pair of parallel sides" is given as an option in Section 16.3. If you adopt it, an occasional answer to a Learning Exercise may not be correct.

INSTRUCTOR NOTE 16.1C

Some students may need a review of the vocabulary and the common notations.

Rather than leave all the numerical work with measurement to the later chapters, some exposure to length and angle size is assumed. Each state has its own standards, so it is difficult to say that some angle vocabulary will not come up in K–6. But based on elementary school textbooks that we have looked at and the recommendations of the Common Core State Standards, we put together our curriculum for teachers. As indicated, some other angle ideas are introduced later, sometimes in exercises if they do not appear to be mainstream elementary school textbooks that we have looked at. Here are some locations: Central and inscribed angles are in Chapter 21; vertical angles, corresponding angles and alternate interior angles (as with parallel lines), and dihedral angles come up in the Learning Exercises for Section 23.2.

Appendix G ("Using a Protractor to Measure Angle Size") at the book companion website, reviews the use of a protractor. Students should at least on occasion show that they know how to use a protractor.

INSTRUCTOR NOTE 16.1D

Here is a sample of the type of shape called for in Exercise 5(e).

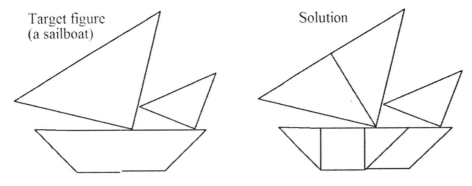
Target figure (a sailboat)   Solution

INSTRUCTOR NOTE 16.2A

Some students find it mysterious that in mathematics classes, squares are considered to be rectangles. Part of this mystery is due to our natural tendency to give the most informative name for a shape, and hence a natural induction is that all the sides of a rectangle cannot have equal lengths. But part of the mystery is likely due to a lack of appreciation for hierarchical classification systems, or taxonomies.

The early paragraphs, having to do with animals, may be familiar to students from their work in biology. The concern here is less with biological accuracy than with the "Why?" for classification schemes. As noted, one reason might revolve around *shared* characteristics rather than differences. Siamese cats, lions, and tigers share many characteristics.

Once a classification system or hierarchy is established, ask questions like, "Is every dog a beagle?" and "Is every collie a dog?" or "Is every salmon a fish?" and "Is every fish a salmon?" to emphasize that subcategories are special cases of the more inclusive categories. The characteristics defining the more inclusive class apply to all its subcategories, but not vice versa.

Similar points should result from the *A Square by Any Other Name...* discussion. One classification scheme for polygons is given in Section 16.3 and in the glossary, under "Polygons." It is likely that many students will have the "only one pair of parallel sides" view for trapezoids because that is commonly taught. That version isolates trapezoids, however, implying that they share no characteristics with any other type of quadrilateral. Yet the area formula for trapezoids *could* be used with parallelograms, and the equality of the lengths of the diagonals and of the sizes of the base angles of an isosceles trapezoid, for example, are shared with rectangles. So we have given first billing to the "at least one pair of parallel sides" version for trapezoids even though, as noted, elementary school books might use an exactly-one version.

INSTRUCTOR NOTE 16.3A

With Activity 3 as a caution, the idea in Activity 4 is to gather facts about types of quadrilaterals from experimental or visual work. Students should have rulers or measuring tapes and protractors. You may wish to have them use geoboards and dot paper (squared/triangular) for more accurate work. The students' 3D shapes might also be handy for Activity 4 as a source of examples of some polygons. In some circumstances it may be more practical for the groups to meet briefly toward the end of one class session to parcel out the work (perhaps two students per shape) and then to meet at the start of the next class session to share results, before a whole-class compilation.

Even though the students have been cautioned about visual evidence by Activity 3, we will make use of symmetry as a means of justification, and the symmetry will be assumed from looking at examples. A student sensitive to mathematical proof may point this danger out.

Students may be confused about what they are supposed to do for Activity 4, as the notion of conjectures may not be familiar to them. You may wish to pick one type of quadrilateral (kites, for example) and form conjectures as a group so that students can see the idea of the exercise. You do not have to find all properties of kites, but have the students brainstorm for a while and write their ideas on the board. If they aren't volunteering anything, prompt them with questions such as: "Do you notice anything about the diagonals of a kite?" and "Is this going to be true for all kites?" Watch for students who give up or are nonparticipators. Occasionally, a student in groupwork decides to let others do the work and then copies their ideas.

Learning Exercise 2 calls for some sort of summary of the conjectures. Make clear in your summary work that the facts they come up with *appear* to be true but that even collectively the class has not examined every possible triangle or quadrilateral (thus the word "conjecture," or "educated guess"). Research suggests that the students won't feel many doubts about their conjectures (or will wait for your evaluation) but will have a high degree of trust in results from their experimental or visual work.

Some fairly standard definitions of the types of quadrilaterals are given next, and then some examples of how one might establish selected results. The word "prove" causes apprehension with some students, so "justify" is used here. The justifications may not be completely sound mathematical proofs anyhow (for example, the argument may use symmetry, which will not be defined carefully), but they will bring out that being asked for justifications is a reasonable expectation, and that justifications can involve more than references to an example or examples. Mention that in many current elementary school curricula, children routinely are expected to justify their results. Do not, however, expect a full appreciation for justifications by all the students.

You may wish to exhibit a hierarchy for types of triangles and quadrilaterals from Section 16.2, Discussion 1, to contrast with the official hierarchy.

Activity 6 is included to alert the students that stopping after noticing a pattern is not enough, mathematically speaking. Students tend to have a great deal of faith in inductive reasoning.

Instructor Notes for Chapter 17: Polyhedra

Sections in Chapter 17:

17.1 *Shoeboxes Have Faces and Nets!* Drawing "shoeboxes," new terms *face, edge, vertex, net.* Isometric dot paper. This section recognizes that students may not have assembled their kits of polyhedra.

17.2 *Introduction to Polyhedra.* Prisms, pyramids, and related vocabulary. Euler's formula for polyhedra.

17.3 *Representing and Visualizing Polyhedra.* Translating among different representations (physical model, word, net, drawing). Drawing prisms and pyramids.

17.4 *Congruent Polyhedra.* Light use of isometry language. (Can be skipped or deferred.)

17.5 *Some Special Polyhedra.* The regular polyhedra. (Can be skipped or deferred.)

17.6 *Issues for Learning: Dealing with 3D Shapes.* Common difficulties.

17.7 *Check Yourself.* Overview of what was covered

INSTRUCTOR NOTE 17.1A

For courses that start with geometry, Section 17.1 allows time for the students to construct their kits of polyhedra for Section 17.2 in the next class meeting. Despite the whimsical title of 17.1, some 3D vocabulary words (face, vertex, edge, net) and a little work on making drawings (including the use of isometric dot paper—see the Masters) are introduced. Students sometimes use informal language (e.g., sides instead of faces). We have found that if the instructor builds a net with plastic polyhedral building kits (like Zome, Polydron, or JOVO) then asks students to anticipate and sketch the polyhedron, they can then use vocabulary as they are asked to discuss how they imagined folding the net. For example, students may say "I visualized folding it so the edge of the blue equilateral triangle adjoins the edge of the yellow square." More vocabulary and work with drawings come up in later sections.

Be certain to assign the Preliminary Homework Activity in 17.2 before starting 17.2 because the work there focuses on the 3D shapes that the students will assemble. We strongly suggest that you have students make and use these shapes. They have proven to be very useful.

INSTRUCTOR NOTE 17.2A

The idea of the preliminary exercise is to have at hand a variety of polyhedra on which to base early discussions, so have the students bring their kits to class. The aim of this section is to introduce several terms that will be new to most students, and to assess the vocabulary that students bring and to lead to Euler's formula for polyhedra ($V + F = E + 2$).

Try to make sure that the vocabulary is used correctly once it is introduced. As you may know from Lakatos (1976), a careful definition of "polyhedron" has a long history. We'll settle for something like, "a closed surface made up of planar regions." This section begins a further breakdown of polyhedra into pyramids (shapes A, D, G, I), prisms (shapes B, C, E, F) and "others" (H, J, K). The term "cube" (E) should also come up.

If you choose to make the *Sorting Shapes* discussion a small-group discussion, write any vocabulary words you overhear or wish to introduce on the board (with sketches if appropriate). You can then follow up the small-group discussion with a whole-class summary (prior to the next discussion), in which you have groups share some of their ideas and attach importance to the vocabulary that will be used.

You are likely to get several types of sortings from your students, often based on characteristics such as the number of faces, the types of faces (triangles, rectangles, etc.), or similarity of appearance (that is, "looks like a . . ."). Early finishers can be asked to devise another type of sort. The terms students know will likely be terms for two-dimensional objects. Make positive remarks about students' sorting methods that won't get much attention after the conventional "pyramid" and "prism" come up. Some students may get confused as to why their sorting method should be any "worse" than that of traditional mathematics. You may want to justify this by telling students that there are relationships that apply to all pyramids or prisms, but in general there are no relationships that apply to all 3D shapes. You may also want to briefly introduce the notion of a **convention**—that is, sometimes one way of doing things is not necessarily better than another, but we choose one to standardize and to ease communication.

One aim of this section is to get a feel for the vocabulary level of your students. Reintroduce the terms *face*, *edge*, and *vertex*. You may have to repeat that *face* is used in mathematics for the planar regions instead of the colloquial *side*, with "side" reserved for (sides of) polygons and angles. The term "*n*-gon" may also need some reinforcement.

Here are some "official" definitions:

- **Pyramids** are polyhedra for which one face is any sort of polygonal region (often called the *base* of the pyramid), and all the other faces are triangular regions with one "corner" or vertex in common.

- **Prisms** are polyhedra having two faces (called **bases**) that are congruent ("exactly alike") and parallel, and whose other faces (called *lateral faces*) are parallelogram regions formed by joining corresponding vertices of the bases.

Pyramids and prisms may be further described by naming the type of polygon making up the bases: triangular pyramid, rectangular prisms, and so on. A prism is a right prism if the lateral edges (those not on the bases) are perpendicular to the edges at the bases, and an oblique prism otherwise. A regular pyramid has a regular polygonal region (equal sides, equal angles) as base, with the other faces all isosceles triangular regions. (This forces the more visual, "The other vertex is right over the center of the base.")

In a follow-up to *Defining Types of Polyhedra*, you may want to draw a Venn diagram (for example, as below) or some other sort of classification diagram (such as below, with the adjectives "right," "oblique," and "regular" given as subcategories rather than through a breakdown by type of base) on the board to show that pyramids and prisms are "special" polyhedra. Test the vocabulary by holding up any additional shapes you have and asking for names and "best" names, using the type of base (and right/oblique if you have introduced them). For example, *right rectangular prism* is the sophisticated name for a shoebox shape. Have on hand or name some nonpolyhedral shapes—balls, most tin cans.

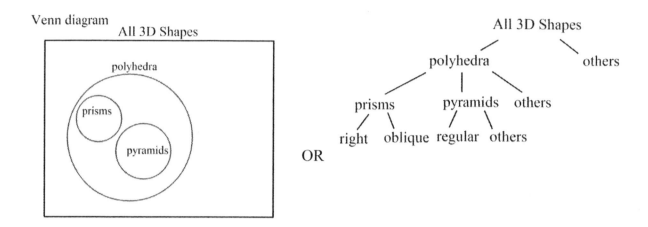

You might consider an activity such as *Possible Polyhedra from Polygon Regions* as an open type of in-class exploration. Although no write-up is required, it gives an opportunity for a relatively nondirected exploration. This activity does require access to polygonal regions (for example, the commercial Polydrons) that can be connected to make polyhedra and serves to familiarize the students with the material.

INSTRUCTOR NOTE 17.2B

As noted, the two *V, F, E...* activities aim toward Euler's formula: $V + F = E + 2$ (or any algebraic equivalent), which holds for polyhedra as we usually think of them. If the polyhedron has one or more "holes" in it, the formula must be adjusted: $V + F = E + 2 - 2h$, where h is the number of holes. Any biographical data you know about Euler (pronounced "oiler")—Swiss, b. 1707, d. 1783, 886 books and articles, 13 children—might be of interest to your students. For those students liking biographies, E. T. Bell's *Men of Mathematics* contains a chapter on Euler. The book by Lakatos (1976) traces the history of Euler's formula, but to make a philosophical point.

These two activities may involve some visualization and abstraction (for example, seeing that all the vertices of an *n*-gonal prism are at the vertices of the two bases). A class discussion in which students explain how they arrived at answers for the 100-gonal, *n*-gonal, and (*x* + *y*)-gonal cases should be worthwhile; some will have used only the patterns suggested by the other cases and can profit from hearing others use their general knowledge of the shapes.

INSTRUCTOR NOTE 17.3A

The primary aims of this section focus on making and reading two-dimensional drawings of polyhedra, along with more visualization practice. An overview of, and some practice with, other possible representations are included. Insofar as possible, the students should have practice at making a drawing, or sketching a net, without the original shape present. The exercises also give a little more practice with drawings on isometric dot/grid paper (see the Masters toward the end or the textbook's companion website if you need another master). Again, have various 3D objects at hand to illustrate particular points. The framework of a cube from Tinkertoys, straws, or plastic polyhedral building kits that are frames for example, may be helpful to students. Call on them to visualize and anticipate perspective as frequently as possible.

INSTRUCTOR NOTE 17.3B

The twelve possible pentominoes in Exercise 13(a) are available in plastic, and may be in some schools. If you have a set, here is a way for students to check: Place the pieces on the overhead to practice visual memory as they look at the screen, and then look on their papers, perhaps having to mentally manipulate the shape seen on the screen.

The 12 pentominoes were once boxed in a 6 ×10 container as a puzzle—dump out the pieces and then fit them back into the box without pieces overlapping. There are two other excellent activities with an 8 × 8 board and the pentominoes. One is a solitaire game: Can you put all the pieces on the board? (A harder version specifies a 2 × 2 square not to be used on the board ahead of time!) The second is competitive: Taking turns, place a pentomino on the board. If you cannot, you lose. (This can end in a tie, with no pieces left.) More visualization is forced in the last game if an additional rule is imposed: If you touch a piece, you must move it.

INSTRUCTOR NOTE 17.4A

Whether these two shapes in Think About, G and H, are "exactly the same" may be argued. The copy requires a reflection in a plane (thus the hint); the two shapes cannot be made to coincide in 3D space without a reflection. Like the shoes in a pair of shoes, the right fender and left fender on a car, or the gloves in a pair of gloves, the two are exactly alike but somehow different because they are not interchangeable. Conventionally, these are regarded as congruent; in advanced work, the label *oppositely congruent* (versus *directly congruent*) might be used. Doubting students may be convinced by their familiarity with a similar issue in the 2D case, as in the congruent halves from the altitude to the base of an ordinary isosceles triangular region. In the 2D case, one can physically flip a shape in a third dimension. Under the motion approach to be adopted, each of two congruent shapes can be mapped to the other by a rotation or translation or reflection (or the composition thereof). Parts that match—corresponding parts—will have the same size.

INSTRUCTOR NOTE 17.5A

Nets for the five convex regular polyhedra are all included in the student kits—the regular tetrahedron (shape A), the regular hexahedron or cube (E), the regular octahedron (H), the regular dodecahedron (L), and the regular icosahedron (M). Craft stores sometimes have styrofoam regular icosahedra, and there is often a set of regular polyhedra around a mathematics department.

That these five types are the only types of convex regular polyhedra can be discussed once one knows how to determine the size of each face angle in a convex polyhedron. (See Learning Exercise 29 in Section 23.2.) Here is the gist of the argument: Study all the possibilities of each face angle at a given vertex; their sum must always be less than 360° for the polyhedron to be convex. Since there must be at least three faces that meet as a vertex, the face angles for a regular polyhedra must be less than, or equal to, 120°, and thus the only faces that can possibly work are the triangle, the square, and the regular pentagon. If one allows concave polyhedra, there are four more regular polyhedra, called *star polyhedra* because they resemble starbursts (one example: imagine putting regular pentagonal pyramids on each face of a dodecahedron). A Web search—for example, with star polyhedra, or star polytopes—can lead to some interesting sites. In particular, the Geometric Solids lessons at http://illuminations.nctm.org have an online program that deals mainly with the regular polyhedra. It is highly recommended, both for the students and class sessions.

Instructor Notes for Chapter 18: Symmetry

Here are the section titles for this chapter:

18.1 *Symmetry of Shapes in a Plane.* Reflection and rotational symmetry only. Symmetry defined. Using symmetry to justify conjectures.

18.2 *Symmetry of Polyhedra.* Reflection and rotational symmetry only. Usually skipped or deferred.

18.3 *Issues for Learning: What Geometry Is in the Pre-K–8 Curriculum?*

18.4 *Check Yourself.*

INSTRUCTOR NOTE 18.1A

This section introduces just two types of planar symmetry: reflections in lines and rotations about points. The other two types of symmetry in the plane, translation symmetry and glide-reflection symmetry, are not usually in the elementary school curriculum and are not covered until late in Chapter 22. Feel free to introduce them, particularly if a question about other types of symmetry comes up (both of the later types require an infinite figure, like a line with regularly spaced barbs).

If you have access to a plastic device that can serve as a two-sided "mirror," you might wish to have your students find lines of symmetry and create symmetric figures with the device. (One version is called the Mira.) Nonpolygonal shapes come up in this section as well since symmetry is not confined to polygons.

You or someone in your class may know how to cut a string of paper dolls from a piece of paper. Such an exercise can be a good visual aid to understanding symmetry. Or it may be as simple as asking them to cut out a heart shape.

It is a good idea to bring a cardboard square so that you can illustrate the symmetries of a square region. A parallelogram region may also be useful later in the section.

Because we do not assume that the students have acquired function ideas from Part II, you may need to elaborate on, say, why a 360° rotation clockwise and a 360° rotation counterclockwise are not different symmetries. (They have the same net effect on every point, even though the motion may be different, so as functions they are considered to be the same.) And, because every shape has a 360° rotational symmetry (with any center!), the 360° rotational symmetry is called the *trivial* symmetry and not even counted unless there are other symmetries for a shape.

Web activities for reflection symmetry (Mirror Tool, Grades 9–12) and for rotational symmetry (Cyclic Figures, Grades 6–8, and Frieze Patterns, Grades 6–12) at http://illuminations.nctm.org may be useful for your students to try.

INSTRUCTOR NOTE 18.2A

You may choose to omit or delay this section if you anticipate running short of time. The section does show that symmetry is not confined to 2D shapes and does give more visualization practice, but it is more difficult than Section 18.1.

Remember to have students bring their cutout polyhedra to class for this section. It is useful to have a cube and other 3D figures on hand for these discussions. (Larger ones are more easily seen, of course.) Shapes made from Polydrons have holes that allow a piece of wire (from a coat hanger, say) to be used as an axis of rotation.

In space, one can reflect not only in a plane but also in a point or a line, so the longer "symmetry with respect to a plane" is less ambiguous. Rotational symmetry about a point is also possible but is not brought up here, nor are the other types of three-dimensional symmetries.

After the first activity, you may wish to show how to draw a plane intersecting a polyhedron. (Perhaps the simplest way is to show only the cross-section of the plane with the polyhedron. Alternatively, see the drawing for Learning Exercise 9.) There are nine different planes of symmetry for the cube, including those joining diagonally opposite edges. (Try picking out one edge, and see how it can be reflected by different planes to the seven other edges coplanar with it, and twice to itself.) For the general right rectangular prism, discuss why the planes joining diagonally opposite edges are *not* planes of symmetry. As with the rectangle and its diagonals, although the two parts are congruent, they are not positioned as mirror images. A Play-Doh right rectangular prism may be useful to illustrate the congruence.

INSTRUCTOR NOTE 18.2B

A cube has 13 axes of rotational symmetry: three giving 90°, 180°, 270°, and 360° rotational symmetries; four (the diagonals) giving 120°, 240°, and 360° symmetries; and six (through midpoints of opposite edges) giving only 180° and 360° symmetries. Notice that the 360° rotational symmetry has at least 13 different descriptions, but each one of them results in every point ending up at its original position. So there are only 24 total rotational symmetries. That these are different can be settled by looking at fixed points (where the axis intersects the cube).

The equilateral-triangular right prism (shape C in the kit) has 4 axes of rotational symmetry and six different rotational symmetries. (The 360° rotation counts just once.)

During (or after) the activity, raise the question of whether a 360° rotation should "count." Explain that any figure, with any line as axis, would have a 360° rotational symmetry, so the 360° rotational symmetry is called a ***trivial*** symmetry. It is usually counted only if there are other rotational symmetries for a particular axis. Again, although the *movement* may be different for 360° rotations with different axes, their net effects are all the same, so they are just different descriptions of the same symmetry.

It may also be worth noting that using the same axis and rotating 180° clockwise or rotating 180° counterclockwise has the same effect on every point, and hence these are just two descriptions for the same symmetry. On the other hand, 90° clockwise and 90° counterclockwise rotations do not have the same final effect on every point, so they are different symmetries. Points end up in the same places by 90° counterclockwise and 270° clockwise rotations, however, so these are just two descriptions for the same rotational symmetry.

Instructor Notes for Chapter 19: Tessellations

Here are the section titles for this chapter:

> 19.1 *Tessellating the Plane.* Regular polygonal regions. Triangular and quadrilateral regions. Designing a figure that will tessellate.
>
> 19.2 *Tessellating Space.* A short section, usually deferred or skipped.
>
> 19.3 *Check Yourself.*

(There is no Issues for Learning section in this chapter.)

INSTRUCTOR NOTE 19.1A

This chapter just touches on tessellations of the plane and of space and gives a breather before the more demanding work with similarity. The two activities (with the second one given as a take-home exercise) and perhaps an artwork assignment might give an adequate treatment if you are short of time.

Cardboard cutouts are very useful in showing tessellations. There are also multitudinous websites dealing with tessellations and software for tessellations (TesselMania! is used here). The Tessellation Creator (Grades 3–8) activity at http://illuminations.nctm.org should be of interest to students, even though it is restricted to regular polygons. A set of activities is also available at Tessellations, via http://nlvm.usu.edu/en/nav.

INSTRUCTOR NOTE 19.2A

This brief section can give more experience with polyhedra and can continue the idea of tessellation, but we have often skipped it for reasons of time. Tessellations of the plane are more commonly encountered in the elementary curriculum than are tessellations of space, but the common measurement of volume by filling with cubes is related to space-filling. Make sure that students bring their polyhedra to class when you discuss this section.

Instructor Notes for Chapter 20: Similarity

Here are the sections in this chapter:

20.1 *Similarity and Dilations in Planar Figures.* Similarity definition, using scale factor language. Similar figures through dilations. Finding missing measurements in similar figures.

20.2 *More about Similar Figures.* Relationships between perimeters and areas of similar figures. AA similarity criterion for triangles. Finding missing measurements in similar triangles.

20.3 *Similarity in Space Figures.* Extension of the above to 3D shapes. Relationship between volumes of similar 3D shapes.

20.4 *Issues for Learning: Similarity and Proportional Reasoning.* Prevalence of additive thinking.

20.5 *Check Yourself.*

The optional software lesson on transformation geometry in the instructional pieces for the Geometer's Sketchpad allows you to illustrate dilations.

INSTRUCTOR NOTE 20.1A

Because similarity involves comparing lengths multiplicatively (instead of the use of additive comparisons), this section is extremely important. "Seeing" that a multiplicative relationship should describe lengths in similar figures is not at all obvious, and can be quite difficult conceptually. The bulk of the conceptual focus will probably be during the *A Puzzle about a Puzzle* activity, so avoid too much intervention (that is, telling) during those discussions.

One erroneous but common approach is to use an additive approach in making the puzzle pieces (see Lee in Discussion 1), so some students may think that adding 3 cm to each length will give a piece of the same shape. The hope is that such students, after seeing that this approach does not give pieces that fit together to give a larger version of the original puzzle, will be receptive to other explanations. It is easier to see that an additive relation does not work than to see that a multiplicative relation does. It is handy to have the additive version to show that the pieces do not fit together. The one following shows how the pieces would look if they were built on the right angles available, and the indicated lengths were obtained from those in the original puzzle by adding 3 cm. You may wish to copy this drawing and cut out the pieces so that you can illustrate that adding 3 cm does not even give pieces that fit together.

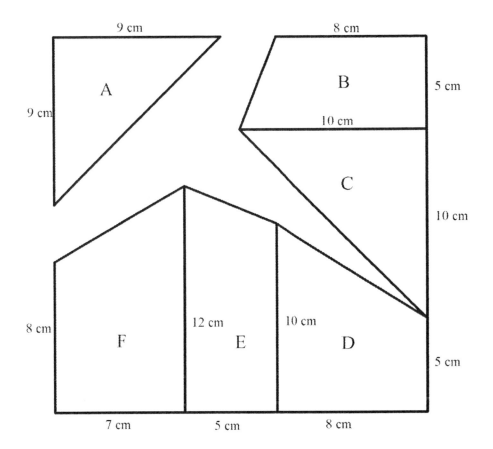

Listen during the discussion and activities to gauge how to follow up. One difficulty that some students have with similarity is dealing with the numbers, often fractions and decimals, that arise, and the different forms (ratio with colon, ratio in fraction form, equation form).

After the discussions, give visibility to both the ratio form (for example, length in new puzzle: corresponding length in original = $1\frac{3}{4}$) and also the scale-factor form (for example, length in new puzzle = $1\frac{3}{4}$ × corresponding length in original puzzle). Although you may ask your students to compare Maria's and Olivia's thinking, you may have to turn Olivia's correct "75% bigger" argument into a "175% as long as the original length" description to see its equivalence to Maria's description. Ask also, as a reminder, how they handled the angles, to emphasize that corresponding angles should be the same size.

At least occasionally stay with fractions instead of changing to decimals. Always changing fractions to decimals gives "fraction-avoider" students an indirect but undesirable confirmation that fractions *should* be avoided.

You will notice that the use of scale factors downplays the common use of proportions with similarity, and the solving of a proportion by cross-multiplying. On the other hand, the use of "related proportionally" instead of "related multiplicatively" is quite acceptable.

INSTRUCTOR NOTE 20.1B

You may wish to illustrate the rubber-band method for changing the size of a shape before you introduce the ruler method. It is practical only on a chalkboard or whiteboard but allows the conjecturing of what scale factor is involved and illustrates the key role of the center of the size change. It also works nicely with curved shapes, whereas the ruler method is practical only for polygons and other objects made up of straight pieces.

Draw a closed curve, such as a face or heart, on the board (plan ahead a bit, so the enlargement will fit on the board). Use a chain of, say, three linked rubber bands, as identical as you can find. Have a (trustworthy) student hold one end of the chain firmly against the chalkboard. You hold the chalk or marker in the loop at the other end of the chain. Adjust the tension in the chain so that the first knot from the student's thumb is over the curve and trace over the curve, keeping that knot over the curve. In the meantime, as you move the first knot, mark with the chalk or marker end. The resulting curve may be wobbly, but it is usually close enough to be visually convincing that it is an enlargement of the original curve.

The center of the size change is at the point where the student was holding the chain; the scale factor is (about) 3 if you used three identical rubber bands. Other good questions are these: What if (the student) had held the end at a different point? What if I had traced over the original with the second knot? Can one shrink a shape with this method? (This is possible but difficult to do without obstructing the students' view; trace over the shape with a tracing finger at the *end* of the chain and the chalk in the loop at some intermediate knot.) What would be possible with a chain of four rubber bands, or five? Emphasize that in step 3 of the ruler method, both distances are measured *from the center* and not from the point whose image is being found.

You will probably need to put in some rays emanating from the center so that the relation to the upcoming ruler method is clear. Surprisingly, sometimes students do not see the ruler method as the same, in particular the important role played by the rays in the stretched chain of rubber bands. The ruler method gives a dilation, the basic motion for similarity in transformation geometry.

Some computer software—for example, the Geometer's Sketchpad—also allows one to show enlargements or reductions of given figures. As with the rubber-band method, putting in the rays from the center will probably be advisable.

INSTRUCTOR NOTE 20.1C

You may need to work through these examples, or preferably others of the same type, since some students are often rusty at solving similar triangles, particularly with the emphasis here on scale factors rather than on ratios. The examples involve the angle sum for a triangle. As noted, in Example 3 the correspondence of sides is not as visually obvious as is often the case. Once corresponding angles are identified, corresponding sides can be located either by looking at the angles opposite the sides or by looking at the two angles adjacent to the side of concern.

Look for both of the following approaches to come up in finding lengths *BC* and *WX* in Example 2 (once a scale factor has been found):

1. Use of that one scale factor to find both lengths

2. A change of view about "new" and "old" to get the inverse of that scale factor to find the second length.

Students who remember the ratio = ratio approach may resist using the scale factor. We have usually said that they should be able to do it both ways.

INSTRUCTOR NOTE 20.2A

The main topics in this section are the relationships between the perimeters of similar shapes (equal to the scale factor) and between the areas of similar shapes (equal to the *square* of the scale factor), along with the AA method for recognizing that two triangles are similar. An example of a justification for the AA method is included in Section 22.5. Students seem to have difficulty with the relationship between the areas of similar shapes, so it usually needs special attention.

INSTRUCTOR NOTE 20.3A

This section treats similarity of polyhedra and, by generalization, similarity of all 3D shapes. Similarity with curved 3D shapes come up in other sections. This section does not depend on Section 20.1 (theoretically, but it is condensed), to allow for courses that treat primarily 3D material. For courses that include Section 20.1, this section should go fairly quickly.

Allow 30 seconds or so for "thinktime" before calling for responses to the *Related Shapes* question in Discussion 3. Reward any suggestions that won't be pursued (for example, "the ones made up of five cubes"), explaining that only two ways of being related will get most of the attention here: Congruence ("the same shape, but possibly rotated or reflected"—A, C, G, H, I) and similarity ("the same shape, usually enlarged or shrunk and perhaps rotated or reflected"— the congruent-to-A family, plus F and J). The ideas of congruence and similarity are of great importance in elementary geometry. Examine why B, D, and E do not fit in with our narrow focus on congruence and similarity; E may be attractive ("a stretched-out shape I"). Some students may need to maneuver cube figures to see some congruences.

Watch for this error: Some students count points rather than intervals between points.

Vocabulary (similar polyhedra, scale factor) and key relationships among corresponding angles (they are the same size) and corresponding lengths (their ratio is the scale factor) should be emphasized in this section. Surface area ("how many squares to cover") and volume ("how many cubes to fill") comparisons should also be insinuated into the development, partly to start building on what the students know but also to assess what knowledge about area and volume measurement the students bring. For some, $A = lw$ and $V = lwh$ will be the only meanings they have for area and volume, so be careful not to assume too much prior knowledge. Area and volume for similar shapes are revisited in the measurement chapters.

It is almost essential that the students be able to build things from cubes. We have always had them on hand during our courses, and, in fact, have on occasion required the students to buy a package of 100 cubic centimeters.

You may wish to have the students make their drawings on separate dot paper.

INSTRUCTOR NOTE 20.3B

Depending on your students' backgrounds, you may need to "seed" this Think About task by referring to several lengths (of various dimensions, diagonals, etc), angle sizes, areas of faces, total area, and volumes. At this point, students may be vague on area and volume. Use a "square regions to cover" meaning for area, and a "cubes to fill" meaning for volume, pointing to show the sizes of squares and cubes you mean.

In your summary, here are some important considerations that repeat the technical meaning for similar shapes from Section 20.1: Points on the two shapes can be matched so that (a) every pair of angles that match have the same size, and (b) the ratio of the values of the lengths of any two matching segments will be the same. (The ratios must be formed in a consistent fashion, either always larger to smaller or always smaller to larger.) This ratio is called the *scale factor*. A useful form is this one: (new length) = (scale factor) × (original length), as well as the ratio or fraction form. Show both, with an example. The language for multiplicative comparison used earlier fits well: The new length is scale factor times as long as the corresponding original length.

Multiplicative comparisons of surface areas and volumes are sought in the important Think About; the ratio of the areas is the *square* of the scale factor, and the ratio of the volumes is the *cube* of the scale factor. In this section these are just experimental conjectures. In the measurement sections, there is an attempt to add conceptually to these two relationships. If your students know the length × width × height formula for the volume of a right rectangular prism, then you can show the three appearances of the scale factor in the corresponding formula for the image. In Section 24.2, for volume the focus is on one cubic region and its image.

As with 2D shapes, in most situations, which shape is the new and which is the original is arbitrary. Point this out, emphasizing that so long as the ratios are formed consistently the choice of new and original can be made either way.

Instructor Notes for Chapter 21: Curves, Constructions, and Curved Surfaces

Section headings in this chapter are as follows.

21.1 *Planar Curves and Constructions.* Circle vocabulary, including inscribed angle size. Standard ruler-compass constructions.

21.2 *Curved Surfaces.* Sphere, cylinder, cone vocabulary.

21.3 *Check Yourself.*

21.4 *Issues for Learning: Standards for Mathematical Practice.*

INSTRUCTOR NOTE 21.1A

The names of the curves in the first figure (part of a sine curve, parabola, ellipse, circle, hyperbola) are not too important for our purposes, but the circle vocabulary should be mastered. *Major* versus *minor* arc, *sector*, and *segment* may be new to many students.

Use the vocabulary as a focus for the discussion of the properties of a circle. Key, and likely to come up, are these:

- A radius is a line segment with its endpoints at the center of the circle and a point on the circle.

- All radii of a circle have the same length.

- A diameter is a chord that goes through the center of the circle.

- A diameter has the length of two radii.

Also of importance is the fact that the words *radius* and *diameter* are used not only for the segments but for the measurement (that is, length) of these segments as well. Students may recall circumference and area formulas, but those do not get attention in this section.

Secants are not included and tangents to a circle are relegated to Learning Exercise 22. Although these are nice to know, studying them beyond vocabulary takes time away from other topics.

Activity 1 on inscribed angles gives an opportunity to explore the relationship between the size of an inscribed angle and its intercepted arc. Learning Exercise 7 starts a justification, if you wish to pursue it.

Activity 2 provides an opportunity to review AA for similar triangles and to prove SAS and ASA for congruent triangles.

The constructions illustrated are the standard ones. You may know whether constructions are a "need to know" or a "nice to know" in your locale. No justifications are given, but symmetry is mentioned as a way to see that the results are reasonable. Learning Exercise 17 in Section 16.1 introduces some paper-folding methods.

INSTRUCTOR NOTE 21.2A

A globe offers familiar great circles in the equator and the meridians. Students probably do *not* know that the path along a great circle is the shortest path (on the sphere) between two points on a sphere.

The descriptions given for a cylinder and cone are intended to be general, but virtually all of the work in measurement will be with circular cylinders and circular cones. If it comes up, a flower-pot shape could result from cutting off the sharp end of a cone, with a plane parallel to the base of the cone (a truncated cone).

INSTRUCTOR NOTE 21.2B

This discussion topic is intended to bring in a cross-cultural element. You may have to be enthusiastic about the topic since students often react with a "this isn't going to be on the test" attitude. Mention that this is a topic that can become a good source for cross-disciplinary work in elementary school. (Refer them to "People Who Live in Round Houses," by C. Zaslavsky, *Arithmetic Teacher*, September, 1989, vol. 37, pp. 18–21.)

The shapes of houses are often influenced by tradition but originally were influenced by factors such as the kinds of materials available, the weather, and the style of life (for example, nomadic versus stationary). A sphere encloses the greatest volume for a given amount of surface area, so the rounded features of some of the "primitive" houses can be defended quite well mathematically!

Instructor Notes for Chapter 22: Transformation Geometry

Chapter 22 is a long chapter, and we usually—in a one-semester course devoted solely to geometry and measurement—cover only the first section, valuing the later work with measurement more highly for an elementary school teacher audience. Middle school teachers should be exposed to more transformation geometry, ideally with help from Geometer's Sketchpad. The website http://nlvm.usu.edu has several activities dealing with transformations.

Sections in this chapter are as follows.

22.1 *Some Types of Rigid Motions.* Rigid motion/isometry; translation, reflection, rotation, glide reflection (visually); image; congruent figures. Section 22.1 is relatively brief, to introduce only the basic vocabulary for courses that must skip the rest of the chapter.

22.2 *Finding Images for Rigid Motions.* Using tracing paper (and grids) to find images (translation, reflection, rotation).

22.3 *A Closer Look at Rigid Motions.* Defining characteristics; given figure and image, identify and describe motion.

22.4 *Composition of Rigid Motions.* Composition introduced.

22.5 *Transformations and Earlier Topics.* Translation and glide-reflection symmetries; reprise of earlier topics with transformation geometry focus.

22.6 *Issues for Learning: Promoting Visualization in the Curriculum.*

22.7 *Check Yourself.*

If you are not familiar with transformation geometry, here are some pieces of the big picture, which includes much more than further practice with visualization, a part of the aim here. With its emphasis on functions (transformations), transformation geometry is closer to the current mathematical mainstream than is classical Euclidean geometry. The coverage here does not include the fact that the isometries of the plane, with composition, give a non-Abelian group. The four standard types of 2D rigid motions (isometries) are introduced in the first section—reflections, rotations, translations, and glide-reflections. The glide-reflection is treated more fully in Section 22.4.

INSTRUCTOR NOTE 22.1A

The preliminary activity should be given as homework, with enough discussion so that students understand that rotations and reflections of a four-toothpick shape do not give new shapes. The activity comes from an excellent compilation of lessons for the primary grades (Burns & Tank, 1988). Nonetheless, the activity involves enough visualization to make it worthwhile for college students, and it gives a springboard for introducing technical terms. Notice that in checking, comparing, or copying shapes, as from a chalkboard or a screen display of students' answers, one likely does some mental visualization and perhaps exercises some spatial memory. For example, showing answers to the preliminary activity with an overhead transparency "forces" students to hold a shape in memory, and perhaps mentally manipulate it, when searching for the shape among their answers. Having answers, perhaps from a version of the answers below or from several students on separate transparencies, allows a figure to be rotated or flipped over (whereas figures on the board must be maneuvered mentally) and in a fairly efficient manner. Students who still consider themselves poor visualizers may need encouragement ("You'll continue to get better") or advice on coping strategies ("Study how the toothpicks are put together"). Having everyone number the shapes the same way allows some quick communication.

Burns and Tank describe follow-up activities such as the following. With a "deck" of the 16 shapes on, say, 3 × 5 cards and as a cooperation game or competition game, students are to make a "one-difference" train, with a starting card; then, each subsequent card must be obtainable from the previous card by the movement of *one* toothpick. Children are often surprised when different trains are possible. Variations are to make a complete circle, with the caboose and engine also differing by one toothpick, or to make a "two-difference" train. Each of these can give potentially valuable extra experience at mental manipulation.

INSTRUCTOR NOTE 22.1B

Some of the terms here may be familiar to students who have worked with 2D rigid motions or symmetries before.

The definition for rigid motion is not, of course, very precise in using movement to define a motion, but it avoids a side-trip into function considerations. If you are familiar with isometries, you will recognize that the definition is redundant since angle congruence can be proved from length invariance with the common congruent-triangle apparatus.

Students who did not have any transformation geometry in precollege work may question its relevance for their teaching careers. Mention that there is an increasing awareness that spatial visualization activities should be an explicit part of the curriculum. The dynamic nature of transformation geometry invites visualization and is recognized in the Common Core State Standards.

As noted above, transformations, as a special case of functions, are also much closer to the mathematical mainstream than a "name this shape" curriculum. In elementary text series, you may be able to find other sample pages that introduce transformation geometry terms. Most curriculum guides call for at least an exposure to translations, reflections, and rotations.

A note in the margin calls attention to the nontrivial nature of Learning Exercise 7. "Shapes from Four Triangles" in the Auxiliary Materials could give a form of the problem more in keeping with an outside assignment.

INSTRUCTOR NOTE 22.3A

Activity 6 is the most involved of this type of problem (given figure and image, describe fully the rigid motion). First of all, seeing that a rotation is involved is visually more difficult for most people. If you have given attention to (clock) orientation, you can note that with a rotation both figures have the same (clock) orientation, and here it does not look at all as though a translation would give the image (joining what should be corresponding points will give nonparallel, noncongruent segments). Once a rotation is considered, it looks reasonable, but finding the center (and then the angle) involves the construction of perpendicular bisectors of two segments joining corresponding points. If you did not assign Learning Exercise 12 in Section 21.1, you might do so now. So it is also important to join two pairs of corresponding points (*A-R*, *B-S*, *C-T*, *D-U*, *E-P*, *F-Q*). Here is a solution, using the perpendicular bisectors of segments *DU* and *CT* (and not showing the construction marks).

INSTRUCTOR NOTE 22.4A

This section introduces the composition of rigid motions, with a closer look at the fourth type of rigid motion, the glide-reflection. The glide-reflection is psychologically awkward because it is defined in terms of *two* motions. Its value is that its addition completes a catalog of rigid motions that is adequate to describe *any* composition of rigid motions. Although a "rotation-reflection" might be an alternate way of getting a particular image, one of a reflection or a glide-reflection can be found to give that image. Some elementary school mathematics textbooks do include glide-reflections in their treatments of rigid motions.

In the earlier work, a rigid motion has been an operator that "moves" shapes. With composition, a rigid motion becomes an operand. Some students find this change difficult.

The approach here is informal. You may want to examine more closely such points as the composition of rigid motions *being* a rigid motion (since each of the rigid motions preserves lengths, so will their composition), or to follow up some of the exercises about compositions to arrive at such results as the predictability of the vector of the translation resulting from the composition of two reflections in parallel lines. The exercises include several hints about further theoretical results (for example, the composition of two reflections in intersecting lines is a rotation with center at the intersection of the lines, and angle of size twice that of the angle made by the intersecting lines) in case your taste and the time in the course allow their pursuit.

As with the earlier sections, you may choose to use MIRAs or software if you have either available. As the outline in Appendix C indicates, the Geometer's Sketchpad can carry out isometries. Transformation-Composition at http://nlvm.usu.edu gives two activities involving compositions.

INSTRUCTOR NOTE 22.5A

Discussion 3 could be lengthy (or optional). The answer to the question is "Yes," but it cannot be answered solely on the basis of the 3D transformations hinted at in the students' earlier study of 3D symmetries—reflections in a plane, and rotations about an axis—and their exposure to 3D size changes—enlargements and shrinks. However, the only missing 3D rigid motions are the translation, and then the compositions of pairs of those three: rotation about axis, with translation (= "twist"); reflection in plane, with translation (glide-reflection); and rotation about axis, with reflection in plane (= "rotatory reflection").

Only the 3D analogue of the 2D size change, along with the 3D rigid motions, is needed for similarity. The 28-minute video, *Similarity* (from Project Mathematica) shows the 3D size change; the video is too fast-paced for a first exposure but is serviceable as a summary.

Instructor Notes for Chapter 23: Measurement Basics

These are the sections in Chapter 23:

23.1 *Key Ideas of Measurement.* Meaning of measurement; standard units—metric system and prefixes; approximate nature of measurements; additivity.

23.2 *Length and Angle Size.* Key ideas of measurement applied to length and angle size; perimeter and circumference; units for angle size; review of angle-sum formula for *n*-gon.

23.3 *Issues for Learning: Measurement of Length and Angle Size.*

23.4 *Check Yourself.*

INSTRUCTOR NOTE 23.1A

As a lead-in homework exercise or an opening question, ask students to list several things that are measured. Then ask them, "What does it mean to *measure* something?" (Collecting their writing helps motivate the passive student, and reading them gives you an idea of how your students are thinking.) The term "quantity" is given careful attention in *Reasoning about Numbers and Quantities*. Briefly, a quantity is any characteristic that can be measured or counted; the measurement or count, with the unit involved, is the *value* of the quantity. We try to place an emphasis on thinking about the quantities and their relationships rather than the *values* of the quantities and the calculations. Lord Kelvin (1824–1907), a physicist and engineer and for whom the Kelvin temperature scale is named, once said, "If you can measure that of which you speak, and can express it by a number, you know something of your subject; but if you cannot measure it, your knowledge is meager and unsatisfactory."

INSTRUCTOR NOTE 23.1B

How you handle Discussion 1 will depend on your students' backgrounds with science classes or with Part I. If they have had earlier experience with the metric system or with the Part I work on quantitative reasoning, then they should have some familiarity with metric units and you could just continue on, either skipping or quickly reviewing the discussion questions.

For Discussion 1:

1. Standard units make for ease of communication and are usually defined in such a fashion as to be permanent and reproducible; using a random twig as a unit for measuring length is certainly possible, but it suffers on all those counts.

2. Units of different sizes allow one to choose an appropriate unit for the object being measured. For example, measuring the weight of a shipment of coal in ounces, or the height of a child in kilometers, would not be sensible, either because the resulting values would be numerically awkward or, in the case of the coal, the choice of unit would imply a precision of measurement that is not reasonable.

3. Nonstandard units, like a twig for length measurement, allow the *process* of measurement to be the focus and involve contexts that are often familiar to children.

Some important points to bring out regarding the metric system:

- Standard units are needed for ease of communication within and across cultures, as well as across time, so that some ease of reproducibility is desirable.

- The metric system, a decimal system, was born during the French Revolution; the French even tried to decimalize time.

- One question you might ask your students is, "When have you used the metric system either in or out of school?"

A couple of notes: The official SI spelling is *metre*, not *meter*. You occasionally see *metre* in books published in the United States. Besides the United States, the only other countries that have not adopted the metric system as their official system are Burma and Liberia (although Liberia seems to be leaning toward metrication). This fact does not mean that a metric country is exclusively metric; the United Kingdom, for example, continues to use the English system in many everyday matters.

You may need to "sell" the usefulness of the metric system to your students, as there is usually resistance to anything unfamiliar. The Olympic games and car engine sizes, for example, are familiar places in which your students have probably encountered metric units. Ford Motor Co., with all its multinational ties, was one of the first large companies to go metric. It is interesting— and informative—that in the United States the English units have been officially defined in terms of metric units since 1893, first by one yard = $\frac{3600}{3937}$ meter, and later (1959) by one yard = 0.9144 meter! Since 1988, the federal government has had a program to adopt metric units for all of its contracts.

The exercises neglect conversions that are unusual in practice, as in "how many centimeters are in 4 hectometers." Our preference is for a "metric sense" approach, in which the student has a feel for the sizes of the units. Some instructors use a rule like "Make a row of the prefixes, starting with the largest and leaving a space for the basic unit. To convert, move the decimal point as many places as you do with the prefixes, and in the same direction." We do not present such a rule, preferring the "think metric" approach and avoiding complicated conversions.

Even though we use "the English system" to refer to the common one used in the United States, you may know that the U.S. version is not exactly the same as the English version. For example, a U.S. gallon is a different size than the English (or Imperial) gallon. Most of the other commonly used units are the same, however.

INSTRUCTOR NOTE 23.1C

The approximate nature of most actual measurements is an important point. (Counting, if regarded as measuring, can be exact.) Unfortunately, measurements in school are often treated as exact (at least implicitly). Point out the width of scale marks, or imagine magnifying the scale marks and the "end" of the measured object, or mention hair thickness and compressibility in measuring height, or cite the fact that because our vertebrae settle during the day, we are slightly shorter in the evening than in the morning.

Illustrate with a drawing the different lengths that might all be reported as 21 inches, or the more difficult 25.2 inches. Students do not seem as comfortable in dealing to the nearest tenth or hundredth, for example, compared with dealing to the nearest whole.

Instructor Notes for Chapter 24: Area, Surface Area, and Volume

Following are the section titles for Chapter 24. The *ideas* of area, surface area, and volume are the focus, leaving formulas to Chapter 25.

24.1 *Area and Surface Area.* Meaning; units; areas of dot paper/geoboard figures; area relationship for similar figures (formulas are in Chapter 25).

24.2 *Volume.* Meaning, capacity, SI units, direct counting of cubes, volume relationship for similar figures (formulas are in Chapter 25).

24.3 *Issues for Learning: Measurement of Area and Volume.* Selected research on children's understanding of area and volume measurement.

24.4 *Check Yourself.*

INSTRUCTOR NOTE 24.1A

This section focuses on the concepts of area and surface area, and the key ideas as applied to area. Hence, area formulas should continue to be downplayed (they will come up in Chapter 25). In demonstrating the relationships among metric area units, a meter stick (or four) is handy, as are a square centimeter and a square decimeter. Faces of base ten materials that you may have are also possible sources for showing a square centimeter and a square decimeter because many types are based on metric units. Four meter sticks can show a square meter, as can a piece of cardboard cut from a large box, like a packing box for a large appliance. *Geoboards* are arrangements of pegs, usually arranged in rows to give squares. Stretching a rubber band around the pegs allows illustrating a variety of polygons. A master for a paper geoboard can be found at the back of the text or on the book companion website: www.whfreeman.com/reconceptmath2e.

The first discussion question in Discussion 1 may be difficult; many students' only idea of area is "length times width" (and their only idea of volume might be "length times width times height"). In earlier sections, students should have counted square regions or cubical regions, so students may have the basic ideas but without the allied vocabulary of area and volume.

You may wish to assign the first discussion question as a homework exercise, so students have a chance to give more than their off-the-top-of-head answers. The marginal discussion question is often the basis for an elementary-school activity with area, and it is included as Learning Exercise 4(f) in the section if you want to postpone its discussion; students might start by finding the area of their hands by tracing their hands on grid paper and later lying down on a large sheet of paper (perhaps grid paper), tracing the outline and then counting squares, to estimate the area of one "side" of their bodies.

When a unit like square inch or square centimeter comes up, ask students to show with their fingers, or a sketch, what the phrase means.

INSTRUCTOR NOTE 24.1B

In Discussion 2 each of the regions could theoretically be used. Regions with straight edges, however, can be made to fit next to each other exactly and to many shapes in western civilizations, so less approximation is needed. If the students have been exposed to tessellations, you can point out that any shape that tessellates the plane would be quite usable because the estimation of any part units could be confined to the edges of the region being measured. Regions in Discussion 2 are used to emphasize the attribute of area.

INSTRUCTOR NOTE 24.2A

As noted, this chapter emphasizes the conceptual side of volume, rather than volume formulas, which will come up in Chapter 25. It is useful for the students to have some hands-on experiences with a cubic centimeter and a cubic decimeter and to at least see a cubic meter outlined and compared to a cubic centimeter and a cubic decimeter. Having 12 meter sticks, or a commercial cubic meter set, enables a demonstration of the size of the unit, and relationships among units, as in Discussion 5. (Notice that unusual units like cubic hectometers, cubic millimeters, and so on, do not get attention.) The pieces in some place-value kits are based on metric units, and you may have a supply of cubic centimeters available. If you have a waterproof cubic decimeter container and a one or two liter bottle, seeing a demonstration that a liter and a cubic decimeter are the same size is more convincing than is just eyeballing the two.

As noted in the margin after Discussion 7, the k^3 ratio between the volumes of similar 3D shapes seems not to be easy for students, so you may need to place some emphasis on it, and perhaps give additional problems in class, *a la* Learning Exercises 20(b) and 21 and Supplementary Learning Exercises 6 and 7.

Instructor Notes for Chapter 25: Counting Units Fast: Measurement Formulas

Here are the sections in this chapter.

25.1 *Circumference, Area, and Surface Area Formulas.* Justifications for the usual circumference and area formulas. There are many exercises, reflecting the richness of the section. You will likely have to pick and choose the ones best suited for your class and your aims (see Instructor Note 25.1F).

25.2 *Volume Formulas.* Prisms and cylinders ($V = Bh$), pyramids and cones ($V = \frac{1}{3}Bh$), and spheres ($V = \frac{4}{3}\pi r^3$).

25.3 *Issues for Learning: What Measurement Is in the Curriculum?*

25.4 *Check Yourself.*

INSTRUCTOR NOTE 25.1A

The development of area formulas here follows a line common in elementary school—common there since it does not involve any algebraic proficiency: rectangle (and square), then parallelogram, then triangle (and trapezoid), and then circle. As you may know, a mathematically "cleaner" sequence follows a rectangle, then right triangle, then general triangle, then other quadrilaterals, and so on, in order of development, and you may prefer that. Whatever order you follow, the students should understand that the formulas *can be justified*, and they should feel responsible for giving justifications.

For in-class work, you may wish to try an approach used by Simon & Blume (1994). Each group of students is given a small rectangular (but not square) region and asked to find how many such regions would be needed to cover their table (or desk or a chalkboard section) and to be prepared to discuss their method. Possibly after concern about whether all the regions should be oriented the same, groups usually decide to multiply the number of regions that fit along the length and width of their (rectangular) table. The key post-activity questions are: "Why did you multiply those numbers together?" "Will this method always work?" and "*Why* does it work?" Let the class answer the questions, perhaps not until the next class session.

A commercial volume-relationships kit includes a transparent cube, pyramid, cylinder, cone, and sphere. The pyramid has base and height equal to those of the cube, and the bases and heights of the cone and cylinder are equal. The diameter of the sphere is like that of the base and the height of the cylinder. Water (or rice) can be poured from one to the other to give experimental evidence for the formula $V = \frac{1}{3}Bh$ for the cone, and some instructors use them to arrive at $V = \frac{4}{3}\pi r^3$ for the sphere (from the experimental pouring that suggests that the volume of the sphere is $\frac{2}{3}$ of the $V = Bh = 2\pi r^3$ for the cylinder). (See Instructor Notes 25.1D, 25.1E, and 25.2B.)

INSTRUCTOR NOTE 25.1B

In the United States, $m \times n$ is interpreted as telling how many are in m groups of n each. (This is reversed in some countries.) Hence, the square regions can be counted by rows: $m \times n$ can tell how many squares in all are in m rows, with n in each row. Both m and n can be determined by measuring a *length* because the unit squares have sides equal to 1 length unit.

Although students may come up with clever ways of cutting individual squares to find the areas in the second and third examples, these methods may not support the desired $A = lw$. You may have to intercede. As you know, almost uniform is the practice in advanced mathematics of regarding rows as horizontal (as opposed to vertical). A partial row, such as $\frac{1}{2}$ of a row of 4 square regions in the second rectangle, fits the part-of-an-amount interpretation of multiplication. Hence, the total area is $(3 \times 4) + (\frac{1}{2} \times 4)$. Using the distributive property, this gives the total area as $(3 + \frac{1}{2}) \times 4$, or $3\frac{1}{2} \times 4$, with $3\frac{1}{2}$ and 4 interpretable as the lengths of the two dimensions of the rectangle. Similarly, in the last example, $(2 \times 2\frac{1}{2}) + (\frac{1}{4} \times 2\frac{1}{2}) = (2 + \frac{1}{4}) \times 2\frac{1}{2} = 2\frac{1}{4} \times 2\frac{1}{2}$.

INSTRUCTOR NOTE 25.1C

This alternative approach to the formula for the area of a sphere uses a result from the historically significant figure, Archimedes (ca. 287–212 B.C.) Archimedes discovered that the surface area of a sphere of radius r is two-thirds the (total) surface area of a circular cylinder with radius r and height $2r$. Thus, $SA(\text{sphere}) = \frac{2}{3}(2\pi r^2 + 2\pi r \cdot 2r) = \frac{2}{3} \cdot 6\pi r^2 = 4\pi r^2$. Advantages of this approach are that it gives some practice with finding the surface area of a special cylinder and that it introduces an important mathematician; the disadvantage is that Archimedes' result is just stated (as is ours, for the surface area of the sphere).

INSTRUCTOR NOTE 25.1C

You may prefer an alternative development of the $A(\text{circle}) = \pi r^2$ formula. The method involves a bit less algebra and about the same amount of hand-waving as the text method; it assumes that $C = 2\pi r$ and $A(\text{parallelogram}) = bh$ are available. In short, a circular region is cut into a (large) number of sectors that are then rearranged to give, approximately, a parallelogram, as in the following drawing.

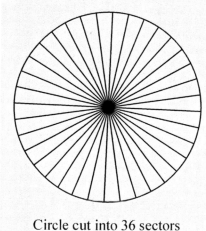

Circle cut into 36 sectors

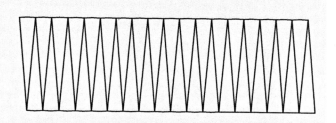

Sectors rearranged, to give (nearly) a parallelogram with base (nearly) πr and height (nearly) r, with area = πr^2.

The base of the near parallelogram is about half the circumference ($\frac{1}{2} 2\pi r = \pi r$) and the height of the near parallelogram is about r. And hence

$$A(\text{circular region}) \text{ is nearly } \pi r \cdot r = \pi r^2$$

Surprisingly, this $\frac{2}{3}$ relationship also holds true for the volumes of the sphere and cylinder. (See Instructor Note 25.2D.) (http://en.wikipedia.org/wiki/Archimedes, April 11, 2012)

INSTRUCTOR NOTE 25.1E

One reviewer preferred an alternative sequence that makes good use of a volume-relationship kit to which you may have access. It leads to a derivation that would occur *after* work with the volume of a sphere and again involves the idea of limits, along with some algebra. First, experimentally relate the volume of a sphere to that already established for a cylinder and use the resulting formula for the volume to make plausible the formula for the surface area. Here are details. Some kits have a sphere, radius r, that fits tightly into a cylinder (so that the cylinder has height $2r$ and a base with radius r); the sphere has a hole so that water can be put inside. The water from a sphereful is poured into the cylinder, filling it $\frac{2}{3}$ full. Hence, the volume of the sphere is $\frac{2}{3}$ that of the cylinder, or $\frac{2}{3}\pi r^2 2r$, which gives the usual $\frac{4}{3}\pi r^3$. Then, to get the *surface area*, imagine concentric spheres with radii r and $r + h$. The difference in the volumes of the two spheres gives a thin layer (thickness h), so it is plausible that dividing the difference in volumes by h, and letting h get arbitrarily small, will give the surface area. Some algebra, with the most complicated being cubing $r + h$, gives the usual $4\pi r^2$.

$$\frac{\frac{4}{3}\pi(r+h)^3 - \frac{4}{3}\pi r^3}{h} = \frac{4}{3}\pi\frac{r^3 + 3r^2h + 3rh^2 + h^3 - r^3}{h} = \frac{4}{3}\pi\frac{3r^2h + 3rh^2 + h^3}{h} = \frac{4}{3}\pi(3r^2 + 3rh + h^2) \rightarrow 4\pi r^2 \text{ as } h$$

approaches 0.

INSTRUCTOR NOTE 25.1F

You will likely have to pick and choose from these exercises. Some of them involve a considerable amount of work, and some could be small-group or discussion exercises. Students will need a ruler and square-dotted grid paper for some of the exercises. Usually, the exercise lists have not been organized in any particular order, partly so that students do not expect a later numbered exercise to be more difficult that earlier numbered ones. But this section is so long that the exercise list is quite long, and there has been a degree of organization, as follows:

#2–#7 deal with circumference or π.

#8–#17 deal with areas of polygons.

#18–#24 involve areas of circular regions/sectors/spheres, and regions to be "cut up."

#25–#26 ask for surface areas of simple polyhedra.

#27–#28 are conceptual items (area under a curve, units for area).

#29–#30 involve areas of similar figures.

#31 has a new formula for the area of a kite.

#32 treats Pick's formula, a way of finding areas of polygons with vertices at the dots on dot paper. (We often skip it because students attach too much importance to it and use it instead of the more fundamental "surround with a rectangle" approach.)

#33–#36 suggest alternative derivations of some area formulas.

#37 involves the surface area of a cylinder.

Some of the exercises for Section 25.2 involve area as well as volume, to help keep the ideas distinct.

INSTRUCTOR NOTE 25.2A

You may wish to ask what volume formulas your students already know. Again, the emphasis here is on what the formulas tell one and on where the formulas come from. For some students, this may be their first encounter with anything besides $V = lwh$.

Here is an overview of the work coming up with volume formulas. For prisms and cylinders, the derivation of volume formulas is centered on layers. For pyramids and cones, it is centered on extrapolation from an experiment with a special case in *Three Coins in the Fountain, or...* (and perhaps a demonstration, if you have suitable equipment). Thus, the main formulas are $V = Bh$ for prisms and cylinders, and $V = \frac{1}{3}Bh$ for pyramids and cones.

The formula for the volume of a sphere is given, but the argument may be too dense without support from you (and a soccer ball or basketball, perhaps). Alternative derivations are in Instructor Note 25.2C.

INSTRUCTOR NOTE 25.2B

Activity 3 requires shape I from the polyhedra kit. The group size should be three or more, since three copies of shape I are needed to make the smallest prism possible (a cube). The $V = \frac{1}{3}Bh$ formula is revealed soon in the student notes, but be certain to make it explicit in a post-activity discussion. Having groups of just three, along with the title of the activity, is something of a big hint, although many think that two shape Is can be put together to make a prism. (Aside: Your students—and you—may be too young to recognize the activity title as the title song from an old movie.)

There are commercial kits with a plastic pyramid and prism sized so that the pyramid has the same area base and height as the prism. These allow either a water- or rice-pouring demonstration that the volume of the pyramid is, plausibly, $\frac{1}{3}$ that of the prism. Ask your students to predict a relationship before such a demonstration; many will think the pyramid has half the volume of the prism. If you have access to such a kit, it is a good substitute or supplement to Activity 3. The commercial kits also have a cone and cylinder for the same type of demonstration. A make-do cone and cylinder can be devised fairly easily from card stock, with rice or beans used for pouring.

An alternative derivation for a special case involves cutting a cube into six identical pyramids, each with a face of the cube as its base (see the following sketch). Then, the volume of each pyramid is given by $\frac{1}{6}e^3$, where e is the length of each edge of the cube. Noting that each pyramid has a base with area $B = e^2$ and height $h = \frac{1}{2}e$, you can argue that the volume, $\frac{1}{6}e^3$, for each pyramid could be obtained by taking one-third of $e^2 \cdot \frac{1}{2}e$. That is, $V(\text{pyramid}) = \frac{1}{3}Bh$.

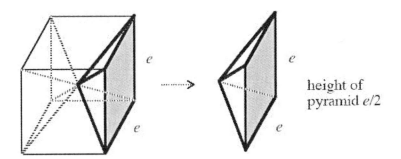

height of
pyramid $e/2$

INSTRUCTOR NOTE 25.2C

If your students are strong (perhaps planning to be middle school teachers), you may want to give more careful or different arguments. Here are three ways that you can do so.

1. The derivation of the formula for the volume of a sphere given in the text could be strengthened by also considering pyramids with the vertex at the center and height r so that the sphere is now surrounded by the pyramids. As the number of pyramids increases and all their bases get smaller and smaller, the combined areas of the bases of the pyramids grow ever closer to the surface area of the sphere. Thus, the volume of the sphere is between the sum of the volumes of the pyramids inside the sphere (as in the text development) and the sum of the volumes of those outside the sphere. As the number of pyramids inside the sphere grows, the height of the inside pyramids approaches r, and as the number of pyramids enclosing the sphere grows, the bases become ever closer to the surface of the sphere, so the volume of the sphere is "trapped" between the two.

$$\sum \tfrac{1}{3}h(\text{base of an inner pyramid}) \leq \text{volume of sphere} \leq \sum \tfrac{1}{3}r(\text{base of an outer pyramid}).$$

As the number of inner pyramids grows larger and larger, the common h approaches r and the total of the bases of the inner pyramids approaches the surface area of the sphere,

$$\sum \tfrac{1}{3}(\text{base of an inner pyramid}) \cdot h = \tfrac{1}{3}h \sum (\text{base of inner pyramid}) \rightarrow \tfrac{1}{3} \cdot r \cdot 4\pi r^2 = \tfrac{4}{3}\pi r^3.$$

As the number of outer pyramids with height r increases, the bases of the pyramids again approach the surface area of the sphere,

$$\sum \tfrac{1}{3}(\text{base of an outer pyramid}) \cdot r \rightarrow \tfrac{1}{3} \cdot 4\pi r^2 \cdot r = \tfrac{4}{3}\pi r^3.$$

So the volume of the sphere must be between $\tfrac{4}{3}\pi r^3$ and $\tfrac{4}{3}\pi r^3$—that is, the volume must *be* $\tfrac{4}{3}\pi r^3$.

2. Another way to derive the formula for the volume of a sphere again appeals to a result from Archimedes. (See Instructor Note 25.1C.) Archimedes also discovered that the *volume* of a sphere of radius r is two-thirds the volume of a circular cylinder with radius r and height $2r$. Thus, $V(\text{sphere}) = \tfrac{2}{3} \cdot \pi r^2 \cdot 2r = \tfrac{4}{3}\pi r^3$. (Learning Exercise 11 gives other results known to Archimedes and allegedly used on his gravestone.) The drawback is that the result from Archimedes is not justified.

3. Finally, a common way of finding the formula for the volume of a sphere introduces Cavalieri's principle, a generalization of our layers arguments:

> Suppose that two solids have equal altitudes and that *all* plane sections parallel to their bases at equal distances from the bases are equal. Then, the solids have the same volume.

Using Cavalieri's principle for the volume of a sphere requires the Pythagorean theorem, which in this text is not covered until Section 26.1. However, any students likely to understand this method of finding the volume of a sphere probably know the Pythagorean theorem.

To use Cavalieri's principle, we first consider a sphere with a cross-section (which of course is a circle), with a radius of c. The area of this circle is πc^2. If the center of this circle is d units from the center of the sphere, then a right triangle can be formed with c and d as sides and r as the hypotenuse. Then, $c^2 = r^2 - d^2$ and the area of the circle is $\pi(r^2 - d^2)$ or $\pi r^2 - \pi d^2$. (We will relate this expression to a new figure made up of a circle of radius r with a donut hole of radius d, as in Figure 1.)

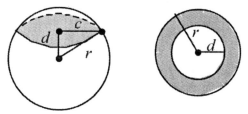

The gray areas are equal.

Figure 1. Circular and donut regions with equal area.

To use Cavalieri's principle, we must find another solid with a cross-section of the same area, that is, an area of $\pi(r^2 - d^2)$ or $\pi r^2 - \pi d^2$. Consider a cylinder of radius r and height $2r$ with cones with height r and bases at the two ends of the cylinder and intersecting in the middle of the cylinder (Fig. 2). The cylinder has volume $\pi r^2 \cdot 2r$ or $2\pi r^3$, and the cones together have volume $2(\frac{1}{3}\pi r^2 \cdot r) = \frac{2}{3}\pi r^3$. The part of the cylinder *outside* the cones must be $2\pi r^3 - \frac{2}{3}\pi r^3 = \frac{4}{3}\pi r^3$.

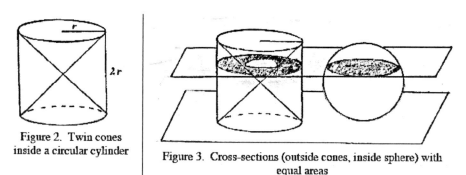

Figure 2. Twin cones
inside a circular cylinder

Figure 3. Cross-sections (outside cones, inside sphere) with
equal areas

Let this cylinder sit on the same plane as the sphere. Now, consider a cross-section of this cylinder-cones shape but *outside* the cones, and with the cross-section on the same plane as a cross section of the sphere, d units from the center of the sphere (Fig. 3). This new cross-section will also be donut-shaped, with an outer circle of area πr^2 and a cutout inner circle of area πd^2, giving an area $\pi r^2 - \pi d^2$, the same as that of the circular section, for every value of d above or below the point at which the cones meet (and less than *r*); see Figure 1. Thus, by Cavalieri's principle, this cylinder with the cones cut out must have the same volume as the sphere. Because that value from the cylinder is $\frac{4}{3}\pi r^3$ from the earlier argument, the volume of the sphere must be $\frac{4}{3}\pi r^3$.

Although this third derivation will introduce Cavalieri's principle, visualizing the cross-sections may be difficult.

INSTRUCTOR NOTE 25.2D

You will have to pick and choose from this exercise list, as with that for Section 25.1. Some of the exercises involve a considerable amount of work, and some could be small-group or discussion exercises. Usually, the exercise lists have not been organized in any particular order, partly so that students do not expect a later numbered exercise to be more difficult that earlier numbered ones. But this section is so long that the exercise list is quite long, so there has been a degree of organization, as follows:

> #1 focuses on the reasoning for the volume formula for prism/cylinder.
>
> #2, #3, and #5–#7 focus on prisms and pyramids (*V* and *SA*).
>
> #4 and #8–#16 involve spheres and cylinders (*V* and *SA*).
>
> #17 returns to polyhedra.
>
> #18 returns to curved shapes to "cut up" (*V* and *SA*).
>
> #19–#20 deal with cubes.
>
> #21 involves the k^2 and k^3 relationships for areas and volumes (respectively) of similar shapes.
>
> #22 develops alternate formulas for spheres and hemispheres (in terms of the diameter).
>
> #23 is an open-ended problem of design.
>
> #24 connects some area/volume situations with algebra.
>
> #25 introduces Fermi problems, which are good for estimating both measurements and calculations.

Areas of curved surfaces, besides that of a sphere, get minimal attention, as an astute student may observe. An example and a few exercises treat it as obvious that thinking about a net for, say, a right circular cylinder or cone, suggests how to get the surface area. An exercise in the next chapter goes from a net of a cone to its volume. Here are the usual formulas in case a student asks whether they exist, although we view these formulas as only "nice to know," but not "need to know."

SA(circular cylinder) $= 2\pi r^2 + (2\pi r)h = 2\pi r(r + h)$, where *r* is the radius of the base and *h* the height, with the second term coming from the rectangle in the net.

SA(right circular cone) $= \pi r^2 + \pi rs = \pi r(r + s)$, where *r* is the radius of the base and *s* is the "slant height," the distance from the vertex to any point on the circle at the base.

Instructor Notes for Chapter 26: Special Topics in Measurement

Here are the sections in this chapter.

26.1 *The Pythagorean Theorem.* Justification via areas; the converse; applications; Pythagorean triples are mentioned in the Learning Exercises.

26.2 *Some Other Kinds of Measurements.* A sample of nongeometric quantities and units; Caution when adding rates.

26.3 *Check Yourself.*

(There is no Issues for Learning section for this chapter.)

INSTRUCTOR NOTE 26.1A

The Pythagorean theorem is important in its own right, of course, but it also has a rich history, with only a few references given here. *Was Pythagoras Chinese?* (Swetz, 1977) and *The Pythagorean Proposition* (Loomis, 1968) are books dealing with the theorem.

The exercises offer good opportunities for reviewing the area and volume formulas. As noted in the margin, Learning Exercise 17 can lead to an attractive but incorrect pattern.

You will recognize the familiar Pythagorean triples in the examples and exercises: 3-4-5 and 5-12-13 or their multiples (for example, 0.6, 0.8, 1) in particular. (Learning Exercise 13(e) aims toward knowing that their multiples are also Pythagorean triples.) Here are a few other Pythagorean triples, although they involve a bit more calculation if you do not allow calculators:

7-24-25   8-15-17   12-35-37   16-63-65
20-21-29   28-45-53   36-77-85   48-55-73

If x and y are odd positive integers with $x > y$, then the a, b, and c values given as follows form a Pythagorean triple: $a = xy$, $b = \frac{x^2 - y^2}{2}$, and $c = \frac{x^2 + y^2}{2}$. For example, $x = 7$ and $y = 1$ give the 7-24-25 triple.

INSTRUCTOR NOTE 26.2A

Other units identified as *base units* in SI are the ampere (for electrical current), the degree Kelvin (for temperature; the size of degree Kelvin = the size of degree Celsius although the two scales have different zero points), the mole (for a standard amount of a given chemical substance), and the candela (for luminous intensity). *Derived units* are then defined in terms of those, even though the derived unit may have some special name—for example, the unit of force is called the newton (N) but defined as $m\,kg/s^2$. These units are not brought up in the text because of their technical natures, but you may choose to allude to them so that students do not think SI covers only the units they have encountered. Still other units—for example, the hour, the degree for angle size—are allowed because of their wide, uniform use (they are given precise definitions in SI terms—1 h = 3600 s, for example). An earlier exercise referred to a website that currently exists, http://lamar.ColoState.edu/~hillger/; they should maintain the "last word" on the metric system, which is reviewed periodically by an international body. Alternatively, you can type "metric system" in the search engine.

Mass and *weight* are technically different, although everyday usage treats them as the same. A body has a mass that is the same no matter where the body goes; weight depends on the gravitational pull on the body, so the weight of a body can differ from place to place. A person weighs less on the moon than on Earth, but her/his mass will be the same in both locations.

INSTRUCTOR NOTE 26.2B

The terms ratio and rate do *not* have universally agreed-upon meanings. We use ratio to refer to a multiplicative comparison for one static situation, in contrast to a rate, the multiplicative comparison that is the same for all of several variations of the situation with different values for the quantities being compared. Hence, each of the parts from Discussion 4 might be expressing a *ratio*, perhaps in simplified form, for a single situation: "I went 130 miles in 2 hours; what was my average speed?" But each part might also involve a *rate*, which can be applied to any measure of the quantity after the *per*: "I drove a long time at a steady speed of 65 miles per hour." Some rates, as in parts (b) (per child) and (d) (numbers of questionnaires) of Discussion 4, can involve counts.

References

Ascher, M. (1991). *Ethnomathematics: A multicultural view of mathematical ideas.* Pacific Grove, CA: Brooks-Cole.

Bell, E. T. (1937). *Men of mathematics.* New York: Simon and Schuster.

Beckmann, P. (1971). *A history of pi* (3rd ed). New York: St. Martin's.

Burns, M., & Tank, B. (1988). *A collection of math lessons: From grades 1 through 3.* Math Solutions.

Campbell, P. F. (1983). Cardboard, rubber bands, and polyhedron models. *Arithmetic Teacher, 31*(2), 48–51.

Fuys, D. J., & Liebov, A. K. (1997). Concept learning in geometry. *Teaching Children Mathematics, 3*(5), 248–251.

Golomb, S. W. (1965). *Polyominoes.* New York: Scribner.

Klein, H. A. (1974). *The world of measurements.* New York: Simon and Schuster.

Lakatos, I. (1976). *Proofs and refutations: The logic of mathematical discovery.* New York: Cambridge University Press.

Loomis, E. S (1968). *The Pythagorean proposition.* Reston, VA: National Council of Teachers of Mathematics.

National Council of Teachers of Mathematics. (1994). *Measurement in the middle grades.* Reston, VA: Author.

National Governors Association for Best Practices, Council of Chief State School Officers (2010). *Common Core State Standards for Mathematics.* Washington, D.C.: Author.

Simon, M. A., & Blume, G. W. (1994). Mathematical modeling as a component of understanding ratio-as-measure: a study of prospective elementary teachers. *Journal of Mathematical Behavior, 13*(2), 183–197.

Swetz, F. J., & Kao, T. I. (1977). *Was Pythagoras Chinese?* University Park, PA: The Pennsylvania State University Press.

Zaslavsky, C. (1989). People who live in round houses. *Arithmetic Teacher, 37*(1), 18–21.

Overview of *Part IV: Reasoning About Chance and Data (RCD)*

Goals Our major goal is to prepare elementary and middle school teachers to teach the probability and statistics content that is now a part of the usual elementary and middle school mathematics framework and curriculum. But we also believe that teachers, as professionals, should have a basic understanding of these topics because they affect their daily home and workplace lives.

Key Ideas These are the key ideas presented in *Reasoning about Chance and Data*, although not necessarily in this order:

Chance

- A probability statement is based on the assumption that a process is repeated a large number of times.

- Probabilities can be determined both experimentally by undertaking an experiment many times (often simulated) and noting the result each time, or theoretically by calculating the portion of times an event would occur under ideal circumstances.

- Probabilities for multiple events happening concurrently or in succession can be determined by first determining whether or not the events are disjoint or independent. When one event cannot affect the outcome of another event, the events are independent.

- Conditional probability allows the calculations of probabilities when events are not independent.

- The expected value of some random phenomenon with numerical values associated with the outcomes is based both on the probabilities of the outcomes and on the numerical amounts associated with the outcomes. (This goal is addressed later in Chapter 33, the final chapter.)

Data

- A random sample is one in which every element in the sample has the same chance of being selected as every other element in the sample. Randomness is of vital importance in collecting data to be analyzed statistically.

- To obtain accurate information, a random sample must contain a large number of elements. However, there comes a point when additional data do not provide useful information.

- Two equally important ways of interpreting data are to determine the "center" of the data—the mean, the median, or sometimes the mode—and the "spread-outness" or distribution of the data, that is, the range, quartiles, percentiles, or standard deviation.

- Data displays such as bar graphs, circle graphs, histograms, stem-and-leaf plots, line graphs, boxplots, and scatterplots help to represent data so that interpretations can be made about the data.

- The normal distribution (bell curve) is common for very large data sets of certain kinds (such as many physical characteristics) and provides information about the distribution of data in terms of the standard deviation and the mean.

- When working with two sets of data, the relationship between the variables measured by the data can be analyzed by finding the regression line and the correlation coefficient. Strong correlations cannot be interpreted in terms of causal relationships.

- A confidence statement tells us the level of confidence we can have that the statistic taken from a sample is within a certain margin-of-error of the population parameter.

Assumed background Students are expected to have completed the content of *Part I: Reasoning about Numbers and Quantities*, particularly work with fractions, decimals, percents, and proportional reasoning, and they are expected to know the $y = mx + b$ form of a straight line (see *Part II: Reasoning about Algebra and Change,* Chapter 12*)*. In addition, they should have had sufficient coursework to have achieved a certain maturity in mathematics, that is, this should not be their first university course in mathematics. No knowledge of probability and statistics is assumed, although some of your students may have studied them, perhaps as early as elementary school or as late as an Advanced Placement or college course. Even students with the latter background, however, often have only some familiarity with the vocabulary and computational procedures but little experience and skill in explaining what terms mean or what the result of a calculation tells one.

Problem solving Part IV begins with an introduction to two well-known probability problems that students are able to solve after study of the probability chapters. This early introduction to these interesting but puzzling problems is intended to motivate students and to show them that problems such as these can be solved by using what is learned in the Chapters 27 and 28. They learn that intuition can sometimes lead them astray.

The second two problems at the beginning of Part IV deal with collecting and interpreting data and serve as an introduction to Chapters 29 through 33. Problems dealing with sampling, displaying data, and interpreting data are found throughout these chapters. There is an (optional, multiweek) opportunity presented for groups of students to undertake a project that requires developing a good survey question, proper sampling, and the display and interpretation of the data they collect. Finally, more general problems of sampling and interpreting are studied in terms of confidence levels and margins of error.

Using manipulatives Simple materials should be on hand for probability experiments. Two-color chips or marbles or multilink cubes (which you may have used in other parts of this text) will be useful. Dice and decks of cards can be used in some experiments. Spinners can easily be made with paperclips unbent to use as the spinner. We show circular spinners here, but you might want to use other shapes, such as squares, and check whether students think these are "fair" spinners (see Learning Exercise 9 in Section 27.2). At one point, we do an experiment tossing thumbtacks, and some boxes of thumbtacks will be needed. (You can replace the tacks with Styrofoam cups. A compass and a protractor will be needed to make circle graphs. Graph paper will be useful for other types of graphs. Paper clips can be used to make spinners. Some boxes or opaque bags will be useful to have. You can, of course, use other handheld materials for probability and graphing, such as bags of M&Ms in which you consider numbers of each color. Results could be used to make a bar graph on the front board using the smallest paper stickies.

Technology Part IV on *Reasoning about Chance and Data* involves the use of more technology than do Parts I–III. A survey of users indicated that they believed that these topics should not be taught without using technology. This survey also showed that different institutions have different types of technology available. Some had Fathom (software from Key Curriculum

Press), some had TI-73s (calculators from Texas Instruments), and some had Excel (part of Microsoft Office). Almost all offered students access to the Internet (and thus to the Illuminations website*)*. To accommodate instructors we have therefore provided information in appendices on how to use Fathom, the TI-73 Explorer, and Illuminations in both the Chance and Data sections, and how to use Excel for a selected number of statistical analyses. A Table of Randomly Selected Digits (TRSD) together with instructions for using this table is provided for instructors of students who have no access to technology. Use of the Illuminations activities also offers the added benefit of exposing your students to the website for the National Council of Teachers of Mathematics (NCTM). Data sets are provided both in printed form (Appendix E) and electronically at www.whfreeman.com/reconceptmath2e. Detailed instructions are provided in appendices for each of these forms of technology, and for using the TRSD. **You need to make the decision, early on, about what data processing software and hardware you will require in this course.**

Appendices H, I, J, and K contain instructions on how to use several technologies for the tasks in Part IV. Here is a run-down on the capabilities of some of the tools. URLs given are current but may change, as you know. The primary site URL is likely to continue to be accessible, however.

	C/M*	Illuminations	Excel	Fathom 2	TI 73
Random numbers/simulations		√	√	√	√
Circle graph	C	√[1]	√		√
Bar graph	C	√[2]	√	√	√
Histogram	M	√[3]	**	√	√
Boxplot	M	√[4]	**	√	√
Scatterplot	M	√[5]	√	√	√
Line of best fit	M	√[5]	√	√	√
(Broken) line	M			√[6]	

*C - categorical data; M - measurement data
**The Analysis ToolPak for Excel allows histograms, but the technique might be a bit much for our audience and the usual time constraints, especially with other tools available. Boxplots do not appear to be available as part of the standard Excel package.
[1] Circle Grapher http://illuminations.nctm.org/ActivityDetail.aspx?ID=60
[2] Bar Grapher http://illuminations.nctm.org/ActivityDetail.aspx?ID=63
[3] Histogram Tool http://illuminations.nctm.org/ActivityDetail.aspx?ID=78
[4] Boxplotter http://illuminations.nctm.org/ActivityDetail.aspx?ID=77
[5] Line of Best Fit http://illuminations.nctm.org/ActivityDetail.aspx?ID=146
[6] Called "line scatterplot"

Calculators? As noted earlier, too often students want to change all fractions to decimal form. Although a no-calculator restriction might not be necessary in other classes, we want to encourage teachers to be comfortable using fractions because they will someday teach fractions. When the calculations are easy ones, they should be completed without using a calculator. Of course, there will be times when using a calculator is necessary and efficient.

Assign a project? In a full-semester probability and statistics course we have assigned a project (Section 29.5), with teams of roughly three students. The group formulates a question, designs a survey and a method of sampling, gathers the data, undertakes an analysis of the data (using graphs), and reports the team's findings. Occasionally, the reports reveal a surprising lack of understanding of sampling or reporting issues! Most of the work is done outside of class, although we have found it essential in our urban environment to allot some class time for team planning and to ask for planning reports. (What question? What sample planned? Planned time-line? See Section 29.5.) Often, the planning starts before graphing and statistical descriptions have been fully covered, so the final report should be due toward the end of the semester. If you have only a few weeks for these chapters, you may wish to skip this project.

Suggested Timing for a Full-Semester Course on *Reasoning about Chance and Data*
Following are some rough time estimates, based on classes that have used *RCD* in a three-unit, semester-long (15 week) course. The chapters are ordered in a manner that attempts to give first attention to the "must-know" topics for teaching. Hence, more advanced topics in probability and statistics do not appear until Chapters 31, 32, and 33, with the advanced topics in probability (expected value and combinations) at the end rather than with the other probability topics (Chapters 27–28). Ideally, if the group project (Chapter 29) is undertaken, time at the end of the semester should be allowed for class reports on the projects. If this content is used in a half-semester course, we recommend skipping the project and focusing on the remaining parts of Chapters 27, 28, 29, and 30. Topics from Chapters 31, 32, and 33 could be selected judiciously. Chapter 31 contains some children's work that could be considered without completing the entire chapter. You might also want to take time to study expected value in Chapter 33.

In the introduction, four well-known problems dealing with probability are introduced, to be discussed now at an intuitive level and solved later, thus requiring only a short time at the beginning of the semester. But if you are pressed for time, you may decide not to discuss these problems at the beginning of the course.

27 Quantifying Uncertainty (2 weeks)

In the first section, the message is that a probability statement assumes that a situation will occur many times. Later sections on assigning probabilities and simulating probabilistic situations will require more time because students will need to learn to run simulations on available software or calculators, or learn to use the Table of Randomly Selected Digits.

28 Determining More Complicated Probabilities (2+ weeks)

The first three sections of this chapter on multistep experiments, probabilities of events related to other events, and conditional probability are challenging and require time and work to learn.

29 Introduction to Statistics and Sampling (1.5–2 weeks)

Techniques for unbiased, representative sampling are discussed. Instructions for a group project to gather, display, and interpret data are given. If you decide not to undertake this project, Chapters 29 and 30 could be interchanged.

30 Representing and Interpreting Data with One Variable (2.5 weeks)

A variety of ways to organize and display data via graphing are discussed. Measures of distribution and central tendency are developed as ways to understanding data sets. The normal curve is introduced. Once again, there is a great deal of "meat" in this chapter and time is required to understand the concepts here.

31 Dealing with Multiple Data Sets or with Multiple Variables (2 weeks)

Scatterplots are quite easy to understand, and even in a reduced course, this section may be used. The discussions of regression lines and correlations are conceptually based and once again take time and work to understand.

32 Variability in Samples (1.5 weeks)

The fact that samples must be large, but not necessarily too large, for sampling to produce accurate results is difficult for students to understand. Confidence statements can be made with an acceptable margin of error depending on the size of a sample.

33 Special Topics in Probability (1.5 weeks)

Some knowledge of expected value is worthwhile. Combinations and permutations are not usually taught in elementary school, or even in most middle schools, so this section is optional. Keep in mind, however, that some exposure makes the teacher aware of the bigger picture. The Issues for Learning section may offer you a quick look at combinations and permutations.

Instructor Notes for Chapter 27: Quantifying Uncertainty

INSTRUCTOR NOTE 27

We begin Chapter 27 by introducing students to some probability problems that invite intuitive reasoning and solutions. The first two problems are not actually solved until Section 28.3, the third in Chapter 29, and the fourth in Chapter 32. They are intended only for discussion now. The solutions should be kept and compared with their later solutions. If you are short on time and cannot take time at the end of the unit to go back and solve these problems, they could be skipped over here.

These are the sections in Chapter 27: Quantifying Uncertainty

27.1 *Understanding Chance Events.* A probabilistic situation is defined and clarified in examples and class discussions.

27.2 *Methods of Assigning Probabilities.* Students learn to find both experimental and theoretical probabilities.

27.3 *Simulating Probabilistic Situations.* Simulations with random numbers and with drawing balls from a hat are used to show how to find probabilities of events. **The instructor needs to choose which to use: TI-73, Fathom, Excel, Illuminations, or a Table of Randomly Selected Digits.** Five appendices are included, one for each, to show how the software or Web sites are used.

27.4 *Issues for Learning: What Do Large-Scale Tests Tell Us about Probability Learning?* Items from both national and international testing is discussed.

27.5 *Check Yourself.*

We have found that many of the ideas in this and the next chapter make more sense to students if they have opportunities for hands-on activities. **Coins** certainly will be used. For Activity 1, you will need a large number of **thumbtacks** or **Styrofoam cups.** We have included these because they are so readily available. However, we do not intend that these materials be the only ones used. Some people have used Hershey's kisses. **Paper clips** will be needed for making spinners. (Do not buy spinners because you will want to divide the circles up in different ways.) **Multilink cubes** (see, for example, http://www.etacuisenaire.com) can be used in multiple ways, including activities in the chapters in *Part III: Reasoning about Shapes and Measurement.* Simple inexpensive **counters** can also be found at this site—the transparent ones work particularly well. **Dice** (of two colors) can be used. You may have other materials you like to use. If you look online for math manipulatives, you will find other sources.

Dice (of two colors), other regular polyhedra, and homemade spinners (made by straightening one end of a paper clip, and spinning the other end around a pencil tip) can be very useful in dealing with many of the concepts in this and future chapters. For example, we asked one group of students to take a pair of dice of different colors, find the sample space for tossing the dice, and note the number of dots on top of each die. Some did the usual summing and listed 2 through

12; others listed all possible pairs without regard to color, and had a sample space of 21. When reminded that a green 3 and red 4 outcome was different from a red 3 and green 4 outcome, they simply doubled the 21 to 42 possible outcomes. Then one prospective teacher noticed that pairs should not be counted twice and reduced the sample space to 36 outcomes. We feel that this type of experimentation is helpful, and we urge instructors to gather some materials and set up some additional activities with these materials.

INSTRUCTOR NOTE 27.1

Students may have a difficult time perceiving a difference between the two sets of situations. They may feel that the comments from the first set also imply that the person is thinking of a repeating process. For example, when Rishad exclaims, "That's impossible," her statement makes no sense if we assume that she is only thinking of that one instance, because in that one event, it did happen! Instead, her statement reflects that she might be thinking of past experiences with rolling a die.

So if the characters in both sets of examples are thinking of repeated events, why are we bothering to make a distinction between the two? The reason is that in the first example, this thought process is implicit, and in the second example, it's explicit. We want to draw the students' attention to how we think of probability in terms of repeated events. This frequentist conception of probability, when made explicit, can become a powerful tool for them to use throughout the remainder of this and following chapters. To help students make their conceptions of probability explicit and assist them in refining these conceptions, it is important to engage them in the discussion of the language people use to talk about probabilistic situations. Students should see the reformulations in the second set of examples as a meaningful way of making explicit the implicit ideas in the first set of examples.

One way to help students see a difference between the two sets of situations would be to ask them what the people in the first set of situations meant by their statements of disbelief. In fact, the instructor can take the situation one step further by suggesting how the first person might reply. For example, in the first Rishad scenario, the instructor could say something such as: "Betty said, 'Don't be stupid. It's not impossible. I just did it!'" This will help students see the contradictions inherent in the comments made in these two examples. The instructor can then follow up with a question asking students what they think Rishad meant by her statement, "That's impossible!" This will help to open a dialogue about what kind of thinking is going on in these situations and whether or not it is important to be explicit about this thinking.

INSTRUCTOR NOTE 27.2A

A Tackful Experiment: Students should determine at least one probability experimentally. You can replace this thumbtack experiment with another of your choice, if you wish. Hershey's chocolate kisses are a popular choice. An experiment that requires even less equipment is one in which a Styrofoam cup is tossed, and the experimental probability of its landing open side up is found. The advantage of the thumbtack or Styrofoam cup or chocolate kisses experiments is that they give experience with unequally likely outcomes that cannot easily be guessed.

You might want to begin this activity by asking students the following questions: Is tossing a thumbtack a certain or an uncertain situation. Why? Is tossing a thumbtack a probabilistic or a non-probabilistic situation? Why? You might also encourage the groups to think about what fraction of the tosses resulted in a tack pointing up. You should allow students to create their own method for recording the experiment. As groups share their results, you can ask students to share the format they used to record their data. This sharing could lead to a discussion about what information is included in the different formats students used, and which formats seem to be most appropriate for the experiment. This type of discussion can help guide students to learn how to select data recording methods that organize the data they are collecting.

INSTRUCTOR NOTE 27.3A

In this section we begin to use technology, chiefly for selecting numbers at random. Choices are given because various institutions have different resources. Only ONE of the following needs to be used for this section.

1. The TI-73 (Texas Instruments) serves the purposes of providing random numbers and also performing other simulations very well. (See Appendix H.)

2. Fathom (Key Curriculum Press) is a powerful software program that works extremely well with statistics. Random numbers can be quite simply generated. Simulations can also be performed using Fathom, but not in such straightforward way as with representing statistical data. The directions in Appendix I look difficult, but because this is the first lesson using Fathom, very detailed information is provided. Finding random numbers using Fathom is not all that difficult. (See Appendix I.)

3. Some students may have access only to Excel (part of Microsoft Office). Generating random numbers on Excel is very easy to do. (See Appendix J.) Bar graphs, circle graphs, scatterplots, and regression lines can also be done using Excel.

4. Almost all students have access to the Internet (but perhaps not during class). The Illuminations website has many relevant activities in the form of applets. (See Appendix K.) See, for example, the Adjustable Spinner activity http://illuminations.nctm.org/ that allows simulations of a spinner, giving the theoretical results as well as the results from the simulation. (See also the Random Drawing Tool at this web site, as well as other simulations)

5. Finally, if students do not have access to any technology, a table of randomly distributed digits can be used. Directions (and the table) are in Appendix D.

Instructor Notes for Chapter 28: Determining More Complicated Probabilities

INSTRUCTOR NOTE 28

Chapter 28 is a more difficult chapter for students. The ideas here will take some time to develop. Use many examples with lots of class discussion. We have found Section 28.4, on conditional probability, to be a favorite of students. They are very surprised with the results of the AIDS testing problem, and many say that this problem alone convinces them of the worthwhileness of knowing some probability. With Sections 28.1, 28.2, and 28.3, students are now able to tackle the first two problems presented in 27.1. These problems are again presented either in the text or in the Learning Exercises. Section 28.5 presents some of the research findings about probability learning.

These are the sections in Chapter 28: Determining More Complicated Probabilities

28.1 *Tree Diagrams and Lists for Multistep Experiments.* Multistep experiments with and without replacement are studied. Tree diagrams are used to determine probabilities.

28.2 *Probability of One Event* or *Another Event.* The Addition Rule for Probability is introduced and used.

28.3 *Probabilities of One Event* and *Another Event.* Disjoint/mutually exclusive events are distinguished from independent events. A formula for finding the probability of independent events is reached.

28.4 *Conditional Probability.* Contingency tables are used to find probabilities of events that are not independent. The P(A|B) notation for conditional probability is introduced. An alternative definition for independent events based on conditional probability is given.

28.5 *Issues for Learning: Research on the Learning of Probability.*

28.6 *Check Yourself.*

INSTRUCTOR NOTE 28.1A

Although there are times that one wants to distinguish among the different red balls and among the different green balls, in tree diagrams they are usually lumped together to give a "condensed" tree diagram, rather than a correct but much more unwieldy one in which there are different branches for the different red and green balls.

Here are examples of condensed tree diagrams for the two experiments in the Brownbagging Again activity. Pay attention to the key differences in the probabilities for the second drawings, for the with-replacement (Experiment 1) and without-replacement (Experiment 2) situations. The outcomes and their probabilities are also given.

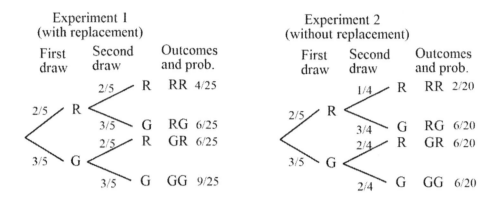

In the without-replacement experiment, the probabilities for the second draw are conditional probabilities, showing one of the advantages of tree diagrams. A more relaxed treatment of conditional probability and its notation is in Section 28.4, introduced with a contingency table.

INSTRUCTOR NOTE 28.1B

Here is an icosahedron from lrt.ednet.ns.ca with a top and bottom face showing.

INSTRUCTOR NOTE 28.2A

Sometime during this section, perhaps after independence has been treated, introduce the "birthday problem": What is the probability that at least two students in a class have the same birthday? (Students do not have this problem in the text.) The problem has a nonintuitive answer, with the usual thinking focusing on the 365 possibilities and the far fewer class members. Yet if there are at least 23 students in a class, the probability of at least one match is about 50%. Here is one explanation. The probability of at least one match is 1 minus the probability of no matches. So the idea is to find the probability of no matches—that is, that all the birthdays are different, and subtract that from 1. It is reasonable to assume that the birthdays are independent (adjust if you have twins in class). Person 1 has some birthday; the probability that Person 2 avoids that date is 364/365 (we will omit leap year concerns). Then the probability that Person 3 avoids both those dates is 363/365. So far, the probability that Persons 1, 2, and 3 have different birthdays is $1 \times (364/365) \times (363/365)$, or 0.991796, and so the probability of a match with just 3 people is $1 - 0.991796$, or 0.008204. But as additional people are involved, the product $1 \times \frac{364}{365} \times \frac{363}{365} \times \frac{362}{365} \times \frac{361}{365} \times \frac{360}{365} \times \frac{359}{365}$ and so on becomes smaller and smaller, so the desired probability, $1 -$ the product, becomes larger and larger. A tree diagram, with a focus just on misses of earlier birthdays, can give the same argument. Here is a summary of the calculations for different class sizes.

Number of people	Probability of one match or more	Number of people	Probability of one match or more
1	0.000	21	0.444
2	0.003	22	0.476
3	0.008	23	0.507
4	0.016	24	0.538
5	0.027	25	0.569
6	0.040	26	0.598
7	0.056	27	0.627
8	0.074	28	0.654
9	0.095	29	0.681
10	0.117	30	0.706
11	0.141	31	0.730
12	0.167	32	0.753
13	0.194	33	0.775
14	0.223	34	0.795
15	0.253	35	0.814
16	0.284	36	0.832
17	0.315	37	0.849
18	0.347	38	0.864
19	0.379	39	0.878
20	0.411	40	0.891

INSTRUCTOR NOTE 28.3A

Many students have difficulty seeing that $P(A) + P(B)$ and $P(A \text{ and } B)$ are different. If they see no difference between the two, then they will be confused about how this formula could generate any answer other than 0. There are at least two different conceptions that lead to this difficulty. First, students may equate "and" with addition. The instructor needs to draw students' attention to the fact that in this case, the word "and" is used very differently from their experience with arithmetic. It may be helpful to use a Venn diagram to illustrate the different outcomes and where each one falls on the diagram. Then the instructor can talk about two ways we often think about multiple events happening: having either event A and/or event B happen, or having event A and event B occur simultaneously. Have students identify which part of the Venn diagram corresponds to each case. It may help to have students generate a few more examples of two events happening together. Have them place the possible desired outcomes in a Venn diagram and talk about the union and intersection. (Some students may not know this language.) Follow up by saying that statisticians have decided to use "or" for the first situation and "and" for the second. It is important that students understand that this set of terms is only one possible way that statisticians *could* have used to talk about these two cases, but that because statisticians have adopted these conventions and they are widely used, they will also be used in the class.

A second difficulty that students may have is that they may think that they can "distribute" the P over the "A and B": $P(A \text{ and } B) = P(A) \text{ and } P(B) = P(A) + P(B)$. They may or may not be consciously aware that they are doing this. To help them change this conception, return to the Venn diagram and talk about which outcomes get counted for $P(A$ and $B)$ and which get counted for $P(A) + P(B)$. Ask them what each of $P(A$ and $B)$ and $P(A) + P(B)$ means. Because this meaning of "and" may be very new to them, it may be necessary for you, the instructor, to ask this question often throughout the rest of this probability section, even if you are confident that all the students understood the difference between $P(A$ and $B)$ and $P(A)$ and $P(B)$ the first time it was discussed in class. It is very likely that students' conceptions of "and" as meaning addition will be very resistant to change, and thus may continue to resurface.

One other possible difficulty students may have with the formula is that they may feel that by subtracting $P(A$ and $B)$, they are not counting the case when both events happen simultaneously. Showing the parts of the Venn diagram may help them to see that the outcomes in the intersection get counted twice, and thus their probabilities need to be subtracted.

INSTRUCTOR NOTE 28.4A

This problem is adapted from Paulos (p. 66), and from the NCTM Addenda Series (1991, p. 33). In the HIV Testing activity, the incidence of the HIV virus and the accuracy of the test are relevant, but not the size of the population. Below is the contingency table for a population of size n but with the same incidence and test accuracy figures; it will give the same probabilities for any n:

	Has the virus	Does not have virus	Totals
Positive	$0.98(0.005n) = 0.0049n$	$0.02(0.995n) = 0.0199n$	$0.0248n$
Negative	$0.02(0.005n) = 0.0001n$	$0.98(0.995n) = 0.9751n$	$0.9752n$
Totals	$0.005n$	$0.995n$	n

INSTRUCTOR NOTE 28.4B

There are three possible scenarios, each with equal probability (1/3). Assume that there are 2 pigs and a car behind the three doors:

* The player picks pig number 1. The game host picks the other pig. Switching will win the car.
* The player picks pig number 2. The game host picks the other pig. Switching will win the car.
* The player picks the car. The game host picks either of the two pigs. Switching will lose.

Hence, switching gives a 2/3 probability of winning. You may want to refer to these two (or other) websites for people interested in the Monty Hall problem. Just Google it.

http://www.letsmakeadeal.com/problem.htm

http://mathforum.org/dr/math/faq/faq.monty.hall.html

Instructor Notes for Chapter 29: Introduction to Statistics and Sampling

INSTRUCTOR NOTE 29

If you do not plan to assign the survey project (Section 29.5), Chapters 29 and 30 may be done in either order. The project assignment appears early so that students can start to work on it, even though all of the tools for the final report have not yet been covered.

Chapter 29, Introduction to Statistics and Sampling, focuses on sampling techniques and the importance of having an unbiased sample. Here are the titles of the sections and sketches of their content.

> 29.1 *What Are Statistics?* "Statistics" is explained as the plural of "statistic," a quantitative aspect of a situation, and also "statistics" as a discipline. A warning about misuses of statistics is given.

> 29.2 *Sampling: The Why and the How.* Why use just a sample? Ways of finding representative samples and how they are treated, and their role in providing information about a population. A sample statistic is contrasted to population parameter.

> 29.3 *Simulating Random Sampling.* Sampling via random numbers is the topic of this chapter.

> 29.4 *Types of Data.* Categorical data and measurement data are contrasted.

> 29.5 *Conducting a Survey.* This is an optional section that describes a group assignment to gather data that will be displayed and interpreted during the time period for this unit of study. You may want to modify it.

> 29.6 *Issues for Learning: Sampling.* This section describes some research on children's understanding of "sample."

> 29.7 *Check Yourself.*

While piloting these materials, we have uncovered several misconceptions that our students have, many of which have been documented elsewhere. By knowing the misconceptions ahead of time, you may be able to guide discussions in a way that will minimize the formation and the influence of these misconceptions.

The main misconceptions we have found are as follows: (1) The best way to sample is to draw many samples and then average the results. (2) The population parameter is computed from the sample. (3) We can either identify groups for a stratified sample, or we can sample and then identify the groups. It does not matter which we do first. (4) Random sampling means selecting items or individuals so that there is chance involved in the selection process (as opposed to having every item or individual in the population have an equal chance of being selected). Closely related to this issue is the difficulty students have with defining populations. That is, do we try to find an unbiased sample for a certain population? Or do we take a sample and then talk about what population it represents? Or do we try to find a compromise between the two? (5) Anyone can produce a list of random digits or outcomes. A random number generator is not necessary. (6) The imprecision caused by low sample size is a bias in sampling.

In reference to misconception 5, first have students make a list of 100 tosses of a coin for which they guess the outcomes and then look as some actual tosses 100 times. The student lists are apt to have no more than three of one kind in a row, but the truly random lists often have more than three in a row. The literature provides several ideas for convincing students that they cannot produce a random sequence. Scheaffer, Gnangadesikan, Watkins, and Witmer, in their book *Activity-Based Statistics,* show a page of randomly sized rectangles, have students randomly select a sample of rectangles and calculate the mean size of the sample, and then use a random number generator to select the rectangles and compare the two mean sizes. Often the smaller rectangles are missed when a student chooses them. Another way to convince students that they are unable to do a good job at trying to guess randomly is to provide a sheet of paper with a grid of, say, 20 by 20 squares, and ask students to shade in 100 squares at random. It will be quite easy to see that the students carefully place the shaded squares so that two are very seldom touching. If the shading is done in a random fashion, there will often be two or more touching.

INSTRUCTOR NOTE 29.2A

As a motivation to learn about sampling, we suggest beginning with Activity: A Fifth Grade Task, a sampling problem given to elementary school students, and the following discussion. (The problem was designed and used in a research study by Jacobs, 1997.) Sampling considerations were important to these students. There were four types of responses: Some children focused on potential bias and recognized that random samples were not biased, whereas some focused on bias but missed some sources of bias. Other children focused on fairness, on practical issues, or on whether the results met their expectations. What will your students focus on? In your class, you might have your students work through this activity in groups or pairs, then you could lead a class discussion of the activity. You could also have your groups rank-order the sampling methods and write their rankings on the board. After discussion of the sampling methods, some groups may change their rankings.

INSTRUCTOR NOTE 29.2B

A fifth reason is that data from a sample may actually be more accurate, an argument that has been made regarding bot the Census 2000 and the Census 2010. A mathematical argument was made by Fritz Scheuren (1997) in *Consortium,* where he applied a margin of error simplification to show that when $n \geq (1/b)$, where b is the possible bias in the census and n is the size of the sample, the sample will be more accurate than the census 95% of the time. We did not include this reason in the list for your students because it is not as intuitively clear and probably is less important. Whether or not to sample for the census has been was hotly debated by Congress.

The same issue of *Consortium* provides some history on the census. The first modern census in the United States was in 1790, more than 100 years before sampling techniques were introduced as a formal discipline in 1895. Sampling is now used in some aspects of the U.S. census, but the Census Bureau wants to expand the use of sampling even though some members of Congress say sampling is "inadequate and could be used for political manipulation" (page 5). The Web sites at http://www.census.gov and http://www.censusscope.org might be of interest to some students.

INSTRUCTOR NOTE 29.3A

You may have introduced the Table of Randomly Selected Digits (TRSD) in Chapter 27, or you may have used a calculator or software for generating random numbers, as in the Appendices. Whichever you used there should be used here. The major goal is for students to come to understand what random means and to know how to simulate random sampling.

We strongly advise an activity such as the first one, where students draw simple random samples "the hard way," to gain an intuitive idea of what is going on. Multilink cubes of two colors could be used, or beans of two different colors but same size, or, if neither of these is available, just cut up two colors of paper into pieces of the same size. You should choose based on what materials you have available. For example, suppose you use blue and yellow paper and you place in a box 48 pieces of blue paper and 72 pieces of yellow paper, all the same size, all mixed together. Tell the students there are pieces of paper in the box to simulate fish, and all are either yellow or blue. Holding the box so that students cannot see the colors, have a student take out 10 pieces, record the colors, and replace the papers in the box. Ask what the population is (all the papers in the box) and what a sample is (Activity questions 1 and 2). Ask them if every piece of paper in the box had an equal chance of being selected and why (Activity question 2). Repeat this process several times with other students. Ask them if they think every sample should have the same percents as the population and why the results varied (Activity question 3). Finally, after they have made their prediction (Activity question 4), tell them what the distribution actually is (60% yellow in the case outlined here), and ask if anyone was surprised.

You can return to this activity in later lessons because it illustrates that a sample statistic can vary from sample to sample, even when the samples are randomly chosen. If you have time to collect several samples, you might record the results for possible reference later on (Chapter 32).

INSTRUCTOR NOTE 29.4A

This section prepares the way for the work on graphing by distinguishing between categorical and measurement data.

You may be familiar with a more elaborate breakdown of the uses of numbers: nominal (or categorical, when numbers are used), ordinal, interval (units are all the same), and ratio (ratios of scale differences make sense). Our use of "categorical" sometimes allows ordering. We have chosen not to spend time on all the categories but to lump the uses into either categorical or "measurement." Nor have we distinguished between discrete measurements and continuous measurements, even though the distinction could have some bearing on the appropriateness of a bar graph or a histogram (a minor point, in our view).

INSTRUCTOR NOTE 29.5A

You may wish to change this project in ways you feel would be helpful. For example, you may decide on a choice of one of three questions you design for the project rather than leaving that up to students. You should probably stick to a simple yes/no type of question, or ask your students to ask such a question, thus limiting the many avenues they may not be prepared to take even after later chapters. (If you do not have a full semester for this course, you may wish to skip this project.)

We usually use (self-selected) groups of two to four for the survey project. This practice gives the students more experience working in a group, and it cuts down on the grading (usually done late in the semester). We have used a minimum of class time, usually just a part of a class session to introduce the project assignment, and a little time for establishing who is in which group. Many times we have asked, separately from the (single?) final write-up, each student to describe each group member's contribution to the project, as is suggested in Section 29.5. The write-ups are sometimes quite revealing about the students' grasp of some ideas.

We usually weight the project so that it carries enough weight to matter, but not enough to give a very weak student a much better grade for the course. Evaluating the projects will be easier if you decide beforehand how you will do this. You might set up a scheme such as this and share it with your students:

Development of a good choice of question to investigate	? points
Development of an adequate and appropriate sample	? points
Description of carrying out the study	? points
Using appropriate tools to represent the data	? points
Providing an appropriate interpretation of the data	? points
Clarity of presentation (oral? poster?)	? points
Correct spelling, punctuation, organization of written report	? points

Instructor Notes for Chapter 30: Representing and Interpreting Data with One Variable

INSTRUCTOR NOTE 30

In Chapter 29, we focused on the collection of data, particularly on finding an appropriate sample. With Chapter 30, we begin our consideration of organizing and interpreting data. This chapter deals with data on one variable, and Chapter 31 touches on two-variable situations. Chapter 30 could be covered before Chapter 29. Chapter 30 is quite long, so plan to spend considerable time on it.

Chapter 30: Representing and Interpreting Data with One Variable contains these sections:

30.1 *Representing Categorical Data.* Bar graphs and circle graphs are both used to display data. The two are compared in terms of what we can and cannot learn from them.

30.2 *Representing and Interpreting Measurement Data.* Stem-and-leaf plots are used to generate histograms.

30.3 *Examining the Spread of Data.* The range is introduced as a gross measure of spread. Percentiles, quartiles, and median are introduced, as are the five-number summary and box and whiskers (or just box) plots.

30.4 *Measures of Center.* All the usual measures of central tendency—mean, median, mode—come up. The standard deviation and its interpretation are treated.

30.5 *Deviations from the Mean as Measuring of Spread.* The shapes of distributions are considered, including the normal distribution and *z*-scores.

30.6 *Issues for Learning: Understanding the Mean.* The section reviews some research about children's understanding of the mean.

30.7 *Check Yourself.*

There is a particular emphasis here on measuring the "spread-outness" of data and how this information relates to measures of central tendency. Students should learn how to create bar graphs, circle graphs (or pie charts), stem-and-leaf plots, and histograms; how to determine what type of graph is appropriate for a particular situation; how to recognize what type of information is portrayed or not portrayed in each graph; and how to start with a graph of a data set and make relevant conclusions about that set. Elementary and middle school textbooks do not deal with all of the ideas in this unit; some are here (percentiles, standard deviations, the normal distribution) because teachers ought to be able to interpret test scores from standardized tests.

The singular form of *data* is actually *datum* in Latin, so etymologically *data* is a plural form. However, the *American Heritage Dictionary* has this to say about data versus datum: "Although *data* came from a Latin plural form, scientists and researchers think of data as a singular mass entity like information and use it with a singular verb, a practice adopted by many others." So you or your students should be comfortable with using *data* as a singular noun.

Software Among other software programs, we have used Fathom and Excel in the past. But Fathom may not be readily available at some sites, and Excel is unable to produce easily some of the graphs we want. And some calculators, such as the TI-73, do provide many graphing capabilities. We seek simplicity and transparency in the software we use. There are now websites with applets that do almost everything needed here. Two sources are the NCTM Web site http://illuminations.nctm.org, and the Math Forum website, http://mathforum.org/mathtools. The safe rule of thumb is to check the availability and appropriateness before assigning exercises calling for a particular tool.

Appendices H–K provide details of the type needed for the Learning Exercises in this chapter. We have provided a range of choices because different institutions (and students) often have access to only one or two of the types described. As the instructor, you should choose one that you want your students to use and then spend some time with the appropriate appendix lessons. See the chart in the General Instructor's Note for information on what various technologies can do.

Keep in mind (and alert your students) that different software may use different conventions, so results from different software may not be identical. In most cases, the results will be close enough so that the students can be assured that their thinking was probably correct.

A software program called Tinker Plots is also available from Key Curriculum Press. This software was developed for fourth to eighth grade students and allows for dynamic data explorations. Hence, its use might be of value to the college students when they are teaching. However, most universities are unlikely to have Tinker Plots available, and thus we do not use it here. You should have little difficulty switching to that software program if you do have it at hand.

Data sets Most of the data sets used in this chapter can be found online at www.whfreeman.com/reconceptmath2e. Students do not need all of them, but you may want them for demonstration purposes. Those needed by students should be readily available so that insofar as possible students do not waste time entering data rather than thinking about data. Data sets called for in student work are also printed in Appendix E.

We have often found that students are interested in data on themselves, so we usually collect a variety, both categorical and measurement, from ideas suggested by the class. Age in months, height in inches, (ideal) weight, shoe size, favorite kind of ice cream or beverage, favorite movie star (usually from a small list), marital status, number of siblings, approximate grade point average, home distance from school, and so on. Getting all the collected data into an accessible form can involve some work (perhaps by a student who is a skilled data-entry person), as does getting the data into a form usable by all the students (print copies, computer file). You may want to replace data from the 60 Students file and use your own, with appropriate modifications of Learning Exercises that call for the use of the 60 Students data.

INSTRUCTOR NOTE 30.1A

An occasional student may have difficulty with the use of fractions in this section. However, because the focus of this unit is on representing data, it may be better to spend more time on the representations rather than conduct an extensive review of fractions and percents at this point. You might want to refer students to the *Appendix F: A Review of Some Rules*. Do not, however, legitimize fraction avoidance by encouraging the exclusive use of decimal notation.

In Learning Exercise 5, students can be referred to the National Council of Teachers of Mathematics Web site to track down the Circle Grapher applet.

INSTRUCTOR NOTE 30.2A

One issue to be aware of arises in defining what values a cell will represent. Our use of the stem-and-leaf plot as a lead-in to histograms results in natural boundaries (20–30, for example) as *not* including the upper bound, 30. But it is common to include counts of values at the upper boundary value in a particular cell (perhaps motivated by advanced work with distributions such as the normal distribution, or tables for the cumulative binomial distribution values). Try not to get bogged down in dealing with this nuance. In particular, for quiz or test questions calling for histograms, avoiding values at the likely (or specified) boundaries can also avoid the possibility of students producing histograms with different conventions but all being correct (and more difficult to grade quickly).

Our experimentation suggests, for example, that these resources define a cell with boundaries a and b in these ways:

Fathom 2 and TI-73: $a \le values < b$

Histogram Tool (from http://illuminations.nctm.org/ActivityDetail.aspx?ID=78):

$$a < values \le b$$

INSTRUCTOR NOTE 30.2B

Here are samples for the three histograms with different cell sizes, showing that too small a cell size gives too much detail, and the overall shape of the graph is lost. Students may correctly say that the smaller cell size loses less information about the individual data values. Nonetheless, the overall picture for the data is sacrificed. The extreme case would be an interval just one unit wide. You may wish to illustrate the effect of changing the cell size with the Histogram Tool at http://illuminations.nctm.org/, using the SAT data provided. The tool allows one to change the interval size (but includes a count of values at the upper bound in a cell).

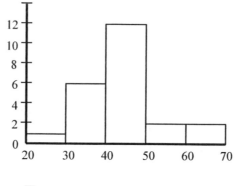

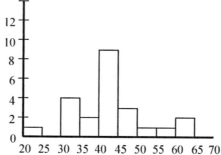

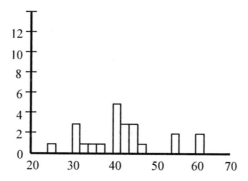

INSTRUCTOR NOTE 30.2C

Students might find this advice helpful. Some software allows copying-and-pasting, usually in the Edit menu. If you develop a graph with a software tool that does not allow copying, you want to copy the on-screen version, or part of it, to a Word document. On Macs, you likely have a utility, such as Grab. Most PCs have a Print Screen key and a similar screen capture utility. Others may require some relatively inexpensive software to print screens or excerpts of screens.

INSTRUCTOR NOTE 30.3A

As the title of this section indicates, we focus first on the variability of data rather than on measures of central tendency. Some statisticians think that understanding this variability is central to understanding statistics. Using percentiles is one way to look at the variability and spread of data. We introduce percentiles and show how they provide us with information, but we do not expect students to actually calculate all percentiles. Different texts in statistics use different ways of calculating percentiles, but our reason for only introducing them here rather than spending time calculating all of them is that, for this audience, the information gained is not worth the time spent. Teachers often need to interpret percentiles that they are given, but they have no need of actually calculating most percentiles.

What is useful, however, and found in middle school texts, is the ability to make box (or box-and-whiskers) plots of data. This ability requires knowing how to find quartiles, so we do expect students to be able to find all three quartiles values, and hence the median. We focus then on finding and interpreting quartiles in terms of what they tell us about the spread of the data and how to use them to make and interpret boxplots. Some texts refer to the "five-number summary" for a data set, which consists of the lowest score, the first quartile, the median, the third quartile, and the highest score. These five values are used to make a boxplot.

One caution is in order, when percentiles (and hence boxplots) are involved. When the values on which the percentiles are based are themselves in percents (as is common with test results), students may have difficulty in keeping the two kinds of percent-looking values straight. Our examples having data sets about examination scores have scores expressed in "points" rather than percents.

INSTRUCTOR NOTE 30.4A

There is some confusion about when to use the mean and when to use the median. Students should know when the mean is preferred over the median and why, and vice versa, when the median might be preferred to the mean and why.

The *average rate per person,* that is, the leveling out view of the "mean," is used throughout. Because average rate is itself a puzzle to some, you may have to spend time on the idea that, if all the values were replaced by the average value, then the sum of the values would be the same. Looking at the area of a histogram versus the area of a rectangle with height equal to the average (and length across the x-range) gives a visual way of thinking about the average. The mean as a "balance point" for a set of data is also handy and comes up in Section 30.7, but you may wish to mention it here. This view of the mean could be acted out, or be the subject of a thought experiment, by thinking of the distribution being made of linking blocks for each of the n scores; the mean is then the value such that n piles of that value would balance the earlier assemblage.

INSTRUCTOR NOTE 30.5A

Statisticians usually prefer to divide by $n-1$ rather than n. Some statistics calculators have keys for both $n-1$ and for n. So be aware that students may offer slightly different values for the standard deviation if they are using different calculators. We use n here rather than attempting to explain why the less intuitive $n-1$ is used. For large n, the difference in the two is small. While we are on the topic of standard deviation, we urge you to attach units to both the mean and the standard deviation when they are expressed so that students can see what is being measured by these values.

Instructor Notes for Chapter 31: Dealing with Multiple Data Sets or with Multiple Variables

INSTRUCTOR NOTE 31

These are the sections in Chapter 31: Dealing with Multiple Data Sets or with Multiple Variables.

   31.1 *Comparing Data Sets.* Separate boxplots or histograms are used to compare two data sets. Scatterplots are used to represent two variables. Positive and negative associations are introduced, along with the warning that relationship does not mean causation. Line graphs.

   31.2 *Lines of Best Fit and Correlation.* Software-generated regression lines are used, and correlation coefficients are introduced.

   31.3 *Issues for Learning: More Than One Variable.* The topic is a research study on children's difficulty in analyzing data from two sources.

   31.4 *Check Yourself.*

This chapter focuses on how to organize and interpret two (or more) sets of data, as well as two ways to graph and relate two variables, scatterplots, and the more limited line graph. Students should understand that correlations are meaningful only when the data are somewhat linearly distributed and that correlation does not imply causation. You may wish to use some of the data sets from the text (available electronically at www.whfreeman.com/reconceptmath2e or in print form in Appendix E) for demonstration purposes or to do some of the activities in class. Students should have some experience entering data so that they can enter data about their own interests, but with more variables (or with large data sets) the typing is time-consuming and subject to errors. Hence, you may wish to supply students with the data sets for the exercises.

At times, one might have more than one set of data and want to know how these data compare, such as test scores of males compared to test scores of females. Again, there are several ways to display the data. At other times, you may want to know how two sets of data are related, such as years of education and wages. This last type of analysis must be carefully considered because if two sets of data are closely related, it is all too easy to mistakenly think one *causes* the other when in fact that might not be true. For example, you might find a high correlation between mathematics scores and science scores at a particular school. But one cannot say that doing well in mathematics causes one to do well in science. Perhaps the factor causing both is degree of motivation.

INSTRUCTOR NOTE 31.1A

Possible answers:

a. Graphing the data for each player could allow some comparisons. Boxplots and histograms are reasonable choices. Boxplots give quartiles, and histograms usually attach means and standard deviations.

b, c, and d. Below are three boxplots (from Tinker Plots), together with pertinent information for each set of data. Each graph represents only games played.

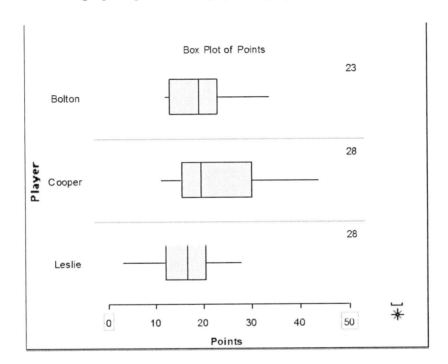

The boxplots suggest that Bolton and Cooper score better than Leslie does (acknowledging that other aspects of their play are also important). Of the two, Cooper appears to be the top scorer. Her scores are more spread out, but on the high end.

Other statistics also support Cooper's case for being the top scorer of the three. The boxplots make clear that her greater standard deviation is due in part to her high scores. Leslie can make a case for being the most consistent scorer because of her smallest standard deviation (hers and Bolton's ranges from the boxplots seem to be about the same. (Note that standard deviations might vary some depending on whether one divides by n or by $n - 1$.)

	Bolton	Cooper	Leslie
Mean	19.5	21.9	16.1
St Dev	6.4	8.8	5.9
Median	19.0	19.5	16.5
1st Quart	13.0	15.5	12.0
3rd Quart	23.0	30.0	20.5

INSTRUCTOR NOTE 31.1B

The Trends in International Mathematics and Science Study (TIMSS) also looked at thirteen-year-olds and students in the last year of school (and there are reports for those grades as well). The sampling for TIMSS was carried out more carefully than in some other international studies, with good sample sizes, so the results have been much discussed. Although the U.S. fourth graders scored about average in mathematics, U.S. eighth graders did not do as well. Total scores, however, disguise that most of the U.S. eighth graders' deficiencies might be with topics such as geometry and measurement. The data here were taken from *Mathematics Achievement in the Primary School Years: IEA's Third International Mathematics and Science Study (TIMSS),* June 1997, and *Science Achievement in the Elementary School Years: IEA's Third International Mathematics and Science Study (TIMSS),* June 1997. Both were downloaded from the TIMMS Web site: http://nces.ed.gov/timss/. Reports on more recent studies may be available now.

An interesting case of bias was described in Blastand's and Dilnot's book *The Numbers Game.* You might want to share it.

> All kinds of characteristics can, and do, cause bias…. In one famous case it was found that a sample of Democrat voters in the United States were less satisfied with their sex lives than Republicans, until someone remembered that women generally reported less satisfaction than men, and that more women tended to vote Democrat than Republican (2009, Gotham Books, p. 124).

Instructor Notes for Chapter 32: Variability in Samples

INSTRUCTOR NOTE 32

Chapter 32, Variability in Samples, contains information that all citizens should know, but this content is not in the elementary or middle school curriculum. Thus, you should decide whether or not you want to undertake the sometimes subtle and difficult ideas in this chapter. Of course, the time you have will be crucial in deciding whether to include it. The chapter has only two sections, but the content is more sophisticated than that in the previous chapters on data analysis.

32.1 *Having Confidence in a Sample Statistic.* Students should learn that sample statistics are quite accurate for large samples, but that the samples need not be extremely large to make good estimates.

32.2 *Confidence Intervals.* A confidence statement can be made with an acceptable margin of error, depending on the size of the sample.

32.3 *Issues for Learning: What Probability and Statistics Should Be in the Curriculum?*

32.4 *Check Yourself.*

The ideas in this chapter, on variability in samples (32.1) and the meaning of a confidence interval (32.2), seem to be particularly difficult ones for students to grasp. Do not expect these ideas to come easily to them. Too often, students come away from a statistics class feeling that because a sample statistic can be "far away" from a population parameter, then sampling is a bad thing to do. They also believe that samples must be *very* large to provide valid information. These sections try to clarify just what we can expect from sampling.

We first tackle the problem of whether or not we can be confident that a sample will provide the information we need to make decisions. That people mistrust samples is recognized in the fact that the U.S. government refused the Census Bureau permission to sample rather than to undertake a complete census in 2000. In 2010 sampling became a partisan matter, when Obama's pick as Commerce Secretary withdrew over arguments about whether sampling would be used in the 2010 Census. Yet sampling can give a quite accurate picture of a population, even when the sample is relatively small compared to the population. As an instructor, you need to help students understand that population size is not an issue, assuming that it is substantially large. Sampling can provide quite accurate information, at substantially less cost, than a census of the entire population.

Of particular importance in this chapter is the fact that *we assume we know a parameter*, because that knowledge helps one understand how sampling can provide quite exact information on the parameter. In real life, of course, we do *not* know the parameter. If we did, sampling would be pointless.

Most of our familiarity with sampling comes from poll reports in the news, yet few people understand what is meant by a margin of error. The second section in this chapter focuses on confidence intervals and what information they provide.

We consider only surveys in this chapter, and primarily dichotomous data for which we can find proportions. Students might therefore form the idea that a statistic and a parameter refer only to proportions. To counter that idea, you might discuss the idea of an experiment in which you are comparing the effects of two different methods of teaching a statistics class. You randomly assign 60 students to one of two classes, where each class is taught using a different method. All students are given the same exam, and the mean scores for the groups are found. Ask what the samples, statistics, populations, and parameters would be in this situation. Tell them that there are statistical ways of comparing the means to see if they are significantly different. A confidence interval can be found to tell us how confident we can be that the two methods really do lead to different results. We will not spend time here considering other types of parameters and statistics, but students should know they exist. They should also know that the two major uses of statistics are in surveys and in experiments. In this course, we are considering only surveys, but students may need to know more about experiments in the future.

INSTRUCTOR NOTE 32.1A

Leading up to Understanding Table 1: Simulating random samples from a known population

Table 1 has been used many times in many classes, enough to know that students have difficulty understanding the messages of the table:

> *For a large enough sample we can be quite confident that the population parameter is very close to the sample statistic. However, there comes a time when increasing the sample size really isn't going to give additional information of substantial value.*

The following notes are adapted from a lesson by Mike Maxon at San Diego State University developed to help his students understand Table 1. His students did come to a better understanding with this lesson than they had in past times. He used a simulation with Fathom (with the figure for the 50 samples used in the activity What 50 Samples of Size 10 Say, adapted for the context there). You might choose to use your own version, perhaps with a different method of simulation, such as Adjustable Spinner from Illuminations (described in Appendix K) or using the TI-73. You could use the Table of Randomly Selected Digits (TRSD) or even just a bag of cubes, 63% of one color and 37% of another color to conduct these simulations, but doing so would take a great deal more time.

Lesson

1. Suppose that you work in the admissions office at State University, where 63% of the student body is female.

   > *Would you be surprised if only 2 or fewer of the next 5 students to walk into the admissions office are female? How about 4 or fewer of the next 10? 20 or fewer of the next 50? 40 of the next 200?*

2. We can design an experiment to test the likelihood that a sample provides a statistic far different from the population parameter of 63%, say 40% or fewer females.

Appoint pairs to run an experiment that tests each of the questions above. Different groups should work with different sample sizes of 5, 10, 50, or 200. Before running the experiment, have them guess at the results. Run the experiments as many times as is possible, given time constraints.

3. Discuss ways of recording their results. You should settle on a table similar to Table 1 in the text and chunk the percents by below 40%, 40–44.5%, 45–49.5%, … 80–84.5%, 85–89.5%. Pool data to fill the table.

Here is a sample of 50 experiments of size 10, using Fathom.

Sample of 10 Students and Percent Female									Collect More Measures
40%	50%	60%	30%	60%	80%	70%	60%	40%	70%
70%	70%	90%	70%	60%	70%	50%	60%	40%	70%
80%	50%	70%	60%	50%	80%	50%	50%	80%	70%
40%	60%	70%	70%	80%	70%	50%	90%	60%	50%
80%	80%	60%	70%	70%	10%	70%	80%	70%	30%

Depending on the software you use, you may also want to show the shape of the data. Here is a histogram for this set of data.

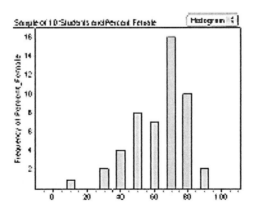

Groups that are using sample size 100, with 1000 such samples, might generate percentages such as these (also found using Fathom, with only a few of the 1000 cases showing in the display of the results) and the accompanying histogram for all 1000 samples.

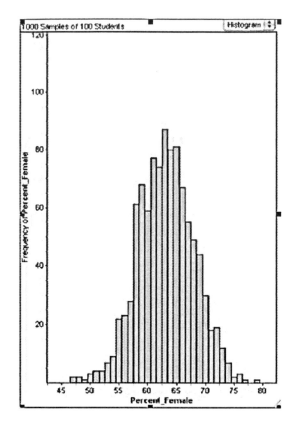

4. Ask questions each time, such as: What fraction of the time do we have 40% or less females? 50% or less females? Of all our sample statistics, what is the greatest percent away from the population parameter of 63%? How do you describe the overall shape of these graphs?

    Be sure to ask: How large a sample do we need to take before most or all of our sample percents are close to the population parameter? What would you consider close? What percentage of the sample statistics would you want in that interval to feel comfortable with saying that a random sample is representative of the population parameter?

5. Now go to Table 1 in the text.

    In the *n* = 2000 column there is a "73." Talk to your partner and explain in a complete sentence what the 73 tells us.

    Given sample sizes of 100, what percent of the time will we get a sample statistic of less than 50% when our true population parameter is 63%?

    In each of the 1000 samples of differing sample sizes (that is, in each column), what percent of the sample statistics are within ± 3% of the true population parameter?

    In what interval centered at 63% are 95% of our sample statistics found?

INSTRUCTOR NOTE 32.1B

The sample statistics in Table 1 for $n = 100$ have about 97% of the samples with statistics in the 53–73% interval, and about 77% within the 58–68% interval.

For your information, the distribution of the sample percents for a large number of samples would be a normal distribution, with a mean equal to the population proportion. So, for example (see Instructor Note 32.1C below), we can make statements with 95% accuracy that the sample proportion falls within two standard deviations of the mean. This fact is alluded to when we say that statisticians apply probability to make statements with some confidence level attached.

INSTRUCTOR NOTE 32.1C

The margin of error most used in sampling a population of size N and with percent p with a sample of size n is equal to $\sqrt{\dfrac{4\left[1-\frac{n}{N}\right]p\left[1-p\right]}{n}}$. When n is small relative to N, the quantity $1-n/N$ is close to 1, and if p is close to 1/2, the expression simplifies to $\sqrt{\frac{1}{n}} = \frac{1}{\sqrt{n}}$. Thus, the $\frac{1}{\sqrt{n}}$ expression works best when the true proportion for the population is 0.5, but it is fairly accurate even when the true proportion is between 0.4 and 0.6 and the sample size is much smaller than the population size.

In addition, if the underlying distribution is approximately normal, the $\frac{1}{\sqrt{n}}$ expression is roughly 2 standard deviations. Hence, the calculation, observed proportion $\pm\, 1\frac{1}{\sqrt{n}}$, gives a confidence interval with confidence level about 95% ("pretty good," we say in class). Students should know that the method used by statisticians is different from this one and works no matter what the true parameter is.

INSTRUCTOR NOTE 32.1D

Dr. Susan Nickerson interviewed college students completing a course in statistics. She focused on one student, who insisted (for Exercise 9) that because the ratios 2 to 3 and 200 to 300 were equal, getting 2 heads out of a three coin toss was equally likely to getting 200 heads in a toss of 300 coins. In Exercise 10, the student first said 8 to 10, then 8 or 9, then 7 to 9. However, when asked about the sample of 100, she said it would be 40, then returned to the first part and said she would get 8 browns. This student did not understand that sampling has variability, and that sample size affects variability. This student and others interviewed showed common errors on these two problems, so it is likely that at least some of your students will have the same thinking.

INSTRUCTOR NOTE 32.2A

Here are some answers for the activity Finding Confidence Intervals.

Within…of 63%	$n = 100$	$n = 500$	$n = 1000$	$n = 2000$	$n = 3000$
10 percent (53–73%)	97.5%	100%	100%	100%	100%
5 percent (58–68%)	77.5%	98.7%	100%	100%	100%
3 percent (60–66%)	56.1%	91.8%	98.5%	99.9%	100%
1 percent (62–64%)	24.6%	53.1%	67.0%	83.7%	89.8%

Instructor Notes for Chapter 33: Special Topics in Probability

INSTRUCTOR NOTE 33

We pick and choose from this chapter, depending on the audience and time available. Here are the sections in Chapter 33: Special Topics in Probability.

33.1 *Expected Value.* Calculating and interpreting the expected value are the topics.

33.2 *Permutations and Combinations.* The fundamental counting principle is applied to counting the number of permutations. The number of combinations is determined by counting the number of permutations in two ways. Formulas are given, and the ideas applied to probability problems.

33.3 *Issues for Learning: Children Finding Permutations.*

INSTRUCTOR NOTE 33.1A

This example is from Utts, 1996, p. 275. Students may want to know how the probabilities were determined. Their background so far could enable them to calculate the probability of 4 matches, $(\frac{1}{13})^4$ or 0.000035, and the probability of 0 matches, $(\frac{12}{13})^4$ or 0.726025. The other probabilities are somewhat advanced with the coverage so far. If there is time, you might return to this situation after the work with combinations in Section 33.2. With the whole number factors being the number of combinations,

$P(1 \text{ match}) = 4 \cdot \frac{1}{13} \cdot (\frac{12}{13})^3$, or 0.2420;

$P(2 \text{ matches}) = 6 \cdot (\frac{1}{13})^2 \cdot (\frac{12}{13})^2$, or 0.03025; and

$P(3 \text{ matches}) = 4 \cdot (\frac{1}{13})^3 \cdot (\frac{12}{13})$, or 0.00168.

Another approach would be to look at the situation for a smaller "deck" of cards, such as A–4 in the four suits.

References

American Statistical Assocation. (2005) Guidelines for assessment and instruction in statistics education (GAISE) Reports. Alexandia, VA: Author.

Blastland, M., & Dilnot, A. (2009) *The numbers game.* New York, NY: Gotham.

National Council of Teachers of Mathematics. (1991) *Dealing with data and chance: NCTM addenda series.* Reston, VA: Author.

Paulos, J. A. (1988) *Innumeracy.* New York NY: Hill and Wang.

Scheaffer, R., Gnangadesikan, M., Watkins, A., and Witmer, J. A. (2005) *Activity-based statistics.* Emeryville, CA: Key Curriculum Press.

Scheuren, F. (Winter 1997). The Census sampling controversy: When can a sample be better than a census? *Consortium,* no. 64. (*Consortium* is published by COMAP in Bedford, MA.)

Utts, J. M. (1996). *Seeing through statistics.* New York: Duxbury Press (Wadsworth).

Solutions to Exercises

Note to Instructors: We recommend playing down algebraic approaches in *Reasoning about Numbers and Quantities* in favor of more conceptually driven solutions accessible without algebra because the college students or teachers will be teaching elementary or middle school students who likely not yet have taken algebra. See the Instructor Notes for additional information on the approach to take in addressing problem situations.

Note to Students: The selected answers below give you some indication about whether you are on the right track. They are NOT intended to be the type of answers you would turn in to an instructor. **Your complete answers should contain all the work toward obtaining an answer**, as described in the Message to Students.

Examples of Complete Answers:

Learning Exercise 2a in Section 1.2

The quantities and their values are:

Regular price of CDs	$9.95
Regular price of tapes	$6.95
Discount this month	10%
Discounted price of CDs	90% of $9.95 = $8.96
Discounted price of tapes	90% of $6.95 = $6.26
New discount on 3 items	20%
Number of CDs bought	1
Number of tapes bought	1
Amount spent on CDs	$8.96
Amount spent on tapes	$6.26
Sales tax	6%
Amount spent	?

This drawing represents the problem.

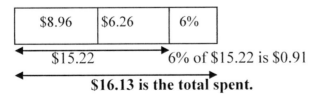

$15.22   6% of $15.22 is $0.91

$16.13 is the total spent.

Learning Exercise 9 in Section 3.1

We need to find the weight of the sum of the medicine available from companies A, B, and C. A diagram will help. Here is one possible diagram.

1.3 mg

A ————————————————

(1.3 − 0.9) mg = 0.4 mg   0.9 mg

C ——————|···

0.4 mg   (0.5 × 1.3) mg = 0.65 mg

B ——————···

Company A's medicine is represented by a line marked 1.3 mg. Company C's medicine is represented next because it is easier to find—it is 0.9 mg less than A's medicine. Thus, Company C has 0.4 mg of medicine. The difference between Company B's medicine and Company C's medicine is half of 1.3 mg, so it is 0.65 mg over and above Company C's medicine, which is 0.4 mg. Thus, Company B has 0.4 mg + 0.65 mg which is 1.05 mg. The total medicine furnished by the companies is (1.3 + 0.4 + 1.05) mg, or 2.75 mg.

Learning Exercise 2 in Section 5.4

$3 \times 10^4 \times 4 \times 10^6 = 12 \times 10^{10}$. This expression is not in scientific notation because 12 > 10. In scientific notation, this product would be expressed as 1.2×10^{11}.

Part I: Reasoning About Numbers and Quantities

Answers for Chapter 1: Reasoning About Quantities

1.2 Quantitative Analysis

1 a.

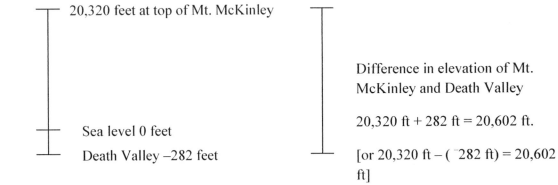

20,320 feet at top of Mt. McKinley

Difference in elevation of Mt. McKinley and Death Valley

20,320 ft + 282 ft = 20,602 ft.

[or 20,320 ft – (⁻282 ft) = 20,602 ft]

Sea level 0 feet

Death Valley –282 feet

  b.

Created   Sold

1727   1998

Age when sold = 1998 – 1727 = 271 years.

  c.

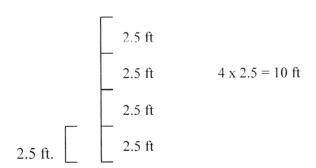

2.5 ft

2.5 ft   4 x 2.5 = 10 ft

2.5 ft

2.5 ft

2.5 ft.

  d.

$20		$4.75	$4.75
$3.50	$3.50	$3.50	$5.00	????

Money to spend is $20 + $4.75 + $4.75 = $29.50.

Money spent is 3 ($3.50) + $5.00 = $15.50.

Remaining amount is $29.50 – $15.50 = $14.00.

e.

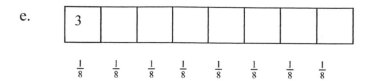

Each box represents 3 students. There are 8 boxes. Thus, there are 24 students.

f.

| 15 yrs | 10 yrs | 3 | 3 | 3 | 3 | |

Each box represents one dog year. Thus, the dog is 37 years old in human years.

2. a.   See page A1.

b.   Quantities and values

     a. Length of yard   9 meters
     b. Width of yard   7.5 meters
     c. Width between posts   1.5 meters
     d. Price per post $2.19
     e. Number of posts needed   ??
     f. Price for posts bought   ??
     g. Meters of wire needed   ??
     h. Price of mesh wire per meter $5.98 per meter
     i. Price for mesh wire needed   ??
     j. Number of gates needed   1
     k. Price per gate $25.89
     l. Number of staples needed   ??
     m. Cost of staples $3.99 for 50
     n. Cost of staples bought   ??
     o. Total cost for fencing yard   ??

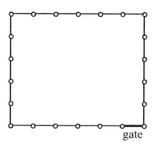
gate

The drawing shows that there are 7 posts needed for top and bottom, including corners, and 4 needed for each side, for a total of 22 posts. At $2.19 each, this would be $48.18.

The perimeter of the yard is 2(7.5 m + 9 m) = 33 m. But 1.5 will be a gate. Thus, 31.5 m of mesh wire is needed. Price per meter is $5.98, so the total would be $188.37.

Each post will need 7 staples. There are 22 posts, so 154 staples are needed. Thus, 4 boxes of 50 are needed, each costing $3.99, for a total of $15.96.

One gate is needed, for a total of $25.89.

The total price of materials before tax is $48.18 + $188.37 + $15.96 + $25.89 = $278.40.

3. This problem is an example of a word problem typically found in an algebra textbook that can be solved quite easily when all of the quantities to be used are listed and a drawing is made.

Quantities	Values
Speed of Train A	84 mph
Speed of Train B	92 mph
Distance traveled by Train A to meeting point	? miles
Distance traveled by Train B to meeting point	? miles
Total distance traveled by trains	132 miles
Time traveled by both trains, departure to meeting point	? hours

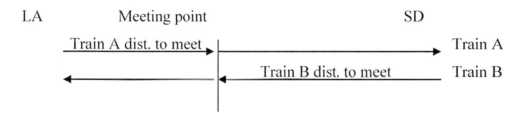

One solution: In 1 hour, the trains together will go 84 + 92 = 176 miles. Since they need go only 132 miles, they will meet after $\frac{132}{176} = \frac{3}{4}$ hours. *A second solution* looks at how far each train goes in 1 minute: $\frac{84}{60}$ miles and $\frac{92}{60}$ miles, or $\frac{84}{60} + \frac{92}{60} = \frac{176}{60}$ miles together. Again, since they need to go 132 miles, the calculation $132 \div \frac{176}{60}$ will tell the number of minutes needed. Here is a *third solution*, the traditional algebraic one that also follows from a quantitative analysis. Note that the time traveled by both trains is the same, t hours.

Distance A + Distance B = 132 miles

$84t + 92t$ = 132, so $176t$ = 132 and t = 132÷176 = 0.75 hour

Distance Train A travels in 0.75 hours is 0.75 hr × 84 mph = 63 miles.

Distance Train B travels in 0.75 hours is 0.75 hr × 92 mph = 69 miles.

Notice that algebra is not necessary for this problem and need not be used in elementary school.

4. a. Here is one way to find that the answer is 24 minutes. (Advice: Work through each step of this problem slowly and thoughtfully.)

An important issue involves the assumptions that one must make when analyzing a situation quantitatively. In Brother and I, for example, we must assume things like:

- both brother and I walk at a constant speed

- brother and I go to the same school

- brother and I take the same route to school

It is important to be aware of the assumptions that you make when analyzing a situation because thinking about these assumptions helps you understand the situation better.

Consider the following diagram depicting the situation at, say, 8 minutes after my brother takes off for school.

What other distances besides the distance from home to school are made evident by this diagram?
Consider these quantities and their values. (You may list more than what is here.)

Distance from home to school: unknown

Time taken for brother to go from home to school: 40 minutes

Time taken for me to go from home to school: 30 minutes

Difference between the time brother left for school and I left for school: 8 minutes

Distance traveled by brother in 1 minute: $\frac{1}{40}$ of total distance

Distance traveled by me in 1 minute: $\frac{1}{30}$ of total distance

Distance I gain on brother each minute: $\frac{1}{30} - \frac{1}{40} = \frac{1}{120}$ of total distance

Distance between brother and me at time zero: $\frac{8}{40} = \frac{1}{5}$ of total distance

If brother has covered $\frac{1}{5}$ of the distance when I begin, and I catch up to him at the rate of $\frac{1}{120}$ of the total distance each minute, it will take me $\frac{1}{5}$ distance $\div \frac{1}{120}$ distance/minute or 24 minutes to catch up.

b. The parts of the distance covered by brother and me in 1 minute.

c. 15 minutes

5. a. There are different approaches likely. One is to focus on the catch-up amount (the additive comparison), 50 boxes per day, that D can achieve. They need to catch up by 300 boxes, so it will take them 6 days.

b. No, knowing the difference in their rates does not tell what the rates themselves are.

6. First, each quantity is listed, and then the value of each quantity is determined, if possible.

1. Distance (length) of the last part of the triathlon: 10,000 m

2. Distance between Aña and Bea at the start of the last part: 600 m

3. Distance between Aña and Bea during the last part: varies

4. Distance between Aña and Bea at the time they meet: 0 m

5. Distance between Aña and Bea at the end of the 10,000 m race: not known

6. Average speed (rate) at which Aña runs: 225 m/minute

7. Average speed (rate) at which Bea runs: 200 m/minute

8. Distance Aña runs in 1 minute: 225 m

9. Distance Bea runs in 1 minute: 200 m

10. Difference between the average speeds: Aña runs 25 m/minute faster than Bea

11. Difference between the distance Aña runs in 1 minute and the distance Bea runs in 1 minute: 25 m

12. Time it takes Aña to run the last part of the triathlon: 10,000 m ÷ 225 m/minute = 44.44 minutes

13. Time in takes Bea to run the last part of the triathlon: 10,000 m ÷ 200 m/minute = 50 minutes

14. Time from when Aña begins the last running part to the time she passes Bea: not known

15. Time from when Bea begins the last running part to the time when Aña catches up: not known

Make a drawing (or drawings) to represent the problem and the relationships among the quantities.

Consider the following diagram depicting the situation at the start of the running part of the triathlon. Aña and Bea are 600 m apart.

Now, consider the situation 1 minute later. Aña has run 225 m, Bea has run 200 m + 600 m headstart so is at 800 m. After 1 minute they are 575 m apart.

Using this process, I know they would be 550 m apart after 2 minutes, 525 m after 3 minutes, etc. Notice that the value of that distance between Aña and Bea *varies,* that is, it is not 600 m except at the beginning. A critical value of the distance between Aña and Bea will occur when Aña overtakes Bea (if she does). At this time, the distance would be 0.

Finally, solve the problem using the drawings.

One way is to think the following: In each minute of the race, Aña gains 25 m on Bea. Because Aña begins the race 600 m behind Bea, it will take Aña 600 m divided by 25 m/minute, or 24 minutes, to catch up to Bea.

7. A quantitative analysis would produce the following quantities, values, and relationships:

Length of board: 200 inches

Width of board: 12 inches   (Note that we do not need this information.)

Length of each shelf: unknown

Number of shelves: 4

Total length of shelves placed end to end: not given, but can be found by the relationship of length of each shelf and total number of shelves: 4 times length of one shelf

Length of the part of the board left over: 36 inches

Length of the part of the board used for shelves: Total – left over = 200 – 36 = 164

Length of one shelf is length of board used divided by the number of shelves:

   164 ÷ 4 = 41. Each shelf is 41 inches.

8. a. A walked 12 km, B walked 18 km, for a total of 30 km.

   b. A walked $\frac{4}{10}$ of the distance. $\frac{4}{10}$ of 27 km is 10.8 km. Thus, A walked 10.8 km at 4 km/h; 10.8 ÷ 4 is 2.7 hours. Also, B walked $\frac{6}{10}$ of 27 km, or 16.2 km, at 6 km/h; 16.2 ÷ 6 is 2.7 hours.

   c. A walked 3h × 4 km/h = 12 km. 27 km – 12 km = 15 km. To walk 15 km in 3 hours would require that B walked 5 km/h.

9. Speed of train leaving Moscow: 48 km/h

   Speed of train leaving Sverdlovsk: 54 km/h

   Time of travel: 12 hours

   Distance traveled by first train: 48 km/h × 12 h = 576 km

   Distance traveled by second train: 54 km/h × 12 h = 648 km

   Distance between cities: 1822 km

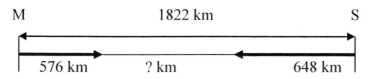

Distance apart after 12 hours is 1822 km – (576 km + 648 km) = 598 km.

Supplementary Learning Exercises for Section 1.2

1. Finding a unit with which to measure "prettiness" and with which everyone agreed would be extremely difficult.

2. a. Quantities: Walt's height, Sheila's height, Tammi's height, and possibly the differences in pairs of the three people's heights, and even the difference in those differences. A drawing (for example, line segments, thin rectangles) should show the relative sizes and be labeled.

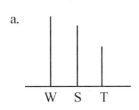

a.   W   S   T

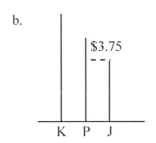

b. $3.75

K   P   J

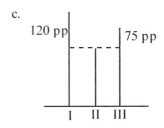

c.   120 pp   75 pp

I   II   III

   b. Quantities: Pedro's salary, Jim's salary, Kay's salary, the difference in Pedro's and Jim's salary, etc. Your drawing should have labels and show the known $3.75 value for the difference in Pedro's and Jim's salaries.

   c. Quantities: The number of pages in each of the three books and the differences in page numbers (first and second, second and third, first and third). One could even consider the difference in the differences if that was appropriate for a particular question.

3. Acting it out, a drawing showing different times, or a table for the runners' positions after various numbers of minutes can be helpful in seeing that Les catches up by 25 meters every minute, so she can catch up in $800 \div 25 = 32$ minutes (if the race is not over). In 32 minutes, Les would have covered $32 \times 250 = 8000$ meters, so the race is not over. Les will take $10,000 \div 250 = 40$ minutes to make the run. In 40 minutes, Pat will have covered $40 \times 225 = 9000$ meters, plus the 800 meters she was ahead at the start gives 9800 meters for Pat after 40 minutes. So Les is $10,000 - 9800 = 200$ meters ahead when she wins.

4. a. Even an abstract drawing like the one to the right could be helpful. The entire drawing could be repeated until there are 24 B's.

    C C C C C C C C for
       B B B B B B

   b. Your drawing could focus on the 12 pictures, with $4.80 being associated with the whole group of 12, and then 35¢ associated with each picture.

   c. Three stacked rectangles can stand for the number of students at each of the 3 games. The rectangle representing the number of people in attendance at the first game is the longest. The rectangle representing the number of people in attendance at the second game is shorter and the difference in length is marked as 18. Continue for third rectangle.

5. Height, width, number of rooms, size of rooms, size of entrance hall, cost, …

6. Points scored, number of points more than (or less!) than the opponent, number of errors, number of rebounds, number of shots made, number of free-throws made, number of fouls,… Would your answers change if it had been the football team?

7. a. A drawing definitely helps most people. Here is one possibility.

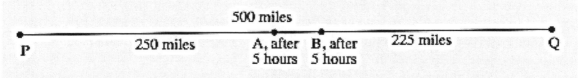

The trains have traveled $250 + 225 = 475$ of the 500 miles, so the locomotives are $500 - 475 = 25$ miles apart.

   b. 260 miles. Train A has traveled 400 miles, and Train B has traveled 360 miles. So the trains have passed each other, as a drawing shows.

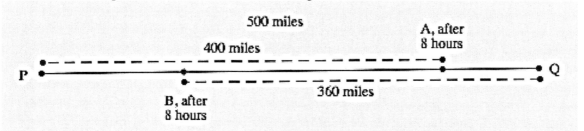

There are different ways of reasoning, but one way is to note that B is 140 miles from P, whereas A is 400 miles from P. Hence, the two locomotives are $400 - 140 = 260$ miles apart.

8. a. 490 miles. Make a drawing and keep in mind that Train D is heading *away from* P.

   b. 430 miles.

   c. Train C will eventually catch Train D. It is catching up by 10 miles every hour, so it will catch up in 50 hours.

1.3 Values of Quantities

1. a. Cupfuls, liters, cubic inches, milliliters, height in cup…

   b. Feet or meters (why not inches?)

   c. Miles, kilometers, time of car/plane travel (non-standard)

   d. Gallons, liters

   e. Number of pounds or kilograms or number of people

   f. Inches or centimeters

2. a. Good means more miles for each gallon

   b. Miles per gallon

   c. Divide the number of miles traveled by the number of gallons used for that travel.

    d. No; city vs. highway driving, low speed vs. high speed, etc.

    e. Gallons per mile, or gallons per 100 kilometers, say

3. Rain gauges, radar, and satellites are used to measure rainfall. The answer will probably reflect the source of the information.

4. See side-note in text.

5. a. Width of a fingernail

    b. A paperclip

    c. A quart

    d. Width of a door

    e. A little more than half a mile

    f. Three cans of mushroom soup

    Of course, you may have others. You might want to compare your answer with the answers of others.

6. An inch is approximately 2.5 cm, a mile is approximately 0.6 km, and a quart is approximately 1 liter.

Supplementary Learning Exercises for Section 1.3

1. Perhaps a little finger

2. A car might be 5 meters long, and perhaps also a kite tail and a python.

3. a. A meter is 100 centimeters.   b. A centimeter is one-hundredth of a meter.

    c. A decimeter is 10 centimeters.   d. A centimeter is one-tenth of a decimeter.

    e. A kilometer is 1000 meters.   f. A meter is one-thousandth of a kilometer.

4. The Latin word *mille* means 1000. In the metric system, the labels for units smaller than 1 are suggested by Latin words: 1 millimeter = one-thousandth meter

5. a. cm   b. mi   c. kg

6. 2 m (smallest)   510 cm = 5.1 m   300 dm = 30 m (largest)

7. a. 5   b. 0.5 (or just .5. So that the decimal point is not overlooked, SI recommends that a "0" be written to the left of the decimal point: 0.5.)
    c. 340   d. 0.034   e. 0.2 (or 0.200)   f. 200 000

1.4 Issues for Learning: Ways of Illustrating Story Problems

1.

| $4.25 | | | |

$17 weekly allowance

2.

Sara

| |

Calle

| | | | | |

Juniper

| 25 stickers |

Calle: 50 stickers, Sara 10 stickers
In all, 85 stickers

3.

| | | $32 |

$128 weekly earnings

4.

Hat

| |

Sweater

| | |

Coat

| | | |

<------- $114 ------->

Hat $19 (Sweater $38)

5.

| |

| | | | |

5285 in all,
so 1057 in each.

First number: 1057
Second number: 4228

6.

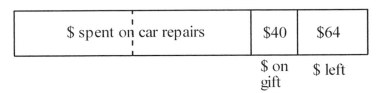

Dollars in paycheck

| $ spent on car repairs | $40 | $64 |

$ on gift $ left

Each third of the paycheck is $40 + $64, or $104, so Jinfa's whole paycheck is $312.

7.   104 students in 4th grade

| (104 − 11 = 93) | 11 |

There are 104 − 11 = 93 students in the three classrooms, so there are 31 students in each classroom.

8.

Karen

Jacqui   12

Lynn

The 7 equal-sized small boxes have 124 − 12 = 112 in them. Each small box has 112 ÷ 7 = 16.
So, Karen has 48 stamps, Jacqui has 60, and Lynn has 16.

9.

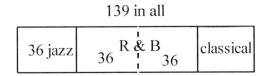

139 in all

| 36 jazz | R & B 36   36 | classical |

31 are classical.
(36 + 36 + 36 + c = 139, or 108 + c = 139, and c = 139 − 108, missing addend).

Answers for Chapter 2: Numeration Systems

2.1 Ways of Expressing Values of Quantities

1. Different answers possible

2. There are five fingers on one hand and ten on both.

3. The Spanish and French words resemble one another. Both languages are Romance languages, all of which have similar words for similar things.

4. a. 2113   b. 185   c. 1507

5. a. MMLXVI   b. LXXVIII   c. DCV

6. a. 903   b. 49   c. 409

7. Twins, couple, dyad, brace, duet, duo, double, twosome, twice; bicompounds like bicycle, both; and dicompounds like dipolar are others.

8. IV V VI VII VIII IX X XI XII XIII XIV XV XVI XVII XVIII XIX XX

9. a. IC, CI   b. MIM, MMI   c. CMXIII, CMXV

2.2 Place Value

1. a. 35.7; 35   b. 43.62; 43   c. 436.2; 436   d. 456.654; 456

    e. 4566.54; 4566   f. 45665.4; 45,665   g. 234.7; 234   h. 23,470; 23,470

    i. 23.47; 23   j. 2347; 2347   k. 23470; 23470   l. 2347; 2347

2. No. The ones place, not the decimal point, divides the number into two parts with similar names on both sides.

3. a. True

    b. It depends on the placement of the decimal point, so there is no safe general conclusion.

4. Three thousand two hundred; thirty-two hundred. They have the same value because they have the same number of hundreds: three thousand is thirty hundreds.

5. a. Four hundred seven *and* fifty-three thousandths

    b. Thirty *and* four hundredths

    c. Thirty-four hundredths

    d. Two hundred *and* sixty-seven thousandths

    e. Two hundred sixty-seven thousandths.

6. a. and b. No regrouping into tens

    c. Regrouping (in this case "borrowing" is not understood)

    d. Digits are misplaced in quotient.

e. No regrouping into tens. In all cases, the work indicates a lack of understanding of place value.

7. 1635 is exactly 1635 ones, 163.5 tens, 16.35 hundreds, 1.635 thousands,…, 16,350 tenths, or 163,500 hundredths.

8. 73.5 is 73.5 ones, 7.35 tens, 0.735 hundreds, or 0.0735 thousands; it is also 735 tenths or 7350 hundredths. (If possible, think of it this way: 7.35 ten dollar bills, 0.735 hundred dollar bills, 0.0735 thousand dollar bills, 735 dimes, or 7350 pennies.)

9. To the right, yes; to the left, no (for whole numbers)

10. The word "billion" means different things in different countries. In the United States, it means "one thousand million," whereas in Britain and some other countries, it means "one million million."

Supplementary Learning Exercises for Section 2.2

1. a. 1000   b. 53   c. 538,649   d. 67   e. 6794   f. 8   g. 824,753,298

2. a. 8,500,000 (metric: 8 500 000)

   b. 92,000,000,000 (metric: 92 000 000 000) In Britain, a billion is a million million rather than the thousand million in the U.S. A British billion would be a trillion in the U.S.

   c. $6,450,000,000,000 (metric: $6 450 000 000 000)

3. a. "Six hundred and twenty-three thousandths"

   b. "Six hundred twenty-three thousandths" (Notice the "and" in part (a).)

   c. "Twenty and eight hundredths"   d. "Twenty-eight hundredths"

4. 8.7645 tens, 87.645 ones, 876.45 tenths, 8764.5 hundredths, 87645 thousandths, 876450 ten-thousandths, and 0.87645 hundreds

5. 0.5 ones, 5 tenths, 50 hundredths

6. a. four hundred seven hundred-thousandths
   b. fifty-one and 5 ten-thousandths
   c. four hundred and 5 hundredths (Notice the use of "and" here.)
   d. four hundred five thousandths (No "and"—remember to use "and" only for the decimal point in a decimal greater than 1, as in parts b and c.)

7. a. 3.2   b. 7.53   c. 2000.017   d. 2.017

2.3 Bases Other Than Ten

1. Different answers possible.

2. a. 22_{four} b. 20_{five} c. 12_{eight}

3. a. 10_{four} b. 10_{eight} c. 10_{twenty} d. 10_b

   e. 100_b f. 1100_b g. 1002_{three} h. 430_{five}

   i. 1000101_{two} j. 1000_{twelve}

4. 1, 10, 11, 100, 101, 110, 111, 1000, 1001, 1010, 1011, 1100, 1101, 1110, 1111, 10000, 10001, 10010, 10011, 10100

5. a. There cannot be a "4" with base three.

   b. There cannot be a "7" with base seven.

   c. There cannot be a "5" with base four.

6. a. Forty-three   b. Thirty-four

   c. Two hundred seven and twenty-four ten-thousandths

   d. Eight   e. Sixty-four   f. Twenty-five and two-thirds

7. Usually the base-two numeral will have more digits because its place values are smaller than those in base twelve. The exceptions are 0 and 1, which appear the same in both systems.

8. Base six and greater

9. a. <   b. =   c. >   d. >   e. =   f. >

10. Base four ... fin-na, fin-obi, fin-fin, fin-mus, mus-na, mus-obi, mus-fin, mus-mus, obi-na-na, obi-na-obi, obi-na-fin, obi-na-mus, obi-obi-na, ...

11. a. Twenty   b. Twenty   c. Twelve   d. Sixty

12. 3 fives $+ 4$ ones $+ \frac{2}{5}$; 19.4_{ten}

13. a. $9\frac{11}{16}$ b. $40\frac{3}{12} = 40\frac{1}{4}$

14. a. $\frac{1}{4}$ in base twelve is the same amount as in base ten. $\frac{1}{4}$ is $\frac{3}{12}$ in base 10. $\frac{3}{12}$ in base 12 would be $\frac{3}{10}$, or 0.3_{twelve}.

    b. 0.9_{twelve} c. 0.2_{eight}

15. a. 42_{ten}, or just 42. The place values in the base-two numeral given are, starting at the right, 1s, 2s, 4s, 8s, 16s, 32s. Taking into account the digits, $101010_{two} =$ $(1\times32)+(1\times8)+(1\times2)=32+8+2=42$.

    b. 1310   c. 161   d. $33\frac{5}{8}$ e. 221

16. a. 13_{nine} b. 14_{eight} c. 15_{seven}

    d. 20_{six} e. 22_{five} f. 30_{four}

    g. 110_{three} h. 1100_{two}

17. a. 202_{seven} b. 400_{five} c. 91_{eleven}

    d. 1100100_{two} e. $37_{thirty-one}$

18. a. 212   b. 78   c. 54   d. 355   e. 64   f. $\frac{1}{2}+\frac{1}{4}+\frac{1}{8}=\frac{7}{8}$

19. Three longs and 4 small blocks; 3 flats and 4 longs

20. a. You should have 2 flats, 3 longs, and 4 small cubes where the flat is 5 units by 5 units.

    b. You should have 2 flats, 3 longs, and 4 small cubes where the flat is 6 units by 6 units.

21. 5413_{six} is 5413 *ones* (in base six), is 541.3 *sixes*, 54.13 *six²'s; is* 5.413 *six³'s.*

22. You should have 2 flats, 3 longs, and 4 small cubes.

23. a. If the small cube is the unit, then 3542 could be represented with 3 large cubes, 5 flats, 4 longs, and 2 small cubes.

    b. 0.741 could only be represented if the large block is the unit. Then 0.741 would be represented with 7 flats, 4 longs, and 1 small cube.

    c. If the flat represents one unit, then 11.11 would be represented with 1 large cube, 1 flat, 1 long, and 1 small cube.

24. Let the unit be the same in both cases: say, a flat. Then 5.21 would be represented as 5 flats, 2 longs, and 1 small unit; 5.4 would be represented as 5 flats and 4 longs. More units would be needed to make 5 flats and 4 longs. (Some children actually say: "5.4 is bigger because it's got more wood.")

25. A number could be written in different numeration systems. (The idea of several different ways of writing a number is extremely important with fractions.)

26. Base five or greater

Supplementary Learning Exercises for Section 2.3

1. 1, 2, 3, 4, 5, 10, 11, 12, 13, 14, 15, 20, 21, 22, 23, 24, 25, 30, 31, 32, 33, 34, 35, 40, 41, 42, 43, 44, 45, 50 51, 52, 53, 54, 55, 100. A third digit is needed at 100_{six}, which is the square of six, or thirty-six.

2. 111, 1000, 1001, 1010, 1011, 1100, all in base two.

3. The digit 3 does not appear in base three. Eighteen = 200_{three}.

4. First, write the base-ten values of each place value in the unfamiliar system. Then calculate how many of each place value is needed, starting with the largest needed.

    a. 2101_{five} b. 424_{eight} c. 100010100_{two}

5. a. 774   b. 1882   c. 649

6. 354, with the small cube as the unit; 35.4, with the long as the unit; 3.54, with the flat as the unit; 0.354, with the large cube as the unit (any two)

7. 35.4_{seven}, with base-ten value $26\frac{4}{7}$.

8. Notice that each has four place values, so all four sizes of the usual kit of blocks will be needed for each.

    a. With the small cube as the unit, 4 large cubes and 2 small cubes

    b. With the large cube as the unit, 4 large cubes, 3 flats, 2 longs, and 5 small cubes

    c. With the long as the unit, 7 large cubes, 5 flats, 2 longs, and 3 small cubes

9. In binary (base two), 10 = two.

10. a. b^4
    b. $3b^3 + 2$ (or $3b^3 + 0b^2 + 0b + 2$)
    c. $b^5 + 2b^3 + 3b$ (or $1b^5 + 2b^3 + 3b$, or $1b^5 + 0b^4 + 2b^3 + 0b^2 + 3b + 0$)

11. a. 2030_b b. 41023_b c. 301026_b

2.4 Operations in Different Bases

1. Answer, either way: 10220_{three}

2. Block answers should yield:

    a. 1111_{five} b. 1011_{two} c. 132_{four} d. 268_{ten}

3. (Assigns work on Internet)

4. a. 3204_{five} b. 611_{nine} c. 1110_{seven} d. 176_{eleven}

5. a. 101_{nine} b. 506_{seven} c. 2203_{five} d. 524_{eleven}

6. More difficult because we don't know our basic multiplication and division facts in bases other than ten.

7. a. 1030_{four} b. 413_{five} c. 360_{eight} d. 1111_{two}

8. Block or cut-out answers should yield the following:

    a. 121_{four} b. 132_{five} c. 165_{eight} d. 1_{two}

9. Cutouts for base-six would consist of small squares, longs the length of 6 small squares, and flats the size of 6 longs side-by-side.

Supplementary Learning Exercises for Section 2.4

1. If you work right-to-left and record them in the numerical work, the actions with the cutouts support exactly the usual record-keeping with the "standard" algorithm.

    a. 413_{five}

b. 1030_{four} (Notice that the final answer involves a larger piece than is in the cut-outs. With 3D materials, it would be a big $4 \times 4 \times 4$ cube; with the 2D, it could be a strip of four sixteens.)

c. 361_{seven}

d. 10101_{two} (Notice that the final answer involves larger pieces than are in the cut-outs. With the 2D, you need, for example, a square made up of two strips of two fours for the sixteen.)

2. If you trade as necessary to work right-to-left and record the trades in the numerical work, the actions with the cut-outs support exactly the usual record-keeping with the "standard" U.S. algorithm. Notice also that you can check these by adding the difference to the subtrahend (the number being subtracted).

   a. 213_{four} b. 224_{five} c. 246_{seven} d. 101_{two}

3. Base seven: small squares (1s); strip (long) of seven small squares (seven, 7^1); square (flat) of seven of those strips (forty-nine, 7^2)

4. Different answers possible.

5. a.   four entries   b.   nine entries

+	0	1
0	0	1
1	1	10

+	0	1	2
0	0	1	2
1	1	2	10
2	2	10	11

c. forty-nine (seven rows, with seven in each row)
d. one hundred
e. n^2

Answers for Chapter 3: Understanding Whole Number Operations

3.1 Additive Combinations and Comparisons

1. a. Subtract the value of Laura's height from that of Bob's height.

   b. Add the value of Laura's height to that of the difference.

2. The time it took to swim the first lap can be found by subtracting the time it took to swim the last two laps from the time it took to swim all three laps.

3. 50 students

4. C and D are combined, A and B are combined, A and D are compared, B and C are compared.

5. a. The point is that here there will be many answers. Any scores giving a difference between B's and B's opponents' scores = 34, with B's score greater, will solve the problem (but not uniquely).

   b. The point here is that there is no answer meeting the condition (without deciding that team A actually lost, which does not seem consistent with the "argument" between the captains).

   c and d. See the important points in parts (a) and (b). Both types of answers give potentially valuable information in mathematics. If there are many answers, perhaps one will be cheaper, say. If there are no answers, then that gives potentially valuable information about an endeavor.

6. Here is one drawing. You may have another that works better for you.

   Note that the "found" quantities are bolded.

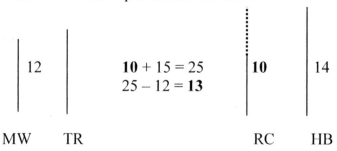

   Connie bought 13 Tootsie Rolls.

7. a.   Annie weighed $1\frac{3}{4}$ pounds less than Carmen on that day.

   b. Many values can lead to the same differences.

8. A drawing of the two pieces, one under the other, shows that once the difference of $\frac{1}{4}$ lb is "removed," the remaining two pieces are equal in weight (and total $\frac{3}{4}$ lb), so the smaller piece

weighs $\frac{3}{8}$ lb and the larger weighs $\frac{5}{8}$ lb. Notice that algebra is not necessary, especially with the help of a drawing.

9. See page A-2.

10. $\frac{1}{8}$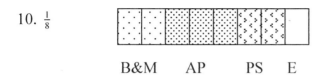

11. Example: For #6, one additive combination is the number of Tootsie Rolls combined with the number of Milky Ways. One additive comparison is the number of Reese's Cups is 4 fewer than the number of Hershey Bars.

Supplementary Learning Exercises for Section 3.1

1.   Each value (120 pages, 75 pages) refers to an additive comparison.

2.   a. The sample drawing to the right shows how the additive comparisons can lead to either subtraction (23.4 − 0.064 = 23.336 s for the winner) or addition (23.4 + 0.92 = 24.32 s for third place), depending on how the quantities are related. Often the scales for the values are off because the values are unknown at the start.

Time for race

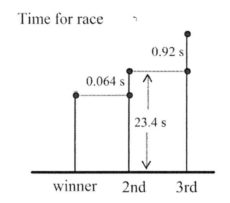

   b. The drawing suggests that if the difference is subtracted from the total, the result ($48.60) will equal twice the first trip's amount. So, the first trip's amount was $24.30, and the second $36.15.

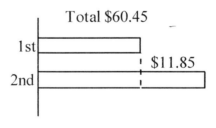

   c. The possible drawing to the right shows that and Xavier have 49 cards, so Will has 49 − 23 = 26 cards.

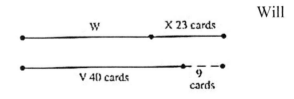

3.   a. Compared: Nia and sister's collection vs. Dan and Ian's. Combined: Nia and her sister's collections; Dan and Ian's collections; the four collections

b. Compared: Assets of Bank X vs. those of Bank Y; total of Banks X's and Y's assets vs. those of Bank Z. Combined: Assets of Bank X and Bank Y

4.   There are many possibilities, so others may have different answers. Check that your values fit all parts of the stories.

5.   Many possibilities. It is likely, however, that "how much more" or "how much less" appears in your story.

6.   a. One possibility is to the right. It shows that Tia's current GPA is 2.7 and so Sue's current GPA is 2.7 + 0.3 = 3.0.

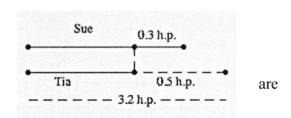

b. Tia's current GPA and the 0.5 improvement additively combined.   are

c. Sue's and Tia's current GPAs are being additively compared.

3.2 Understanding for Teaching about Addition and Subtraction

Long line is 8 units

1.   a. Take-away   in each case below

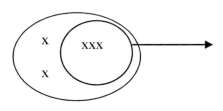

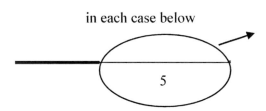

b. Comparison

x x x x x x x x

x x x x x

c. Missing addend (5 + ? = 8)

x x x x x + (?) = x x x x x x x x

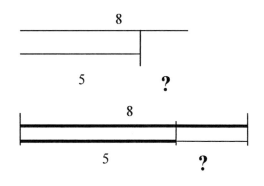

2. a. Student answers will vary.

   b. Example: Colleen had pennies in her piggy bank. She took out 17 and gave them to her brother. She counted the ones she had left and found she had 24 pennies. How many pennies did she have in her piggy bank before she gave some to her brother?

3. a. "Spent" as a key word suggests subtraction, but this problem requires addition.

b. "Altogether" suggests adding 32 and 12, but multiplication is needed.

c. "Divided" naturally suggests division, but multiplication is needed.

d. "Times" suggests multiplication, but division is needed.

e. "In all" suggests addition, but subtraction is needed.

f. "Total" may signal addition of 6, 12, and perhaps 4, but multiplication is needed.

4. a. The baseball team has 12 players and 9 were wearing gloves. How many players were not wearing gloves?

b. There are 28 children in a teacher's class. The teacher gave suckers to 20 of them. How many did not get suckers? (This is just one possible phrasing.)

5. a. $2 + 6 = 8$; $6 + 2 = 8$; $8 - 2 = 6$; $8 - 6 = 2$

b. $12 + 49 = 61$; $49 + 12 = 61$; $61 - 12 = 49$; $61 - 49 = 12$

c. $m - p = x$; $m - x = p$; $p + x = m$; $x + p = m$

6. Possibilities:

Addition: Latima had $12 and her grandfather gave her $49. How much does she have now?

Take-away subtraction: Carla had $61 and gave her brother $12. How much did she have left?

Missing-addend subtraction: Carol has $12 but needs to buy new running shoes that cost $61. How much more does she have to earn?

Comparison subtraction: Kim has $12 and her brother has $61. How much more money does her brother have?

7. The teacher handled the situation by having 8 girls and 12 boys line up next to each other, so the match of the 8 girls with 8 of the boys was obvious. The children then saw that "taking away" 8 boys from the 12 boys was all right.

8. a. Missing-addend   b. Missing-addend   c. Take-away

d. Comparison   e. Comparison

10. Mr. Lewis's students did not recognize the comparison problem as a problem calling for subtraction because they had only worked with take-away problems in class.

11. The drawings are quite easy to make.

a. 8.25 ft.   b. $\frac{6}{15}$ of the students   c. 6 cm

d. $\frac{1}{6}$ part   e. 25 beads   f. 15.36 pints

Supplementary Learning Exercises for Section 3.2

1. You should have illustrations for the take-away, the comparison, and the missing-addend views. The illustrations should differ.

2. The differences is 83.5, the minuend is 165.8, and the subtrahend is 82.3.

3.   a. Take-away   b. Missing-addend   c. Comparison

4. $y - z = x$

5.   Here are examples, using marbles. There are many possibilities.
a. Joe has 28 marbles, and Jean has 7. How many fewer marbles does Jean have than Joe? (Or, How many more marbles does Joe have than Jean?) Notice that two separate amounts are being compared in a how-much-more or how-much-less sense.

b. Joe has 28 marbles. Only 7 of them are solid colors. How many of his marbles are not solid colors?

c. Joe had 28 marbles but lost 7 of them in the park. How many marbles does Joe have now?

6.   There are many possibilities. Here are examples.
a. He had 36 feet of black irrigation pipe. How much less black pipe did he have? (The clearest earmark for a comparison subtraction situation occurs when two separate amounts are being compared in a how-much-more or how-much-less sense.)

b. She needs 75 feet of pipe to finish the job. How many feet of pipe does she need?

c. He used 29 feet for a flower bed. How many feet of pipe does he have now? (Clearest examples involve a taking-away, using, erasing, removing,… action.)

3.3 Children's Ways of Adding and Subtracting

1. Answers will vary.

2. Case A: 40 and 50 is 90, 8 more is 98, then 9 more is 99, 100, 101, 102, 103, 104, 105, 106, 107.

Case B: 50 and 60 is 110. Then take 2 away to get 108, then take away 1 to get 107.

Case C: 50 and 59 is, 50 and 50 is 100, and 9 more is 109, but take 2 away, so it's 107.

Case D: 254 + 367: 2 plus 3 is 5 so it's 200 + 300, so it's somewhere in the 500s. Now add tens. They are 5 and 6. Start at 60, 70, 80, 90, 100. You are in the 500s because of the 200 + 300, but now you're in the 600s because of the 60 and 50. But you've got one more ten. So 500 + 60 + 50, you'd have 610. Now add 4 more onto 10, which is 14. And add 7 more: 15, 16, 17, 18, 19, 20, 21. This is 621.

Case E: 58 – 9. 58 – 8 is 50, and take away 1 more to 49.

Also: 9 + 9 is 18, then 10 is 28, and 10 more is 38, and 10 more is 48, and 10 more is 58. Four tens is 40, and 9 more is 49.

Case F: 368 – 132. 3 take away 1 is 2, and you make it into hundreds, so 200. Then you add 60 and get 260, – 30 is 230, + 8 is 238, – 2 is 236.

Case G: 800 – 452. 8 to get to 460, then 40 to get to 500, then 300 more, so 348.

3 and 4. Case A: (3) The student is first adding the tens (30 + 30), then each of the ones: 60 + 9, then 69 + 7. The 7 is added by counting on. (4) This will not be difficult to remember and is a form of mental computation that is quite natural. Children should be able to continue using this procedure.

Case B: (3) The student is rounding up on both addends, then subtracting the appropriate number of ones. (4) This is also a common way of mental adding and should not be forgotten.

Case C: (3) The student rounded the first number up to 40, then added the tens and the ones and compensated for the rounding. (4) This method might be slightly more difficult because it would be easy to forget the need for compensating at the end.

Case D: (3) The student is adding from left to right; hundreds, then tens; then ones. So many steps and intermediate sums are hard to remember mentally, and so the student does make one error, then corrects it. (4) The method itself will not be difficult to remember because the direction from left to right is the way we read. However, the difficulty is remembering all the partial addends, so this might be easier if the solver could jot down partial sums along the way.

Case E: (3) The student is using a variation of adding on to the second number to reach the first number. The student adds an 8 to get to 15, then adds tens to get to 65. Another example of this method might be 43 – 9: Add 4 to get 13, then 10 more to 23, 10 more to 33, 10 more to 43, so I've added 3 tens and a 4, or 34. (This is sometimes called shopkeepers' math, because if you gave a shopkeeper $10 for something that cost $6.25, she might count out money saying, "$6.25, $7.00, $8.00, $9.00, $10.00" while giving you 3 quarters and 3 one-dollar bills.) In some curricula, the "empty" number line might be used (see Learning Exercise 5). (4) This is not too difficult to remember, but it might, for some people, be easier to add to ten, then tens, then whatever more is need: 43 – 9 would be 1 to get to 10, then 30 to get to 40, then 3 more: 1 + 30 + 3 is 34.

Case F: (3) The student is working from left to right, first getting 300 from the hundreds, then adds in the 50 from 354 to get 350, and then subtracts the 30 from 350, for 320. He/she then adds the 4 from 354 and has the subtraction of 9 from 339 remaining, which he/she does by seeing 9 as 4 + 5 and subtracting each part. (4) Despite the jumping back and forth between the numbers and the operations, this child shows good number sense. Children for whom the jumping might be difficult to keep track of might have trouble with understanding this student's explanation.

Case G: (3) The student is using a missing-addend approach: What must you add to 268 to get 500? (4) This approach also shows good number sense and an awareness of different ways of thinking about subtraction. There is a memory load (without paper), so some children might have difficulty with keeping track of how much has been added. An "empty" number line might help keep track of the numbers added. See the next exercise.

5. There are different possibilities. Do not leave the impression that there is one correct way.

6. The child appears to be working left-to-right and, if necessary, adjusting in a place value to make the subtraction possible.

7. In the example given, a child might start with 4 flats, 5 longs, and 7 small cubes. There are no hundreds to be taken away, so start the work writing the 4. But $5-6$ requires more longs, so trade one of the four flats for ten longs, leaving 3 flats. Now $15-6$ is possible, giving 9 longs. Similarly, the $3-5$ requires trading one of the longs for 10 small cubes, leaving 8 longs and enabling $13-5$.

Supplementary Learning Exercises for Section 3.3

1. The child seems not to have any idea of what "+" really means.

2. These are sample directions for the arrows; different approaches could give different answers.

   a. Start at 189, go to 190, then to 192, then to 202, and finally to 232.

   b. Start at 936, go to 940, then to 1000, then to 1020, and finally to 1025.

   c. Start at 1000, go to 300, then to 270, then to 268.

   d. Start at 381, go back to 380, then to 320, and then to 319.

3.   a. Probably $550 - 400$ b. $400 - 75$

4. Child 3 could start with 3 flats, 6 longs, and 4 small cubes. Starting on the right, trades of 1 long for 10 small cubes and then 1 flat for 10 longs would enable the take-aways. Child 6 would do similar trades, but in a different order.

5. No hints given! Be sure that your algorithm works for the second example.

3.4 Ways of Thinking about Multiplication

1. a. 6×2: XX XX XX XX XX XX
       2×6: XXXXXX   XXXXXX

b. Possibly…

$5 \times \frac{1}{2}$ and

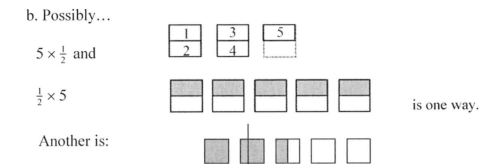

$\frac{1}{2} \times 5$

is one way.

Another is:

c. Did you get 25 different possibilities?

2. Sometimes the difficulty is coming up with a context in which the numbers you want to involve are not realistic. For whole numbers, think of things that are usually counted; for fractions or decimals, think of things that are measured.

3. Not any fraction, but multiplying by a fraction less than 1. If the multiplier is a whole number or a fraction greater than 1, then "multiplication makes bigger" is correct.

4. Repeated addition does not make sense for $^{-}2 \times 4$ (what on earth could it mean?) or $\frac{2}{3} \times 8$ (add 8, two-thirds times??), but it does for the others: $^{-}2 + ^{-}2 + ^{-}2 + ^{-}2$ and $\frac{2}{3} + \frac{2}{3} + \frac{2}{3} + \frac{2}{3} + \frac{2}{3} + \frac{2}{3} + \frac{2}{3} + \frac{2}{3}$.

5. 6 twelves, plus $\frac{1}{2}$ twelve—a repeated-addition multiplication as well as a part-of-an-amount multiplication.

6. a. Just a sample: How much will 32 pencils cost at 29¢ each? (answer in pennies)

b. The situation will likely involve four copies or four groups of 6.98.

c. The situation may involve 7% of the number.

d. Make sure that the situation would involve twelve $\frac{3}{8}$'s.

e. Make sure that $\frac{2}{3}$ of six (pizzas?) is featured.

f. One can imagine situations such as discounts.

7. a. Eight chicken breasts, $1\frac{1}{3}$ cups onion, $1\frac{1}{3}$ tbsp olive oil, $2\frac{2}{3}$ cups apples, $1\frac{1}{3}$ tbsp margarine, 2 cups apple juice, $3\frac{1}{3}$ tbsp honey, $\frac{2}{3}$ tsp salt

b. Four chicken breasts, $\frac{2}{3}$ cup onion, $\frac{2}{3}$ Tbsp olive oil, $1\frac{1}{3}$ cups apples, $\frac{2}{3}$ tbsp margarine, 1 cup apple juice, $1\frac{2}{3}$ tbsp honey, $\frac{1}{3}$ tsp salt

8. a and b. Mimic the 3×5 and 5×3 example.

c. To do the 90°-turn technique might be a bit strained here because the approach in #1, part (b), seems more natural. But one could *start* with something like the second drawing in #1, part (b), and "see" the $6 \times \frac{1}{2}$. Alternatively (and similarly to the second drawing, with the squares right next to each other), use an area approach with a rectangular region 6 units by $\frac{1}{2}$ unit.

9. a. Property: Multiplication is distributive over addition.

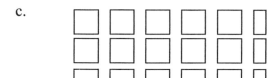

      6   2   6   2

b. Note that no drawing is called for. A demonstration might be as follows:

    $3 \times (4 \times 5) = 3 \times 20 = 60$

    $(3 \times 4) \times 5 = 12 \times 5 = 60$

c.

If turned 90 degrees, this would show 6.5×3. The area is the same for both.

10.   a.   R1, R2, R3, R4, R5, R6

           W1, W2, W3, W4, W5, W6

           B1, B2, B3, B4, B5, B6

           G1, G2, G3, G4, G5, G6

Thus, the answer is 24. The rest are not listed: only the final number is provided.

    b. 12   c. 20   d. 36

11. $2^8 = 256$, so there must be eight ways to choose between two things to arrive at 256 different kinds of hamburgers.

12. a. 62

    b. Counting the orders as different gives $31 \times 31 \times 2 = 1922$ possibilities. Counting vanilla on top of chocolate as the same as chocolate on top of vanilla illustrates that, when order is not important, the problems are more involved: Count the flavors, different ones first, then the same flavors. There are $31 \times 30 = 930$ ordered choices of different flavors, but that counts, say, van-choc and choc-van, twice, so there are $930 \div 2 = 465$ possibilities for different flavors, plus the 31 both-same-flavor possibilities, for 496 choices for the two scoops. Each can go with either cone, giving 992 in all.

13. $(3 \times 4 \times 3) \times 12,486$, with the first multiplications from the fundamental counting principle and the last from repeated addition: $449,496.

14. a. See (b).

    b. $26^2 \cdot 10^4$ is 6,760,000 and 10^6 is 1,000,000, so 5,760,000 larger. 6.76 times as large.

    c. Answers vary. Decisions likely relate to the number of possibilities.

15. a. 77.1   b. 0.76 (or just .76)   c. 17.85   d. 1.46   e. 0.14924   f. 0.09022

16. 9,039,600,000 miles, from $13.5 \times (60 \times 60) \times 186000$, where 60×60 tells the number of seconds in one hour. Can you read, in words, the 9,039,600,000?

17. 86,400 seconds in a day, from $24 \times (60 \times 60)$

18. 31,536,000 seconds in a 365-day year, from $365 \times 24 \times 60 \times 60$ or, using Exercise 17, 365×864000

19. 5,865,696,000,000 miles! (Can you read that answer, in words?) Using Exercise 18, $31,536,000 \times 186,000$. Example 5 in Section 5.4 also addresses the length of a light year.

20. a. $\frac{2}{3} \times (4 - 1\frac{3}{4}) = n$ Notice the order of the factors. Final answer, if required: $1\frac{1}{2}$ cups

   b. $\frac{1}{2} \times 2\frac{1}{4} = n$ Notice the order of the factors. Final answer, if required: $1\frac{1}{8}$ cups

   c. $5 \times 3 = n$ will tell the number of biscuits needed (notice the order of the factors). Then one way is to notice that 15 biscuits is one full recipe plus $\frac{6}{9}$ of another, and so $(1 + \frac{6}{9}) \times 2\frac{1}{4} = m$ or the equation $2\frac{1}{4} + (\frac{6}{9} \times 2\frac{1}{4}) = x$ will give the number of cups needed. Final answer, if required: $3\frac{3}{4}$ cups. It may be that you think of a proportion, such as

   $$\frac{2\frac{1}{4}}{9} = \frac{x}{5 \times 3}$$; proportions will come up later.

21. $4 \times 3 = n$. Final answer, if required: 12 possible orders

22. $(20 \times 25) + (12 \times 18) = n$. Final answer, if required: 716

23. For Exercise 16: repeated additions, with the 13.5 involving a part-of-an-amount for the half.
   For Exercise 17: repeated additions
   For Exercise 18: repeated addition(s)
   For Exercise 19: repeated addition
   For Exercises 20: part of a quantity multiplication
   For Exercise 21: fundamental counting principle
   For Exercise 22: (two) arrays, although you could defend repeated additions

24. In $5 \times 3 = 3 + 3 + 3 + 3 + 3$, there are only 4 additions.

Supplementary Learning Exercises for Section 3.4

1. To find the total when a number of same-sized quantities are combined (repeated-addition multiplication); to find the area of a rectangle or the number in an array (area or array multiplication); to find a fractional part of a quantity (part-of-an-amount multiplication); to find the number of possible occurrences of two or more events in succession (fundamental-counting principle).

2. With the repeated-addition view, 4 × 3 should be shown as 4 groups, each with 3 objects, and 3 × 4 as 3 groups, each with 4 objects. With the array/area view, 4 × 3 would have 4 rows with 3 in each row, and 3 × 4 would have 3 rows with 4 in each row. These would be the most common ways of showing 4 × 3 and 3 × 4.

3. Commutativity of multiplication (4 × 3 = 3 × 4)

4. Samples; be sure that your problem reflects the order of the factors (not in the written story as reported, but in the meaning for the operation).

    a. At $1.99 a bag, how much would Sean pay for 5 bags of chips?

    b. For a project, the teacher figures that she needs 12 pieces of construction paper for each of her 35 students. How many pieces of paper will she need?

    c. Dana bought 6 packages of dates, each of which weighed $\frac{3}{4}$ pound. How many pounds of dates did she buy?

    d. Eddie bought a six-pound bag of grapefruit and gave away $\frac{3}{4}$ of the bag to his relatives. How many pounds did he give away?

5. a. Your equation for associativity should follow the form $a \times (b \times c) = (a \times b) \times c$, or $(a \times b) \times c = a \times (b \times c)$. The two sides should calculate to give the same answer.

    b. Your equation for distributivity should be of one of the forms

    $a \times (b + c) = (a \times b) + (a \times c)$ OR $(a \times b) + (a \times c) = a \times (b + c)$ OR

    $(b + c) \times a = (b \times a) + (c \times a)$ OR $(b \times a) + (c \times a) = (b + c) \times a$. Again, the two sides should calculate to give the same answer.

6. a. Fundamental counting principle

    b. Repeated-addition multiplication

    c. Part-of-an-amount multiplication

    d. Array multiplication, or possibly repeated-addition multiplication

7. Part (a) should yield a tree diagram. Contrast your drawings for parts (b) and (c)—they should be different! Diagram for part (d) likely is an array.

8. a. $\frac{92}{113}$ is less than 1, so the product will be less than $\frac{578}{234}$.

    b. $\frac{578}{234}$ is greater than 1, so the product will be greater than $\frac{92}{113}$.

9. a. <u>multiplier</u> × <u>multiplicand</u> = <u>product</u>

b.   <u>factor</u> × <u>factor</u> = <u>product</u>

10. Any multiplication with a fraction less than 1.

11.
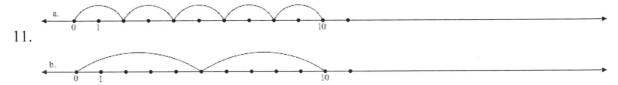

12. 4 × 3. Notice the order of the factors.

13. Apparently the student has not had experience with story problems involving the fundamental counting principle (or the student has forgotten it).

14. Only one was going to St. Ives! The others were going the opposite way. But other interpretations of the situation are possible, so if you use the riddle with children, you may hear other answers. See Wikipedia for the St. Ives riddle.

3.5 Ways of Thinking about Division

1. Answers may vary.

2. Repeated-subtraction: Put 12 into groups of 3: xxx xxx xxx xxx (four groups)

    Sharing: "Deal out" 12 into 3 equal groups: xxxx xxxx xxxx (four in each group)

3. Samples:

    a. The 12 friends picked 150 pints of strawberries. How many pints will each get if they split them evenly?

    b. Some friends picked 150 pints of strawberries. If they put them in flats of 12, how many flats will they have?

    c. Four friends on a hike have 3 liters of water. How much water is that for each person?

    d. How much of an empty four-liter container will three liters fill?

4. Division with the divisor as a fraction or decimal less than 1 will give a quotient greater than the dividend.

5. b. Sample: Abe went up the long trail and came down by the 3.5-km one. Bert went up and down the 2.4-km trail. Who walked farther, and by how much?

    c. The workers put up 3 trail markers on the 4.5-km trail, spaced equally. How far apart are the signs?

    d. You can hike 3 km in an hour on trails like the 4.5-km one. How long should you plan for going up the 4.5-km trail?

    e. Sample: A runner prepares for a 10K run by running on Mt. Azteca. How many times would it take her to run the 2.4-km trail to make 10 km?

6. a. In the testing, eighth graders would give the results of the division calculation, $1500 \div 36$ ($41\frac{2}{3}$ or 41 R 24), as though those were the number of buses needed. But the company should actually supply 42 buses.

   b. i. 38

      ii. 4. Did you get your answer from the division calculation?

7. Samples: About how many ounces do they expect to get per acre (sharing division)? How many tons of ore and rock do they have to process to get an ounce of gold (sharing division)? How much will they get for each ounce of gold (sharing division)? How many tons can they process each year (sharing division)?

8. a. Repeated subtraction. Draw a large rectangle for the 900-kg piece, and then mark off some smaller 12-kg pieces to get the idea across. The division tells how many there would be (75).

   b. Sharing. Use a rectangle for the 525 kg with several pretend-1-kg pieces shown, and then draw arrows to 3 empty spaces for the weeks to show the 1-kg pieces being distributed equally.

   c. Sharing.

   d. Repeated subtraction. (Think how you would act it out.)

   e. Sharing.

   f. Repeated subtraction, although it does not really require calculation.

9. 8, 8, 8, 8, 8. $10^{n}a \div 10^{n}b = a \div b$.

10. Answers will vary.

Supplementary Learning Exercises for Section 3.5

1. The repeated subtraction view entails removing or indicating groups of 2, giving three groups. The sharing equally view entails putting the 6 into 2 equal groups, giving 3 in each group.

2. a. and b. 1620 is the dividend, 36 the divisor, and 45 the quotient. Notice the different orders of the 1620 and the 36 in the two forms.

3. a. There will be 9 groups of 10, with 6 left over.

    b. There will be 9 in each of the 10 groups, with 6 left over.

4. a. No number makes sense. Removing 0 things from 6 things any number of times will never use up the 6.

    b. There are too many answers. Any number of removals of 0 things from 0 things makes sense.

    c. The related $n \times 0 = 6$ has no values for n that check.

    d. In the related $n \times 0 = 0$, *every* value for n checks.

5. Samples: check that yours do fit the indicated views.
   a. There are 150 children in Grades 5–6. How many teams of 5 children can be made for playground clean-up duty?
   b. There are 150 children in Grades 5–6. There are 5 buses available to take them on a field trip. How many children will be on each bus to keep the loads as equal as possible?
   c. The area of a rectangular banner that is 5 inches tall is 150 square inches. How long is the banner?

6. a. There are 23 fourteens in 322 (or 23 fourteens make 322).
   b. With 322, each of 14 equal shares will have 23.
   c. The solution to either $n \times 14 = 322$ or $14 \times n = 322$ is 23.

7. a. Sharing-equally division. $12 \times n = 168$ indicates that there are 12 groups of unknown size, totaling 168.
   b. Repeated-subtraction division. $n \times 12 = 168$ indicates that there is an unknown number of groups of size 12, totaling 168.

8. a. 500 seconds (from $93,000,000 \div 186,000$)
   b. $8\frac{1}{3}$ minutes (from $500 \div 60$)
   c. Both can be viewed as repeated-subtraction divisions.

9. There are different possibilities. Check to see that your finishes do fit the given ways of thinking about division.

10. a. The 15 meters is cut into 6 equal pieces.
    b. The 15 meters is cut into pieces each 2.5 meters long.

11. Do you have 3 equal pieces (for sharing-equally), or do you have pieces each 3 units long (for repeated-subtraction)?

12. It is praiseworthy that the child is trying to make sense of $0 \div 0$, but the child does not seem to be attending any meaning of division. You might say: "I see what you're thinking. But what does the division sign mean?"

13. You might ask the child how you can check a division by multiplying, say, $12 \div 6 = 2$ — probably easier to answer from the algorithm form $6\overline{)12}$. Then ask how the child could check $0 \div 0 = 100$.

14. If you are not sure, read Discussion 5.

15. 17, from $(12 \times 500) \div 350 = 17 \, R \, 50$ (repeated-addition multiplication, repeated-subtraction division)

16. 19.2 miles (if you and your friend are along a straight line from you to the lightning). One way: You and your friend are 1.5 minutes apart. The sound will travel $768 \div 60 = 12.8$ miles

in one minute. Then $1.5 \times 12.8 = 19.2$. Another way is to calculate how far each of you are from the lightning, and then subtract.

3.6 Children Find Products and Quotients

1. The first student's method is related to estimating because she first estimated the quotient to be between 2080 and 2240, then found the remainder to obtain the exact answer.

2. Possibly: $10 + 10 + 10 + 10 = 40$. $6 \div 4 = 1$ rem 2. $10 \div 4 = 2$ rem 2. $2 + 2 = 4$. $4 \div 4 = 1$. So $10 + 1 + 2 + 1 = 14$. Note that the student knows that there are ten 4s, then one 4 (in 6) then two 4s (in the other 10, ten make 50), then one 4 (from the remainders).

3. Advantages: Attaches repeated-subtraction to division conceptually; need not make best guesses (as in eventual algorithm); involves familiar subtraction rather than multiplication. Others advantages?

   Disadvantages: Slower; must understand a meaning for division (is this a disadvantage?); many subtractions so there is more possibility of error. Other disadvantages?

4. The method used here is taught by some teachers because the steps are more easily understood than the traditional algorithm most of us learned. The major advantage of this method is that it can be easily understood, based on the subtraction notion of division. We ask: How many 27s are in 3247? We know there are at least 100 because $27 \times 100 = 2700$ is less than 3247, so we first subtract one hundred 27s. We could next take away ten 27s, or we could take away twenty 27s; the choice depends on one's number facility. This is another advantage. The disadvantage is that it takes longer than the standard algorithm (but perhaps not if one counts all the additional time needed to learn the standard algorithm for division).

5. This procedure was invented by a very precocious child. Most first graders would not have been able to do this. However, prospective teachers should recognize that they will sometimes have very bright students whose thinking is not always easily followed.

   To find $63 \div 9$:
   $60 \div 10 = 6$
   $6 + 3 = 9$
   $9 \div 9 = 1$
   $6 + 1 = 7$, so $63 \div 9 = 7$

6. Answers will vary.

Supplementary Learning Exercises for Section 3.6

1. In the first division, the child apparently saw the $28 \div 4$ and passed over the tens place in the quotient. In the second division, the child calculated correctly but was mixing up the "R" format (R = 2 here) with the fraction form $\frac{\text{remainder}}{\text{divisor}}$.

2. It appears that the child is carrying over the algorithms from addition and subtraction in which the calculation is handled a place value at a time. So the child does 3×2 and 2×4, not realizing that the 3 also multiplies the 40 in the top factor and the 2(0) from the factor underneath also multiplies the 2 in the top factor.

3. a. 4×432 b. $520 \div 15$

4. Yes, the technique and its generalization are all right. The $560 \div 20$ might be seen as how many 2-tens are in 56-tens, but it may be easier to use what you may remember: $x \div y$ is equal to $\frac{x}{y}$ (this relationship is examined in Section 6.1). Then $(na) \div (nb) = \frac{na}{nb} = \frac{a}{b}$.

3.7 Issues for Learning: Developing Number Sense

1. a. $135 + 98$ because each addend is greater than the corresponding addend in $114 + 92$

    b. $46 - 17$ because more is taken away in $46 - 19$

    c. $1\frac{1}{2}$ because $\frac{3}{4} < 1$

    d. $0.0016 + 0.313$ because the 3 tenths in the sum is itself greater than 0.0358

2. 46×91 is less than $5000 = 50 \times 100$ ($46 < 50$, and $91 < 100$) but more than $3600 = 40 \times 90$ ($46 > 40$, $91 > 90$).

3.

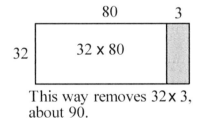

This way removes 32×3, about 90.

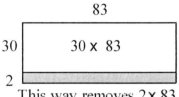

This way removes 2×83, about 160.

Thus, more is lost the second way, so the first way gives a closer estimate.

Or, if 32 is rounded to 30 and the 83 is not rounded, the answer is off by 2×83, or about 160. If 83 is rounded to 80 and the 32 is not rounded, the answer is off by 3×32, or about 90, so rounding the 83 yields a closer estimate. (The temptation is to say "round the 32 because only 2 is being dropped, but if 83 is rounded to 80, 3 is being dropped.")

4. a. All of the addends have 0 in the ones place, so the sum can't have a 1.

    b. The addend 940 itself is more than 602.

    c. I know that $25 \times 3 = 75$, so 27×3 will be a little more, not 621.

    d. I am asking how many halves are in 36. The answer will be a whole number.

5. a. Necessarily false   b. Necessarily false   c. Possibly true

    d. Necessarily true   e. Necessarily true

6. a. 47 and 52 are "compatible," adding to about 100, and 36 and 69 are somewhat compatible, with sum about 100. Sum about $200 + 20$ or 30: 220 or 230.
    b. About 40×40, or 1600
    c. $1200 - 900$ is easy to calculate.
    d. $35,000 \div 50 = 700$

e. $26 + 74 = 100$, $79 + 19 \approx 100$, so about 200 to 210

f. $4200 \div 70 = 60$

7. a. Repeated subtraction: There will be more 9.35s in 56 than there are 10s.

   Sharing: "Splitting" 56 into 10 amounts will give less than splitting it into fewer than 10 amounts.

   b. The 71.5 is obtained from $715 \div 10$. Repeated subtraction: There will be fewer 10.2146s in 715 than there are 10s. Sharing: Sharing 715 among more than 10 will give smaller amounts than sharing among 10.

8. 0.68×5 is trivial compared to 0.34×150, which is about a third of 150.

9. Each digit-place value in each numeral is multiplied by each digit-place value in the other numeral, so there is not the "nice" place-value by place-value consideration that exists with addition and subtraction.

Answers for Chapter 4: Some Conventional Ways of Computing

4.1 Operating on Whole Numbers and Decimal Numbers

1. a. Let the flat be the unit because a unit that can be cut into hundredths is needed. Then large cubes represent tens, longs represent tenths, and small cubes represent hundredths.

> Step 1. Lay out two rows: The first has 5 large cubes, 6 flats, and 2 longs. Directly below are 3 large cubes, 4 flats, 5 longs, and 2 small cubes.

> Step 2. Begin filling a third row. First bring down (directly below) the small cubes; there are 2 thousandths.

> Step 3. Bring down (to the third row) the longs. There are 7, representing 7 tenths.

> Step 4. Bring down the flats. There are 10. Trade for a large cube and place the cube in the next left column with the other cubes. The flats column is now empty, representing 0 ones.

> Step 5. Bring down all the large cubes. There are 8 plus the one from Step 4, for a total of 9, representing 9 tens.

> Step 6. Write down the number represented, from left to right: 9 cubes, 0 flats, 7 longs, and 2 small cubes, representing 90.62.

b. Choose a unit that can show hundredths (because of the 0.39) say, a flat. Then 0.39 is 3 longs and 9 small cubes. Show four of these amounts. For the usual algorithm, work with the small cubes first, noticing that you can trade 30 of them for 3 longs (0.3), to go with the four groups of 3 longs already there. Since there are now 15 longs, 10 of them can be traded for a flat. Final display: 1 flat, 5 longs, 6 small cubes. This represents 1.56.

c. 45.6 – 21.21

> i. Using the flat as the unit, place 4 large cubes, 5 flats, and 6 longs on the table.

> ii. Trade 1 long for 10 small cubes, and remove 1 small cube, leaving 4 large cubes, 5 flats, 5 longs, and 9 small cubes. (0.01 has been removed.)

> iii. Remove 2 longs, leaving 4 large cubes, 5 flats, 3 longs, and 9 small cubes. (0.2 has been removed.)

> iv. Remove 1 flat, leaving 4 large cubes, 4 flats, 3 longs, and 9 small cube. (1 has been removed.)

> v. Remove 2 large cubes, leaving 2 large cubes, 4 flats, 3 longs, and 9 small cubes.

> (20 have been removed.) The remaining blocks represent 24.39.

d. $2912 \div 8$

> Here is one way this could be acted out and written, using the sharing notion of division. The small block is used to represent 1.

> Place or draw 2 blocks, 9 flats, 1 long, and 2 small blocks. Write: $8\overline{)2912}$

Think of how to place the blocks in 8 piles with the same amount in each pile. Change the 2 blocks to 20 flats; there are now 29 flats; place 3 in each of 8 piles.

$$
\begin{array}{r}
3 \\
8\overline{)2912} \\
\underline{24} \\
5
\end{array}
$$

There are 5 remaining flats. Change them to longs; there are now 51 longs.

Distribute the longs; there will be 6 longs in each pile, with 3 longs remaining.

$$
\begin{array}{r}
36 \\
8\overline{)2912} \\
\underline{24} \\
51 \\
\underline{48} \\
3
\end{array}
$$

Change the 3 longs to 30 units. There are now 32 units. Distribute them to the piles, 4 per pile.

$$
\begin{array}{r}
364 \\
8\overline{)2912} \\
\underline{24} \\
51 \\
\underline{48} \\
32 \\
\underline{32}
\end{array}
$$

In each pile there are 3 flats, 6 longs, and 4 units per pile. The quotient is therefore 364.

2. These involve just whole numbers, so the small cube can be the unit. It is instructive to act them out with base materials or toothpicks, noticing the trades.

   a. 1123_{five} b. 1_{six}

3. Answers will vary. Look for some attention to separate partial products and quotient pieces.

4. Samples, with 57×623

$$
\begin{array}{r}
57 \times623 \\
28 \times \cancel{1246} \\
14 \times \cancel{2492} \\
7 \times 4984 \\
3 \times 9968 \\
1 \times 19936 \\
\hline
35511
\end{array}
$$

5. a.   500 (twice as many as for $4000 \div 16$)

b. 1000 (e.g., four times as many as for 4000 ÷ 16)

c. 125 (half as many as for 4000 ÷ 16)

d. 125 (half as many as for 4000 ÷ 16 because 32 is twice 16)

e. $62\frac{1}{2}$ (half as many as for 4000 ÷ 32)

f. 500 (twice as many as for 4000 ÷ 16)

g. 1000

h. 10,000

6.   Lining up the decimal points for addition and subtraction assures that digits with the same place values are aligned. This alignment is not necessary for multiplication.

7.

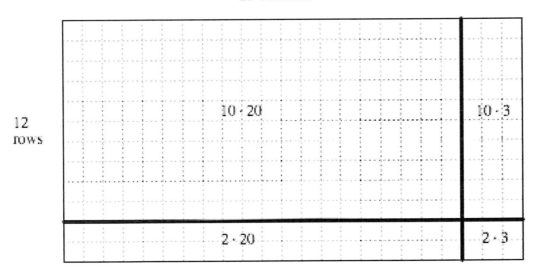

8.   a. Start with 3 flats, 9 longs, and 6 small cubes. Start with the flats, and put 1 flat into each of 3 separate piles. Continue with the longs, putting 3 longs into each of the started piles. Finally put 2 small cubes into each pile, giving 1 flat, 3 longs, and 2 small cubes in each pile. The answer is 132. Trying a repeated-subtraction is not practical, because removing only 3 small cubes 132 times would involve extensive trading and a lot of time.

b. Proceed much as in part (a), but the 2 flats will have to be traded for 20 longs (giving 25 longs), and after putting 6 longs into each of 4 piles, trade the remaining 1 long for 10 small cubes, giving 12 small cubes to be shared. There should be 6 longs and 3 small cubes in each of the four piles: 63.

c. This time, after trading the flat for 10 longs, sharing, trading the remaining 2 longs for 20 small cubes (giving 27 small cubes), and sharing, there are 3 small cubes remaining. The answer is 46 R 3.

9.   a. Repeat-subtraction is much more practical when the divisor is large. Start with 2 flats, 8 longs, and 4 small cubes. You can remove 1 flat, 4 longs, and 2 small cubes twice, so the answer is 2.

b. Start with 9 flats and 6 longs. You can remove 3 flats and 2 longs three times, so the answer is 3.

c. Start with 1 large cube, but trade it first for 10 flats, then one of the flats for 10 longs, and one of the longs for 10 small cubes. The status at this point is 9 flats, 9 longs, and 10 small cubes. Remove 2 flats, 7 longs, and 5 small cubes (one 275), leaving 7 flats, 2 longs, and 5 small cubes. Trade a flat for 10 longs, giving 6 flats, 12 longs, and 5 small cubes. Remove 2 flats, 7 longs and 5 small cubes (a second 275), and leaving 4 flats and 5 longs. Continue trading to get a third 275. There will be 1 flat, 7 longs, and 5 small cubes remaining. Hence, $1000 \div 275 = 3 \text{ r } 175$.

10. $127 \times 25 = 3175$

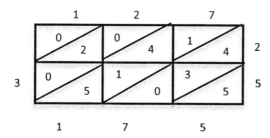

Supplementary Learning Exercises for Section 4.1

1.   Part (a) is not illustrated because the digit (0) for the flat place value is missing. The other parts are all right. Part (b) has the small cube as the unit. Part (c) has the long as the unit. Part (d) has the large cube as the unit. In part (e), the pieces could be base seven pieces.

2.   Letting the small cube be the unit, you could show 1 flat, 3 longs, and 6 small cubes. Because it is to be take-away, you want to remove 8 longs and 9 small cubes. To support the usual algorithm, you would start with the small cubes. Because there are only 6 small cubes and you want to remove 9, you will have to trade 1 long for 10 small cubes (and this is exactly what you do symbolically), giving 1 flat, 2 longs, and 16 small cubes. Removing 9 small cubes leaves 7 small cubes. Dealing with the longs will involve another trade, getting 10 more longs for the flat (as in the algorithm). At this stage, there are 12 longs (and 7 small cubes), so you can remove 8 longs, leaving 4 longs and 7 small cubes, for 47.

3.   (It is worthwhile to contrast how you worked Exercise 2.) You will start with two displays, one being 1 flat, 3 longs, 6 small cubes, and the other being 8 longs and 9 small cubes. To compare the small cubes first (to support the usual algorithm), you would again need to trade, as in exercise 2, and find that there are 7 more small cubes in the display for 136. Another trade of the flat for 10 longs allows you to compare the (now) 12 longs and 8 longs, showing that there are 4 more longs from the 136 display. Notice that the answer is perhaps less visible using the comparison method.

4.   (It is worthwhile to contrast Exercises 2 and 3.) For the missing-addend view, you want to mimic $89 + ? = 136$, so you will start with 8 longs and 9 small cubes. This start makes it

difficult to lead to the usual algorithm, which shows that missing-addend is not a good starting point if you have in mind leading to, or supporting, the usual algorithm. Nonetheless, you can keep adding to the 8 longs and 9 small cubes, with trades necessary to get to the final 1 flat, 3 longs, 6 small cubes.

5. Using take-away and the long as the unit (why the long?), you would start with 5 flats, 2 longs, and 3 small cubes. Trades would enable you to remove 6 small cubes, 4 longs, and 3 flats, leaving 1 flat, 7 longs, and 7 small cubes, or 17.7.

6. Three groups, each with 2 longs and 4 small cubes, would allow you to focus on the 3 groups of 4 small cubes (the usual algorithm starts with the ones), trading 10 for a long and combining that with the 3 groups of 2 longs to get 7 longs and a product of 72. Notice that the 3 is not illustrated with 3 small cubes, but as the 3 groups.

7. You need only change the unit from the small cube to something that would allow hundredths. The flat would work for 3×0.24, and the large cube for 3×0.024. Otherwise, the display would be the same.

8.

So, $286 \times 492 = 140,712$

9. a. Think $64 = 2 \times 32$, so $64 \times 95 = (2 \times 32) \times 95 = 2 \times (32 \times 95) = 2 \times 3040 = 6080$. (You would probably think, "Oh, just twice as much.")

b. 9120   c. 12160   d. 95   e. Half as many, or 47.5   f. 190

10. Each gives the same product, because the first factor has been halved and the second factor doubled, in effect multiplying by 1: $\frac{1}{2} \times 2 = 1$. Part (d) is easiest to do mentally.

Answers for Chapter 5: Using Numbers in Sensible Ways

5.1 Mental Computation

1. These are some possible ways:

   a. $43 \times (10 - 1) = 430 - 43$ (using the distributive property) $= 430 - 30 - 13 = 387$

   b. $23(98 + 2)$ (using the distributive property) $= 23 \times 100 = 2300$

   c. $72 \times 30 = (70 + 2) \times 30 = 70 \times 30 + 2 \times 30 = 2100 + 60 = 2160$

2. These are some possible ways:

   a. $365 + 35 + 40 = 400 + 40 = 440$ b. $758 - 30 = 728$ c. $1000 + 431 = 1431$

   d. $500 - 50 = 450$ e. $124 \times \frac{100}{4} = 31 \times 100 = 3100$ f. $43 - 30 = 13$

   g. $44 \times \frac{100}{4} = 11 \times 100 = 1100$

   h. $(0.75 \times 100) \times 88 = 100 \times 0.75 \times 88 = 100 \times 66 = 6600$

   i. $8 \times (30 + 2) = 240 + 16 = 256$ (Some students might use $2^3 \times 2^5 = 2^8 = 256$.)

3. a. $\frac{1}{4}$ of $60 = 15$ b. 7.8 c. 4.5

   d. $8 \times 10\%$ of $710 = 8 \times 71 = 8 \times 70 + 8 \times 1 = 560 + 8 = 568$

   (or $4 \times 20\%$ of $710 = 4 \times 142 = 400 + 160 + 8 = 568$)

   e. $6   f. 57

   g. $1\frac{1}{4} \times 40 = 50$ h. 100 i. 3.2

4. a. 120 b. 380 c. 89 d. 40

5. Draw all three diagonals. You have that the 6 parts are 120%, so each part is 20% and 5 parts is 100%.

6. First row: $\dfrac{1}{2}$ $\dfrac{1}{3}$ $\dfrac{3}{4}$; second row: $\dfrac{2}{3}$ $\dfrac{1}{8}$ $\dfrac{1}{5}$

Supplementary Learning Exercises for Section 5.1

1. a. 1567, seeing that $988 + 12 = 1000$ b. 211, using $67 + 33$, then $198 + (2 + 11)$

   c. 635, left-to-right   d. 3111.6, just $29 - 18$

   e. 3600   f. 1800, half as much as in part (e)

   g. 900, using (f), or every four 25s gives 100   h. 2700, 3 times as much as part (g)

   i. 1900 because nineteen 85s plus nineteen 15s is the same as nineteen (85 + 15)s— that is, the distributive property.

   j. 2300, because ninety-six 23s plus four 23s would be one hundred 23s.

2.   a. 850   b. 1700   c. 32   d. 320   e. $8 \times 32 = 256$

f. $13.20   g. $4.80   h. $7.50

5.2 Computational Estimation

1. 0.76 is about $\frac{3}{4}$ and 62 is about 60. $\frac{3}{4}$ of 60 is 45.

2. Now I want to be sure I have enough money, so I must be careful not to underestimate. I could say 80¢ × 60, or $48, would be close, and $50 (accounting for 2 more tablets) is more than enough.

3. The second. The first would be less than 84.63, and the second would be more than 84.63.

4. If I round the bill to $28, then 10% would be $2.80, half of that is $1.40, which together is $4.20. Or just round to $30, in which case 15% would be $3.00 + $1.50, or $4.50.

5. All of the ways shown are acceptable, depending on the degree of accuracy needed. Shawn's way is pretty far off. Jack's way is better because it focuses between an overestimate and an underestimate. Maria understands how rounding one factor up and the other down produces a fairly good estimate. Jimmy's way provides a very good estimate, perhaps more so than needed for many situations. Debbie's is just a little better than Shawn's. Sam's is good.

6. Only some ways of estimating the answers are shown here.

a. $50 \times 900 = 45000$

b. A few ways: $\frac{100}{4} \times 80 = 2000$ (so the estimate should be less than 2000)

$25 \times 76 \approx 25 \times 75 = 25 \times 25 \times 3 = 625 \times 3 = \underline{1875}$

or $25 \times 75 = 20 \times 75 + 5 \times 75 = 1500 + 375 = \underline{1875}$

or $25 \times 80 = 80 \times 25 = 8 \times 25 \times 10 = 2000$, so 25×76 is <u>a little less than 2000</u>

or $25 \times 80 = 5 \times 5 \times 80 = 5 \times 400 = 2000$, so 25×76 is <u>a little less than 2000</u>

or $20 \times 70 = 1400$ and $30 \times 80 = 2400$, so 25×76 is about in the middle of 1400 and 2400, which would be <u>about 1900</u>.

(There are more ways than what are shown here.)

c. $15 \times 650 = 10 \times 650 + 5 \times 650 \approx 6500 + $ half of $6500 \approx 6500 + 3200 = 9700$

d. 350×6000 is between 300×6000 and 400×6000, or between 1,800,000 and 2,400,000, so a good estimate would be 2,100,000.

e. $3 \times 500 + 3 \times 30$ is $1500 + 90 = 1590$

7. a. The price is about $\frac{1}{4}$ off $50, or $12.50 off. About $37.50.

b. The price is 15% of about $20, or $3 off—a little less since I rounded up. A little over $14. Or 10% of 17 + 5% of 17 is 1.7 + 0.65 = $2.35, and $17 − $2.35 is about $14.65.

c. 75% of $20 is $15. So the actual cost is about $5.

d. 40% of $110 is $44.

8. b. 32% is close to $\frac{1}{3}$, so an estimate is 4.

   c. Something under 500. 5% of 500 would be 25, so 475. (Here it is easy to get the exact answer, 470, since 94% of 100 is 94 and 500 is five 100s.)

   d. About $\frac{1}{2}$ of 800, or 400

   e. About $\frac{1}{4}$ of 80, or 20

   f. A bit more than $\frac{1}{3}$ of 21, or 7

   g. About $\frac{3}{4}$ of 200, or 150

9. a. The student does not realize that rounding the $19 to $20 takes care of the 95¢, and that the answer should be less than $20 \times \$20 = \$400$. A better estimate would be just $20 \times \$20 = \$400$.

   b. The student does not take advantage of the fact that 25.3% is about $\frac{1}{4}$. A better estimate would be 30.

   c. Similarly to part (b), the student does not recognize that treating 0.514 as one-half gives a much more sensible answer, 4.

Supplementary Learning Exercises for Section 5.2

1.   a. 10.5% is about one-tenth, so about $15.

     b. About 5% of $50, or about $2.50

     c. 10% would be about $7.50, so about $\frac{3}{4}$ of $7.50. Something under $6.

     d. A 10% tip would be about $1.70, so 15% would be about $1.70 + 0.85, or about $2.50.

2.   a. 35,000 (about 50×700)

     b. 33×40 is 66×20, or 1320. (You could add another 33, for 1353.)

     c. 4800 (about 8×600)

     d. $400 (about 2/3 of $600). If a closer estimate is needed, notice that $600 is about 15 more than $584.38, so since $\frac{2}{3}$ of 15 = 10, $390.

     e. A little less than $20 (about $\frac{1}{4}$ of $80)   f. $12 (one-third of $36)

5.3 Estimating Values of Quantities

No answers are given for Section 5.3.
(Instructor: Students do not have answers to any of these exercises.)

1. These are some possibilities:

    a. 3 miles is about 30 city blocks. (Of course, sizes of blocks vary, so this needs to be adjusted to where you live.)

    b. Runners may picture 5 10Ks.

    c. This is likely based on where an individual lives.

    d. 3000 miles is approximately the distance from the west coast to the east coast of the United States.

    e. 30,000 miles is crossing the country 10 times and may be about the number of miles needed for a free airline ticket for frequent flyers.

2. Divide each by your usual speed to get the number of hours. For example, if you drive 50 miles per hour, divide each by 50. If the number of hours is large, you can divide that by 24 to get the number of days, then by 7 to get the number of weeks, or by 365 to get the number of years. . .

3. Student answers will vary.

4. When discussing this problem, keep in mind that in the year 2000, the net budget outlay for the United States was $1,788,000,000, which is getting close to $2 trillion.

Supplementary Learning Exercises for Section 5.3

1. About 400, using a class size of about 30.

2. You can check how your benchmark worked by actually measuring.

3. 25 pounds or more, depending on the size of raccoons in your area.

5.4 Using Scientific Notation for Estimating Values of Very Large and Very Small Quantities

1. a. 1.836×10^7 b. 2.04×10^2 c. 2.04×10^{-2}

2. See page A-2.

3. a. 9.9×10^{18} b. 3×10^{-4} c. 8×10^{-17} d. 2.1×10^3

4. a. 1.5×10^9 b. 4.27×10^{12}

5. $314 \times 10^4 + 2.315 \times 10^4 = 316.315 \times 10^4 \approx 3.16 \times 10^6$. Numbers must have the same power of ten to be added.

6. Calculator exercise (no answers given).

7. Suppose n is 5. Then $2n$ is 10; $2^n = 32$; $n^2 = 25$; $10^n = 100,000$.

8. 277,777.8 hours, 11,574.1 days, 31.7 years

9. Computer search engine

10. A gigabyte. 2^{30} is 1,073,741,824. See http://encyclopedia.thefreedictionary.com/gigabyte

Supplementary Learning Exercises for Section 5.4

1.　The first factor is not ≥ 1 and < 10. 21.7×10^5 should be 2.17×10^6.

2.　a. 5,804,000　　b. 8,000,000,000　　c. 186,000　　d. 3,900,000,000,000

　　e. 0.0175　　f. 0.00002703　　g. 0.000000074　h. 0.0052368

3　a. 2.6829×10^{13}　　b. 8.236×10^3　　c. 9.45×10^8

　　d. $4.18923722 \times 10^{-1}$　e. 2.3×10^{-1}　　f. 4.85×10^{-4}

4.　1 thousand = 10^3; 1 million = 10^6; 1 billion (US) = 10^9; 1 trillion (US) = 10^{12}

5.　a. $26 \times 10^9 = 2.6 \times 10^{10}$　　b. 5×10^5　c. $26 \times 10^{12} = 2.6 \times 10^{13}$

6.　a. 4.2×10^{10}
　　b. 6.8×10^{13}
　　c. $23 \times 10^{10} = 2.3 \times 10 \times 10^{10} = 2.3 \times 10^{11}$
　　d. 1 million = 10^6, so $5 \times 4 \times 10^{3+6} = 20 \times 10^9 = 2 \times 10 \times 10^9 = 2 \times 10^{10}$

7.　If your display allows 8 digits, the largest number (without scientific notation) is 99,999,999.

8.　a. 10^8 = 100 million, so 5×10^{-8} = five hundred-million<u>ths</u>, or 0.000 000 05
　　b. 10^4 = 10 thousand, so 166×10^{-4} = one hundred sixty-six ten-thousand<u>ths</u>, or 0.0166
　　c. 10^6 = 1 million, so 19×10^{-6} = nineteen million<u>ths</u>, or 0.000 019

Answers for Chapter 6: Meanings for Fractions

6.1 Understanding the Meanings of $\frac{a}{b}$

1. Infinitely many ways, even with straight cuts! Cuts through the point where the diagonals intersect will give two congruent and therefore same-sized pieces. Curved or zigzag cuts through that point can also give halves.

2. a. One possibility: A circular region marked into three equal parts with two parts shaded.

   b. One possibility: Two circular regions, with the second marked off in fourths. Shade in all of the first circle and three parts of the second circle.

   c. One possibility: Three circles, with the third marked off in eighths. Shade all of the first two circles and shade 3 parts of the third circle.

   d. One possibility: A rectangular region could be marked into four equal pieces, with none shaded.

   e. One possibility: Three rectangular regions are shaded (showing that $3 = \frac{3}{1}$).

3. Be sure to contrast parts (a) and (b). In part (a), the unit is the whole piece of licorice whip. In part (b), the unit is the segment between any two consecutive whole numbers, and the labeling convention would have the $\frac{3}{4}$ in only one place. Mark halfway between 0 and 1, then halfway between $\frac{1}{2}$ and 1. The second mark is at $\frac{3}{4}$.

4. John's unit: the whole cake

   Maria's unit: Just the remaining $\frac{3}{4}$ of the cake was there for Maria.

5. a. Two square regions of the same size, each marked into 2 equal pieces, with 3 of the pieces shaded.

   b. Start with 3 square regions; how you show the division can vary. Think of how 3 brownies could be shared by 2 people. One way would be to cut one brownie in half: $3 \div 2$. Each person gets $\frac{3}{2}$, or $1\frac{1}{2}$, brownies. Another way would be to cut each brownie in half; then each person would receive three halves.

6. a. Hexagon = 1; trapezoid = $\frac{1}{2}$; blue rhombus = $\frac{1}{3}$; triangle = $\frac{1}{6}$

   b. Hexagon = 2; trapezoid = 1; blue rhombus = $\frac{2}{3}$; triangle = $\frac{1}{3}$

   c. Hexagon = $\frac{1}{2}$; trapezoid = $\frac{1}{4}$; blue rhombus = $\frac{1}{6}$; triangle = $\frac{1}{12}$

7. Here are several, without distinguishing between different orders of the fractions (different orders might make different visual appearances with pattern blocks): $\frac{1}{2} + \frac{1}{2} = 1$, $\frac{1}{2} + \frac{1}{3} + \frac{1}{6} = 1$, $\frac{1}{2} + \frac{1}{6} + \frac{1}{6} + \frac{1}{6} = 1$, $\frac{1}{3} + \frac{1}{3} + \frac{1}{3} = 1$, $\frac{1}{3} + \frac{1}{3} + \frac{1}{6} + \frac{1}{6} = 1$, $\frac{1}{3} + \frac{1}{6} + \frac{1}{6} + \frac{1}{6} + \frac{1}{6} = 1$, $\frac{1}{6} + \frac{1}{6} + \frac{1}{6} + \frac{1}{6} + \frac{1}{6} + \frac{1}{6} = 1$.

8. Instructor note: Student work must include drawings.

9. Drawings should show that each of the following is the larger of two fractions.

   a. $\dfrac{3}{4}$　　　　　　　　b. $\dfrac{4}{7}$　　　　　　　　c. $\dfrac{1}{8}$

   d. $\frac{12}{17}$ is larger because something cut into 17 equal pieces gives larger pieces than something cut into 19 equal pieces does, and there are 12 pieces in each.

   e. $\frac{11}{9}$　　　　　　　　　f. $\frac{62}{101}$ is larger (see the reasoning for part (d)).

10. a. A is fair, B is fair (each piece is a quarter of the total rectangle), C is not fair, D is fair. (Can you see why? Recall the formula for the area of a triangle and apply here.) E is fair, F is not. (Try tracing and matching parts.) G and H are not fair, I is fair, J is not fair, and K and L are both fair in that in each case the pieces are the same. However, in K, if $1.25 is charged for each of two pieces, then $5.00 is the cost of 8 pieces. Thus, 7 pieces would be less than $5.00—a good deal for the buyer but not for the Student Education Association. In L, the total number of pieces is more than 8, so the Student Association would make more money selling pieces of 2 rather than selling the whole cake.

    b. Answers vary.

    c. None

    d. The pieces a fraction brings to mind should be the same size but not necessarily the same shape. Those considered not fair are those with pieces that are not the same size.

11. The shaded part of the second region shows $\frac{1}{4}$ (compare it to the equally sized first region). How the other markings are made is irrelevant with the first region as a guide. Without the first region as a guide, it would be just an "eyeball" estimate to say $\frac{1}{4}$.

12. a. In both cases, one piece is $\frac{1}{4}$ of the cake.

    b. Part (b) could be an interesting mini-project if your course calls for such.

13. The key is realizing that the unit for the fraction is some unspecified set of asterisks—what is here is only $\frac{5}{6}$ of the unit set. If the asterisks are divided into 5 sets, then there are 4 asterisks (*) in each set. Each set would be $\frac{1}{6}$ of the whole set, and a sixth $\frac{1}{6}$ of the whole set can be added with four additional asterisks (thus, six such sets joined to give all $\frac{6}{6}$). Two-thirds of the set would then be $\frac{4}{6}$, or 16 asterisks.

14. If you are interested in children's thinking, these examples from a real third-grade classroom should be investigated. Sandy's thinking is really quite advanced for a child so young. Sally thinks of $\frac{3}{4}$ only in the context of parts of a square, but she has provided several examples. Sam is thinking of $\frac{3}{4}$ in terms of size and the relationships to other fractions. Sandy has made a chart to show all possibilities through sixteenths: The first row is 12 sixteenths, the second is 1 eighth and 10 sixteenths, etc.

15. a.

The gray region is three-fourths, so each of its pieces is one-fourth. Add another fourth to make the original bar.

b. $2\frac{1}{6}$ would be two of the whole box (all four pieces) in part (a), plus $\frac{1}{6}$ of another whole box.

16. a. Begin by partitioning the rectangle into 8 equally sized parts. (Why 8?) Then mark off *one* unit. Then find $\frac{3}{4}$ of that unit.

b. You have the rectangle cut into 8 pieces of which each represents $\frac{1}{3}$ of a unit. Four more thirds need to be added on to reach four units.

c. The piece is cut into thirds. You need 4 of the thirds. (No drawing shown here.)

d. Each of the 8 one-third unit pieces would be 60¢, so a whole unit (three-thirds) would be $1.80 (requires a drawing).

17. a. Mark the strip into 5 equal parts. Mark them 0, 0.25, 0.5, 0.75, 1, 1.25.

b. If the 1.25-decimeter piece costs $1.60, then each of the 0.25 decimeter lengths should cost $1.60 ÷ 5, or 32¢, so 4 lengths (1 decimeter) would cost 4 × 32¢,   or $1.28.

18. Start by cutting the 0 to 1.5 segment into 3 equal pieces. (Why 3?)

19. $\frac{7}{10} > \frac{7}{11}$ because if the whole is divided into 10 equal pieces. Each piece is larger than when the whole is divided into 11 equal pieces, so 7 of the bigger pieces is more than 7 of the smaller pieces.

20. Suppose a whole is cut into 7 pieces. $\frac{1}{3}$ of those would be more than $\frac{2}{7}$ because $\frac{1}{3}$ of only 6 pieces would be 2 pieces. Actually $\frac{1}{3}$ of 7 pieces would give $\frac{2\frac{1}{3}}{7}$, and $\frac{1}{4}$ of those would be less than $\frac{2}{7}$ since $\frac{1}{4}$ of 8 pieces would be 2. Actually $\frac{1}{4}$ of 7 pieces would give $\frac{1\frac{3}{4}}{7}$, so $\frac{1}{4} < \frac{2}{7} < \frac{1}{3}$. (It might help to draw a line segment with seven equal pieces. Begin with one line segment and repeat it six times.) Draw another line segment of the same length below the first one. Mark the second one into six equal pieces. Draw a third line segment the same length as the first one, this one marked into 4 equal pieces. (Note: this is a real problem given by a child to his father, who related it to us.)

21. a. Discrete because...

b. Continuous because...

c. Continuous because...

d. Discrete (if asked for milk drunk, it would be continuous, but in this case it is discrete because...)

22. a.

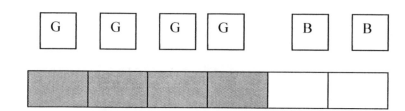

b.

The sketches are the same for a few parts. Parts (e) and (g) have the same answer as (c). Parts (f) and (h) have the same answer as (d).

c.

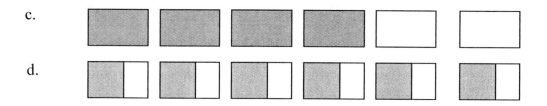

d.

23. The distance between the given points is 1/3 unit long, so for part (a), go the left that distance. For part (b), go to the right that distance to locate the point for 1, then use the distance between 0 and 1 to get fourths, and go one of the fourths farther to the right. Similarly, for part (c), cut the 0 to 1 distance into six equal parts, use the 0 to 1 distance from 1 to get the point for 2, and then go one of the sixths farther to the right.

24. The distance between the given points is 2/3 unit. One way: Cutting that distance into two equal parts gives 1/3 unit. Go to the left from the point for 1 three of the 1/3 units to get 0 (part (a)). Part (b) is then easier: cut the 0 to 1 distance into 4 equal parts, and locate the point for ¾. For part (c), build onto the 1 2/3 location with two more 1/3 units.

25. a. $x = 4$ b. $y = 21$ c. $z = 230$

d. Parts (a)–(c) suggest that regarding whole numbers as having fractional values is reasonable.

Supplementary Learning Exercises for Section 6.1

1.   Be sure to mention the unit (what = 1). $\frac{5}{9}$ means the unit is thought of as cut into 9 equal pieces, and you are considering 5 of those pieces.

2. Parts (a) and (c) have 6 equal pieces, so they are all right. Parts (b) and (d) do not have 6 equal pieces.

3. $\frac{17}{5}$. Your drawing should show 3 wholes, each cut into 5 equal pieces, giving 15 equal pieces in all. Those 15, plus 2 more fifths in another whole, give the 17 fifths.

4. Showing $\frac{19}{4}$ involves making copies of a whole, each cut into 4 equal pieces, and shading until 19 pieces are shaded. Each 4 pieces makes up a whole, so the shading, or the calculation 19 ÷ 4 = 4 R 3, tells that four wholes will be involved, with three pieces, or three-fourths, left over. $\frac{19}{4} = 4\frac{3}{4}$

5. a. $3\frac{1}{7}$ b. $12\frac{13}{15}$ c. $14\frac{1}{4}$ d. $19\frac{19}{35}$ e. $1\frac{1}{384}$ f. $3\frac{194}{219}$

6. $\frac{x}{y}$ can be interpreted as $x \div y$. So the sharing equally meaning would be that $\frac{x}{y}$ tells how much is in each if x's are shared equally among y's. The repeated subtraction would be that $\frac{x}{y}$ tells how many y's make, or are in, x.

7. Fifths and tenths are easy to show, using a point in the "center" to give the divisions. But how to cut the region into three equal parts is not at all clear.

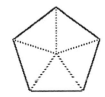 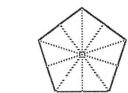

8. The unit for $\frac{1}{3}$ is the amount of money in the paycheck. The unit for $\frac{3}{4}$ is the amount spent on groceries. The unit for $\frac{1}{2}$ is the amount of space in the grocery cart. The unit for $\frac{4}{5}$ is the amount of money left from the paycheck (which is $\frac{2}{3}$ of the paycheck).

9. a. There is the same number of pieces (2) being considered in each, so the decision depends on which has larger pieces. Cutting a whole into 3 pieces gives larger pieces than does cutting it into 9 pieces, so $\frac{2}{3}$ is larger.

   b. Again, there is the same number of pieces (15) being considered in each, so the decision depends on which has larger pieces. A whole cut into 23 pieces will have smaller pieces than one cut into 22 pieces, so $\frac{15}{22}$ is larger.

   c. The number of pieces in the whole is the same in each case (53 × 62), so the decision will depend on which fraction has more pieces. 2 × 27 = 54, but 3 × 20 = 60, so $\frac{3\times20}{53\times62}$ is larger.

   d. $\frac{197}{192}$ is greater than 1, and $\frac{349}{360}$ is less than 1, so $\frac{197}{192}$ is larger.

10. a. The cake shown is 2 of 3 equal pieces, so cut it into 2 pieces (each will be $\frac{1}{3}$ of the cake). Tack on another such piece to get $\frac{3}{3}$ of the cake, the whole cake.

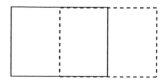

b. Make 2 and ¾ copies of the answer in (a).

c. The whole cake would be worth $6.75, each third being worth $2.25.

11. One way: The distance between the given points is 1 unit. Cut that distance into 4 equal parts to get ¼ unit. For part (a), go to the left of the point for ¼ by one of those ¼ units. For (b), go to the right of the point for 1¼ three of the ¼ units. Finally, for part (c) go another ¼ unit to the right of the point for 2.

12. $109.5 = 109\frac{1}{2} = 109\frac{4}{8}$, so the distance between the given points is 3/8 unit. Cut that distance into 3 equal parts to get 1/8 unit. Then for part (a) go up from the point for $109\frac{7}{8}$ by one of those 1/8 units, for part (b) go down four 1/8 units from the point for 109.5, and from that point, for part (c) go up two of the 1/8 units.

6.2 Equivalent (Equal) Fractions

1. a. $\frac{4}{6}, \frac{6}{9}, \frac{8}{12}, \frac{10}{15}, \frac{12}{18}, \frac{14}{21}, \frac{16}{24}, \frac{18}{27}, \frac{20}{30}, \frac{22}{33}, \cdots$ and $\frac{10}{16}, \frac{15}{24}, \frac{20}{32}, \frac{25}{40}, \frac{30}{48}, \frac{35}{56}, \frac{40}{64}, \frac{45}{72}, \frac{50}{80}, \frac{55}{88}, \cdots$

b. 24 is a common denominator. If the first row is carried out to more places, 48 would also appear in both lists. Actually, any common denominator of both $\frac{2}{3}$ and $\frac{5}{8}$ would be a multiple of 24.

c. Common denominators are useful when adding and subtracting fractions.

2.

  a. One way

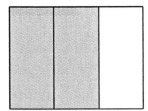 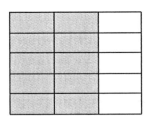

Parts (b) and (c) can be similarly drawn.

3. Part (b) is shown for $\dfrac{3}{4} = \dfrac{6}{8}$. The fractions are equal if the distance is the same on both number lines; in this case, they have the same location on the number line. Both parts (a) and (c) would be similarly drawn.

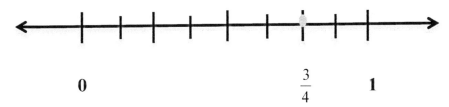

$$0 \hspace{5cm} \frac{3}{4} \hspace{1cm} 1$$

4. $\dfrac{6}{10}$. GG GG GG BB BB shows the 6 girls in 3 of 5 equal-numbered groups.

5. a. $\dfrac{5}{8}$ b. $\dfrac{45}{32}$ c. $\dfrac{25}{16}$ d. $\dfrac{xz^3}{y}$ e. $\approx 1.3 \times 10^{11}$

6. a. $\dfrac{3}{4} > \dfrac{3}{5}$ because fourths are larger than fifths.

  b. $\dfrac{102}{101} > \dfrac{75}{76}$ because $\dfrac{102}{101} > 1$ and $\dfrac{75}{76} < 1$.

  c. $\dfrac{8}{9} = \dfrac{40}{45}$ because $\dfrac{8}{9} = \dfrac{8 \times 5}{9 \times 5}$.

  d. $\dfrac{8}{9} < \dfrac{9}{10}$ because $\dfrac{8}{9}$ is $\dfrac{1}{9}$ away from 1, but $\dfrac{9}{10}$ is $\dfrac{1}{10}$ away from 1.

  e. $\dfrac{13}{18} > \dfrac{29}{62}$ because $\dfrac{13}{18} > \dfrac{9}{18} = \dfrac{1}{2}$, but $\dfrac{29}{62} < \dfrac{31}{62} = \dfrac{1}{2}$.

7. a. Show the 24 in 6 groups of 4 crayons each.

  b. Show the 24 in 4 groups of 6 crayons each.

  c. Show the 24 in 12 groups of 2 crayons each, and then group pairs of 2s to make 6 groups of 4 crayons each.

8. a. A set of 10 (or 20 or 30 or...) popsicle sticks will work.

   b. 18 marbles

   c. 6 children

   d. 18 of your objects

9. The diagram involves units of two different sizes, 4 letters and 12 letters. The student meant, "Multiply both numerator and denominator by 3." Multiplying the fraction by 3 would certainly not give the same value.

10. Reducing usually refers to making something smaller, but equivalent fractions are equal to one another.

11. a. C   b. D   c. B   d. G   e. A

12. a. $\frac{2}{5} < \frac{40}{80} < \frac{6}{10} = 0.6 < \frac{2}{3} < \frac{7}{10}$; logic varies, of course. One might think about 80 being twice 40 and then placing numbers as either greater than one-half or less than one-half. Comparing numerators and denominators, then $\frac{2}{5}$ is the only one less than one-half. Need to read decimal as $\frac{6}{10}$ and then with equal sized parts, 6 is fewer than 7.

   b. $\frac{1}{10} = 0.1 < 0.2 = \frac{1}{5} = \frac{3}{15} < 0.4$

13. Internet exercise

14. a. $\frac{2}{3} > \frac{1}{2}$ b. $\frac{3}{5} < \frac{7}{11}$ c. $\frac{3}{10} < \frac{5}{12}$

    d. $\frac{2}{5} > \frac{5}{16}$ e. $\frac{3}{4} > \frac{7}{11}$ f. $\frac{5}{14} > \frac{5}{16}$

Supplementary Learning Exercises for Section 6.2

1. Equivalent fractions have the same value.

2.
   a. 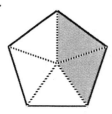   b.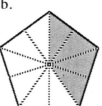

   c. Show $\frac{6}{5}$, as in part (a), but using two pentagons. Then cut each fifth into two equal pieces, as in part (b).

3. a. Samples (there are others): $\frac{5}{6}, \frac{10}{12}, \frac{15}{18}, \frac{20}{24}, \frac{25}{30}, \frac{30}{36}, \frac{35}{42}, \frac{40}{48}, \frac{45}{54}, \frac{50}{60}, \frac{500}{600}, \frac{5000}{6000}, \cdots$

   b. The fractions are all equal to one another.

4.

a.

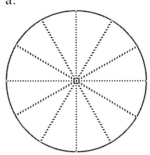

b. Shade 9 pieces.

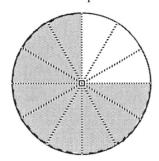

5. a. $\frac{3}{4}$ b. $\frac{21}{32}$ c. $\frac{7}{40}$ d. $\frac{3}{4}$ e. $\frac{36}{125}$

f. $\frac{y}{z}$ g. $\frac{1}{150}$ h. $\frac{1}{ab^6}$ i. $\frac{5x}{6}$ j. $\frac{1}{x^4}$

6. a.

b.

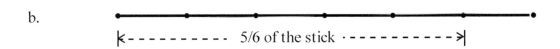

c. The units are different, with the unit on the number line the length between any two consecutive numbers, and the unit for the stick is the length of the whole stick.

7. a. $\frac{163}{190}$ because it is larger than a half, and the other fraction is less than a half.

b. $\frac{29}{65}$ because $\frac{29}{65} = \frac{3 \times 29}{3 \times 65} = \frac{87}{195}$.

c. $\frac{44}{81}$ because $\frac{44}{81}$ is more than $\frac{3}{81} = \frac{1}{27}$ more than a half, but $\frac{37}{72}$ is only $\frac{1}{72}$ more than a half.

d. $\frac{83}{108}$, using a common denominator of 216.

8. $\frac{12}{15}$ of the marbles are black. In your diagram, to show 5 equal parts, put the marbles in clusters of 3 so that the black marbles are in 4 of the clusters.

9. Because $\frac{2}{3} = \frac{4}{6}$, the distance between the given points is 1/6 unit. One way: From the point for 2/3, go to the left four of the 1/6 units to get the point for $\frac{0}{6} = 0$. For part (b), go two of the 1/6 units to the right from the point for 5/6. For part (c), go two of the 1/6 units to the left of the point for 5/6.

10. Because $1\frac{1}{3} = 1\frac{4}{12}$, the distance between the given points is 5/12 unit. Cut that distance into five equal parts to get 1/12 unit. One way: Go to the left of the point for 11/12 by five of the 1/12 units to get to 6/12 (= ½). For part (b), go to the left of the point for 11/12 by two of the 1/12 units to get to the point for 9/12 (= ¾). For part (c), from the point for 9/12, go one 1/12 unit to the left to get to the point for 2/3 (= 8/12).

6.3 Relating Fractions, Decimals, and Percents

1. a. 0.375   b. 2.3   c. $0.428571428571428571... = .\overline{428571}$

   d. $0.27272727... = 0.\overline{27}$ e. 0.375   f. $0.8\overline{3}$

   g. $\frac{3}{8}$ and $\frac{9}{24}$ are equivalent fractions.

2. a. $\frac{5}{8}$ b. $\frac{49}{100}$ c. $\frac{274}{3}$

   d. $\frac{17}{10}$ e. $\frac{1}{1}$ f. $\frac{28}{30}$ or $\frac{14}{15}$ (Hint: $100x - 10x = ...$)

   g. $\frac{53}{99}$ h. No, so this number is irrational and cannot be written as a fraction.

   i. $\frac{53}{990}$ j. $4\frac{76}{99} = \frac{472}{99}$ k. $8\frac{94}{999} = \frac{8086}{999}$

3. a. Yes, infinitely many—can you find ten? How do you know $\frac{1}{2}$ works? Here are two others: $\frac{29}{60}$, $\frac{31}{60}$.

   b. Yes, infinitely many—can you find ten?

4. a. One possibility is 0.45.   b. One possibility is 0.4445.

   c. One possibility is 1.35672.   d. One possibility is 0.00000111011.

5. $\frac{3}{17}, 0.21, \frac{1}{4}, 0.\overline{26}, \frac{11}{29}, \frac{11}{24}, 0.\overline{56}, \frac{2}{3}, \frac{12}{15}, \frac{5}{6}, 1.23$. Many can be ordered by using number sense. For example, $\frac{3}{17} < \frac{3}{15} = \frac{1}{5} = 0.2 < 0.21$. One more difficult ordering is $\frac{2}{3}, \frac{12}{15}, \frac{5}{6}$, but $\frac{12}{15} = \frac{4}{5}$, and ordering $\frac{2}{3}, \frac{4}{5}, \frac{5}{6}$ yields to number sense (compare to 1).

6. The repeating block has 8 digits in it. With a divisor of 7, there are only 6 nonzero remainders possible, so the longest possible repeating block would have 6 digits.

7. a. It could be 8.124973200000. . . , that is, there are only 0s after the 2.

   b. It could be 8.1249732732732. . . , that is, the 732 repeats.

   c. It could be 8.124973212112111211112 . . . .(There is a pattern but it does not repeat.)

8. 0: 5%

   $\frac{1}{4}$: 24%, 0.29 (slightly closer to $\frac{1}{4}$ than to $\frac{1}{3}$ —look at decimals)

   $\frac{1}{3}$: 32%

$\frac{1}{2}$: 0.52, 0.49

$\frac{2}{3}$: 70% (slightly closer to $\frac{2}{3}$ than to $\frac{3}{4}$ —look at decimals)

$\frac{3}{4}$: 0.78

1:   94%

9.   Complete the following table:

Decimal form	Fraction	Percent
0.48	$\frac{48}{100}$	48%
0.8	$\frac{4}{5}$	80%
4.57	$\frac{457}{100}$	457%
0.001	$\frac{1}{1000}$	0.1%

10.   a. Lars is correct. Answers may vary.

   b. 0.64   0.645   0.7

   c. Chris, Sam, Lars

11. Your response could point out that calculator answers are cut off (truncated) or rounded and may or may not be exact. If you divide 1 by 13 and continue indefinitely, you will find that the decimal number continues beyond 0.0769231.

12. Your response could point out that calculator answers are cut off (truncated) or rounded and may or may not be exact. If the student multiplies the 1.4142136. by itself (by hand), he/she will see that it is not an exact square root. With more decimal places, $\sqrt{2} \approx 1.414136$, and even that is not exact. $\sqrt{2}$ is an irrational number.

13.   (Table is filled by using an Internet site.)

Fractions	Decimal	Percent
$\frac{1}{4}$	0.25	25%
$\frac{11}{10}$	1.1	110%
$\frac{31}{10}$	3.1	310%
$\frac{13}{20}$	0.65	65%
$\frac{5}{2}$	2.5	250%
$\frac{17}{4}$	4.25	425%
$\frac{9}{5}$	1.8	180%
$\frac{14}{5}$	2.8	280%
$\frac{17}{5}$	3.4	340%
$\frac{3}{10}$	0.3	30%

14. Some fraction equivalents might have different forms. (Table is filled by using an Internet site.)

Fraction	Decimal	Percent
$\frac{100}{20}$ or $\frac{5}{1}$	5	500%
$\frac{50}{54}$	0.9259	92.59%
$\frac{95}{67}$	1.4179	141.79%
$\frac{15}{10}$ or $\frac{3}{2}$	1.5	150%
$\frac{4}{100}$ or $\frac{1}{25}$	0.04	4%
$\frac{73}{100}$	0.73	73%
$\frac{47}{20}$	2.35	235%
$\frac{1}{3}$	0.3333	33.33%

Supplementary Learning Exercises for Section 6.3

1.   Each has a terminating decimal, because only factors of 2 and/or 5 appear in the denominators. The factor of 3 in the denominator of $\frac{699}{300}$ is not essential because $\frac{699}{300} = \frac{233}{100}$.

2.   a. $\frac{3333}{10,000}$ b. $\frac{8374}{1000} = \frac{4187}{500}$ c. $\frac{7}{9}$ d. $\frac{63}{99} = \frac{7}{11}$

   e. $\frac{632}{999}$ f. $\frac{431.4}{99} = \frac{4314}{990} = \frac{2157}{495} = \frac{719}{165}$ (Your instructor might accept $\frac{4314}{990}$.)

   g. $\frac{154.73}{9} = \frac{15473}{900}$ h. $\frac{2299.2}{999} = \frac{22992}{9990} = \frac{11496}{4995} = \frac{3832}{1665}$ ($\frac{22992}{9990}$ may be enough.)

3. A rational number is any number whose decimal is either a terminating decimal or a repeating decimal. An irrational number is any number whose decimal neither terminates nor repeats. A real number is any number that can be represented by a decimal.

4. Whole number are rational numbers because they can be written as terminating decimals. For example, $173 = 173.0$.

5. The decimal form of $\sqrt{5}$ goes on forever without any repeating block of digits.

6. π is indeed irrational. $\frac{22}{7}$ is only an approximate value for π.

7. Samples (There are actually infinitely many possibilities for each.)

    a. 0.985, 0.988   b. 1.0401, 1.0402,... c. 0.49991, 0.49992,...

8. The equation is not true. 3.1416 cannot be *exactly* equal to π.

9. a. Half of an eighth, or half of 0.125. 0.0625, or 6.25%

    b. $3 \times 0.125 = 0.375$, or 37.5%

    c. Half of one-third, or half of $33\frac{1}{3}\%$. This is a slightly more difficult mental calculation, but half of 32 is 16, and then half of $\frac{4}{3}$ is $\frac{2}{3}$. So $\frac{1}{6} = 16\frac{2}{3}\%$. ($0.16\frac{2}{3}$, a mix of decimal and fraction within a single number, is usually avoided.)

    d. Half of $\frac{1}{6}$, or $8\frac{1}{3}\%$. Note the use of part (c).

    e. $\frac{11}{12}$ is $\frac{1}{12}$ less than 1, so $100 - 8\frac{1}{3} = 91\frac{2}{3}$ percent. Note the use of part (d).

6.4 Estimating Fractional Values

1. The remark is cynical because the friend knows that $\frac{5}{4}$ is more than 1 (and is allowed by the sign), so the sale price is more than the original price.

2. $\frac{7}{12}$ is more than $\frac{1}{2}$ and $\frac{5}{8}$ is more than $\frac{1}{2}$, so the sum is more than 1. But $\frac{23}{24}$ is less than 1, so it is incorrect.

3. Yes, fractions can have negative values. For example, $^-\frac{1}{2} < 0$ but $\frac{1}{2} > 0$.

4. $\frac{2}{9}, \frac{11}{108}$ are close to 0; $\frac{4}{7}, \frac{99}{152}, \frac{17}{35}, \frac{15}{34}$ are close to $\frac{1}{2}$; $\frac{11}{12}, \frac{9}{8}$ are close to 1; and $\frac{3}{12}$ could be considered as close to 0, $\frac{1}{2}$, or both because it is halfway between 0 and $\frac{1}{2}$. Also, $\frac{99}{152}$ is about $\frac{2}{3}$, so not really close to $\frac{1}{2}$, but closer than it is to 1.

5. A fraction is close to $\frac{1}{3}$ when the denominator is about 3 times as large as the numerator. A fraction is close to $\frac{2}{3}$ when the numerator multiplied by 3 is about the size of the denominator multiplied by 2. (For some, there could be more than one answer.)

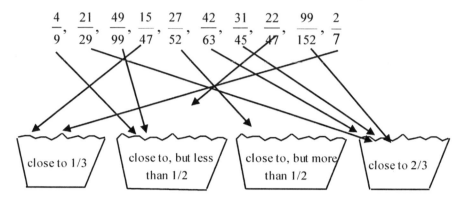

$$\frac{4}{9}, \frac{21}{29}, \frac{49}{99}, \frac{15}{47}, \frac{27}{52}, \frac{42}{63}, \frac{31}{45}, \frac{22}{47}, \frac{99}{152}, \frac{2}{7}$$

close to 1/3   close to, but less than 1/2   close to, but more than 1/2   close to 2/3

6. a. $\frac{3}{4} > \frac{1}{2}$ and $\frac{4}{9} < \frac{1}{2}$, so $\frac{4}{9} < \frac{3}{4}$.

   b. $\frac{1}{3}$ is further away from 0 than $\frac{1}{4}$, so $\frac{1}{4} < \frac{1}{3}$.

   c. $\frac{3}{4}$ and $\frac{9}{10}$ are both close to 1, but $\frac{3}{4}$ is $\frac{1}{4}$ away from 1 and $\frac{9}{10}$ is $\frac{1}{10}$ away from 1. But $\frac{1}{10} < \frac{1}{4}$, so $\frac{9}{10}$ is closer to 1 and therefore $\frac{9}{10} > \frac{3}{4}$.

   d. $\frac{2}{5} < \frac{1}{2}$ but $\frac{3}{6} = \frac{1}{2}$ so $\frac{2}{5} < \frac{3}{6}$.

   e. $\frac{1}{20} > \frac{1}{24}$, $\frac{13}{24}$ is $\frac{1}{24}$ more than $\frac{1}{2}$, and $\frac{11}{20}$ is $\frac{1}{20}$ more than $\frac{1}{2}$, so $\frac{11}{20} > \frac{13}{24}$.

   f. $\frac{17}{15} > 1$ but $\frac{11}{25} < 1$, so $\frac{11}{25} < \frac{17}{15}$.

7. The denominator is about 4 times the numerator (or the numerator is about one-fourth the denominator).

8. a. $\frac{2}{5}$ is less than $\frac{1}{2}$ and $\frac{3}{5}$ is greater than $\frac{1}{2}$, so $\frac{1}{2}$ is in between.

   b. One way: $\frac{8}{15} < \frac{9}{15} = \frac{3}{5}$ and $\frac{9}{12} = \frac{3}{4}$, so we need a fraction between $\frac{3}{5}$ and $\frac{3}{4}$. Rewriting as twentieths will give an answer. But symbolically at least, $\frac{3}{4\frac{1}{2}}$ looks as though it should work. $\frac{3}{4\frac{1}{2}} = \frac{3 \times 2}{4\frac{1}{2} \times 2} = \frac{6}{9} = \frac{2}{3}$, and $\frac{2}{3}$ is between the two.

   c. $\frac{7}{8} < \frac{8}{9}$ because $\frac{1}{8} > \frac{1}{9}$, and $\frac{8}{9} < \frac{9}{10}$ because $\frac{1}{10} < \frac{1}{9}$, so $\frac{8}{9}$ is between $\frac{7}{8}$ and $\frac{9}{10}$.

   d. One fraction is less than 1, and the other greater than 1.

e. One way: Use equivalent fractions with 12 as the denominator.

9. Focus on the sizes of the missing pieces.

10. a. $\frac{1}{8} = 0.125 = 12.5\%$ b. $\frac{1}{5} = 0.2 = 20\%$ c. $\frac{1}{4} = 0.25 = 25\%$

d. $\frac{1}{3} = 0.3333... = 33.\overline{3}\%$ e. $\frac{2}{5} = 0.4 = 40\%$

f. $\frac{3}{8} = 3 \times \frac{1}{8} = 3 \times 0.125 = 0.375 = 37.5\%$ g. $\frac{5}{4} = 1.25 = 125\%,$

h. $\frac{1}{2} = 0.5 = 50\%$ i. $\frac{3}{5} = 0.6 = 60\%$

j. $\frac{5}{8} = 5 \times \frac{1}{8} = 5 \times 0.125 = 0.675 = 67.5\%$

k. $\frac{2}{3} = 0.66666... = 66\frac{2}{3}\%$ l. $\frac{3}{4} = 0.75 = 75\%$ m. $\frac{4}{5} = 0.8 = 80\%$

n. $\frac{7}{8} = 7 \times \frac{1}{8} = 7 \times 0.125 = 0.875 = 87.5\%$ o. $1 = 1 = 100\%$

p. $\frac{7}{4} = 1\frac{3}{4} = 1.75 = 175\%$

11. a. Slightly less than $\frac{1}{4}$ b. Slightly less than 1   c. Slightly more than 1

d. Slightly more than $\frac{1}{3}$ e. About $4\frac{2}{3}$ f. About $\frac{1}{8}$

12. Here is just one possible way to estimate each.

a. 10% of 800 + 5% of 800 is 80 + 40 = 120.

b. 10% of 150 is 15. 90% is about 150 − 15, which is 135.

c. 100% is 56, 25% is 14, so an estimate is 56 + 14 = 70.

d. This is about $\frac{2}{3}$ of 24, which is 16.

e. 50% is 360 and 10% is about 70, so an estimate could be 360 + 70 = 430.

f. 10% of 59 is 5.9.

g. 100% is 32 and 50% is 16; 32 + 16 = 48.

h. No need to estimate here; 10% is 2.4; 1% is 0.24, 0.1 % of 24 is 0.024.

i. A third of 69 is 23.

13. Sketch $\frac{4}{5}$ and then cut each fifth into two equal pieces.

14. After drawing $\frac{4}{5}$, there is room in one unit only for $\frac{2}{10}$. So you will have to introduce another unit, divided into tenths, and take one of those in addition to the other unit whole.

15. $\frac{3}{4}$

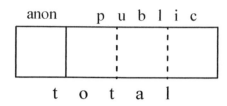

16. Your response should somehow note that the sizes of the cake and the cookie are quite different. Have the child shade to show $\frac{1}{2}$ in each.

17. a. About $\frac{1}{2} + 1 = 1\frac{1}{2}$ 　　　　　　　 b. About $1\frac{1}{2} + 4 + 7 = 12\frac{1}{2}$

　　 c. About $15 - 5 = 10$ 　　　　　　　　　 d. About $5 - 3 = 2$

　　 e. About $\frac{2}{3} - \frac{1}{3} = \frac{1}{3}$ 　　　　　　　　 f. About $4\frac{1}{2} + 6 - 2 = 8\frac{1}{2}$

18. a. Estimates should be in the neighborhoods of these percents:

A) 25%;　　 B) 11%;　 C) any estimate close to 18%;　　 D) 10%;　 E) any estimate close 36%... The sum of the percents should be 100%.

b. Estimates should be in the neighborhood of these fractions:

A) ¼ 　　　 B) about 1/10　C) 1/5 　　　　 D) 1/10 　　　 E) between 1/3 and 2/5

The sum of the fractions would be 1.

Supplementary Learning Exercises for Section 6.4

1.　 Each addend is greater than $\frac{1}{2}$, so the sum should be more than $1\frac{1}{2}$. But the given answer is less than $1\frac{1}{2}$.

2.　 a. $\frac{1}{2}$ 　　 b. $\frac{1}{3}$ 　 c. $\frac{3}{4}$ 　 d. $\frac{2}{3}$ 　 e. $\frac{2}{3}$

3.　 a. About $125, using $2\frac{1}{2} \times \$50$. The estimate is too small because each factor used is less than the corresponding factor in the original.

b. About 18. The first two addends should give about 11, and the last two, about 7. The estimate is a little large because the 11 and 7 are a bit large.

c. About 27, using $13\frac{1}{2} \div \frac{1}{2}$ and thinking, how many $\frac{1}{2}$ s are in $13\frac{1}{2}$? Because $\frac{8}{15}$ is larger than $\frac{1}{2}$ (and $13\frac{1}{2}$ is larger than $13\frac{7}{16}$), 27 is too many.

4. About $15

5. a. Larger: a numerator larger than 35 but close to 35. Smaller: a numerator smaller than 35 but close to 35.

   b. Larger: a numerator larger than 20 but close to 20. Smaller: a numerator smaller than 20 but close to 20.

   c. Larger: a numerator larger than 120 but close to 120. Smaller: a numerator smaller than 120 but close to 120.

6. The drawing was created to make the following percents and fractions; your estimates should be in the neighborhood of the following. (Note the use of Supplementary Learning Exercise 9 in Section 6.3.)

   A and B each 25%, ¼;   C and D each $16\frac{2}{3}$%, $\frac{1}{6}$;   E and F each $8\frac{1}{3}$%, $\frac{1}{12}$. Your total for the percents should be about 100%, and for the fractions, about 1.

7. Somewhat more than 25%, by thinking of the 3.8 as a little less than 4.

8. 68% is about two-thirds, so cut the segment into two pieces, each one-third, and make the new segment two such pieces longer than the one given.

9. Candidate A received 59% of the vote, and B received 41%. Did you use a drawing, and the fact that the total vote would be 100%?

Answers for Chapter 7: Computing with Fractions

7.1 Adding and Subtracting Fractions

1. One way: $8 = 2^3$, $6 = 2 \times 3$, and $15 = 3 \times 5$. The denominator must have all of these factors, that is, it must have at least 2^3, 3, and 5 as factors. $2^3 \times 3 \times 5 = 120$ is the smallest common denominator. Any other denominator must be a multiple of 120.

   (For another way, see Exercise 11 below.)

2. The student relying on the drawing has lost track of the unit, whereas in the story problem, the context helps keep the unit clear.

3. Parts (a) and (b) will require more than one unit and some extra markings to get pieces of the same size.

   c. $\frac{2}{3} - \frac{1}{2}$

   $\frac{2}{3}$ is first shaded; $\frac{1}{2}$ is double-shaded. The portion of light shading is the difference: $\frac{1}{6}$ of the whole rectangle.

4. a. Let the yellow hexagon be the unit. Then $\frac{1}{2}$ is represented by 1 red trapezoid and $\frac{1}{6}$ by a green triangle. Placed together, they can be replaced by 2 blue rhombuses, which represents $\frac{2}{3}$.

   b. Let the yellow hexagon be the unit. Then $2\frac{1}{2}$ is represented as two hexagons and 1 trapezoid, and the $\frac{2}{3}$ is represented by two blue rhombuses. Placed together, 1 blue rhombus must be replaced by 2 green triangles. The red trapezoid, 1 rhombus, and 1 triangle make the shape of a hexagon. There is 1 triangle left. The total is $3\frac{1}{6}$.

   c. Let the yellow hexagon be the unit. Then $\frac{5}{6}$ would be represented with 5 triangles, (each is $\frac{1}{6}$) which can be exchanged for a trapezoid ($\frac{1}{2}$) and a rhombus ($\frac{1}{3}$). Remove the trapezoid. The rhombus remains, for an answer of $\frac{1}{3}$. Or let 2 hexagons be the unit. Now the rhombus represents $\frac{1}{6}$. Three of the 5 rhombuses can be replaced with a hexagon (which is $\frac{1}{2}$) leaving 2 rhombuses, representing $\frac{2}{6}$, which is $\frac{1}{3}$.

   d. Again the hexagon can the unit. $2\frac{2}{3}$ can be represented by 2 yellow hexagons and 2 blue rhombuses. I want to remove 1 hexagon and 5 green triangles. Trade 1 of the two yellow hexagons for 6 triangles. Remove the other hexagon and 5 triangles. You have 5 triangles left: $\frac{5}{6}$.

   e. Let 2 hexagons represent the unit. Now the trapezoid represent $\frac{1}{4}$. The number 4 would be represented by 8 hexagons. I need to take away $2\frac{1}{4}$. How much needs to be removed from 4 to reach $2\frac{1}{4}$? Replace 1 of the 8 hexagons with 2 trapezoids. Remove $2\frac{1}{4}$ (4 hexagons and a trapezoid), leaving 3 hexagons and 1 trapezoid, or 2 hexagons and 3 trapezoids, which represents $1\frac{3}{4}$.

    f. This is essentially the problem $2\frac{2}{3} - \frac{5}{6}$. Let the hexagon represent the unit. $2\frac{2}{3}$ would be represented by 2 hexagons and 2 rhombuses. Replace 1 hexagon by 6 triangles. Remove 5 triangles. There are 1 hexagon (1), 2 rhombuses ($\frac{2}{3}$) and 1 triangle ($\frac{1}{6}$). Each rhombus can be exchanged for 2 triangles. There are now 1 hexagon (1) and 5 triangles ($\frac{5}{6}$), that is, $1\frac{5}{6}$.

5. a. $\frac{8}{10}$

    b. Each loaf may have been cut into 10 parts.

    c. Yes (Place a dark line over each $\frac{3}{10}$ to show that there are exactly ten $\frac{3}{10}$ s.)

6. Each of the original four gets $9 \div 4 = 2\frac{1}{4}$ bags. After Johnny comes, each of the five gets $11 \div 5 = 2\frac{1}{5}$ bags. So Johnny gets $2\frac{1}{5}$ bags. Chico had $2\frac{1}{4} + 2\frac{1}{5} = 4\frac{9}{20}$ (about $4\frac{1}{2}$ bags).

7. He ate $\frac{1}{3} + \frac{1}{6} = \frac{1}{2}$ of a pizza. (Note: not $\frac{1}{6}$ of what was left, but $\frac{1}{6}$ of the whole pizza.)

8. $1 - (\frac{1}{3} + \frac{2}{5} + \frac{1}{6}) = \frac{1}{10}$

9. One way: $\frac{2}{3} + \frac{1}{16} + \frac{1}{16} + \frac{1}{16}$, or $\frac{2}{3} + \frac{3}{16} = \frac{41}{48}$, so there will be $\frac{7}{48}$ of her estate left.

10. One way: $29\frac{1}{2} + 42\frac{3}{4} + 118 = 190\frac{1}{4}$, so he will be able to do the three jobs. But $200 - 190\frac{1}{4} - 9\frac{3}{4}$, so he will not have enough for the fourth job, being $24\frac{5}{8} - 9\frac{3}{4} = 14\frac{7}{8}$ feet short.

11. $4 \times 1\frac{1}{4} = 5$, so the jug holds 5 quarts. $1\frac{3}{4} + 1\frac{3}{4} + 1\frac{3}{4} = 5\frac{1}{4}$, so $\frac{1}{4}$ quart of drink will be left over.

12. $\frac{5}{8} + \frac{5}{8} + \frac{1}{2} + \frac{2}{3} = 2\frac{5}{12}$ gallons, so he cannot mow all four yards on one tank. He will be $2\frac{5}{12} - 2\frac{1}{3} = \frac{1}{12}$ of a gallon short.

13.

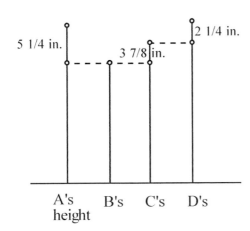

The diagram shows that D is $3\frac{7}{8} + 2\frac{1}{4} = 6\frac{1}{8}$ inches taller than B. So Donell is taller than Arnie, by $6\frac{1}{8} - 5\frac{1}{4} = \frac{7}{8}$ inches.

14. a. Caution: A common error is to lose track of the unit, which should be the same for the two fractions. Why is "Pam had $\frac{2}{3}$ of a cake. She ate half of it. How much cake did she eat?" incorrect (even though it does give the correct numerical answer)?

b and c. The mixed numbers encourage you to think of a measurement situation, using English system units.

15. a. $\frac{3}{4} + \frac{1}{4} = 1$, and $1 + \frac{5}{6} = 1\frac{5}{6}$

b. $\frac{3}{8} + \frac{4}{8}$ is $\frac{7}{8}$

c. $3\frac{1}{2} + 1\frac{1}{2} = 5$, so the total of the two fractions being subtracted total 5. $1\frac{3}{4}$

d. The fractions alone make 1 and $11 - 4 = 7$.

e. $4\frac{13}{16}$

f. $\frac{7}{16}$ ($\frac{0}{72}$ is just 0!)

g. $\frac{20}{63}$

16. a. LCD = 40. $\frac{17+95-8}{40} = \frac{104}{40} = \frac{13}{5} = 2\frac{3}{5}$

b. LCD = 540. $\frac{375+248}{540} = \frac{623}{540} = 1\frac{83}{540}$. (Compare doing this with 36×135 as the common denominator!)

c. $0.7 = \frac{7}{10}$, so LCD = 100. $\frac{75+70-68}{100} = \frac{77}{100}$

17. a. Almost any example you try will show that subtraction is not commutative. Avoid subtracting a fraction that is equal to the other fraction, however, such as $\frac{12}{18} - \frac{18}{27}$, and $\frac{18}{27} - \frac{12}{18}$.

b. So long as you avoid 0 as the third fraction, you should find a counterexample to $(\frac{a}{b} - \frac{c}{d}) - \frac{e}{f})$ being equal to $\frac{a}{b} - (\frac{c}{d} - \frac{e}{f})$.

18. $\frac{5}{18}$. A drawing may help. Leslie's glass had $\frac{1}{2}$ of a Jenny-sized glassful of chocolate syrup, so together they had $\frac{1}{3} + \frac{1}{2} = \frac{5}{6}$. Jenny-sized glassful of syrup in the pitcher with 3 Jenny-sized glassfuls of chocolate milk. So the pitcher contains $\frac{\frac{5}{6}}{3} = \frac{5}{18}$ chocolate syrup.

19. $1\frac{2}{3} - 1\frac{1}{2} = 1\frac{4}{6} - 1\frac{3}{6} = \frac{1}{6}$, so go left from the 1½ point three 1/6 unit distances to get the point for 1. For part (b), continue to the left three more spaces to get the point for ½. For part (c), $\frac{11}{6} = 1\frac{5}{6}$, so the point will be one 1/6 unit to the right of the point for 1 2/3.

20. $12\frac{1}{3}-11\frac{5}{6}=12\frac{2}{6}-11\frac{5}{6}=11\frac{6+2}{6}-11\frac{5}{6}=\frac{3}{6}$, so the distance between the given points can be either cut into three equal pieces (for 1/6 unit pieces) or used as is (for ½ unit). For part (a), go two 1/6 unit pieces to the left from the point for 12 1/3. For part (b), go four 1/6 units to the right from 12 1/3. For part (c), go to the left two ½ unit spaces from the point for 11 5/6 to get the point for 10 5/6, and then go two 1/6 unit distances farther to the left.

21. One way: $2-\frac{3}{4}=1\frac{1}{4}=\frac{5}{4}$, so (part (a)) go to the right from 2 the distance between the given points. For part (b) the distance between the given points can be cut into five equal pieces, each ¼ unit long, so go two ¼ unit distances to the left of the point for 3/4. For part (c), cut one of the ¼ unit pieces into two equal parts, giving a 1/8 unit distance; then from the point for 2, go to the left three of the 1/8 units.

22. The distance between the given points is $3\frac{3}{4}=\frac{15}{4}$, so cut that space into 15 equal pieces to get ¼ unit pieces. (Fifteen equal pieces?! One way that can be fairly accurate is to cut into 3 equal pieces first, and then each of these into 5 equal pieces.) For part (a), then, go right three of the ¼ unit distances from the point for 1. For part (b), go two of the ¼ unit distances to the right from the point for 1¾. For part (c), take half of a ¼ unit piece to get 1/8 unit, and go left the 1/8 unit from the point for part (a).

Supplementary Learning Exercises for Section 7.1

1. $88\frac{7}{8}$ inches. The 8 feet = 96 inches. Did you calculate $(96-4\frac{3}{4})-2\frac{3}{8}$? Or did you calculate $96-(4\frac{3}{4}+2\frac{3}{8})$? Do you see both ways of reasoning?

2. a. $17\frac{3}{4}$ miles, from $5\frac{1}{8}+3\frac{3}{4}+5\frac{1}{8}+3\frac{3}{4}$

   b. $53\frac{1}{4}$ miles. Which did you do: Triple each length and then add, or triple the answer from part (a)? Your instructor may ask the name for the important property involved in assuring that the two methods will give equal answers:
   $3\times(5\frac{1}{8}+3\frac{3}{4}+5\frac{1}{8}+3\frac{3}{4})=(3\times5\frac{1}{8})+(3\times3\frac{3}{4})+(3\times5\frac{1}{8})+(3\times3\frac{3}{4})$.

3. $\frac{7}{12}$ gallon. Do you see that the results from the take-away actions could be determined by adding the amounts used, and then doing a take-away subtraction from the 2 gallons?
   $2-\frac{1}{2}-\frac{2}{3}-\frac{1}{4}=2-(\frac{1}{2}+\frac{2}{3}+\frac{1}{4})$, or more generally, $a-b-c-d=a-(b+c+d)$

4. For part (a), make sure that the $\frac{3}{4}$ (quart of milk, say) is taken away from a $\frac{7}{8}$ (quart of milk), whereas for a clear-cut part (b), the two should be separate quantities. Part (c) should involve an addition situation that could be described by $\frac{3}{4}+n=\frac{7}{8}$.

5. a. $72\frac{1}{4}$ b. $128\frac{1}{8}$ c. $245\frac{2}{9}$ d. $999\frac{1}{18}$

6. a. $7\frac{5}{8}-5\frac{7}{8}=2-\frac{2}{8}=1+\frac{8}{8}-\frac{2}{8}=1\frac{6}{8}$ (=$1\frac{3}{4}$ for us, and perhaps Killie)

b. $10\frac{1}{3} - 6\frac{4}{9} = 10\frac{3}{9} - 6\frac{4}{9} = 4 - \frac{1}{9} = 3 + \frac{9}{9} - \frac{1}{9} = 3\frac{8}{9}$

c. Probably not. because the subtraction does not require any renaming.

d. By now you should appreciate that many times there may be more than the standard way of calculating. So it is to be hoped that you would not immediately rule out Killie's method.

7. $\frac{1}{3} + \frac{4}{9} + \frac{1}{6} = \frac{17}{18}$, so the rancher made an arithmetic mistake (or perhaps a horse had died). The classical solution is that the lawyer added his horse to the herd of 17, gave 6 to Curly, 8 to Buck, and 3 to Cindy Lou—and rode back to town on his horse!

8. a. $1\frac{23}{24}$ 　　　　b. $2\frac{35}{48}$ 　　　　c. $2\frac{25}{36}$

9. $5\frac{1}{4} - 2\frac{3}{4} = 2\frac{2}{4} = 2\frac{1}{2} = \frac{5}{2}$ so we can find ½ unit pieces by cutting the distance between the given points into five equal pieces, and ¼ unit pieces by cutting one of the ½ unit pieces into two equal pieces. For part (a), $6\frac{1}{2} - 5\frac{1}{4} = 1\frac{1}{4}$, so one way is to go the right from the point for 5¼ by two of the ½-unit spaces and one of the ¼ unit spaces (or by five of the ¼-unit spaces). Part (b) is most easily accomplished by going to the left from the 2 ¾ point by the distance (2 ½) between the given points. For part (c), go to the left of the point for 5 ¼ by two of the ½ unit distances.

10. Using associativity and commutativity of addition allows us to rethink of the given problem in the following way: $(\frac{40}{99} + \frac{59}{99}) + (\frac{7}{3} + \frac{2}{3}) + \frac{5}{39}$, which in turn gives $\frac{99}{99} + \frac{9}{3} + \frac{5}{39} = 4\frac{5}{39}$.

7.2 Multiplying by a Fraction

1. a.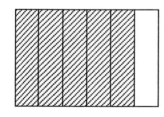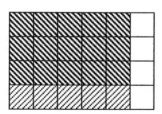

The farmer planted $\frac{15}{24}$ of the field in tomatoes.

b. As above, but first shade in $\frac{3}{4}$ then $\frac{5}{6}$. The answer will be $\frac{15}{24}$ of the field in potatoes.

2. $\frac{1}{4}$ of the candy bar.

3. One way: Cut each circular region into two equal pieces, giving 8 in all; then $\frac{5}{8}$ of the 4 circles would be 5 of the pieces. This is $\frac{5}{8}$ of 4, which is $2\frac{1}{2}$.

A second way: Cut each circular region into 8 equal pieces; shade 5 pieces in each circle to get $\frac{5}{8}$ of the 4 circles. $\frac{5}{8}$ of 4 is $2\frac{1}{2}$ (or $\frac{20}{8}$ with the second method). To represent $4 \times \frac{5}{8}$, draw a region with 8 equal parts, shading 5 of them. Do this four times: $\frac{5}{8} + \frac{5}{8} + \frac{5}{8} + \frac{5}{8} = \frac{20}{8} = 2\frac{1}{2}$.

4.   a.   b.

                                 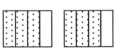

They are the same amount.

5.   a. 4   b. 2   c. 1   d. $\frac{1}{2}$ e. 6   f. 7   g. $\frac{49}{50}$ h. 0

6.   a. $\frac{1}{6} \times 12 = 2$ b. $12 \times \frac{1}{6} = 2$

7.

$4 \times \dfrac{2}{3}$  $\dfrac{8}{3}$

Alternatively, $2\dfrac{2}{3}$

$\dfrac{2}{3} \times 4$

$\dfrac{2}{3} \times 4$  $2\dfrac{2}{3}$

$\dfrac{2}{3}$ of the first 3   + $\dfrac{2}{3}$ of the last one

Alternatively, take $\dfrac{2}{3}$ of each hexagon and get the first row.

8. $\frac{3}{4}$ of the rectangle is shaded. $\frac{2}{3}$ of $\frac{3}{4}$ of 1 is $\frac{1}{2}$.

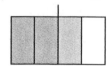

9.

   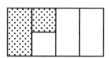

In the first figure, the $\frac{1}{4}$ is $\frac{1}{4}$ of the whole rectangle.

In the second figure, the $\frac{3}{2}$ is $\frac{3}{2}$ of $\frac{1}{4}$ of 1, which is $\frac{3}{8}$ of the original rectangle.

10. a. In each case, the result is one rectangular region. This language is used whenever the product of two numbers is 1.

b. Commutativity of multiplication, or multiplication is commutative.

c. If 1 is a factor in the product of two numbers, the product is just the other factor. Here, $\frac{72}{72}$ and $\frac{103}{103}$ are just fraction names for 1.

11. Do the answers from your pattern-block work agree with answers from calculating the products?

12.   a. Make certain your drawing shows $\frac{2}{3}$ of the $\frac{3}{4}$ pie. The unit for the $\frac{2}{3}$ is the $\frac{3}{4}$ pie. The answer is $\frac{1}{2}$ of the pie, although your work may show $\frac{2}{4}$ or $\frac{6}{12}$ of the pie.

b. You probably used a rectangular region here, rather than the circular regions from part (a). "Pies" suggest circles, but "class" doesn't, so it is natural *not* to use circular regions for part (b).

The whole for the $\frac{3}{4}$ is the number of students in the class; the whole for the $\frac{2}{3}$ is just the part of the class that are girls. The size of the class does not matter, a fact that is surprising to some students, who are not aware that $\frac{2}{3} \times (\frac{3}{4}$ of the number of students in the class) is equal to $(\frac{2}{3} \times \frac{3}{4})$ of the number of students in the class. See Exercise 15.

c. $\frac{7}{6}$ of $\frac{3}{4} = \frac{7}{8}$ of an hour

d. The drawing is correct.

13.   a. Example: A recipe calls for $2\frac{3}{4}$ cups of sugar. Anh is making only $\frac{1}{4}$ of the recipe. How much sugar will she use?

b. Example: A small wedge of cream cheese is $\frac{1}{16}$ of a pound. A small wedge of cheddar cheese is $\frac{1}{8}$ of a pound. If three people each take one serving of each cheese, how much cheese did they take in all?

c. For you to do

14. b. No, "canceling" should be used only with multiplication or as a label for simplifying when using the $\frac{an}{bn} = \frac{a}{b}$ principle for equality of fractions and ratios.

15. a. $\frac{3}{8}$. Here is a drawing to help you. The number of students in the class is irrelevant.

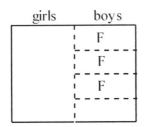 Add lines to make equal pieces.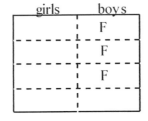

b. The same answer as in part (a). Again, the number of students in the class is irrelevant.

16. a. Yes, the distributive property also works with fractions.

b.

i. One way is just to add the fractions first, then multiply. The distributive property allows you to multiply $\frac{3}{4} \times \frac{4}{5}$ and $\frac{3}{4} \times \frac{8}{15}$ and add those results. Both ways should give an answer equal to 1.

ii. The two ways should give the same answer: 10. (Which way was easier?)

17. Hint: Change to fractions, or use the distributive property: $8 \times (6 + \frac{2}{7})$.

a. $50\frac{2}{7}$ either way   b. $63\frac{1}{3}$ either way

18. a. $\frac{12}{78}$ $\frac{9}{19}$ $\frac{3}{4}$ $\frac{23}{25}$ because $\frac{12}{78}$ is closer to 0 than the others, and $\frac{9}{19}$ is slightly less than $\frac{1}{2}$ and $\frac{23}{25}$ is almost 1.

b. $\frac{3}{14}$ $\frac{3}{9}$ $\frac{3}{7}$ $\frac{3}{4}$ $\frac{3}{2}$ because the denominators are descending, or $\frac{3}{14}$ is close to 0, $\frac{3}{9}$ is $\frac{1}{3}$, $\frac{3}{7}$ is slightly less than $\frac{1}{2}$, $\frac{3}{4}$ is between $\frac{1}{2}$ and 1, $\frac{3}{2} > 1$.

19. a. Jim, Ken, and Len have taken $\frac{1}{4} + \frac{1}{3} + \frac{1}{3} = \frac{11}{12}$ of the bag, leaving $\frac{1}{12}$ of the bag for Max. Because $\frac{1}{12}$ of the bag is 4 bars, there are $12 \times 4 = 48$ bars in the whole $\frac{12}{12}$ of the bag.

b. Jim got 12 bars, and Ken and Len each got 16 bars.

20. a. Jim left $\frac{3}{4}$ of the bars. Ken took $\frac{1}{3} \times \frac{3}{4} = \frac{1}{4}$ of the bars, so Len took $\frac{1}{3}$ of the remaining $\frac{1}{2}$ of the bars, or $\frac{1}{3} \times \frac{1}{2} = \frac{1}{6}$ of the bars. With $\frac{1}{4} + \frac{1}{4} + \frac{1}{6} = \frac{8}{12} = \frac{2}{3}$ of the bars taken, Max's 8 bars were $\frac{1}{3}$ of the bag. So each third of the bag contained 8 bars, with the whole bag containing 24 bars.

b. Jim, 6 bars; Ken, 6 bars; Len, 4 bars

c. The units for the fraction in Learning Exercise 19 are all the same—the whole bag of bars. But in Learning Exercise 20, the units for the given fractions are different.

Supplementary Learning Exercises for Section 7.2

1. Both $\frac{c}{d}$ and $\frac{e}{f}$ refer to the same unit.

2. a.
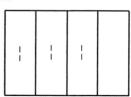

$\frac{3}{4}$ of the region

b.
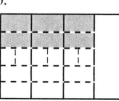

$\frac{2}{5}$ of the $\frac{3}{4}$

c.
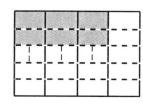

$\frac{2}{5}$ of $\frac{3}{4}$ is $\frac{3}{4}$ of the region

b. There are two rows of 3 darkened regions (2×3), and the whole unit has been cut into 5 rows with 4 equal pieces in each row, or 5×4 pieces of the same size.

3. a. Ronnie paid $\frac{2}{9}$ (from the $\frac{4}{9} + (\frac{3}{4} \times \frac{4}{9}) = \frac{7}{9}$ paid by Ally and Bella). So each ninth of the cost is $400, and the whole cost would be $3600.

b. Ally paid $1600, and Bella paid $1200.

4. a. $\frac{7}{24}$ b. $1\frac{1}{2}$ c. $\frac{1}{9}$ d. 4

e. In multiplication, the numerator in the product and the denominator in the product are the result of multiplying the individual numerators and denominators. "Canceling" just recognizes that common factors in the numerators and denominators can be eliminated before multiplying the fractions rather than waiting until the product of the numerators and the product of the denominators are calculated.

5. $200. The first two payments took care of $\frac{2}{5} + (\frac{3}{4} \times \frac{2}{5}) = \frac{7}{10}$ of the loan. So the $60 represented $\frac{3}{10}$ of the loan, and each tenth of the loan was $20.

6. a. $100\% - 30\% = 70\%$ b. $100\% - x\%$

c. About $60. One way is to calculate the discount first (25% of $79.95) and then subtract the discount from the regular price. Another way is to calculate 75% of $79.95.

7. There are many possibilities. Be sure, for example, that the 5, the 2/3, and the 3/4 apply to the amounts represented by the *second* factors, and that the unit for each of the second factors is clear (e.g., pounds or cups of sugar).

8. a. The technique does not recognize that the first factor affects *all* of the second factor.

   b. $15\frac{5}{4} = 16\frac{1}{4}$

The most common algorithm taught is to change each of the factors to a fraction and multiply. (This algorithm could also be used on part (b), $5 \times \frac{13}{4} = \frac{65}{4} = 16\frac{1}{4}$, but is not necessary.)

   c. $\dfrac{10}{3} \times \dfrac{37}{5} = \dfrac{370}{15} = \ldots = 24\dfrac{2}{3}$ d. $\dfrac{127}{9} \times \dfrac{103}{8} = \dfrac{13081}{72} = \ldots = 181\dfrac{49}{72}$

9. a. One possible drawing:

   b. The 60 new ones must be the additional 20% over last year's, so 1% would be 3 employees, and 100% would be 300 employees last year.

   c. 300 + 60 = 360 employees this year

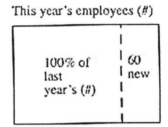

This year's employees (#)

10. a. 20%, the number in the whole student body; ¼, the number of voters; 35%, the number of voters

   b. One possible drawing is to the right.

   c. Is the drawing accurate enough to be trusted? We should check: A and B together have 60% of the vote, leaving 40% of the vote for C, so C does win.

   d. One way: C's 800 votes is 40% of the voters, so 1% of the voters would be $800 \div 40 = 20$ voters, and so 100% of the voters would be 2000 voters. But these 2000 voters are only 80% of the student body. 1% of the student body would be $2000 \div 80 = 25$ students, and so 100% of the student body would be 2500 students.

7.3 Dividing by a Fraction

1. a. 16   b. 8   c. 4   d. 2   e. 1   f. $\frac{1}{2}$

2.

3. b. $5 \times 1\frac{1}{2}$ (or $5 \times \frac{3}{2}$) $= 7\frac{1}{2}$

   c. $24 \times 1\frac{1}{2}$ (or $24 \times \frac{3}{2}$) $= 36$

   d. $7\frac{1}{2} \times 1\frac{1}{2}$ (or $7\frac{1}{2} \times \frac{3}{2}$) $= 11\frac{1}{4}$

e. $\frac{4}{5} \times 1\frac{1}{2}$ (or $\frac{4}{5} \times \frac{3}{2}$) $= 1\frac{1}{5}$

4. 16, 8, 4, 2, 1

5. You can make $1\frac{1}{2}$ recipes. The $1\frac{1}{2}$ refers to the $\frac{1}{2}$ cup amount—the number of recipes that can be made. The $\frac{3}{4}$ refers to the sugar on hand, which is the unit in this case. The $1\frac{1}{2}$ refers back to the unit: $\frac{3}{4}$.

6. There are four $\frac{1}{6}$ units in $\frac{2}{3}$ unit.

7.

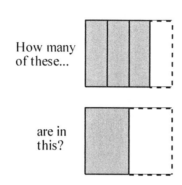

How many of these...

are in this?

What part of the $\frac{3}{4}$ is the same as $\frac{1}{2}$? $\frac{2}{3}$.

$\frac{2}{3}$ refers back to the $\frac{3}{4}$. That is, the referent unit for the $\frac{3}{4}$ is one whole, the referent unit for the $\frac{1}{2}$ is the whole rectangle, but the referent unit for the $\frac{2}{3}$ is the $\frac{3}{4}$ —the shaded area of the first rectangle.

8. a. Using the hexagon as the unit, find $\frac{5}{6}$ of 2 hexagons. To do so, replace the 2 hexagons with 6 rhombuses. $\frac{5}{6}$ would be five rhombuses, which can be replaced with 1 hexagon and 2 rhombuses: $1\frac{2}{3}$.

   b. Let the hexagon be the unit. Replace it with 6 triangles. How many halves (how many trapezoids) can be used to replace the 6 triangles? Four of the triangles would be one $\frac{1}{2}$. The other 2 triangles would be $\frac{2}{3}$ of a half, for a total of $1\frac{2}{3}$.

   Notice that parts (a) and (b) have the same answer. You should do (c), (d), (e), and (f) in a similar fashion, noting equivalent answers.

9. By marking each of the quarters into 3 pieces, 2 lines will coincide with the lines marking the thirds. Notice that 8 of these new slices can be found in the shaded area. Each new slice is also an eighth of the shaded area. Thus, there is one full two-thirds, and an eighth of another two-thirds, so the answer is $1\frac{1}{8}$.

10. With 1 gallon, $\frac{3}{4}$ of the wall can be painted. So $\frac{3}{5}$ of a gallon of paint will cover $\frac{3}{5}$ of $\frac{3}{4}$ of the wall. $\frac{3}{5} \times \frac{3}{4} = \frac{9}{20}$.

11. How many $\frac{3}{16}$ are in $\frac{3}{4}$? $\frac{3}{4} \div \frac{3}{16} = 4$. You make the drawing.

12. You are explaining why $3\frac{1}{2}$ is the answer, referring to your sketch. (Where is the $3\frac{1}{2}$ in your sketch?)

13. a. The $\frac{2}{3}$ refers to the $\frac{3}{4}$ of the unit. The $\frac{3}{4}$ refers to the unit. The $\frac{1}{2}$ refers to the unit.

b. The $\frac{1}{2}$ refers to the unit. The $\frac{3}{4}$ refers to the unit. The $\frac{2}{3}$ refers to the $\frac{3}{4}$ of the unit. (Note that the answers to parts (a) and (b) are the same. We are emphasizing repeated subtraction here.)

14. a. $\frac{1}{4}$ pan   b. $\frac{1}{2}$ cake   c. $3\frac{3}{4}$ recipe   d. $13\frac{1}{8}$ cups   e. 13 banners

f. $1 - (\frac{1}{2} + \frac{2}{5}) = \frac{1}{10}$. You make the drawings.

15. Possible answer: a. Cherie has 6 yards of fabric and wants to make as many identical skirts as possible. Each requires $1\frac{2}{3}$ yards of fabric. How many skirts can she make? (What happens to the remainder here?) Another: Val has 6 cups of flour and wants to make cookies. One batch calls for $1\frac{2}{3}$ cups of sugar. How many batches can he make? (What happens to the remainder in this situation? Can it be used for part of another batch? Can the fabric be used for another skirt?)

16. a. $(\frac{2}{3} \times (2 \times 9)) \div \frac{1}{2}$ b. $(0.5 \times 0.8) \times (6 + 1)$

17. a. No, no—try almost any example.

b. Yes, yes ($\frac{n}{n} = 1$), no

18. a. $\dfrac{8}{9} \div \dfrac{5}{6} = \dfrac{\frac{8}{9}}{\frac{5}{6}} = \dfrac{\frac{8}{9} \times \frac{6}{5}}{\frac{5}{6} \times \frac{6}{5}} = \dfrac{\frac{8}{9} \times \frac{6}{5}}{1} = \dfrac{8}{9} \times \dfrac{6}{5}$

b. $\dfrac{2\frac{1}{2}}{\frac{7}{8}} = \dfrac{2\frac{1}{2} \times \frac{8}{7}}{\frac{7}{8} \times \frac{8}{7}} = \dfrac{2\frac{1}{2} \times \frac{8}{7}}{1}$

Supplementary Learning Exercises for Section 7.3

1. a. There are 6 one-fourths in $1\frac{1}{2}$.

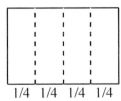

1/4   1/4   1/4   1/4   1/4   1/4

b. Pieces i and ii give one $\frac{2}{3}$, and pieces iii and iv give a second $\frac{2}{3}$. With some added marks, piece v is $\frac{1}{4}$ of another $\frac{2}{3}$. Notice the care necessary in interpreting piece v: What part of another $\frac{2}{3}$ is piece v?

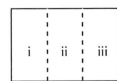
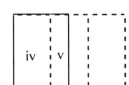

i   ii   iii   iv   v

d. How many $1\frac{1}{2}$ s are in (or make)
1? There is not a whole $1\frac{1}{2}$ in 1;
only a part of a $1\frac{1}{2}$ will make 1.
To get equal parts in the $1\frac{1}{2}$, put
in the other half mark.

What part
of the gray

makes this?

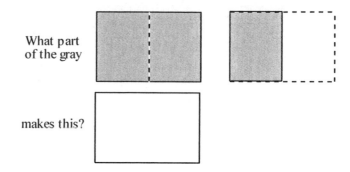

3.   Showing the equal shares may involve
putting in other cutting marks. For
example, for part (a), each share is
$\frac{1}{2} + \frac{1}{4} = \frac{3}{4}$.

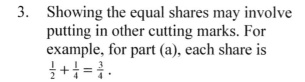

4.   a and b. Each fraction refers to the same unit.

c. The $\frac{c}{d}$ and the $\frac{e}{f}$ refer to the same unit, but the unit for the $\frac{a}{b}$ is the ($\frac{c}{d}$ of the unit).

d. For the repeated-subtraction view, the first two fractions refer to the same unit, but the $\frac{e}{f}$
tells how many of the $\frac{c}{d}$ s of the unit there are in the $\frac{a}{b}$ of the unit.

(For the rarer—in U.S. curricula, for fraction divisors—sharing-equally view, the $\frac{a}{b}$ and the
$\frac{e}{f}$ refer to the same unit, but the $\frac{c}{d}$ is some other unit.)

5.   Notice how important knowing the units for the different $\frac{1}{3}$ s is.

a. $6\frac{5}{12}$ cups   b. $4\frac{1}{2}$ cups

6.   a. $\frac{4}{3}$ times   b. $2 \times \frac{4}{3}$ times (or $2\frac{2}{3}$ times)   c. $3 \times \frac{4}{3}$ times (or 4 times)

d. $4\frac{1}{2} \times \frac{4}{3}$ times (or 6 times)   e. $\frac{7}{8} \times \frac{4}{3}$ times (or $1\frac{1}{6}$ times)

7.   What multiplication will "undo" a multiplication by $\frac{3}{4}$? Multiply by $\frac{4}{3}$, so set the machine
at $133\frac{1}{3}$%, if possible, or if the machine allows only whole numbers, use 133% for a close
approximation.

8. Even without knowing the personality of the child, you can be sure that the child is not applying a meaning for division. You might ask what $6 \div 2 = 3$ tells you to see whether the child does have a "how many 2s are in 6" understanding. If so, ask what $\frac{3}{4} \div \frac{1}{4} = 3$ tells you.

9. a. You can tell how many c's are in $a + b$ by seeing how many c's are in a, how many c's are in b, and adding those results. More algebraically,

$$(a+b) \div c = (a+b) \cdot \frac{1}{c} = (a \cdot \frac{1}{c}) + (b \cdot \frac{1}{c}) = (a \div c) + (b \div c)$$

    b. It is not at all clear that you can tell how many $(b + c)$'s are in a, by seeing how many $(b + c)$'s are in a and then in b, and adding those results. If you avoid zeroes, you will have a "counterexample." For instance, $24 \div (2 + 3) \neq (24 \div 2) + (24 \div 3)$.

7.4 Issues for Learning: Teaching Calculation with Fractions

1. $\frac{1}{5}$, from $\frac{3}{4} \times \left[1 - (\frac{1}{3} + \frac{2}{5}) \right] = \frac{3}{4} \times \left[1 - \frac{11}{15} \right] = \frac{3}{4} \times \frac{4}{15}$

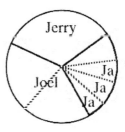

2. $0.9 \div 0.002 = 450$

3. 5 full recipes because $4 \div \frac{3}{4} = 5\frac{1}{3}$.

4. $1 - (\frac{5}{12} + \frac{1}{6} + \frac{1}{12}) = 1 - \frac{8}{12} = \frac{1}{3}$ and the $\frac{1}{3}$ is shared by 3. $\frac{2}{3} of \frac{1}{3} = \frac{2}{9}$.

5. 333 because $75 \div 0.2 = 375$, but $200 \div 0.6$ is only $333\frac{1}{3}$.

6. 10 full days because $(4 \times 2) \div \frac{3}{4} = 10\frac{2}{3}$.

7. $66\frac{2}{3}\%$. The excess amount was $\frac{1}{3} - \frac{1}{5} = \frac{2}{15}$. Comparing the $\frac{2}{15}$ to the planned $\frac{1}{5}$ gives $\frac{2}{15} \div \frac{1}{5} = \frac{10}{15} \approx 66\frac{2}{3}\%$.

8. a. 25%. The excess was $\frac{1}{2}$ cup, and $\frac{1}{2}$ cup compared to 2 cups is $\frac{1}{4}$, or 25%.

    b. 37.5%. You used $\frac{3}{4}$ cup less than the designated 2 cups. $\frac{3}{4} \div 2 = \frac{3}{4} \times \frac{1}{2} = \frac{3}{8} = 37.5\%$

Answers for Chapter 8: Multiplicative Comparisons and Multiplicative Reasoning

8.1 Quantitative Analysis of Multiplicative Situations

1. a. 4:1 or $\frac{4}{1}$ b. $\frac{1}{4}$ c. $\frac{4}{5}$

2. a. 4:3 or $\frac{4}{3}$ b. $\frac{3}{4}$ c. $\frac{4}{3}$ d. $\frac{3}{7}$ e. $\frac{4}{7}$

3. a. $\frac{2}{3}$ b. Twice as many, or 2:1   c. $\frac{1}{3}$ d. $\frac{4}{15}$; 4:15

    e. $\frac{6}{15}$, 6:15   f. 2:3   g. 3, 2   h. $\frac{2}{3}$ i. $\frac{3}{2}$, or $1\frac{1}{2}$

    j. Not enough information is given to answer.

4. If not, here is a drawing that could be helpful for Learning Exercise 3. Notice that you are answering the questions without knowing the actual numbers of seniors, females, or males.

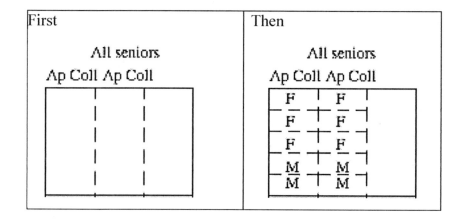

5. a. Here is a possible drawing, with D for drive-to-school, M for male, and F for female.

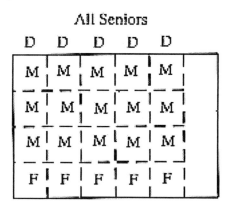

    b. Continuing the horizontal in the drawing gives 24 little rectangles, with the females who drive to school making up 5/24 of the whole senior class.

    c. 15/24 or 5/8; 15/24 or 5/8

d. ¼

e. We cannot tell, because there is no information about the non-drivers.

f. No

Note: For answers to 8.1 and 8.2 Supplementary Learning Exercises, see the end of 8.2 Answers for Learning Exercises.

8.2 Fractions in Multiplicative Comparisons

Instructor: If Exercises 5 and 6 of **Activity 4 Candy Bars** are assigned as homework, the answers are as follows. Making a drawing for part (a) is a good idea.

5. b. $\frac{3}{2}$, or $1\frac{1}{2}$ c. $\frac{2}{5}$ d. $\frac{2}{3}$ (compare b)

6. b. $\frac{4}{3}$, or $1\frac{1}{3}$ c. $\frac{3}{7}$ d. $\frac{3}{4}$

1. a. The ratio, # Anh's spools: # Jack's spools, is 3:8. So reversing the ratio, # Jack's: # Anh's = 8:3. That is, Jack uses $\frac{8}{3}$, or $2\frac{2}{3}$, times as many spools as Anh does. So if Anh uses 2 spools, Jack will use $2\frac{2}{3} \times 2 = 5\frac{1}{3}$ spools. The ratios represent multiplicative comparisons.

   b. Jack. We knew this from the first sentence in the problem because Anh uses less than Jack.

   c. The additive comparison leads to $5\frac{1}{3} - 2 = 3\frac{1}{3}$. Jack uses $3\frac{1}{3}$ spools more in one month than Anh does.

2. The first question, involving a multiplicative comparison, is answered by turning the ratio $9\frac{2}{7} : 5$ into the fraction form and simplifying. $9\frac{2}{7} : 5 = \frac{9\frac{2}{7}}{5} = \frac{65}{35} = 1\frac{6}{7}$. Claudia ran $\frac{9\frac{2}{7}}{5} = \frac{65}{35} = 1\frac{6}{7}$ times as many laps as Juan. The second question involves another additive comparison and leads to Claudia's running $9\frac{2}{7} - 5 = 4\frac{2}{7}$ laps farther than Juan.

3. The first question asks for the multiplicative comparison of 10 to $2\frac{3}{8}$ (sticks used: sticks in recipe). So, $10 : 2\frac{3}{8} = \frac{10}{2\frac{3}{8}} = \frac{80}{19} = 4\frac{4}{19}$, and Les is using $4\frac{4}{19}$ times as much butter as the recipe. The second question, $10 - 2\frac{3}{8} = 7\frac{5}{8}$ sticks of butter, involves an additive comparison.

4. This is like a candy bar problem with an addition—the value (14 meters) for the whole amount. The given sentence translates into a R:S = 3:4 ratio, which gives $\frac{3}{7}$ as the R part of the whole ribbon. So the ribbon part is $\frac{3}{7} \times 14 = 6$ meters, and the strips part is 8 meters.

5. Your quantitative analysis should include the dogs' weights, the two multiplicative comparisons, the additive comparison, and the parts-whole relationships. A drawing is definitely helpful here because there are two multiplicative comparisons and an additive comparison involved.

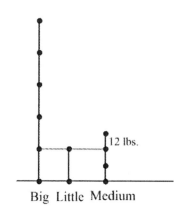

Big Little Medium

The other thirds of the medium dog's weight must also be 12 lb each, so the medium dog weighs 36 pounds. The little dog's weight matches 2 of the 12-lb pieces, so the little dog weighs 24 lb. Finally, the big dog weighs 120 lb.

6. A drawing makes this problem easy. Fractions of geese are shown on the line below:

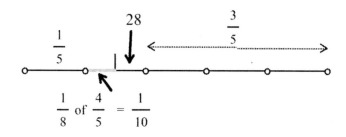

$\frac{1}{5} + \frac{1}{10} + \frac{3}{5} = \frac{9}{10}$ of the geese flew away. So $\frac{1}{10}$ are remaining.

$\frac{1}{10}$ is 28, so the total number of geese at the beginning is 280.

7. a. Your drawing and reasoning should be based on 4 pieces for Al for every 5 pieces for Babs. If the pieces make up the whole bar, there would be 9 pieces in all. Al, $\frac{4}{9}$ of the bar; Babs, $\frac{5}{9}$.

   b. Cameron, $\frac{4}{5}$ of the bar; Don, $\frac{1}{5}$. Notice that there is no multiplicative comparison in part (b).

   c. Emily, $\frac{3}{4}$ of the bar; Fran, $\frac{1}{4}$.

   d. Gay, $\frac{3}{10}$ of the bar; Haille, $\frac{6}{10}$ or $\frac{3}{5}$; Ida, $\frac{1}{10}$.

   e. Judy, $\frac{2}{3}$ of the bar; Keisha, $\frac{2}{9}$; Lannie, $\frac{1}{9}$. (The dashed segments are added to tell the fractions of the whole bar for K and L.)

Judy	Judy	
		Keisha
- - - -	- - - -	Keisha
- - - -	- - - -	Lannie

   f. Mick and Nick, each $\frac{1}{4}$ of the bar; Ollie, $\frac{1}{6}$; Pete, $\frac{2}{6}$ or $\frac{1}{3}$.

8. a. Al, 80¢ (not $0.80¢); Babs, $1

   b. Cameron, $1.44; Don, 36¢

   c. Emily, $1.35; Fran, 45¢

   d. Gay, 54¢; Haille, $1.08; Ida, 18¢

   e. Judy, $1.20; Keisha, 40¢; Lannie, 20¢

   f. Mick, 45¢; Nick, 45¢; Ollie, 30¢; Pete, 60¢

9. a. Recipe I, $\frac{1}{10}$ of the chunk, $\frac{1}{5}$ pound; II, $\frac{3}{10}$ of the chunk, $\frac{3}{5}$ pound; III, $\frac{3}{5}$ of the chunk, $1\frac{1}{5}$ pound

   b. I, 66¢; II, $1.98; III, $3.96

10. Charity A, $16; charity B, $8; charity C, $64

11. Quinn ate $\frac{8}{15} \times \frac{3}{4} = \frac{2}{5}$ of the whole pizza; Rhonda, $\frac{4}{15} \times \frac{3}{4} = \frac{1}{5}$ of the pizza; and Sue, $\frac{3}{15} \times \frac{3}{4} = \frac{1}{5} \times \frac{3}{4} = \frac{3}{20}$ of the pizza. The fifteenths come from thinking of Q:R as 8:4, so that S:R's 3:4 can be used in the same drawing. Note the different uses of $\frac{3}{4}$.

Supplementary Learning Exercises for Sections 8.1 and 8.2

1. a. 5:3 or 5 to 3   b. $\frac{5}{12}$ c. $\frac{5}{3}$ or $1\frac{2}{3}$ d. $\frac{3}{5}$

    e. 8   f. 2   g. 8:4 or 8 to 4

2.

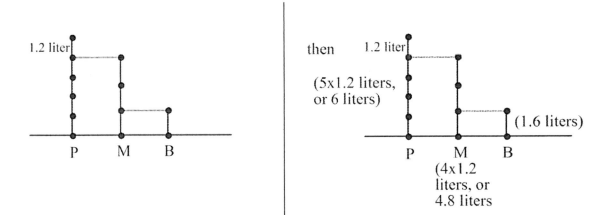

So, the total consumption was 6 + 4.8 + 1.6 = 12.4 liters. How did your quantitative analysis and drawing help you?

3.

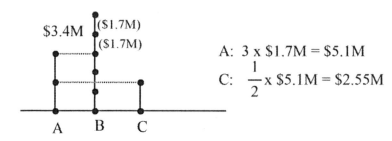

A: 3 x $1.7M = $5.1M

C: $\frac{1}{2}$ x $5.1M = $2.55M

What other quantities do you now know values for?

4. a.

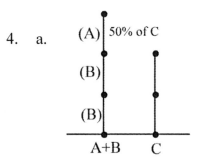

Total of the 5 pieces = 60 games
So each piece = 12 games.
A won 12 games, B 24, and C 24.

b.

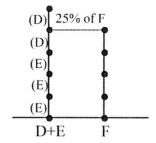

9 equal pieces -- 72 games
1 piece -- 8 games
D won 16 games, E 24,
and F 32.

5.   One possible diagram:

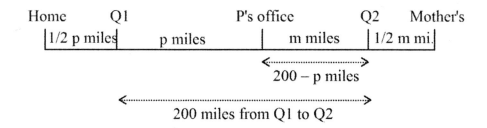

(Algebra could be used to solve this problem, but it is not difficult to find numbers that work: If *p* is 150 then *m* is 50, $\frac{1}{2}$ *p* is 75, and $\frac{1}{2}$ *m* miles is 25 miles. The total distance is (75 + 150 + 50 + 25) miles, or 300 miles. A diagram makes this problem an easy one to solve.)

6. Darla, $0.75; Ellie, $1.50; Fran, $3.75

7. a. Your drawing likely shows 2 boxes for Tom and 3 boxes for Ulysses. Tom is 2/5 of the bar, Ulysses 3/5.

b. Your drawing might show 3 boxes for Vicky, 4 boxes for Willie, and 8 boxes for Xavier. Vicky ate 1/5 of the bar, Willie ate 4/15 of the bar, and Xavier ate 8/15 of the bar.

   c. Your drawing might show 1/3 of the bar for Yolanda, leaving 2/3 of the bar, so Zeb ate $\frac{3}{4} \times \frac{2}{3} = \frac{1}{2}$ of the bar, leaving $1 - (\frac{1}{3} + \frac{1}{2}) = \frac{1}{6}$ of the bar for Arnie.

8. a. Tom, \$1.20; Ulysses, \$1.80

    b. Vicky, \$0.60; Willie, \$0.80; Xavier, \$1.60

    c. Yolanda, \$1.00; Zeb, \$1.50; Arnie, \$0.50

9. 81 M&M's. After Tuesday, there were 5/6 of the original M&M's remaining. After Wednesday, there were $\frac{2}{3} \times \frac{5}{6} = \frac{5}{9}$ of the original M&M's remaining. If 5/9 of the original number is 45, then 1/9 of the original number M&M's is 1/5 of 45, or 9, and then 9 one-ninths of the M&M's would be 81.

Answers for Chapter 9: Ratios, Rates, Proportions, and Percents

9.1 Ratio as a Measure

1. The manager could keep track of how many ounces of coffee beans were used per pot of water. This would yield a ratio for each batch that can then be used to compare for strongest coffee.

2. One way: Determine the change in population from the numbers of live births and deaths. Then divide that difference by the number of 1000s in the population. What does this accomplish? If you do the calculations, are you surprised at the answers, from country to country?

3. a. The usual way for most computers: the size of the tiny dots that make up the display (pixels)

   b. The number of black dots per square inch

   c. The slope, just as you did with the ski slopes

   d. The number of miles or kilometers between them

   e. The number of people per square mile (or square kilometer)

   f. The fraction, $\frac{\text{number of red balls}}{\text{total number of balls}}$ (this is how the "probability" would be assigned)

   g. A common way: the grade point average (the number of honor points per unit of credit)

   h. The ratio of the number of teaspoons of sugar used to the volume of liquid involved

   i. The ratio of the number of tea bags used to the amount of water used

4. Keep the angles the same, but multiply the length of each side by the same number to keep the ratio of new length:old length the same for every side. (The polygons are then said to be "similar," in the technical sense of geometry.)

5. Sizes of corresponding angles, lengths of corresponding sides (the ratio, length in one: corresponding length in other, will be the same from side to side), areas, ratio of the areas, total number of degrees in all the angles.

Supplementary Learning Exercises for Section 9.1

1. Perhaps. "Let's look at drawings. (Make rough drawings.) So the 105 by 100 does look more nearly square. The ratio of the two dimensions is more informative than the difference of the two dimensions."

2. All of the ratios, length:width, length:height, and width:height are closer to 1 for Box 2, so Box 2 is more nearly a cube.

3. In parts (b) and (d), a ratio would be appropriate (# lemons or salt:amount of water). And in part (a), it could be the ratio, maximum weight lifted to the weight of the lifter, or just the

maximum weight the person could lift, and in part (c), it might be the amount of force that would bend the bar.

4. The ratio of the real and mirror heights of your image will be quite different from the ratio of the real and mirror widths of your image, so you will look distorted.

5. The results should taste different, with 5 times as much chili powder but only 1½ times as much garlic powder in the second version.

6. Although his daughter does have twice as many hits, she has batted more than twice as many times.

9.2 Comparing Ratios

1. a. Sample explanation: Using scoops of coffee to cups of water ratios, the two brews give 3:4 or $\frac{3}{4}$:1, versus 4:6 or $\frac{4}{6}$:1 = $\frac{2}{3}$:1. Comparing $\frac{3}{4}(=\frac{9}{12})$ and $\frac{2}{3}(=\frac{8}{12})$ gives that the 3 scoops for 4 cups is stronger.

   b. In the same way (but using number sense to compare the fractions per 1 cup), the 4 scoops for 8 cups is stronger.

   c. These are illustrated in the solutions given above, in case you immediately rewrote the ratios as fractions (4:6 = $\frac{4}{6}$, for example) and reasoned with those forms alone.

2. a. Stronger because $\frac{8}{15} > \frac{1}{2}$ (How did you get the fractions?)

   b. Weaker than the intended recipe since $\frac{9}{19} < \frac{1}{2}$ (number sense?), and weaker than the 8:15 one since we already know it is stronger than the intended recipe.

   c. Many possibilities, as long as your ratios are slightly greater than 1:2—e.g., 11:20

   d. Many possibilities, as long as your ratios are slightly less than 1:2—e.g., 11:24

   e. Many possibilities, as long as your ratios are quite a bit greater than 1:2—e.g., 7:8

   f. Many possibilities, as long as your ratios are quite a bit less than 1:2—e.g., 1:12

3. Answer similarly to the answers in 2 (c), (d), (e), and (f). To get a ratio slightly greater than 1:1, you might have to "jump" to something like 11:10 rather than just 2:1, which would be quite strong.

4. The first question translates into 10:4 = x:50 (or $\frac{10}{4} = \frac{x}{50}$ or $\frac{5}{2} = \frac{x}{50}$), giving x = 125 tbsp. Notice that another, less "mechanical," line of reasoning also makes sense: The cocoa requires 10 ÷ 4 = $2\frac{1}{2}$ tbsp of cocoa per cup of milk. So for 50 cups, they need $50 \times 2\frac{1}{2}$, or 125 tbsp. Then the ratio, 2:$\frac{1}{8}$, for the number of tbsp to the number of cups of cocoa, might lead either to $\frac{2}{\frac{1}{8}} = \frac{125}{x}$, or to the rate,16 tbsp per cup and 125 ÷ 16. Either gives an answer of $7\frac{13}{16}$ cups of cocoa.

5. The rate from # inches: # miles should tell which will give the greater length of line, since the number of miles between the cities stays the same. Adam's rate is 6:9, or $\frac{6}{9}$ inches per mile.

Matt's rate is 8:12, or $\frac{8}{12}$ inches per mile. Since $\frac{6}{9} = \frac{8}{12}$ (each $= \frac{2}{3}$), their lines would have the same length.

6. Try different values for the distances A and B can travel. Suppose B travels 10 miles in 2 hours, and A travels 12 miles in 3 hours; or 18 miles in 3 hours; or 24 miles in 3 hours. Would all of the numbers fit the situation? Now can you answer the question?

7. One possible reason is that doubling recipe 1 gives 6 cups orange concentrate and 8 cups of water, which is easily compared to the 5:8 situation. Recipe 2 does not yield to such easy reasoning (unless one might think to do recipe 1 eight times and recipe 2 five times!).

8. A's rate is $\frac{40}{3} = 13\frac{1}{3}$ km per hour; B's rate is $\frac{67}{5} = 13\frac{2}{5}$ km per hour. So B travels slightly faster (has a slightly greater speed).

9. We need to determine B's rate of working. Using A's rate, A will make $9 \times 13 = 117$ parts in 9 hours, so B must have made $243 - 117 = 126$ parts in the 9 hours. B's rate, then, is $\frac{126}{9} = 14$ parts per hour, slightly faster than A's. So B would be more productive.

10. Finding the price per ounce (the "unit price") gives $\frac{109}{12} = 9\frac{1}{12}$ cents per ounce for the larger can, and $\frac{98}{10.75} = 9\frac{5}{43}$ cents per ounce for the smaller can. So the larger can is a slightly better buy. If you used an ounces:cents approach, you would get the same end result, but your rates, and your reasoning about the final values, would be different from those here.

11. Compare $\frac{4}{9}$ and $\frac{3}{7}$, either by finding equal fractions with a common denominator ($\frac{3}{7} = \frac{27}{63}$ and $\frac{4}{9} = \frac{28}{63}$) or by changing the fractions to decimals. Jane has slightly more crayons left.

12. One approach is to compare the number of girls:number of boys ratios. Another is to see what fractions of the whole class are involved: $\frac{13}{24}$ versus $\frac{15}{28}$. Mrs. Heath's class has a slightly greater representation of girls.

13. Comparing the two rates from $\frac{250}{12} = 20\frac{5}{6}$ miles per gallon and $\frac{145}{7.5} = 19\frac{1}{3}$ miles per gallon shows that car A is more economical.

14. Assume no bigamy! Rather than the algebraic $\frac{2}{3}M = \frac{3}{4}W$ approach, try making a diagram. Start with a rectangle for all the men, and mark the married men. Then, keeping in mind that the number of married men = the number of married women, add to the diagram to show all the women. Adding a few more line segments enables you to see the M:W ratio of 9:8.

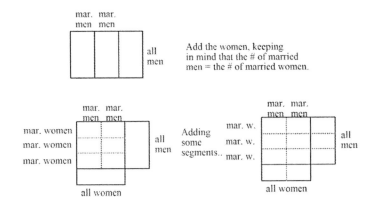

15. There are different ways. (1) Replace the ratios with equal ratios having the same second entries: $(133 \times 115):(161 \times 115)$ and $(95 \times 161):(115 \times 161)$; and then compare 133×115 and 95×161. (2) Change the ratios to fraction form and then use methods that you earlier learned to determine whether or not two fractions are equal. Or (3) Change the ratios to fractions and then to decimals (this way is probably easiest with a calculator). The fact that the ratios are equal may make one suspect that there might be an easier way: Simplify each ratio: $\frac{133}{161} = \frac{7 \times 19}{7 \times 23} = \frac{19}{23}$ and $\frac{95}{115} = \frac{5 \times 19}{5 \times 23} = \frac{19}{23}$! See Exercise 16 for a shortcut.

16. a. $a:b = (ad):(bd)$ (or $\frac{a}{b} = \frac{ad}{bd}$) and $c:d = (bc):(bd)$ (or $\frac{c}{d} = \frac{bc}{bd}$). Then the ratios (or fractions) are equal if $ad - bc$.

    b. $x = 144$; $x = 39$

    c. Not in general. Try it on, say, $\frac{1}{4} + \frac{1}{8}$ and $\frac{1}{2} \times \frac{1}{2}$.

17. Because $\frac{3}{4} + \frac{2}{4} = \frac{5}{4}$, which apparently would mean 5 hits in 4 at-bats, this way cannot be correct. Indeed, 3:4 "+" 2:4 here should equal 5:8, 5 hits in 8 at-bats. (The " " marks are a reminder that this is not the usual addition of numbers.) Critics say that ratios should be added this way: $a{:}b$ "+" $c{:}d = (a+c){:}(b+d)$.

18. From S. Lamon, 1999

Pounds	Cost	Notes
1	4.25	given
10	42.50	a × 10
2	8.50	a × 2
0.1	0.425	a ÷ 10
12.1	51.425	b + c + d
0.05	0.2125	d ÷ 2
0.01	0.0425	f ÷ 5
0.03	0.1275	g × 3
12.13	51.5525	e + h

19. a. The rate is 60 donuts:5 minutes, or $\frac{60 \text{ donuts}}{5 \text{ minutes}}$. This is a rate because it remains the same when quantities change; that is, this same rate applies whether one is determining number of donuts for any particular time period.

   b. $\frac{12 \text{ donuts}}{1 \text{ minute}}$

   c. $\frac{12 \text{ donuts}}{1 \text{ minute}}$, so 60×12 donuts in 60 minutes, or 720 donuts in an hour

   d. $\frac{60}{5} = \frac{x}{60}$. Multiply both sides of the equation by 300 (or cross-multiply, as in Exercise 16). $5x = 3600$. And $x = 720$ donuts.

20. a. The rate is 23 miles:1 gallon (or $\frac{23 \text{ miles}}{1 \text{ gallon}}$). This is a rate because it remains the same when quantities change; that is, this same rate applies whether one is determining number of gallons for any particular number of miles.

   b. $\frac{23 \text{ miles}}{1 \text{ gallon}}$

   c. $\frac{23 \text{ miles}}{1 \text{ gallon}}$ so 12×23 miles with 12 gallons, or 276 miles.

   d. $\frac{23}{1} = \frac{x}{12}$. Multiply both sides of the equation by 12. $x = 276$ miles.

21. a. The desired rate is $\frac{7 \text{ ugrads}}{2 \text{ grads}}$ because as the numbers of undergraduates and graduate students change, the ratio should stay the same.

   b. $\frac{7 \text{ ugrads}}{2 \text{ grads}} = \frac{3.5 \text{ ugrads}}{1 \text{ grad}}$, or 3.5 undergrads per graduate student

   c. 3.5 undergrads for each graduate student, so if there are 100 graduate students, there should be 350 undergrads.

   d. $\frac{7}{2} = \frac{x}{100}$. Multiplying both sides by 100 gives $x = 350$.

22. The ratio of girls to boys is 12:11. The number of girls and the number of boys do not vary.

23. Problem to be done in grocery store. Student does not have answer. There is any unit rate such as cost per pound of cheese or the small labels found on most grocery store shelves that has cost ounce to assist shoppers in comparing unalike quantities.

24. a. Andy drove faster because he covered more miles in less time, so his mph would be greater. (You may be helped by making up values for the quantities.)

   b. Donna swam faster because Carla swam fewer laps in more time, so her laps per minute would be less than Donna's.

   c. We can't tell. Make up numbers to show that any of the first three possibilities could happen.

Supplementary Learning Exercises for Section 9.2

1.   a. A proportion is an equality between two ratios.

     b. A rate is ratio of quantities that change but leave the value of the ratio the same.

2.   a. To sing the same song would take the group of 3 singers about the same amount of time
         as it takes one singer.
     b. A larger crew should be able to do the job in less time, not more time.

3.   a. $\frac{15}{16}$ mile (What was *your* thinking?)

     b. $8\frac{1}{8}$ miles   c. $2\frac{1}{2}$ inches   d. 24 inches   e. $\frac{1}{5}$ inch

4.   a. $1\frac{1}{15}$ cups of sugar   b. $1\frac{19}{45}$ cups of sugar (Now you know why recipes are usually just
         halved or doubled, rather than adjusted to fit the amount of ingredients available!)
     c. $3\frac{3}{4}$ cups of flour   d. $11\frac{1}{4}$ cups of flour
     What methods did you use—mechanical proportion solving? Unit rates?

5.   a. 2.4% loss in fuel efficiency   b. 2.4% gain in fuel efficiency

     c. 1.05% loss in fuel efficiency   d. $166\frac{2}{3}$ lbs reduction in weight

     e. 200 lbs increase in weight

6.   a.   Although the conclusion (that Bob has the best ratio) is correct, the *reasoning* does not
         take into account how many errors Bob took.
     b.   The thinking does not take into account that Andy also had the fewest assists.
     c.   Here are the assist to turnovers ratios: Andy, 4 to $10 = 0.4$ to 1, usually reported as 0.4,

         understood to be a unit ratio; Bob, 13 to $17 = \frac{\frac{13}{17}}{1} \approx \frac{0.76}{1}$, or just 0.76; and Cam,

     9 to $13 = \frac{\frac{9}{13}}{1} \approx \frac{0.69}{1}$. So Bob has the best ratio.

7.   No. The team may have won 8 and lost 6, or won 12 and lost 9, for example. Ratios are often
     simplified.

8.   a. $\frac{2\frac{2}{3}}{1}$ (or $2\frac{2}{3}$ to 1)   b. $\frac{\frac{3}{8}}{1}$ c. $\frac{2\frac{4}{5}}{1}$

9.   The ratio of this year's budget to last year's budget has been 105% to 1 for the last ten years.

10. Dale's rate is $\frac{\$30}{2\frac{1}{2}\text{ h}} = \frac{\$12}{1\text{ h}}$, or \$12 per hour. So in 6 hours, Dale can expect to earn \$72.

11. a. $\frac{\text{number of births}}{92,228,000} = \frac{30.1}{1000} = \frac{92,228 \times 30.1}{92,228,000} \approx \frac{2,776,063}{92,228,000}$, so about 2,776,000 births.

b. $\dfrac{4,058,814}{\text{pop in 1000s}} \approx \dfrac{14.7}{1000} = \dfrac{4,058,814 \div 14.7}{\text{pop in 1000s}} \approx \dfrac{276,110}{\text{pop in 1000s}}$, so about 276,110,000 people.
(Notice that cross-multiplication *avoids* having to think about the situation even though it might lead to the same calculations!)

12. a.   Half of 313,232,000 is 156,616,000, so over these females' lifetimes, the number of births could add about $156,616,000 \times 2.06 = 322,628,960$ children to the population.

b.   TRFs less than 2, if they do not increase, predict that a country's population will decrease (the two parents would not be replaced).

c.   A young woman—probably the TFR, because that gives an idea of the culture's typical number of children she will have. The public health official would probably find the birth rate more compelling in the short term, because it will suggest how the population will grow in the near future.

13. a.   The ratio, number of beats to time, stays the same for different intervals of time (or for different numbers of beats).

b.   Yes; 10 seconds is 1/6 of a minute, so 1/6 of 72 = 12 gives the number of beats. (Sometimes children think that a "per minute" rate does not apply to less than a minute.)

9.3 Percents in Comparisons and Changes

1. The percent discount on the first coat is $\frac{30}{120} = 25\%$, and on the second coat, $\frac{30}{150} = 20\%$. "Which is a better buy?" could be answered by looking at the percent discount. Looking just at the dollars saved, one might argue that they are the same buy, or that the second coat is a better buy because you saved the same amount but got a better coat (perhaps).

2. Test 1: 75%; test 2: 76%. The instructor would probably weight the tests the same, and give the average as $\frac{75\% + 76\%}{2} = 75.5\%$. But combining the points, you received 59 out of the 78 possible, or about 75.6%. If the scores were quite different, the two methods give noticeably different results (try the two methods on 10 out of 20 and 80 out of 100).

3. $\frac{4}{9} = 44.\overline{4}\%$ and $\frac{3}{7} = 42.\overline{857142}\%$, so Jane has more left.

4. a. 58%   b. 42%   c. $25   d. 40%   e. 75%

5. The given box represents $\frac{3}{4}$ of some (unknown) amount, so to represent the whole amount you need another $\frac{1}{4}$ (or 25%) of the whole amount, or $\frac{1}{3}$ of what is showing. Then add another $\frac{1}{4}$ of the whole to get 125%. The given box is then $\frac{3}{5}$, or 60%, of the 125% box. Notice again how important it is to know what your fraction or percent is a fraction or percent *of*.

6. Cut the box into 3 parts; 2 parts represent 100%, the unit rectangle in this case. Cut that into 3 parts. One of the parts represents $33\frac{1}{3}\%$ of the unit rectangle.

7. $4.2 million is 90% of $4.67 million.

8. a. 25%

b. 20%

c. 87,450 – 72,625 is 14,825, which is an increase of about 20.4% from 72,625.

d. 20,125 – 17,750 = 2375, which is a decrease of about 11.8% from 20,125.

9. a. 25% (Notice the "larger than.")

   b. 20% (As "larger" does in 9(a), "less" also connotes an additive comparison)

   c. 125%

   d. 80% (Re-examine your answers for 9(a) and 9(b) with answers for 9(c) and 9(d) in mind.)

10. 50% increase

11. $4.00; $2.40

12. About 10,780 ($10567 \div 0.98 \approx 10782.7$)

13. 420 pages. The given fractions and percent account for 70% of the pages, with the other 30% or $\frac{3}{10}$ being the 65 + 61 = 126 pages. So $\frac{1}{10}$ of the pages must be 126 ÷ 3 = 42 pages, and so $\frac{10}{10}$ of the pages would be 420 pages.

14. 100%

15. Pat's new salary will be $17.98 an hour, and her old salary was $14.50 an hour.

16. About 1120

17. $40 million; one department $800,000, the other $400,000

18. 24 points in the first half. Angie, Beth, and Carlita accounted for $\frac{1}{3} + \frac{3}{20} + \frac{1}{4} = \frac{11}{15}$ of the points (using fractions to avoid inaccuracies with the $\frac{1}{3}$). That means that the other 16 points represent $\frac{4}{15}$ of the total points, so $\frac{1}{15}$ of the total points would be 4 points, giving 60 for the total points scored. 40% of those points, or 24 points, were scored in the first half.

19. About $230. The sketch below may help, with a focus on the $\frac{5}{8}$ of her income being $450.

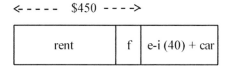

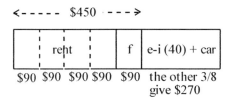

20. a. $\approx \frac{1}{3}$ of 120, or 40 people (Why is $\frac{1}{3}$ better than 0.3 of 120?)

    b. $\approx \frac{1}{2}$ of 12, or 6 pounds

    c. $\approx \frac{2}{3}$ of 66, or 44 kilometers

    d. $\approx$ 15% of 40, or $6 (10% of 40, plus half of that)

    e. $\approx \frac{1}{4}$ of 100 or 25 miles (Why is $\frac{1}{4}$ better than 0.2 or $\frac{1}{5}$?)

    f. $\approx \frac{1}{3}$ of 66, or 22 minutes

g. $\approx \frac{3}{4}$ of 400, or $300

h. 66 is $\approx \frac{2}{3}$ of 100, so $\approx \frac{1}{3}$ of 200, so $\approx \frac{1}{6}$ of 400. $\frac{1}{6}$ is half of $\frac{1}{3}$, so about 16%.

i. 74 miles is $\approx \frac{3}{4}$ of 100 miles, so $\approx \frac{1}{4}$ or 25% of 300 miles.

j. 24 pounds is $\approx 50\%$ of 48 pounds

21. a. 20 people   b. 64 pounds   c. 52 kilometers   d. $9.60

    e. 10 miles   f. 22 minutes   g. $525   h. 20%

    i. 10%   j. 12 pounds

22. a. $2\frac{2}{3}\%$ of all the students already qualify; $1\frac{1}{3}\%$ of all are newly eligible = 3600 students, so 1% of all = 2700 students and 100% of all = 270,000 students; 1200 students are newly eligible from urban schools, 900 from urban areas.

    b. $11\% \approx \frac{1}{9}$, so about $9 \times 1500 = 13,500$ workers

23. About $160 billion. One percent would be $48 billion $\div$ 30 = $1.6 billion, so 100% would be $160 billion. Notice that the $\div$ 30 and $\times$ 100 steps correspond to multiplying by $\frac{100}{30}$, or dividing by $\frac{30}{100} = 0.30$. An algebraic approach might lead to the equation $0.30 \times T = 48$ billion, giving the solution $T = \frac{48 \text{ billion}}{0.30}$, with the same calculation involved.

24. a. About $445,015 \div 54 \approx 8241$ votes
    b. About $100 \times 8241 = 824,100$ total votes

    c. Either about $824,100 - 445,015 = 379,085$ or about $46\% \times 824,100 = 379,086$. A news report might read, "About 379,000."

25. a. The cut of $1 to $9 requires a raise of $\frac{1}{9} \approx 11.1\%$ to return to the original.
    b. The cut of $1.85 to $16.65 requires a gain of $\frac{1.85}{16.65} \approx 11.1\%$ to return to the original.

    c. The answers to parts (a) and (b) suggest that the starting hourly wage does not matter. An algebraic approach shows why: Let W be the starting hourly wage. Then the 10% cut, or $0.1W$, will give $0.9W$ as the new hourly wage, requiring a gain of $\frac{0.1W}{0.9W} = \frac{1}{9} \approx 11.1\%$ to return to the original hourly wage.

26. About 9.1%, from $\frac{16}{176} \approx 9.09\%$. As in Learning Exercise 25, the same loss would apply to any gain of 10%, to return to the original starting value.

27. If S represents the starting value on Monday, then $1.05S$ is the value at the start of Tuesday. So $1.02 \times 1.05\,S = 1.071S$ is the starting value on Wednesday, and $0.97 \times 1.071\,S = 1.03887S$ is the value at the end of Wednesday. So the exact change over the three days is plus 3.887%. With large values of S, this difference from 4% could be significant.

Supplementary Learning Exercises for Section 9.3

1. $\frac{697}{1000}$ is easily expressed in terms of hundreds ($\frac{69.7}{100}$, so = 69.7%), whereas $\frac{7}{13}$ will require calculation.

2. a. 75% (100% of the original price – 25% of the original price)
    b. 60%   c. 85%   d. 50%   e. 75%   f. 100%

3. a. $\approx 6.7\%$ b. $4\frac{1}{6}\%$ c. $6\frac{1}{4}\%, 6\frac{1}{4}\%$ d. $30,000

    e. About \$3:\$20, or 15% (approximating the increase of \$2.95 by \$3 and \$19.95 by \$20)
    f. 20,000 before; 18,800 after (Each 1% loss in the before employment = 200 people.)
    g. The *actual* change in the tax is 1%, but that 1% is a 10% increase over the old 10% tax.

4. a. About 30%   b. About 25%   c. About \$9   d. \$2.49 (drawing?)
    e. About 40¢   f. \$18.94

5. a. About 2738
    b. About 58,460
    c. Between the polling time and the election, events might happen that significantly influence voters, so the 37% could go up or down.

6. a. 6.2 hot dogs per minute
    b. Continuing to eat hot dogs at that rate for an hour is not reasonable.
    c. One way: In 4 minutes, the champion would eat 24.8 hot dogs, and the challenger would eat 21.2. So the challenger would be 3.6 hot dogs behind. Another way: The difference in their rates, $6.2 - 5.3 = 0.9$ hot dogs per minute, gives a difference of 3.6 hot dogs in 4 minutes.
    d. Not likely. Most eaters likely slow down as they continue to eat. You could also argue that the *top* finishers, on the other hand, may be able to maintain a constant rate.

7. a. Proportion: $110:9 = x:14$, $x \approx 171$ calories. Unit rate: $110:9 = 12\frac{2}{9}:1$; so for 14 crackers, $14 \times 12\frac{2}{9} = 171\frac{1}{9}$ calories, or 171 calories. Similarly, about 5.4 grams of fat.
    b. Proportion way: $\dfrac{3.5}{9} = \dfrac{65}{y}$, $y \approx 167$ crackers
    c. $\dfrac{3.5}{65} \approx 0.0538$, so about 5%.

Supplementary Learning Exercises for Chapters 7, 8, and 9

1. Lisa's rate was 1.5 ounces of white per drop of green. Since Rachel had the same shade, her rate of white to green must have been the same. Since Rachel used 6 drops of green, she must have used $6 \times 1.5 = 9$ ounces of white. Alternatively, solve $\frac{6}{4} = \frac{x}{6}$.

2. Drawings may be helpful here. With $\frac{3}{4}$ gallon, Todd should be able to paint $\frac{3}{4}$ as much as he could with 1 whole gallon, or $\frac{3}{4} \times \frac{3}{5} = \frac{9}{20}$ of the wall. For the entire wall question, since 1 gallon paints $\frac{3}{5}$ of the wall, $\frac{1}{3}$ gallon would paint $\frac{1}{5}$ of the wall, and it would take 5 times

as much to paint the whole $\frac{5}{5}$ of the wall, or $5 \times \frac{1}{3} = \frac{5}{3} = 1\frac{2}{3}$ gallons of paint. The two

questions could be addressed "mechanically" with $\frac{\frac{3}{5}}{1} = \frac{x}{\frac{3}{4}}$ and $\frac{\frac{3}{5}}{1} = \frac{1}{x}$.

3. In 8 hours, the worker whose rate is 36 parts per hour will make 288 parts. That means the other worker made 512 − 288 = 224 parts in the 8 hours, a rate of 28 parts per hour.

4. A drawing may be helpful here. The 16 liters fill $\frac{2}{5}$ of the tank, so 8 liters would fill $\frac{1}{5}$ of the tank, and $5 \times 8 = 40$ liters would fill the whole tank. Its volume is 40 liters. Can you also use a proportion here?

5. This situation is just repeated addition, so John needs $15 \times \frac{3}{8} = \frac{45}{8} = 5\frac{5}{8}$ meters of ribbon.

    Notice that the proportion $\frac{\frac{3}{8}}{1} = \frac{x}{15}$ could be used. The (advanced) proportional reasoning has repeated addition as a special case.

6. Since 6 trees represent $\frac{3}{2}$ of the trees, 2 trees would be $\frac{1}{2}$ of the trees, so there would be 4 trees in the park. Alternatively, $\frac{6}{\frac{3}{2}} = \frac{x}{1}$, where the unit for the $\frac{3}{2}$ and the 1 is the number of trees in the park.

7. If $\frac{1}{3}$ of the cars has 18 cars, then all $\frac{3}{3}$ of the cars would have 3 times as many, or 54.

8. Similarly, if the 9 dogs represent $\frac{3}{7}$ of all the dogs, then 3 dogs would represent $\frac{1}{7}$ of the dogs. So the whole $\frac{7}{7}$ of the dogs at the pound would be 7×3, or 21, dogs.

9. One way, focusing on 7 days per week, 3.5 kg per week per 10 persons: 50 people, then, would take $5 \times 3.5 = 17.5$ kg per week. In 28 days (4 weeks), they would require $4 \times 17.5 = 70$ kg of sugar.

10. Ten small glasses will fill $\frac{10}{15}$ or $\frac{2}{3}$ of the large jar, or what nine large glasses will fill. So $\frac{2}{3} \times 9 = 6$ large glasses will fill the small jar. Alternatively, one small glass will fill $\frac{9}{15}$ of a large glass, so 10 small glasses would match $10 \times \frac{9}{15}$ or six large glasses. Still another alternative: Solve $\frac{15}{9} = \frac{10}{x}$. Can you explain where this proportion comes from?

11. In one week, the horse will eat $10 \div 3 = 3\frac{1}{3}$ pounds of hay, so in five weeks, the horse will eat $5 \times 3\frac{1}{3} = 16\frac{2}{3}$ pounds of hay.

12. The 15 chips represent $\frac{5}{6}$ of the unit, so $\frac{1}{6}$ of the unit would be three chips, and $6 \times 3 = 18$ would represent the whole $\frac{6}{6}$ of the unit. Then $\frac{2}{3}$ of the unit would be 12 chips, and $1\frac{1}{2}$ of the units would be 27 chips. The questions could also be handled by proportions; can you write them?

13. 40 kilometers in 16 minutes is a rate of 2.5 kilometers per minute. So in 36 minutes, the trip should cover $36 \times 2.5 = 90$ kilometers. Alternatively, 40 minutes is 2.5 times as much as 16 minutes, so the train should cover 2.5 times as much in 40 minutes as it does in 16 minutes: $2.5 \times 36 = 90$ kilometers. Another method would use a proportion: $\frac{16}{40} = \frac{36}{x}$.

14. Beeburg. Antville's budget was \$12M, as was Cowtown's, but Beeburg's was \$12.5M.

15. 100,000. The unit for the five-eighths is Middletown's population, suggesting looking at eighths of M's population. Then M's excess population of 15,000 over L's shows that each eighth of M's population is 5000. L then has 25,000 and B 100,000.

16. 48. A drawing might suggest an analysis leading to the following reasoning. The known fractions eaten give $\frac{1}{8} + \frac{1}{8} + \frac{1}{8} + \frac{1}{3} + \frac{1}{4}$, or $\frac{23}{24}$ of the bag. So Fran's two chocolates were $\frac{1}{24}$ of the bag, and the whole bag ($\frac{24}{24}$) contained 48 chocolates.

17. Because they paint at the same rate, this amounts to an additive situation. Joel is 80 square yards ahead of Kendrick when Kendrick starts, so he will be 80 square yards ahead when he has painted 600 square yards. Kendrick will have painted 520 square yards.

18. This situation is proportional, with the Lewis to Max ratio of square yards being 120:40 or 3:1. So, Max will have painted 200 square yards when Lewis has painted 600.

19. Tyler: \$7 per hour; Ullie: \$8.50 per hour.

20. Velma will pay $\frac{1}{3}$ of the rent, Winnie will pay $\frac{4}{15}$, and Zoe will pay $\frac{2}{5}$.

Answers for Chapter 10: Integers and Other Number Systems

10.1 Big Ideas about Signed Numbers

1. a. $^-75.2, ^-22, ^-3, ^-1, ^-(\frac{2}{3}), \frac{3}{4}, 1, ^+50$

    b. $^-5, ^-1.2, ^-0.9, ^-\frac{4}{9}, ^-0.1, \frac{4}{9}, 0.5, \frac{13}{10}, 2\frac{9}{10}, 3.1$

2. a. 8. The additive inverse, or opposite, of $^-8$ is 8.

    b. $^-0 = 0$ The "oppositing" across 0 would leave 0 where it is. More exactly, $0 + x = 0$ has $x = 0$ as the solution, so 0 behaves as its own additive inverse.

    c. ^-a is not always negative. For example, if a is a negative number, its additive inverse, ^-a, is positive.

3. a. $^-9$ b. $^-9$ c. 6   d. $^-10.3$

4. a. $^+1$, or 1   b. $^-4$ c. $^-4$

    d. 0   e. 0   f. 0

5. The child might be associating a number only with a point on the number line, rather than the length of a jump.

6. The two styles allow one to contrast the "−" as a signal for a negative or additive inverse number, versus subtraction. The "pro" is that using the different styles allows a distinction between the ideas; in writing, it also requires fewer parentheses for clarity. A "con" is that the use of the one-level form is common and, if one is careful, does not cause any difficulty in reading or in calculating (and it's easier to type!).

7. a. One-fourth of the way between 6 and 7.

    b. Halfway between $^-1$ and $^-2$. One could locate 1½ and then place $^-\frac{3}{2}$ the same distance from zero on the opposite side. One could also think halfway between $^-3$ and 0.

    c. Take the interval between 0 and $^-1$, split into three equal parts, place it two segments away from 0.

    d. $^-5/4 + 5/4$ is 0. If the segment between 0 and 1 is divided into 4ths, it lies at the end of 5 of these fourths.

    e. Opposite of ½; same distance on the left hand side of 0.

8. Many possible answers. Some samples are given.

    a. Jump goes two to the left, such as begins at 1 and ends at $^-1$.
    b. Jump begins 5 and ends at 0.
    c. Additive inverse of 8 (or any number) begins at the given number and ends at zero.

Supplementary Learning Exercises for Section 10.1

1. From smallest to largest, $^-(\frac{53}{6})$ $^-(\frac{53}{7})$ $^-(\frac{5}{4})$ $^-(\frac{3}{4})$ $^-(\frac{1}{10,000})$ $\frac{1}{1000}$ $\frac{53}{7}$ $\frac{53}{6}$

2. a. 2 or +2   b. –3   c. –3   d. 10 or +10

10.2 Children's Ways of Reasoning About Signed Numbers

1.   a. A child starts by marking 1 on the number line and, also, the ending point of ⁻3. Since subtraction means to move to the left, the child counts 4 and places a 4 in the blank.

   b. A child starts by marking ⁻6 on the number line and, since addition means to move to the right, the child moves right 3 and ends on ⁻3.

   c. With an unknown start, Violet would have guessed a number, moved right 5, and after seeing where she landed relative to ⁻1, adjusted the starting point and begun again.

2. ⁻1 + ⁻4

3. Many examples will do. Here are two possible scenarios: 1) adding to get a smaller number; 2) subtracting to get a bigger number.

4. These may involve problems for which the addends or minuend and subtrahend are not the same sign.

10.3 Other Models for Signed Numbers

1. a. 5 blue chips (or 5 more blue chips than gray)

   b. 6 gray chips (or 6 more gray chips than blue)

2. In each case, there should be the same number of blue chips as of gray chips.

3. a. ⁺2, or 2   b. ⁻1   c. ⁻3

   d. 0   e. ⁺1, or 1   f. ⁺1, or 1

4. a. Any negative number that does not have a terminating or repeating decimal. Examples include $-\sqrt{2}, -\sqrt{3}, -\sqrt{5}, -\sqrt{6}, \ldots$, as well as special numbers like $-\pi$.

   b. Any negative number that can be written in the form $-\frac{\text{whole number}}{\text{nonzero whole number}}$.

   c. Not possible. Every integer is also a real number.

   d. A negative rational number like $^{-}\frac{7}{3}$ or $^{-}\frac{11}{12}$ that is not an integer, or any negative irrational number is acceptable. See part (a).

5. (samples)

   a. ⁺10, a paycheck or gain of $10; ⁻4, a bill or loss of $4

   b. Football: ⁺10, a gain of 10 yards; ⁻4, a loss of 4 yards

      Golf: ⁺10, 10 strokes over par; ⁻4, 4 strokes under par

   c. An increase of 10 degrees; a decrease of 4 degrees

   d. 10 degrees above 0; 4 degrees below 0

Supplementary Learning Exercises for Section 10.3

1. a. 0   b. ‾2   c. ‾13

2. 5 chips for positive, 3 for negative. The student is merely counting chips and not evaluating according to the "canceling" effect of two chips of opposite colors.

3. A gain of 4 yards, a gain of 8 yards, losses of 3 and 15 yards, a gain of 11 yards

4. If the child accepts the view of, say, 2 and ‾2 as being on the opposite sides of 0, then it may be plausible that ‾0 must belong to the same point as 0.

10.4 Operations with Signed Numbers

Note: Sometimes we use the –6 form rather than the ‾6 form.

1. a. ●●●● ●●
    $-4 + -2 = -6$

    b. ●●●●
    ○○
    $-4 + 2 = -2$

    c. ●●✖✖
    $-4 - -2 = -2$

    d. ●●●●●●
    ✖✖
    $-4 - 2 = -6$

    e. ○○○
    ○   ●●●   ●
    $(4 + -3)$ $+ -1$
    1              $+ -1 = 0$

    f. ○○○○
    ●●●●●●
    $4 + -6 = -2$

    g. ○○○○○○○
    ✖✖✖
    $4 - -3 = 7$ (See the $4 + 3$?)

    h.
    $4 - -6 = 10$ (See the $4 + 6$?)

2.

a. (sample)

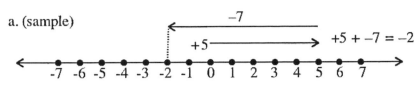

$+5 + -7 = -2$

b. $^-7$ c. $^+3$ d. $^-4$ e. $^+4$ f. $^+8$ g. $^-3$ h. $^-7$

A drawing for f:

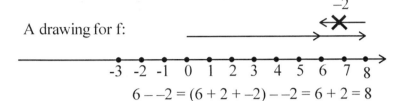

$6 - {}^-2 = (6 + 2 + -2) - {}^-2 = 6 + 2 = 8$

3. a. $^-10$ b. 0   c. 0   d. 0   e. $^-10$ f. 10

4. a. $\frac{1}{3}$ b. $^-4\frac{4}{9}$ c. 0   d. $\frac{1}{9}$ e. $^-3.272$ f. $^-10.4$

   g. $^-7.897$ h. 11.5

5. a. $^-3 + 5 = 2$ $\underline{2 \quad 5 - {}^-3}$
      $5 + {}^-3 = 2$ $\underline{2 - {}^-3 = 5}$

   b. $\underline{3 + {}^-5 = {}^-2}$ $\underline{{}^-2 - 5 = 3}$
      $\overline{{}^-5 + 3 = {}^-2}$ $\overline{{}^-2 - 3 = {}^-5}$

   c. $\underline{{}^-32 + {}^-29 = {}^-61}$ $\underline{{}^-61 - {}^-29 = {}^-32}$
      $\overline{{}^-29 + {}^-32 = {}^-61}$ $\overline{{}^-61 - {}^-32 = {}^-29}$

6. a. 3   b. $^-3$ c. $17\frac{4}{7}$ d. 12   e. 12   f. 0   g. 0

7. **Note:** Using temperature change, rather than temperature itself, allows the addends to represent the same sort of thing.

8. Yes, but one could give a negative answer to something like "How much greater is –2 than 3?" or "How much less is 5 than 1?" With knowledge of which is greater or smaller, these can be avoided so that a positive number answers the question.

9. a. $57{,}000 + 35{,}000 + {}^-16{,}000 + {}^-16{,}000 = n$. Company A earned $60,000 for the year.

   b. $n + 92{,}000 = 15{,}000$. Company B lost $77,000 during the first quarter.

   c. $n + {}^-125{,}000 = 11{,}000$. Company B earned $136,000 during the third quarter.

   d. From (b) and (c), $^-77{,}000 + {}^-125{,}000 = n$, and the company lost $202,000 during those two quarters.

10. Sample:

a. I had a starting balance on my checking account of $105.89. Then I wrote a check for $75 to my sister and deposited two refund checks, one for $92.73 and the other for $11.68. Finally, I wrote a check for $99.15 for my credit card. What should my new balance be? $36.15 is the ending balance

b. The "– ⁻22.75" is a bit more difficult to incorporate naturally. It could be an erroneous bank/credit-card deduction or a cancelled check. $141.33

11. Samples:

a. On successive plays, the football team gained 2 yards, lost 5 yards, gained 14 yards, gained 2 yards, lost 6 yards, and gained 3 yards. How far did those plays advance the team?   (10 yards)

b. Della kept track of how she did on her diet. For the first six months, here is how she did: lost 6 pounds, lost 2 pounds, gained 3 pounds, lost 1 pound, lost 2 pounds, and gained 1 pound. How much weight did she lose (or gain) for those six months, in all? (Della lost 7 pounds.)

12. a. High, 1.0 ft; low, 0 ft
    b. High, 1.1 ft; low, ⁻0.3 ft

13. a. 146.9° (from 135.9 – ⁻11; you may have seen the equivalent 135.9 + 11 immediately)
    b. 225.16°

    c. 138.4°

    d. 189°

    e. 215.4°

    f. 147.4°

14. Sketch an empty number line. Begin at the lowest temperature and jump in "convenient" chunks to benchmark numbers until you reach the highest temperature. For each of these, one jump gets you to zero. From there add the distance of the next jump, typically here it is the highest temperature. In each case, the highest temp plus the absolute value of the lowest temp is the distance. An empty number line does not facilitate adding so much as seeing why adding the absolute values of the numbers yields the difference.

Supplementary Learning Exercises for Section 10.4

1. a. Five chips of one color for 5 and 2 chips of an "opposite" color for ⁻2, giving 3 chips of the color for positive after pairs of opposite colors cancel.

    b. (one way)

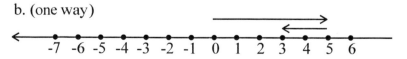

   c.   Sample: In the mail, you received a rebate of $5 but an overdue charge of $2 for a bill you sent in late. How has your financial position changed?

2. a.   Show 5 with 7 positive chips and 2 negative ones. Removing two negative chips gives 7.

   b.   Show 5 negative chips and take away 2 of them. The remainder is ⁻3.

   c.   Show ⁻5 with 7 negative chips and 2 positive chips. Take away the two positive chips, leaving ⁻7 as the answer.

3.   a. ⁻78   b. ⁻468   c. ⁻($\frac{17}{24}$)   d. $\frac{1}{2}$ e. 1.713

4.   a. 57,000 + 35,000 + (16,000) + (16,000)

   b. $750.80   ($1000)   ($110.50)

5.   All of your choices should suggest that ⁻$(a - b)$ = ⁻$a + b$.

10.5 Multiplying and Dividing Signed Numbers

1. $\frac{^-2}{5}$ is the same as ⁻2 ÷ 5, which is negative and can be written ⁻$\left(\frac{2}{5}\right)$.

   $\frac{2}{^-5}$ is the same as 2 ÷ ⁻5, which is negative and can be written ⁻$\left(\frac{2}{5}\right)$.

   Thus, all three expressions are naming the same number.

2. a. ⁻2   b. 8   c. 14   d. 11   e. ⁻$\frac{2}{3}$ f. $\frac{^-1}{10}$

   g. ⁻1   h. 1   i. ⁻126   j. ⁻9

   k. ⁻$\frac{1}{40}$ l. 50   m. 1   n. ⁻1

3. a. 3 × ⁻5 = ⁻5 + ⁻5 + ⁻5 = ⁻15, so draw 3 groups, each with 5 gray chips.

   b. Start with 0 in the form of 15 blues and 15 grays. To find ⁻3 × 5, subtract 5 blues three times, leaving 15 grays, or ⁻15.

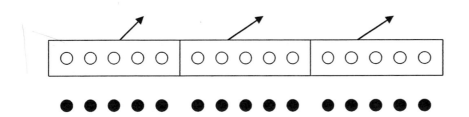

   c. Start with 6 blue and 6 gray chips (0) and remove 3 gray chips twice. Result: 6 blue chips, so ⁻2 × ⁻3 = ⁺6.

d. Again, start with 6 blue and 6 gray chips, but this time remove 2 gray chips 3 times. Result: 6 blue chips, so $^-3 \times {}^-2 = {}^+6$.

4. $^-7 \times 0 = 0$

$^-7 \times (5 + {}^-5) = 0$, substituting $5 + {}^-5$ for the first 0

$(^-7 \times 5) + (^-7 \times {}^-5) = 0$ using the distributive property

$^-35 + (^-7 \times {}^-5) = 0$ using the known $^-7 \times 5 = {}^-35$

So $^-7 \times {}^-5$ must equal $^+35$.

5. Ann may not have heard "when you multiply **two** negatives…"

Bobo did not realize that you were referring to multiplication, not addition.

6. a. $^+5 \times {}^-4 = n$ $(n = {}^-20)$. She will have 20 fewer sheep than at present.

b. $^-6 \times {}^-4 = n$ $(n = {}^+24)$. She had 24 more sheep than at present.

c. $^+6 \times {}^-30 = n$ $(n = {}^-180)$. He will weigh 180 pounds less than at present.

d. $^-3 \times {}^-30 = n$ $(n = {}^+90)$. He weighed 90 more pounds than at present.

7. Yes, the multiplicative identity is 1.

8. a. No, the multiplicative inverse of most integers a is not an integer.

b. 1 is its own multiplicative inverse, as is $^-1$. $(1 \cdot 1 = 1$ and $^-1 \cdot {}^-1 = 1.)$

9. a. Multiplication is commutative.

b. Addition is commutative.

c. Multiplication is distributive over addition.

d. Addition is associative.

e. Multiplication is distributive over addition.

f. Multiplication is commutative.

g. Multiplication is commutative.

h. Every nonzero rational number has a multiplicative inverse, *and* 1 is the multiplicative identity.

i. Zero is the additive identity.

j. Multiplication is distributive over addition.

Supplementary Learning Exercises for Section 10.5

1. Start with, say, $4 \times {}^-5 = {}^-20$, $3 \times {}^-5 = {}^-15$, $2 \times {}^-5 = {}^-10$, etc., continuing to $^-2 \times {}^-5$, and look for a pattern.

2. a. 1088.7   b. $\frac{1}{20}$ c. $^-128$ d. 413.6

3.   With simple calculators, the user must assign the sign to the product.

4.   a. and b. Show the dividend (the ⁻10 and the ⁻16) and repeatedly remove chips for the divisor (–2). The number of groups removed will be the quotient.

5.   Compare your favorite with those of others.

6.   a. Possibilities: "The additive inverse of the product of a and b;" "the additive inverse of a, times b;" and "a times the additive inverse of b."

   b. All of your choices should suggest that the three expressions are all equal.

10.6 Integers and Other Number Systems

1.   3

2. $\dfrac{3}{5}$ 0   ⁻14   ⁻3.67

3.   a. $\frac{-5}{3}$ b. $\frac{1}{14}$ c. $3.67 = \frac{367}{100}$, so the multiplicative inverse of 3.67 is $\frac{100}{367}$.

   d. There is no number that, when multiplied by 0, has 1 as the product.

4.   a. No. An odd number plus an odd number is not an odd number, so the closure property of addition does not hold. Nor are there additive or multiplicative inverses for every odd number (there isn't even an additive identity in the set), and distributivity could be questioned because of the lack of closure.

   b. No. There are no additive or multiplicative inverses (and there is no multiplicative identity in the set).

   c. No. Most integers do not have multiplicative inverses that are integers.

5.   Be sure to set up addition and multiplication tables before doing this problem. When working with clock arithmetic on a 4-hour clock, the multiplicative inverse of 1 is 1 and of 3 is 3. But 2 does not have a multiplicative inverse.

6.   Check multiplicative inverses for a 6-hour clock, and for a 7-hour clock. Multiplicative inverses (of nonzero numbers) exist in a 5-hour system and in a 7-hour system, but not in 4-hour or for 6-hour systems. Conjectures based only on this much evidence would be risky, but looking at other clock systems may suggest a correct conjecture: If there is a prime number of hours on the clock, the clock system gives a field.

7. Between every two real numbers, there is another real number. (Their average is one example.)

8. a. Not dense. There is not another integer between consecutive integers, like 1 and 2.

   b. Yes, dense. There is always a positive rational number between every two given positive rational numbers. For example, the average of two rational numbers is a rational number and is between the two.

   c. Yes, dense. There is always a negative rational number between every two given negative rational numbers.

9. Rewrite the given numbers with a large common denominator. For example, for part (a), use $\frac{3500}{2000}$ and $\frac{3600}{2000}$, and for part (b), $^-(\frac{2000}{3000})$ and $^-(\frac{1860}{3000})$. You can then find several rational numbers between the pairs.

10. a. Yes: The sum of any two even integers is an even integer. $2m + 2n = 2(m + n)$, and if m and n are integers, so is $(m + n)$.

   b. Yes: The sum of any two multiples of 3 is another multiple of 3.

   c. No: Example: $3 + 5 = 8$ is not odd.

   d. No: Example: $3 - 4$ is not positive.

   e. Yes: The sum of any two integers is an integer.

   f. Yes: If you subtract any integer from another integer, the difference is another integer.

   g. No: $\frac{1}{3} - \frac{1}{2}$ is not positive.

11. a. Yes, because addition is commutative
    b. Yes, because addition is associative
    c. Yes, because 0 is the additive identity
    d. Yes, because 4 and $^-4$ are additive inverses
    e. Yes, because 4 and $^-4$ are additive inverses
    f. Yes, because addition is associative
    g. Yes, because the set of integers is closed under addition; $\frac{306}{18} = 17$
    h. Yes, because addition is commutative
    i. Yes, because 0 is the additive identity
    j. Yes, because the numbers are additive inverses of each other

12. a. $^-13$ b. $4\frac{3}{10}$ c. $\frac{4}{9}$ d. $^-\sqrt{11}$

Supplementary Learning Exercises for Section 10.6
1.   There is no whole number between consecutive whole numbers, like 8 and 9.

2.   a. Using equivalent fractions $^-(\frac{300}{400})$ and $^-(\frac{100}{400})$, it is easy to see several.
     b. Infinitely many

3.   a. Possibilities, all keeping the order of the factors the same: $\frac{5}{8} \times [^-20 \times (^-4\frac{5}{6} \times \frac{8}{35})]$; or
        $[(\frac{5}{8} \times ^-20) \times ^-4\frac{5}{6}] \times \frac{8}{35}$; or further applications to the expressions in square brackets.
     b. Change the order of the two factors within either set of parentheses, or change the order of the parenthetical expressions, $(^-4\frac{5}{6} \times \frac{8}{35}) \times (\frac{5}{8} \times ^-20)$.
     c. $(\frac{5}{6} \times 24) + (\frac{5}{6} \times ^-600)$ d. $\frac{2}{3} \times (^-298 + ^-2)$
     e. $(2 + ^-5)x$ f. 1×1 g. $5 \times \frac{1}{5}$

4. a. Samples: $(^-15 + 8) + (7 + ^-3)$; or $(^-3 + 7) + (^-15 + 8)$; or $(7 + ^-3) + (8 + ^-15)$; or combinations of those three

   b. $0 + 0$

   c. $5 + ^-5$

   d. Samples: $[(^-2 + ^-4) + 5] + ^-5$; or $^-2 + [(^-4 + 5) + ^-5]$; or further uses of associativity on the expressions in square brackets. Notice that the order of the addends does not change.

5. a. Yes, the set, $-1, 0, 1$, is closed under multiplication because the product of every choice of pairs of numbers from the set is also a number in the set.

   b. The set, $-1, 0, 1$, is not closed under addition because, for example, $1 + 1 = 2$, and 2 is not in the set.

   c. The set of numbers, $-2, 0, 2$, is not closed under multiplication because, for example, $2 \times 2 = 4$, and 4 is not in the set.

Answers for Chapter 11: Number Theory

11.1 Factors and Multiples, Primes and Composites

1. a. 1, 5, and 25. There are no more because 25 is a perfect square of a prime number.

    b. 25, 50, 75, ... Any whole number multiplied by 25 will be a multiple of 25.

2. a. $k = 25 \times$ some whole number, or $k = 25\,m$, for some whole number m. A rectangular array would need 25 on one side and m on another side.

    b. $w = mn$ for some whole number n.

    c. $v = tx$ for some whole number x.

3. a. $216x = 2376$ or $x = 2376 \div 216$

    b. Solve $144x = 3456$, which involves seeing whether $3456 \div 144 =$ a whole number.

4. 21 squares could be in rectangular arrays only as 1 by 21, 21 by 1, 7 by 3, and 3 by 7. An array with 5 squares on one side would require 4.25 squares on the other side, but rectangular arrays allow only whole numbers on each side.

5. a. A number is a factor of itself.

    b. A number is a multiple of itself.

6. a. 2 and 253   (Others are 1, 11, 22, 23, 46, and 506.)

    b. 506, 1012, 1518 (There are an infinite number of multiples of 506.)

7. True or false? If false, correct the statement.

    a. 13 is a factor of 39. True because there exists a whole number, namely 3, such that $13 \times 3 = 39$.

    b. 12 is a factor of 36. True because there exists a whole number, namely 3, such that $12 \times 3 = 36$.

    c. 24 is a factor of 36. False because there is no whole number n such that $24n = 36$.

    d. 36 is a multiple of 12. True because there exists a whole number, namely 3, such that $12 \times 3 = 36$.

    e. 36 is a multiple of 48. False because there is no whole number n such that $48n = 36$.

    f. 16 is a factor of 512. True because there exists a whole number, namely 32,   such that $16 \times 32 = 512$.

    g. 2 is a multiple of 1. True. Every whole number n is a multiple of 1 because $n \times 1 = n$. 1 is a factor of every whole number.

8. a. $kn = 15$ for some whole number n.

    b. $mn = x$ for some whole number n.

9. a. Yes, because for some whole numbers x and y, $m = kx$ and $n = my$, substituting the first into the second, $n = (kx)y = k(xy)$. The latter also shows that n is a multiple of k.

   b. Yes. Because $m = kx$ and $n = ky$ for some whole numbers x and y, $m + n = kx + ky = k(x + y)$. So k is a factor of $m + n$.

   c. Suppose $k = 6$, $m = 12$, and $n = 15$. Now k is a factor of m, but not of n. $m + n = 27$, and 6 is not a factor of 27. (This is a counterexample.)

10. a. An even number is a number that has 2 as a factor.

    b. An even number is a number that is a multiple of 2.

    c. An odd number is a number that can be expressed as $2n + 1$ for any whole number n.

11.

+	even	odd
even	even	odd
odd	odd	even

×	even	odd
even	even	even
odd	even	odd

   a. The sum of any number of even numbers is even.

   b. The sum of an even number of odd numbers is even (put them in pairs), so the   sum of an odd number of odd numbers is odd.

   c. The product of any number of even numbers is even.

   d. The product of any number of odd numbers is odd.

   e. No, an odd number cannot have an even factor.

   f. Yes, an even number may have an odd factor—for example, 12 is even but has 3 as a factor.

   g. Yes

   h. No (e.g., $3 + 5 = 8$)

   i. Yes

   j. Yes

12. a. 2 is prime because it has only 1 and 2 as factors. 29 is prime because it has   only 1 and 29 as factor. Similarly for 3 and 97.

13. Each of them has only 1 and itself as factors.

    2, 3, 5, 7, 11, 13, 17, 19, 23, 29, 31, 37, 41, 43, 47, 53, 59, 61, 67, 71, 73, 79, 83, 89, 97

14. 3 is a factor of 15, so 15 has at least these three factors: 1, 15, and 3. Hence, it is not prime. Similarly, each of the other numbers has at least three factors. $119 = 7 \times 17$.

15. a. Every number is a factor of 0, so it has more than two factors. Composite numbers have to be greater than 1.

   b. 1 has exactly one factor (1), not two, so it is not a prime. Composite numbers have to be greater than 1.

   c. This definition would allow 1 to be a prime number. One reason that we do not want 1 to be a prime number is that if it were a prime, unique factorization into primes would be messed up (there are reasons in advanced mathematics also).

16.   a. 1 and 829   b. 1 and 5771   c. 1 and 506   d. n and 1

17.   Every even number greater than 2 has 2 as a factor. So the even number greater than 2 will have at least three factors, 1, 2, and itself.

18.   Perhaps surprisingly, the conjecture is false. For example, 6 has more factors than 9.

19.   c. Common factors of 18 and 24 are 1, 2, 3, 6. Common multiples of 6 and 18 are 18, 36, 54, etc. All multiples of 18 are also multiples of 6.

20.   2 is a factor of $n = 2 \cdot 3 \cdot 5 \cdot 7 \cdot 11 \cdot 13 \cdot 17$, but not a factor of 1, so it cannot be a factor of $n + 1$. The same argument holds for 3, 5, 7, 11, and 17.

21. $28 = 1 + 2 + 4 + 7 + 14$

Supplementary Learning Exercises for Section 11.1

1.   A prime number is a whole number that has exactly two different factors. A composite number is a whole number greater than 1 that has more than two factors.

2.   No, composite numbers by definition have more than two factors, and prime numbers are restricted to numbers with exactly two factors.

3.   True. A prime number p can be expressed only by $p \times 1$ or $1 \times p$.

4.   True. Each number crossed out is a multiple of some number greater than 1, so that number would be a third factor of the number crossed out.

5.   b. 361. 23 won't be crossed out (it is the next prime), and 323 is already crossed out, when all the multiples of 17 were crossed out. 20 is also already crossed out, as a multiple of 2.

6.   No. For example, 2 is a factor of 6, but 6 is not a factor of 2.

7.   Many examples exist. For $2 \times 4 = 8$, for example, "8 is a multiple of 2" and "2 is a factor of 8" are both correct.

8.   a. 87 is a factor or 2088.   b. 24 is a factor of 2088.

   c. 2088 is a multiple of 87, or 2088 is a multiple of 24.

9.   a. g is a factor of w.   b. s is a factor of w.

c. *w* is a multiple of *g*, or *w* is a multiple of *s*.

10. a. 1, 7, and 49 are the only factors of 49 because 49 is the square of 7.

   b. Yes, 49 is a composite number because it is larger than 1 and has more than two factors.

   c. 0, 49, 98, 147, 196, 245.... Multiply 49 by any whole number to get a multiple of 49.

11. a. 31 is a prime because it has only 1 and 31 as factors.

   b. 299 is a composite because 13 (or 23) is a third factor besides 1 and 299.

   c. 27 is a composite because 3 (or 9) is a third factor besides 1 and 27.

   d. 999 is a composite because 3 (and 333 or 111 or ...) would be a third factor besides 1 and 999.

   e. "Prime" and "composite" refer only to whole numbers, not fractions different from whole numbers.

12. No, because the product of two primes would have more than two factors and thus not be a prime.

13. a. 0 is the only multiple of 0.

   b. Every whole number *n* is a factor of 0 because $n \times 0 = 0$.

14. Adding the prime number 2 to any other prime number will give a counterexample.

15. Not only 1 and 9991 are factors of 9991. 97 (and 103) are also factors, so 9991 has more than two factors.

16. If a number is composite, it will be a multiple of its smallest factor (not 1) and so would have been marked out when multiples of that factor were marked out.

17. 4 (1, 2, 4) is another one, as are 25 (1, 5, 25) and 121 (1, 11, 121), along with the given 49 (1, 7, 49) (*Hint*: $25 = 5^2$)

11.2 Prime Factorization

1. See this section. The theorem says that 239,417 is either a prime or can be written in exactly one way as a product of primes (except that the order of the factors can vary).

2. a. 102   102   (Note: The remaining parts should also have a factor tree.)

Thus, the prime factors are 2, 3, and 17.

(Note: Factor trees should also be used to find the following prime factorizations.)

b. $1827 = 3^2 \cdot 7 \cdot 29$ c. $1584 = 2^4 \cdot 3^2 \cdot 11$ d. $1540 = 2^2 \cdot 5 \cdot 7 \cdot 11$

e. $121 = 11^2$ f. $1485 = 3^3 \cdot 5 \cdot 11$

3. Different factor trees are possible, but these prime factorizations should be the same for the different factor trees (except possibly for the order of the factors):

a. $5850 = 2 \cdot 3^2 \cdot 5^2 \cdot 13$ b. $256 = 2^8$ c. $2835 = 3^4 \cdot 5 \cdot 7$

d. $10^4 = 2^4 \cdot 5^4$ e. $17280 = 2^7 \cdot 3^3 \cdot 5$

f. A factor tree shows all the prime factors, but most often it does not show all the possible composite factors of the number.

4. a. 2, 3, 7, and 11 are prime factors of $3 \times 7^3 \times 22$. (There are only these four prime factors. Any three of these is a correct answer.)

b. 2, 3, 11 are prime factors of 27×22. (There are no more. Why not?)

c. 29, 11, and 2 are prime factors of $29^4 \times 11^6 \times 2^5$. (There are no more. Why not?)

5. The prime factorization of a number gives all of the prime factors of the number. A prime factor of the number would be just one of those primes.

6. Think about 11^m. This number, in prime factorization, has only 11 and powers of 11 as factors. Now think about 13^n. This number, in prime factorization, has only 13 and powers of 13 as factors. The fundamental theorem of arithmetic says that prime factorizations are unique. 13 does not appear in the list of factors of 11^m. So 13 cannot be a factor of 11^m for any value of m. This says that 13^n cannot equal 11^m for any (nonzero) values of m and n.

7. a. $m = 2 \cdot 67$

b. There is no m that would satisfy the unique factorization into primes.

c. $n = 2 \cdot 17 \cdot 67^2$ would make the equation true.

d. The right-hand side of the equation will have at least 10 factors that are 2s (because $134 = 2 \cdot 67$). But the left-hand side has only nine factors that are 2s, so it is not possible to make part (d) true.

e. $4^m = (2^2)^m = 2^{2m}$ and $8^n = (2^3)^n = 2^{3n}$, so the given equation will be true if it is possible to find m and n so that $2m = 3n$. There are many such pairs of values for m and n that will work, for example, $m = 3$ and $n = 2$ or $m = 6$ and $n = 4$.

f. Perhaps surprisingly, after part (e), the $m = n = 0$ possibility is the only pair of m, n values that work.

Because $6^m = (2 \cdot 3)^m = 2^m \cdot 3^m$ and $18^n = (2 \cdot 3^2)^n = 2^n \cdot 3^{2n}$, we would have to have $m = n$ (from the powers of 2) and at the same time, $m = 2n$ (from the powers of 3). This is possible only when m and n are both 0.

8. a. $2^8 \cdot 7$ could not be a factor of m because m does not have 7 in its prime factorization (which is unique, and hence could not have another factorization with a 7 in it).

   b. Similarly, the part (b) number already has too many 2s to be a factor of m.

   c. The part (c) number is a factor of m because all of its factors appear in the prime factorization of m

   d. $34^3 = (2 \cdot 17)^3 = 2^3 \cdot 17^3$, so it is a factor of m.

   e. $134^2 = (2 \cdot 67)^2 = 2^2 \cdot 67^2$, so it is a factor of m.

9. 5 and 7

10. a. 6   b. $3 \times 4 = 12$ c. $45000 = 2^3 \cdot 3^2 \cdot 5^4$ has 60 factors.   d. 288 factors

   e. $2^6 \cdot 5^6$ has 49 factors   f. 7 factors   g. $(12 + 1)(6 + 1) = 91$ factors

11. a. $19^4 \times 11^3 \times 2^5 \times n$ is a factor of $19^4 \times 11^4 \times 2^5$ if $n = 11$.

   b. $19^4 \times 22 \times 2^5 \times n$ cannot be a factor of $19^4 \times 11^4 \times 2^5$ because $19^4 \times 22 \times 2^5 \times n = 19^4 \times 11 \times 2^6 \times n$ There is one too many 2s in $19^4 \times 11 \times 2^6 \times n$ to be a factor of $19^4 \times 11^4 \times 2^5$.

   c. $19^4 \times 11^4 \times 64 \times n$ is not a factor of $19^4 \times 11^4 \times 2^5 = 19^4 \times 11^4 \times 32$. Note that $64 = 2^6$, so once again there are too many 2s in $19^4 \times 11^4 \times 2^6 \times n$ to be a factor of $19^4 \times 11^4 \times 2^5$.

   d. $19 \times 11 \times 2 \times n$ is a factor of $19^4 \times 11^4 \times 2^5$ if $n = 19^3 \times 11^3 \times 2^4$.

12. a. $19^4 \times 11^8 \times 2^5$. Yes, multiply q by 11^4.

   b. $19^4 \times 22^4 \times 2^5 \times 17 = 19^4 \times 11^4 \times 2^9 \times 17$. Yes, multiply q by $2^4 \times 17$.

   c. $19^4 \times 11^4 \times 64$. Yes, multiply q by 2.

   d. $(19 \times 11 \times 2)^5$. Yes, multiply q by 19×11.

13. a. $64 = 2^6$, so there are 7 factors. They are 1, 2, 2^2, 2^3, 2^4, 2^5, 2^6, or 1, 2, 4, 8, 16, 32, and 64.

   b. $48 = 2^4 \times 3$, so there should be $(4 + 1)(1 + 1) = 10$ factors.

   The factors are 1, 2, 2^2, 2^3, 2^4, 3, 2×3, $2^2 \times 3$, $2^3 \times 3$, and $2^4 \times 3$.

   That is: 1, 2, 4, 8, 16, 3, 6, 12, 24, and 48.

   c. $(4 + 1)(4 + 1)(5 + 1) = 150$ factors

14. a. 11   b. $m + 1$ c. $n + 1$ d. $(m + 1)(n + 1)$ e. $(m + 1)(n + 1)(s + 1)$

15. $2^5 \cdot 5^9$ is one possibility.

16. $2^7 \cdot 11^2$ is one possibility. 2 can be replaced by other primes for other possibilities.

Supplementary Learning Exercises for Section 11.2

1.   No. 2^{10} is just shorthand for $2 \times 2 \times 2 \times 2 \times 2 \times 2 \times 2 \times 2 \times 2 \times 2$, which is a prime factorization.

2.   The UFT says that *every* prime factorization of 1024 will involve exactly ten 2s as factors.

3.   There are different (correct) factor trees for each part, except part (e), which as a prime can have, at most, branches to 29 and 1, and usually branches that end in 1 are not put in. Whatever your factor tree, you should have the following prime factorizations (with your factors possibly in a different order, of course).

   a. $960 = 2^6 \times 3 \times 5$ b. $9600 = 2^7 \times 3 \times 5^2$ c. $1125 = 3^2 \times 5^3$

   d. $8100 = 2^2 \times 3^4 \times 5^2$

4.   No, these different starts do not violate the Fundamental Theorem of Arithmetic because the theorem applies only to prime factorizations, and neither Kim nor Lee has a prime factorization yet.

5.   If k is an odd number, it cannot have 2 as a factor, which is implied by $k = 2m$.

6.   Neither Abbie nor Bonita has a complete prime factorization. $57 = 3 \times 19$, and $171 = 3^2 \times 19$, so with that further work, the complete prime factorizations would agree.

7.   a. 2, 3, 11, and 19 are the only prime factors of 3,972,672.

   b. There are 164 possibilities! Some, besides 33, are 121, 57, 6, 12, 24, 209,… Just be certain that your composite factors involve only a selection of the prime factors in the prime factorization.

8.   No. Unique factorization into primes assures that 7^{15} has only 7 as a prime factor, and that 9^m has only 3 as a prime factor. Thus, the two can never be equal.

9.   a. 630 (Did you realize that this is just the LCM?)

   b. 990   c. 2940

10. a. True. A nonzero multiple of 75 will be $75n$ for some whole number n greater than 1, so the 3×5^2 must appear in the prime factorization of $75n$, by the Unique Factorization Theorem.

   b. True, with reasoning like that in part (a).

   c. The smallest such number must be $2^3 \times 3 \times 5^2 = 600$.

11. Both sides involve only prime factors of 5, so it may be possible. $(5^2)^m = 5^{2m}$, and $(5^3)^n = 5^{3n}$, so any values of m and n that make $2m = 3n$ will be possible values. One example is $m = 3$ and $n = 2$. Any (nonzero) multiples of those will also work.

12. a. $(2 + 1)(3 + 1)(1 + 1) = 3(4)(2) = 24$ factors

b. $(x + 1)(y + 1)(z + 1)$ factors

13. One million $= 1,000,000 = 10^6 = (2 \times 5)^6 = 2^6 \times 5^6$, so one million has $7 \times 7 = 49$ factors.

14. 100, reasoning as in Exercise 12. Two are primes: 2 and 5. 1 is a factor. So the other 97 factors must be composites.

15. At least one 3 and at least one 7 must appear in the prime factorization of the number. Each could be raised to powers so that, from $15 = 3 \times 5$, one exponent is 2 and the other 4: $3^2 \times 7^4$, or $3^4 \times 7^2$, for example.

16. Yes, it is possible. For example, start one factor tree for 36 with 6×6 and a second factor tree for 36 with 4×9. The two factor trees will be different when completed. (But the prime factorization obtained through the different factor trees are the same.)

11.3 Divisibility Tests to Determine Whether a Number Is Prime

1. a. 2, 3, 4, 6, 8, 9 are (some of the) factors of 43,056 (5 and 10 are not factors).

b. 2, 3, 6, 9 are (some of the) factors of 700010154 (4, 5, 8, and 10 are not).

c. 3 is one factor of the number (but 2, 4, 5, 6, 8, 9, and 10 are not).

d. 5 is one factor the number (but 2, 3, 4, 6, 8, 9, and 10 are not).

2. a. The solution is not solely trial and error. If 2 and 3 but not 9 are factors, then the ones digit must be even and the sum of the digits must be a multiple of 3 but not of 9. If 4 is not a factor, then 4 is not a factor of the right-most two digits. By starting with the ones place, here is one result: 200,022. There are many others.

b. The constraints mean that the ones digit must be 5. Then it is just a matter of making certain that 3 is a factor of the sum of the digits. One easy example: 100,005.

c. 8 must be a factor of the number named by the right-most 3 digits. 9 must be a factor of the sum of the digits. Two examples: 3,000,888 and 333,000.

3. 3 must be a factor of the sum of the digits. The known digits give a sum of 29. So if the unknown digit is 1 or 4 or 7, then 3 will be a factor of the number. Similarly, if 9 is to be a factor, then 9 must divide the sum of the digits. With a current sum of 29, the only digit value that works for unknown digit is 7. (Why not 16?)

4. a. Try 18; 2 and 6 are factors of 18, but 12 is not.

b. Try 24; 3 and 6 are factors of 24, but 18 is not.

c. Try 36.

5. In each case, (a) through (d), the two factors are relatively prime, so examples can be found. If the two factors are not relatively prime, then one cannot make such statements. For example, is it true to say, in part (b), 12 is a factor of n if, and only if, 2 is a factor of n and 6 is a factor

of n? No, 18 has both 2 and 6 as factors, but 12 is not a factor of 18. But one could say: 12 is a factor of n if, and only if, 3 is a factor of n and 4 is a factor of n because 3 and 4 are relatively prime.

6. a. 8 and 3 are factors of 24 and are relatively prime. Thus, a number is divisible by 24 if, and only if, it is divisible by 8 and 3. 8 is a factor because it divides 112. 3 is a factor because the sum of the digits is 6. Therefore, 24 is a factor.

    b. 012 is not divisible by 8, so the number is not divisible by 8 or by 24.

    c. Use the 2-test and the 9-test. No, the number is not divisible by 2.

    d. Use the 2-test and the 9-test. Yes.

    e. Use the 5 test and the 9 test. Yes.

7. To be a multiple of 36, the number must be divisible by 4 and by 9. Thus, choose a 2-digit number divisible by 4, say 24, for the final two digits. To be divisible by 9, the sum of the digits must be divisible by 9, so add a number to 24 to obtain the number divisible by 9, say 3. So 300,000,000,000,024 would be such a number. To obtain a number NOT divisible by 36, change the first digit to 2. Now the sum of the digits is not divisible by 9. Or, change the last two digits to form a number *not* divisible by 4, such as 23.

8. One example: eight = 13_{five}. Two is certainly a factor of eight, but not of the 3 in 13_{five}, so the usual 2-test does not work. Or, nine = 14_{five}, and two is not a factor of nine, but 14_{five} ends in an even number.

9. If n is prime, it has *exactly* two factors, 1 and n. Finding a third factor means n is not prime, which means it is composite. For example, 169 has 1 and 169 as factors. But 169 also has 13 as a factor and so is a composite number.

10. $n^2 = (2^3 \times 5^2 \times 7 \times 17^3)^2 = 2^6 \times 5^4 \times 7^2 \times 17^6$ and $n^3 = 2^9 \times 5^6 \times 7^3 \times 17^9$

11. a. 26^2 is 676, so if 667 is not prime one prime factor must be less than 26. Try 23:   23 $\times 29 = 667$, so 667 is not prime.

    b. $289 = 17^2$, so it is not prime.

    c. Divisible by 9, so not prime.

    d. Has more than 2 factors (1, 47, 61, and 47×61 are all factors), so it is not prime.

    e. Through a method of approximation, find 66^2 is 4356, so test for primes less than 66. 7 is a factor, so 4319 is composite.

    f. 1, 29, and 29^2 are factors, so the number is composite.

12. No, because in any two consecutive numbers, one is even so has 2 as a factor.

13. a. 540 is divisible by 2, 3, 4, 5, 6, 9, 10, 12, 15, and 18. It is not divisible by 8.

    b. 150 is divisible by 2, 3, 5, 6, 10, and 15, but not by 4, 8, 9, 12, or 18.

    c. 145 is divisible by 5, but not by 2, 3, 4, 6, 8, 9, 12, 15, or 18.

    d. 369 is divisible by 3 and 9, but not by 2, 4, 5, 6, 8, 10, 12, 15, or 18.

    e. 840 is divisible by 2, 3, 4, 5, 6, 8, 10, 12, and 15, but not by 9 or 18.

14. a. 29 × 23 is not prime. 29 and 23 are factors.

   b. 5992 is not prime because it obviously has a factor of 2.

   $5992 = 2^3 \times 7 \times 107.$

   c. 127 is prime. (Note: Why do you need to check for divisibility only of 2, 3, 5, 7, and 11?)

   d. $121 = 11^2$, so 121 is not prime.

   e. 31^2 has 31 as a factor and is not prime.

   f. $1247 = 29 \times 43$, so 1247 is not prime. (Remember, all primes less than $\sqrt{1247}$ must be tested, that is, for all primes equal to or less than 31 because $\sqrt{1247} \approx 35.3$.)

   g. 3816 is divisible by 2, so is not prime. (In fact, $3816 = 2^3 \times 3^2 \times 53$.)

15. $4 = 2 + 2$; $6 = 3 + 3$; $8 = 3 + 5$; $10 = 5 + 5$; $12 = 5 + 7$ (you finish)

16. If a number is divisible by 3 and by 8, it is divisible by 24. 120 is divisible by 24. (Note that 4 and 6 cannot be used to check for divisibility by 24. For example, both 4 and 6 divide 36 but 24 is not a divisor of 36.)

17. Yes, because they have only 1 as a common factor.

18. (a), (d), (f), (g), (i). (k)—121 and 22 have 11 as a factor in common; (l)—39 and 169 both have the factor 13 in common.

19. 125 and 243. (Note that $125 = 5^3$ and 243 is 3^5. There are many others.)

20. 25 is one possibility.

21. a. $128 + 494 + 381 = 1003$----4.

   128---11---2;   494---17---8;   381---12---3; $2 + 8 + 3 = 13$---4.

   b. $23 \times 45 = 1035$---9   23---5 and 45---9. $5 \times 9 = 45$---9

22. b. Consider $8 \times 9 \times 10 \times 11$, which is 7920. This number is divisible by 3 because the sum of the digits is 18, which is divisible by 3. Also, 920 is divisible by 8: $920 = 8 \times 115$. Thus, 7920 must be divisible by 24.

   c. Suppose these 5 consecutive numbers are chosen: 4, 5, 6, 7, and 8. $4 \times 5 \times 6 \times 7 \times 8 = 6720$. The theorem claims that this number must be divisible by $1 \times 2 \times 3 \times 4 \times 5 = 120$ and $120 = 8 \times 3 \times 5$, with 8, 3, and 5 relatively prime. Because 6720 ends in 0, it is divisible by 5. Because the sum of the digits is 15, which is divisible by 3, 6720 is divisible by 3. Because 8 divides 720, 8 divides 6720. Hence, 6720 is divisible by 8, 3, and 5, and therefore 120.

23. Here is one case. Let $p = 5$ and $n = 4$. Then by this theorem, $4^5 - 4$ should be divisible by 5. $4^5 = 4 \times 4 \times 4 \times 4 \times 4 = 1024$. When 4 is subtracted, the result is 1020, which is divisible by 5. You choose more to try.

24. Three-digit numbers less than 125 that are multiples of 5 are 100, 105, 110, 115, and 120. But 100, 110, and 120 are divisible by 2, so they can't work, leaving 105 and 115. But 7 is a factor of 105, so that too must be discarded, leaving only 115.

Supplementary Learning Exercises for Section 11.3

1. Relatively prime numbers have only 1 as a common factor. So the pairs in parts (a), (c), (d), and (e) are relatively prime. In part (b), the numbers have 5 as a common factor.

2. True

3. a. 2, 3, 4, 6, and 9 are divisors.　　　b. 2, 4, 5, 8, and 10 are divisors

   c. 2, 3, 4, and 6 are divisors.　　　d. 3 and 5 are divisors.

   e. None of 2, 3, 4, 5, 6, 8, 9, 10 is a factor.　　f. Only 2 is a divisor.

   g. Each of 2, 3, 4, 5, 6, 8, 9, and 10. (Was it necessary to multiply 80×54 out?)

   h. 2, 4, 5, 8, and 10 are divisors.

4. With approximate square roots as the guide…

   a. 19 ($\sqrt{401} \approx 20$ and we need check only primes)

   b. 19 (23^2 would be too large)　　c. 29　　d. 37

5. a. $207 = 3^2 \times 23$　b. $121 = 11^2$　c. 83×71　d. 19^3

   e. $247 = 13 \times 19$　f. $119 = 7 \times 17$　g. Prime　h. Prime　i. $297 = 3^3 \times 11$

6. Check that the sum of the digits in your number has 3 as a factor, but not 9, that the number named by the rightmost two digits has 4 as a factor, and that the number named by the rightmost three digits does not have 8 as a factor.

7. If 9 is a factor, then 3 is automatically a factor (because $9 = 3 \times 3$).

8. It is easy to see that 3 and 9 are factors of $(999 + 5 \cdot 99 + 2 \cdot 9)$.

11.4 Greatest Common Factor, Least Common Multiple

1. a. 1, 2, 4, 8 (There are no more.)　　　b. 1, 27, 49, 27×49 (There are more.)

   c. 1, 2, 3, 4 (There are more.)　　　d. 1, 3, 5, 15 (There are no more.)

   e. 108　1, 2, 3, 4 (There are more.)　　f. 1, 5, 25, 125 (There are no more.)

   g. 1, 2, 3, 12 (There are more.)

2. Notice that there are an infinite number of multiples for each case. Here we list just four.

a. $2^4, 2^5, 2^6, 2^7,...$

b. $2 \times 27 \times 49, 27^2 \times 49, 27 \times 49^2, 27^2 \times 49^2,...$

c. 24, 36, 48, 60,...

d. 15, 30, 45, 60,...

e. 108, 216, 324, 432, ...

f. 250, 375, 500, 625,...

g. 72, 144, 216, 288, ...

3. 60 years

4. Suppose hot dogs come 12 to a package and buns come 20 to a package. Buying multiple packs of hot dogs would result in 12, 24, 36, 48, 60, 72,... hot dogs. Buying multiple packs of buns would result in 20, 40, 60, 80, ... buns. Buying 5 packages of hot dogs (60) and 3 packages of buns (60) would work. Note that the LCM provides the least number divisible by both 12 and 20.

5 and 6. One can begin by factoring each of the numbers below.

$72 = 2^3 \cdot 3^2$ $108 = 2^2 \cdot 3^3$ $144 = 2^4 \cdot 3^2$ $150 = 2 \cdot 3 \cdot 5^2$

$350 = 2 \cdot 5^2 \cdot 7$ $567 = 3^4 \cdot 7$ $90 = 2 \cdot 3^2 \cdot 5$ $270 = 2 \cdot 3^3 \cdot 5$

a. The LCM of 72, 108 is $2^3 \cdot 3^3 = 216$.   The GCF of 72 and 108 is $2^2 \cdot 3^2 = 36$.

b. The LCM of 144 and 150 is $2^4 \cdot 3^2 \cdot 5^2 = 3600$.   The GCF of 144 and 150 is $2 \cdot 3 = 6$.

c. The LCM of 72 and 90 is $2^3 \cdot 3^2 \cdot 5 = 360$.   The GCF of 72 and 90 is $2 \cdot 3^2 = 18$.

d. The LCM of 72 and 144 is $2^4 \cdot 3^2 = 144$.   The GCF of 72 and 144 is $2^3 \cdot 3^2 = 72$.

e. The LCM of 144 and 567 is $2^4 \cdot 3^4 \cdot 7 = 9072$.   The GCF of 144 and 567 is $3^2 = 9$.

f. The LCM of 90 and 567 is $2 \cdot 3^4 \cdot 5 \cdot 7 = 5670$.   The GCF of 90 and 567 is $3^2 = 9$.

g. The LCM of 108 and 90 is $2^2 \cdot 3^3 \cdot 5 = 540$.   The GCF of 108 and 90 is $2 \cdot 3^2 = 18$.

h. The LCM of 150 and 350 is $2 \cdot 3 \cdot 5^2 \cdot 7 = 1050$. The GCF of 150 and 350 is $2 \cdot 5^2 = 50$.

i. The LCM of 150, 350, and 270 is $2 \cdot 3^3 \cdot 5^2 \cdot 7 = 9450$.   The GCF of 150, 350, and 270 is $2 \cdot 5 = 10$.

7. a. Three possibilities of many: $2^3 \cdot 3^2$, $2^3 \cdot 3 \cdot 23$ and $2^6 \cdot 3^7 \cdot 7^2$.

   b. and c. There are many possibilities.

8. a. LCM is $5^2 \cdot 7^3 \cdot 13^2$ and the GCF is 5.

b. LCM is $37^6 \cdot 47^5 \cdot 67^6 \cdot 71$ and the GCF is $37^4 \cdot 47^5$.

c. LCM is $2^2 \cdot 7^2 \cdot 11 \cdot 13 \cdot 17$ and the GCF is 2 (note that $26 = 2 \times 13$).

d. $10125 = 5^3 \cdot 3^4$ and $26730 = 2 \cdot 3^5 \cdot 5 \cdot 11$ so the LCM is $2 \cdot 3^5 \cdot 5^3 \cdot 11$ and the GCF is $3^4 \cdot 5$.

e. LCM is $= 2^3 \cdot 3^2 \cdot 5^3 \cdot 7^2$ and the GCF is 7.

f. LCM is $30x^2y^6z^{12}$, and GCF is $2xy^5z^4$.

9. 0 is always a common multiple of two numbers, but it is not useful as a denominator in adding or subtracting fractions, for example.

10. Jogger A is at the start at 0 sec, 90 sec, 180 sec,...

    Jogger B is at the start at 0 sec, 120 sec, 240 sec, and so on.

    The LCM of 90 and 120 is 360. So after 360 sec, or 6 minutes, they are again both at the start. Jogger A has gone around 4 times, Jogger B 3 times.

11. The LCM of 6 and 8 is 24. Cut each piece of the yellow cake into 4 pieces to arrive at 24 pieces. Cut each piece of the chocolate cake into 3 pieces for 24 pieces.

12. The gear with 12 teeth will rotate 5 times and the large one twice to get back to the original positions. Note that 60 is the LCM of 12 and 30: $12 \times 5 = 30 \times 2 = 60$.

13. 8 packages of plates; 5 packages of bowls, and 10 packages of spoons would provide 200 of each. Note that 200 is the LCM of 25, 40, and 20.

14. Order 2 drums of base and 5 drums of color.

15. One gallon of color takes care of 4 gallons of base, so 1 drum of color takes care of 40 gallons of base. LCM(40, 25) = 200. Use 8 drums of base and 5 drums of color.

16. GCF(414,543) = 3, so $3.

17. GCF (198,252,495) = 9, so $9.

18. GCF is 1600. So if 1 cm represents 1600 km, the sun would have a diameter of 875 cm and the earth 8 cm.

19. GCF(216,282) = 6 So if 1 scale inch = 6 classroom inches, the scale drawing would be 36 inches by 47 inches.

20. For example, $m = 2, n = 3$; $m = 4, n = 6$; $m = 6, n = 9$...

21. Hint: Think of "greatest common factor" in this order: first "factor," then "common factor," and finally "greatest common factor."

a. $\dfrac{9}{10}$ b. $\dfrac{3}{4}$ c. $\dfrac{21}{25}$

d. $\dfrac{9}{8}$ e. $\dfrac{3^2}{2}$ f. $\dfrac{y^2}{x}$

22. a. The answer is in simplest form because 9 and 10 are relatively prime.

    b. The answer is in simplest form because 3 and 4 are relatively prime.

c. The answer is in simplest form because 21 and 25 are relatively prime.

d. The answer is in simplest form because 9 and 8 are relatively prime.

23. a. $\dfrac{65}{72}$ b. $\dfrac{3}{8}$ c. $\dfrac{83}{60}$

d. $\dfrac{x^3 + 2x^2 y}{x^2 y^2}$, which can be simplified

e. $\dfrac{33.3 \times 10^5}{6 \times 10^3}$, or 5.55×10^2

24. Another pair: For 24 and 36 the GCF is 12, and the LCM is 72. $12 \times 72 = 864$, and $24 \times 36 = 864$.

25. a. $\dfrac{8}{9}$ b. $\dfrac{853}{4725}$ c. $\dfrac{34}{125}$

26. a. If x is a common factor of m and n, then x is also a factor of $m - n$.

b. One example: If $m = 48$ and $n = 36$, then 6 is a factor of both. 6 is also a factor of $48 - 36 = 12$.

c. $\dfrac{49}{50}$ $\dfrac{35}{36}$ $\dfrac{37}{42}$

d. Yes, for $\frac{81}{86}$, a common factor of 81 and 86 would have to be a common factor of 5. That is, a common factor would have to be 1 or 5. 5 is not a common factor, so there are no common factors of 81 and 86 besides 1, so they are relatively prime.

27. a. $\dfrac{15}{35} = \dfrac{3}{7}$ b. $\dfrac{28}{54} = \dfrac{2^2 \cdot 7}{2 \cdot 3^3} = \dfrac{14}{27}$ c. $\dfrac{150}{350} = \dfrac{3}{7}$

d. $\dfrac{12}{144} = \dfrac{1}{12}$ e. $\dfrac{150}{567} = \dfrac{2 \cdot 3 \cdot 5^2}{3^4 \cdot 7} = \dfrac{50}{189}$ f. $\dfrac{15}{40} = \dfrac{3}{8}$

g. $\dfrac{64}{512} = \dfrac{2^6}{2^9} = \dfrac{1}{2^3} = \dfrac{1}{8}$ h. $\dfrac{21}{49} = \dfrac{3}{7}$

i. $\dfrac{2223}{4536} = \dfrac{3^2 \cdot 13 \cdot 19}{3^4 \cdot 2^3 \cdot 7} = \dfrac{13 \cdot 19}{3^2 \cdot 2^3 \cdot 7} = \dfrac{247}{504}$

28. a. $\dfrac{39}{144} + \dfrac{35}{108} = \dfrac{39}{2^4 \cdot 3^2} + \dfrac{35}{2^2 \cdot 3^3} = \dfrac{39 \cdot 3}{2^4 \cdot 3^2 \cdot 3} + \dfrac{35 \cdot 2^2}{2^2 \cdot 3^3 \cdot 2^2} = \dfrac{117 + 140}{2^4 \cdot 3^3} = \dfrac{257}{432}$

b. $\dfrac{25}{72}+\dfrac{81}{567}=\dfrac{25}{2^3\cdot 3^2}+\dfrac{81}{3^4\cdot 7}=\dfrac{25\cdot 3^2\cdot 7}{2^3\cdot 3^2\cdot 3^2\cdot 7}+\dfrac{81\cdot 2^3}{3^4\cdot 7\cdot 2^3}=\dfrac{1575+648}{2^3\cdot 3^4\cdot 7}=\dfrac{2223}{4536}.$ Or

$\dfrac{25}{72}+\dfrac{81}{567}=\dfrac{25}{2^3\cdot 3^2}+\dfrac{3^4}{3^4\cdot 7}=\dfrac{25\cdot 7}{2^3\cdot 3^2\cdot 7}+\dfrac{1\cdot 2^3\cdot 3^2}{7\cdot 2^3\cdot 3^2}=\dfrac{175}{2^3\cdot 3^2\cdot 7}+\dfrac{72}{2^3\cdot 3^2\cdot 7}=\dfrac{175+72}{2^3\cdot 3^2\cdot 7}=\dfrac{247}{504}.$

Note that $\dfrac{2223}{4536}=\dfrac{3^2\cdot 13\cdot 19}{3^4\cdot 2^3\cdot 7}=\dfrac{13\cdot 19}{3^2\cdot 2^3\cdot 7}=\dfrac{247}{504}.$

On the remaining parts we will simplify fractions before adding or subtracting.

c. $\dfrac{36}{108}+\dfrac{41}{72}=\dfrac{2^2\cdot 3^2}{2^2\cdot 3^3}+\dfrac{41}{2^3\cdot 3^2}=\dfrac{1}{3}+\dfrac{41}{2^3\cdot 3^2}=\dfrac{1\cdot 2^3\cdot 3}{2^3\cdot 3^2}+\dfrac{41}{2^3\cdot 3^2}=\dfrac{24+41}{2^3\cdot 3^2}=\dfrac{65}{72}$

d. $\dfrac{15}{39}+\dfrac{110}{169}=\dfrac{3\cdot 5}{3\cdot 13}+\dfrac{110}{13^2}=\dfrac{5\cdot 13}{13\cdot 13}+\dfrac{110}{13^2}=\dfrac{65+110}{13^2}=\dfrac{175}{169}=1\dfrac{6}{169}$

e. $\dfrac{169}{500}+\dfrac{169}{650}=\dfrac{169}{2^2\cdot 5^3}+\dfrac{13^2}{2\cdot 5^2\cdot 13}=\dfrac{169}{2^2\cdot 5^2}+\dfrac{13\cdot 2\cdot 5}{2\cdot 5^2\cdot 2\cdot 5}=\dfrac{169+130}{2^2\cdot 5^3}=\dfrac{299}{500}$

f. $\dfrac{126}{504}+\dfrac{98}{770}=\dfrac{2\cdot 3^2\cdot 7}{2^3\cdot 3^2\cdot 7}+\dfrac{2\cdot 7^2}{2\cdot 5\cdot 7\cdot 11}=\dfrac{1}{2^2}+\dfrac{7}{5\cdot 11}=\dfrac{1\cdot 5\cdot 11}{2^2\cdot 5\cdot 11}+\dfrac{7\cdot 2^2}{5\cdot 11\cdot 2^2}=\dfrac{55+28}{220}=\dfrac{83}{220}$

29. The GCF of 27 and 36 is 9. A new "ruler" with unit 9 inches gives whole-number answers for the width and length of the desks (3 units by 4 units).

30. (Assignment using Virtual Library)

Supplementary Learning Exercises for Section 11.4

1. a. 12   b. 144   c. Eliminate the GCF: $\dfrac{12\times 3}{12\times 4}=\dfrac{3}{4}$ d. $\dfrac{17}{36}+\dfrac{5}{48}=\dfrac{68}{144}+\dfrac{15}{144}=\dfrac{83}{144}$

2. a. 30   b. 1350   c. $\dfrac{150}{270}=\dfrac{30\times 5}{30\times 9}=\dfrac{5}{9}$ d. $\dfrac{91}{150}+\dfrac{7}{270}=\dfrac{819}{1350}+\dfrac{35}{1350}=\dfrac{854}{1350}\left(=\dfrac{427}{675}\right)$

3. a. LCM = 1056; GCF = 12

   b. LCM = 126; GCF = 42 (Did you see this one quickly?)

   c. LCM = 576; GCF = 4

   d. LCM = x^4y^9; GCF = x^2y^6

   e. LCM = $2^3\times 7^3\times 11\times 13=392{,}392$; GCF = $2^2\times 7^2=196$

4. a. 1800

   b. The algorithm involves finding a common factor, then "removing" it by dividing, and continuing, removing other common factors. At the end, then, the common factors multiplied are the least ones whose product will be a common multiple of the original numbers.

5. a–b. Yes, at any common multiple of 2 and 3: 6, 12, 18, 24, etc.

11.5 Issues for Learning: Understanding the Unique Factorization Theorem

1. k cannot be divided by 5, 11, or 17. Some students try to use divisibility rules to check for divisibility when this is not necessary.

2. 51 is a factor of a because $51 = 3 \times 17$, and both 3 and 17 are factors. Some students would divide 153 by 51 to obtain an answer, but this is not necessary.

3. a and b both have the same number of factors: $6 = (2 + 1)(1 + 1)$. A common error is to think that the larger number has more factors.

Part II: Reasoning About Algebra and Change

Answers for Chapter 12: What Is Algebra?

12.1 Algebra as a Symbolic Language

1. a. 1800. $(ab) + (ac) = a(b + c)$, for every choice of numbers a, b, and c. This property is called the distributive property (of multiplication over addition).

   b. 100. $(ab) + (cb) = (a + c)b$, for every choice of numbers a, b, and c. This property is a variation of the distributive property (of multiplication over addition).

   c. 431. $(a + b) + c = a + (b + c)$, for every choice of numbers a, b, and c. This property is called the associative property of addition.

   d. 1700. $(ab)c = a(bc)$, for every choice of numbers a, b, and c. This property is called the associative property of multiplication.

   e. $\frac{117}{298}$. 1 is the identity for multiplication.

   f. $\frac{13}{35}$. 0 is the identity for addition.

   g. The calculation could be viewed as 4×17, or $4 \times (10 + 7)$, but it could be accomplished by calculating the value of the dimes first, 4×10, and then of all the pennies, 4×7, and adding those results. Hence, $4 \times (10 + 7) = (4 \times 10) + (4 \times 7)$. In general, then, $a(b+c) = (ab) + (ac)$, for every choice of numbers a, b, and c, again the distributive property of multiplication over addition. It is a variation of the property in parts (a) and (b), but the equation is just "backwards," with the right-hand and left-hand sides of the equation replacing each other.

2. a. equal to   b. equal to   c. equal to

   d. One way might be: Is $12 - 4 + 4 = 12$? Is $16 - 7.2 + 7.2 = 16$? Is $b - 9.3 + 9.3 = b$?

3. a. True for =, but not for < or for >.

   b. True for =, for <, and for >.

4. a. $\$2.30 + c = \$4.00$

   b. $8 + 3 = s$

   c. $360 + 6 = n$

   d. $(10 \times 12) \div 30 = m$

5. a. $[(x + 8) \cdot 4 - 3 + 7] \div 4 - 9 = [4x + 32 - 3 + 7] \div 4 - 9$

   $= [4x + 36] \div 4 - 9 = x + 9 - 9 = x$

6. a. Distributive property   b. Commutative and associative properties of addition

c. Commutative and associative properties of multiplication

d. Distributive property   e. Distributive property   f. Distributive property

7. a. $x(x+5)$
   b. $(x \cdot 4)x$
   c. $10(n+m)$
   d. $(y+3y)+2$
   e. $1x^3 = x^3$
   f. $\frac{4}{3}n^2$
   g. $\frac{3}{4}(\frac{x}{y} \cdot \frac{y}{x}) = \frac{3}{4} \cdot 1 = \frac{3}{4}$

8. $2 \cdot 5^3 - 3 \cdot 5 = 250 - 15 = 235$, not 135. So $x = 5$ is not a solution.

9. a. $x = 9.5$
   b. $y = 16$
   c. $n = 19$
   d. $y = \frac{46}{3} = 15\frac{1}{3}$
   e. $x = 4$
   f. $x = 6$
   g. $x = \frac{3}{4}$
   h. $x = {}^-9$
   i. $t = 96$

10. a. $x + 2x + (x+12) + (x-3)$ b. $[x + 2x + (x+12) + (x-3)] \div 4$
    c. $x + 2x + (x+12) + (x-3) - 60$
    d. $x + 2x + (x+12) + (x-3) = 119$, $5x+9 = 119$, $5x = 110$, $x = \$22$, $2x = \$44$, $x+12 = \$34$, and $x-3 = \$19$.
    e. One possibility: When the people combined their money, they had \$36. If they then shared the money equally, how much did each have?
       $5x+9 = 36$, $5x = 27$, $x = \frac{27}{5} = 5\frac{2}{5} = 5.4$ or \$5.40
       The first had \$5.40, the second had \$10.80, the third had \$17.40, and the fourth had \$2.40.

11. a. $x + 10$
    b. $x + y$
    c. $x - 3$
    d. $x - n$
    e. $2x$

12. a. $k - 12$
    b. $k + n$
    c. $\frac{1}{3}(k+n)$
    d. $2(k-12)$

13. a. $\$6d$
    b. $\$nd$
    c. $\$2d + \$17.95$
    d. $\$0.7d$
    e. $\$40 - \$d$
    f. $\$0.07d$

14. a. $2(x+2+x) = 4x+4$ in.   b. $x+x+1+x-7 = 3x-6$ in.
    c. $4S$ in.   d. $n+n+5+2n+8+2n+7 = 6n+20$ in.

15. The total of 3 fifties is *conceptually quite different* from the total of 50 threes, even though we know each will give the same total. The first is easier. We know from the previous section that this is an example of the remarkable relationship that always holds with multiplication of two numbers: the commutative property of multiplication. This property is one that must be learned in school. It is not obvious to young children.

16. a. Example: Associative property of multiplication can be modeled by a two-layer array that is 3×5. This also models a three-layered 5×2 array.

b. Example: Associative property of addition can be modeled with base-ten blocks with the long representing one. Model 1.7 and 3.3. Three small unit cubes shifts from the 3.3 to the 1.7, making 2 longs and 3 longs.

c. The existence of multiplicative inverses is shown with a rectangular array. It is important to identify a rectangular unit. Illustrate $\frac{3}{2}$ and show that $\frac{2}{3}$ of $\frac{3}{2}$ is the original unit.

d. Show on a number line that three jumps of 5 ends at the same place on the number line as 5 jumps of 3. Modeling with an array: three rows of five columns rotated 90 degrees is five rows of 3 columns.

17. a. $3x + 2 = x + 10$,   b. $x + 7 = 1 + 4x$

18. a. Remove two black dots from each side (result $3x = x + 8$) and then an x from each side (result $2x = 8$). Finally, if two x's balance with 8 black dots then one x balances with 4 black dots (result $x = 4$).

b. Remove one black dot from each side (result $x + 6 = 4x$) and then an x from each side (result $6 = 3x$). Finally, if three x's balance with 3 black dots then one x balances with 2 black dots.

Supplementary Learning Exercises for Section 12.1

1. a. Distributive property: $1(x + 3) + 5(x + 3) = 6(x + 3)$

   b. Distributive property (plus computations)

   c. Associative property of addition

   d. False

   e. Rewriting 16 and then using the associative property of multiplication

   f. Distributive property (then computation)

   g. False

   h. False

   i. Distributive property

   j. Associative property of multiplication

   k. False

   l. Zero property of multiplication

   m. Commutative property of addition

n. Identity property of multiplication

2. a. For any value b: $b = b$ is always true; $b \leq b$ is always true; $b \geq b$ is always true.

    b. For any values m and n: If $m = n$, then $n = m$ is always true; if $m \leq n$, then $n \leq m$ is sometimes true (but only when $m = n$); if $m \geq n$, then $n \geq m$ is sometimes true (but only when $m = n$).

    c. For any values r, s, and t: If $r = s$ and $s = t$, then $r = t$ is always true; if $r \leq s$ and $s \leq t$, then $r \leq t$ is always true; if $r \geq s$ and $s \geq t$, then $r \geq t$ is always true.

3. a. True

    b. False. This formula applies only to squares.

    c. True. If each side of the square is $2s$, then the area is $(2s)^2$, or $2^2 s^2$, or $4s^2$.

    d. True. The perimeter of any polygon is the sum of the sides.

    e. False. The circumference is 10π. (You may not remember the formula, $C = 2\pi r$, but you should remember, at least, that π is in the formula.)

4. Let c represent the number of comic books owned by Casey; k represent the number of comic books owned by Kaye; n represent the number of comic books owned by Nancy; j represent the number of comic books owned by Jinfa; f represent the number of comic books owned by Fortuna; and m represent the number of comic books owned by Milissa.

    a. $k = 3c$ b. $n > 2c$ c. $j = \frac{1}{2}c$ d. $f = 3c + 4$ e. $m = 3c + 2$

5. a. $n + (n + 2) + 2n = 4n + 2$ b. $(n + 2) + (n + 2) + (2n - 6) = 4n - 2$ c. $4n - 8$

6. a. Yes   b. No   c. Yes   d. No   e. Yes   f. No

7. a. \$120 million + \$$z$ = \$560 million, or more simply, $120 + z = 560$, so $z = 560 - 120 = 440$. Freddie's company's mortgage debt is \$440 million.

    b. Let t represent the degrees of temperature lost: $104° - t = 99.6°$. So $t = 104° - 99.6° = 4.4°$.

    c. Let a represent the entrance fee in dollars for Air Park for one person. Then $5a$ represents the dollar cost for 5 people. Thus, $5a + 5 \cdot 32 = 300$, so $5a = 140$ and $a = 140 \div 5 = 28$ dollars. The entrance fee for Air Park was \$28.

d. Let d equal the price of one day of the three-day pass. Then $3d = \$81$, so $d = \$27$. Tanya should buy the three-day pass and save $5 per day, or $15 for the 3 days.

e. The price p of 1 ounce of nuts can be used to connect the fact that there are 16 ounces in 1 pound, and the cost of 1 pound $16p = 3.68$, so $p = \$0.23$. Six ounces would cost $6 \times \$0.23 = \$1.38$.

f. Let j represent the cost per ounce of the jellybeans. $8 \times \$0.23 + 8j = \$3.28$, so $j = \$0.18$.

8. a. 5900, using associativity of multiplication

    b. $39.80, using distributivity: $(4 \times 3.98) + (6 \times 3.98) = (4 + 6) \times 3.98 = 10 \times 3.98$

    c. $\frac{97}{106}$, using multiplicative inverses and the identity for multiplication

    d. $144, using distributivity: $(24 \times 1.50) + (24 \times 4.50) = 24 \times (1.50 + 4.50) = 24 \times 6$

9. a. $b + 7$ b. $2b + 9$ c. $b + c$ d. $2b + 12$

10. a. $x = 4$ b. $x = 2.4$ c. $^-28$ d. $^-10$ e. 547

11. a. The result is not 25. "Add 11" should be "Add 13."

    b. Suppose your age is a. Write each of the steps using a instead of your age, then   simplify the expression you have. The result is 25. To obtain your age as the result, subtract 25 instead of subtracting your age.

12.2 Algebra as Generalized Arithmetic

1. a.
$$4 \cdot 10^3 + 0 \cdot 10^2 + 2 \cdot 10 + 6$$
$$\underline{0 \cdot 10^3 + 0 \cdot 10^2 + 4 \cdot 10 + 3}$$
$$4 \cdot 10^3 + 0 \cdot 10^2 + 6 \cdot 10 + 9$$

b.
$$4n^3 + 0n^2 + 2n + 6$$
$$\underline{0n^3 + 0n^2 + 4n + 3}$$
$$4n^3 + 0n^2 + 6n + 9$$

The sum is 4069...   ...or simply, $4n^3 + 6n + 9$.
When 4026 and 43 are written out in long form they are similar in structure to $4n^3 + 0n^2 + 2n + 6$ and $4n + 3$. (Note that the 0 terms do not need to be included. They are placed here for clarity.)

2. a.   b.

$$5 \cdot 10^2 + 9 \cdot 10 + 8$$ $$5x^2 + 9x + 8$$
$$-\ \underline{3 \cdot 10^2 + 4 \cdot 10 + 7}$$ $$-\ \underline{3x^2 + 4x + 7}$$
$$2 \cdot 10^2 + 5 \cdot 10 + 1 = 251$$ $$2x^2 + 5x + 1$$

When 598 and 347 are written out in long form, they are similar in structure to
$5x^2 + 9x + 8$ and $3x^2 + 4x + 7$.

3. a. $6 \cdot 10^2 + 4 \cdot 10 + 2$
     $+1 \cdot 10^2 + 8 \cdot 10 + 8$
       $\overline{7 \cdot 10^2 + 12 \cdot 10 + 10}$
       $8 \cdot 10^2 + 3 \cdot 10 + 0$
       830

    b. $6x^2 + 4x + 2$
     $+ \ x^2 + 8x + 8$
       $\overline{7x^2 + 12x + 10}$

When 642 and 188 are written out in long form, they are similar in structure to
$6x^2 + 4x + 2$ and $x^2 + 8x + 8$.

4. a. $\frac{12}{18} = \frac{2 \cdot 6}{3 \cdot 6} = \frac{2}{3}$ b. $\frac{4x^3}{7x^2} = \frac{4x \cdot x^2}{7 \cdot x^2} = \frac{4x}{7}$

In both cases, the numerators and denominators have common factors.

5. a. $\frac{5}{16} + \frac{7}{16} = \frac{5+7}{16} = \frac{12}{16} = \frac{3}{4}$ b. $\frac{3x}{y} + \frac{2x+1}{y} = \frac{3x+(2x+1)}{y} = \frac{5x+1}{y}$ c. $\frac{5}{x+2} + \frac{x}{x+2} = \frac{5+x}{x+2}$

In all three cases, there are common denominators, so only the numerators need to be added.

6. a. $\frac{5}{8} + \frac{3}{4} = \frac{5}{8} + \frac{3 \cdot 2}{4 \cdot 2} = \frac{5}{8} + \frac{6}{8} = \frac{11}{8}$ (or $1\frac{3}{8}$)

    b. $\frac{3x}{(x+2)(x+3)} + \frac{2}{x+2} = \frac{3x}{(x+2)(x+3)} + \frac{2 \cdot (x+3)}{(x+2)(x+3)} = \frac{3x + 2 \cdot (x+3)}{(x+2)(x+3)} = \frac{5x+6}{(x+2)(x+3)}$

In both cases, one denominator is a multiple of another denominator, making a common denominator easy to find.

7. a. $\frac{7}{9} - \frac{2}{9} = \frac{7-2}{9} = \frac{5}{9}$ b. $\frac{2x}{7y} - \frac{4}{7y} = \frac{2x-4}{7y}$

In both cases, the denominators are the same, so only the numerators need to be subtracted.

8. a. $\frac{3}{4} - \frac{1}{7} = \frac{3 \cdot 7}{4 \cdot 7} - \frac{1 \cdot 4}{7 \cdot 4} = \frac{3 \cdot 7 - 1 \cdot 4}{4 \cdot 7} = \frac{17}{28}$

    b. $\frac{3}{xy} - \frac{4x}{9n} = \frac{3 \cdot 9n}{xy \cdot 9n} - \frac{4x \cdot xy}{9n \cdot xy} = \frac{3 \cdot 9n}{9nxy} - \frac{4x^2 y}{9nxy} = \frac{27n - 4x^2 y}{9nxy}$

In both cases, a common denominator is the product of the two denominators.

9. a. $\frac{2}{3} \times \frac{5}{7} = \frac{2 \cdot 5}{3 \cdot 7} = \frac{10}{21}$ b. $\frac{2a}{b} \times \frac{c}{3d} = \frac{2a \cdot c}{b \cdot 3d} = \frac{2ac}{3bd}$

    c. $\frac{4}{x+2} \cdot \frac{2y}{x+3} = \frac{4 \cdot 2y}{(x+2)(x+3)} = \frac{8y}{(x+2)(x+3)}$

In all three cases, the product was found by multiplying the numerators and then the denominators.

10. a. $\frac{5}{6} \div \frac{2}{3} = \frac{5}{6} \times \frac{3}{2} = \frac{15}{12} = \frac{5}{4}$ or $1\frac{1}{4}$

b. $\frac{x^2}{2y} \div \frac{xy}{3} = \frac{x^2}{2y} \cdot \frac{3}{xy} = \frac{3x^2}{2xy^2} = \frac{3x}{2y^2}$

In both cases, the quotient was found by inverting the divisor before multiplying.

11. a. $\ldots = x^2 + 2xy + y^2$

b. Describe the 8 pieces in the cube and add them.

c. $\ldots = x^2 + xy$

d. $\ldots = x^2 + 2x + 3x + 6 = x^2 + 5x + 6$, with a drawing similar to that of part (a).

Supplementary Learning Exercises for Section 12.2

1. a. $4x^4 + x^3 + 2x + 5$ (It is all okay to include $0x^2$.)

b. $2x^5 + 3x^4 + 4x^3 + x^2 + 2x + 5$

2. a. $9x^2 + 6x + 5$

b. $18x^2 + 8x + 6$

c. $4 + 3x + 8x + 6x^2$, or $6x^2 + 11x + 4$

3 a.   Sum: $12x^2 + 5x + 19$; product: $35x^4 + 31x^3 + 119x^2 + 48x + 90$

b.   Sum: $\frac{13}{12}x + 2\frac{2}{5}$, or $1\frac{1}{12}x + 2\frac{2}{5}$; product: $\frac{1}{4}x^2 + \frac{29}{30}x + \frac{4}{5}$

c.   Sum: $8x + {}^-5$; product: $15x^2 + {}^-19x + 6$

d.   Sum: $41x + 56$; product: $418x^2 + 1139x + 775$

e.   Sum: $14x + 3$; product: $42x^3 + 127x^2 + 2x + {}^-3$

4. a. $\frac{3}{x}$

b. $\frac{11}{2x}$

c. $\frac{7-3y}{2(y+7)^2}$

d. $\frac{2}{y^2}$

e. $\frac{n}{z}$

12.3 Numerical Patterns and Algebra

1. a. ABAB; B

b. ABBA; B (seeing ABBA as repeating)

c. 9.7, 10.5, 11.3, 12.1; 21.7

d. 80, 75, 70, 65; $^-45$

e. 162, 486, 1458, 4374

f. 0.3125, 0.15625, 0.078125, 0.0390625

g. $\frac{1}{6}, \frac{1}{7}, \frac{1}{8}, \frac{1}{9}; \frac{1}{100}$

h. $\frac{5}{6}, \frac{6}{7}, \frac{7}{8}, \frac{8}{9}; \frac{100}{101}$

i. 2, 4, 6, 8; 4 as 30th entry. Instructor: There will be seven full 2-4-6-8 blocks and two extra entries, in the first 30 entries. So the 30th entry will be the second entry in the next 2-4-6-8 block.)

j. 2, 8, 5, 7; 8 (with 1, 4, 2, 8, 5, 7 as repeating numbers)

k. Parts (c) and (d) are arithmetic sequences (not parts (g) and (h), although their numerators are arithmetic sequences, as are their denominators).

l. Parts (e) and (f) are geometric sequences.

2. a. Count how many zeros are in the power of 10 (or look at the exponent) and move the decimal place that many places to make a larger number. If the original number is a whole number, just annex that many zeros.

b. Each place value is made that many times as large as it was originally, so each digit moves to the left that many places. (Instructor: This answer may require an example.)

3. a. Count how many zeros are in the power of 10 (or look at the exponent) and move the decimal place that many places to make a smaller number. If the original number is a whole number, put in a decimal point first.

b. Each place value is reduced by that power, so each digit moves to the right that many places.

c. $1\% = \frac{1}{100}$, so multiplying by 1% is equivalent to dividing by 100.

4. a. 2006

b. $24\frac{3}{4}$

c. 7

d. 16

5. a. 13, 21, 34, 55

b. For $n = 1$, $\dfrac{(1+\sqrt{5})^1 - (1-\sqrt{5})^1}{2^1\sqrt{5}} = \dfrac{2\sqrt{5}}{2\sqrt{5}} = 1$.

For $n = 2$, $\dfrac{(1+\sqrt{5})^2 - (1-\sqrt{5})^2}{2^2\sqrt{5}} = \dfrac{(1+2\sqrt{5}+5)-(1-2\sqrt{5}+5)}{4\sqrt{5}} = \dfrac{4\sqrt{5}}{4\sqrt{5}} = 1$

c. The values get closer and closer to 1.618 ($\frac{1+\sqrt{5}}{2}$, exactly).

6. a. $\frac{1}{2^n}$

b. $\frac{1}{2}+\frac{1}{4}=\frac{3}{4}$, $\frac{1}{2}+\frac{1}{4}+\frac{1}{8}=\frac{7}{8}$, $\frac{1}{2}+\frac{1}{4}+\frac{1}{8}+\frac{1}{16}=\frac{15}{16}$ suggest tentatively that the sum of the first n such fractions would be $\dfrac{2^n-1}{2^n}$.

7. 2. The decimal has a repeating block, 1-4-2-8-5-7, six digits long. So from $99 \div 6 = 16$ R 3, there would be 16 full blocks, with 3 entries into the next block: 1-4-2.

8. a. 9   b. 9   c. 1

    d. The *ones* digits follow a repeating cycle of four digits: 7, 9, 3, 1. Find out how many full cycles there are in n, and look at the remainder by calculating $n \div 4$. The remainder tells you which number to go to in the next cycle. For example, 7^{778} will end in 9 because 778 $\div 4 = 194$ R 2, and the second number in the (next) cycle is 9.

9. The square numbers are so called because they give the areas of squares with whole-number sides. If the side of a square is s, then s^2 gives the area of the square.

10. a. The first eight triangular numbers are 1, 3, 6, 10, 15, 21, 28, and 36, with the differences between two consecutive numbers increasing by 1 each time.

    b. Yes, each bottom row increases by 1 from one triangle to the next.

11. a. The sum would be $\frac{n(n+1)}{2}$.

    b. The successive sums give the triangular numbers, so the nth triangular number is $\frac{n(n+1)}{2}$.

12. a. Yes, the switch can be made.

    b. 15 (If you keep getting 17, there is one crucial point at which you can avoid any moves in the wrong direction.)

    c. $n(n + 2)$

13. Choice II. $\$1000.00 = 100,000¢$. But $2^{20} = 2^{10} \cdot 2^{10} = 1024 \cdot 1024 > 1000 \cdot 1000 = 1,000,000 ¢$, so well before the month was over, Choice II would give more money than Choice I.

Supplementary Learning Exercises for Section 12.3

1. a. (i) This is an arithmetic sequence with $a = 8$ and $d = 4$. That is, the numbers increase by 4 each time, so by the 500th number, there will have been 499 increases of 4, or 1996, over the starting value of 8: $8 + 499(4) = 2004$.

    (ii) The same thinking (or the use of the result for an arithmetic sequence) gives 8 + $(n–1)4$ for the nth number. $8 + (n - 1)4$ also $= 8 + 4n - 4 = 4 + 4n$.

    b. This is an arithmetic sequence with $a = 2.3$ and $d = 1.3$.

    (i) $2.3 + 499(1.3) = 651$

    (ii) $2.3 + (n - 1)1.3$, or $1.3n + 1$

    c. (i) Every odd term is $^{-}1$ and every even term is 1, so the 500th number would be 1.

    (ii) The nth term would be $^{-}1$ if n is odd, and 1 if n is even.

d. This is an arithmetic sequence with $a = 3\frac{1}{4}$ and $d = 1\frac{3}{4}$.

   (i) $3\frac{1}{4} + 499(1\frac{3}{4}) = 3\frac{1}{4} + 873\frac{1}{4} = 876\frac{1}{2}$ (ii) $3\frac{1}{4} + (n-1)1\frac{3}{4}$, or $1\frac{3}{4}n + 1\frac{1}{2}$

e. This is an arithmetic sequence with $a = {}^-100$ and $d = 2$.

   (i) ${}^-100 + 499 \times 2 = {}^-100 + 998 = 898$ (ii) ${}^-100 + (n-1)2 = {}^-102 + 2n$

f. (i) The 4-7-9 pattern is a block of three digits. From $500 \div 3 = 166$ R 2, there would be 166 full blocks and two numbers into the next block, or 7.

   (ii) Calculate $n \div 3$ and use the remainder to see which number in the next 4-7-9 block to choose; if the remainder is zero, then there are full 4-7-9 blocks, so the last number would be 9.

g. This is a geometric sequence with $a = 1$ and $r = 5$.

   (i) The 500th number would be 5^{499}. (ii) The nth term is 5^{n-1}.

h. This is an arithmetic sequence with $a = 2000$ and $d = {}^-1.7$.

   (i) The 500th number would be $2000 + 499({}^-1.7) = 1151.7$.

   (ii) $2000 + (n-1)({}^-1.7)$, or $2000 - (n-1)1.7$, or $2001.7 - 1.7n$

i. This is a geometric sequence with a and r both equal to 3.

   (i) The 500th number would be $3(3^{500-1}) = 3^{500}$.

   (ii) The nth term would be $3(3^{n-1}) = 3^n$.

j. This is a geometric sequence with $a = 1$ and $r = \frac{1}{2}$.

   (i) The 500th number would be $1 \cdot (\frac{1}{2})^{500-1} = \frac{1}{2^{499}}$.

   (ii) The nth term would be $\frac{1}{2^{n-1}}$.

k. This is an arithmetic sequence with $a = 16$ and $d = {}^-4$.

   (i) The 500th term would be $16 + 499({}^-4) = {}^-1980$.

   (ii) The nth term would be $16 + (n-1)({}^-4) = 20 - 4n$.

l. This is an arithmetic sequence with $a = 0.5$ and $d = 0.25$.

   (i) The 500th term would be $0.5 + 499(0.25) = 125.25$.

   (ii) The nth term would be $0.5 + (n-1)(0.25)$, or $0.25n + 0.25$.

2. a. 22.3, 22.65, 23, 23.35, 23.7   b. 1.5, 3, 6, 12, 24

3. Here is one way of reasoning (cf. 1(f) for another way). Notice that the 1st, 4th, 7th etc. digit is 3. The 2nd, 5th, 8th etc. digit is 6. The 3rd, 6th, and 9th digit is 9. The 36th digit is in the sequence 3, 6, 9,... so the digit is 9. The 100th digit is in the sequence 1, 4, 7, ... so the digit is 3. (Notice that 100 is one more than 99, and the digit in the 99th place would be 3 because 99 is in the sequence 3, 6, 9, ... The number following 9 in the given pattern of 369369369...is 3.)

4. $\frac{2}{11} = 0.18181818....$ Notice that the even-numbered digits (2nd, 4th, etc.) are all 8s and the odd numbered digits are all 1s. The 88th digit would therefore be 8.

5. The calculations 2, $2^2 = 4$, $2^3 = 8$, $2^4 = 16$, $2^5 = 32$, $2^6 = 64$, $2^7 = 128$, $2^8 = 256$, $2^9 =$ ...2, $2^{10} = ...4, ...8, ...6, ...2, ...$ suggests that the 2-4-8-6 block of four digits is repeated. From $120 \div 4 = 30$, you know that there will be 30 full blocks of 2-4-8-6 when you get to 2^{120}, so the last digit, 6, will be in the ones place.

6. 85^2 would end in 25. It would begin with 8×9, or 72. Thus, $85^2 = 7225$. Similarly, $19.5^2 = 380.25$, from $19 \times 20 = 380$. (195^2 would equal 38,025.)

7. a. 9   b. 7   c. 1

8. a. $\dfrac{1}{3^{n-1}}$ (or perhaps $3^{-(n-1)} = 3^{-n+1}$)   *Hint*: Make a table:

Term	Number in sequence	Number in sequence rewritten with term number
1	$1 \quad = 3^0$	3^{-1+1}
2	$\dfrac{1}{3} = \dfrac{1}{3^1}$ or 3^{-1}	3^{-2+1}
3	$\dfrac{1}{9} = \dfrac{1}{3^2}$ or 3^{-2}	3^{-3+1}
4	$\dfrac{1}{27} = \dfrac{1}{3^3}$ or 3^{-3}	$3^?$
.	.	.
.	.	.
.	.	.
n	$\dfrac{1}{3^?}$	$3^?$

   b. The sum of the set of numbers *after* the first term (1) will get closer and closer to $\frac{1}{2}$, so 1 (the first term) plus the sum of the set of numbers in the remainder of the sequence will get closer and closer to $1\frac{1}{2}$.

12.4 Functions and Algebra

1. a. Yes, because each and every child has a first name.

    b. Perhaps not, because more than one child might have the same last name, so if you say, "Smith," there might be two or more children respond. If the last names of all the children are different, then the "last name → child" rule *would* give a function.

2. a. Yes, each element in the first set is associated with exactly one element in the second set.

    b. No, the element 9 in the first set is associated with two elements in the second set, 3 and − 3 (and 16 is associated with two elements in the second set, 4 and − 4).

    c. Yes, each first entry in the ordered pairs is associated with exactly 1 second entry in the ordered pairs.

    d. Yes, each first entry in the ordered pairs is associated with exactly 1 second entry in the ordered pairs. (That 1.7 and 1.8 each corresponds to 2 does not violate the definition.)

3. $y = 21x − 12$; $n = 50$

4. $f(x) = 100 − 22x$; $n = 10$

5. *output* $= 8 \times$ *input* $− 8$; $n = 202$

6. *output* $= 0.3 \times$ *input* $− 7$; $n = 76$

7. $y = 5x − 3$; $n = 110$

8. $f(x) = 16x + 3$; $n = 25$

9. $f(x) = \frac{2}{3}x + \frac{1}{2}$; $n = 12$

10. $y = \frac{4}{3}x + 4$; $n = 60$

11. a. $f(x) = x^2$; $n = 30$

     b. $y = x^3$; $n = 9$

12. a. $f(n) = 4n + 1$ (Instructor: Ask for students' justifications first. One justification counts the n vertical ones across the top, plus the n horizontal ones on the top, the n horizontal ones on the bottom, and the $n + 1$ vertical ones in the middle: $n + n + n + (n + 1)$.)

     b. $f(n) = 5n + 2$ (Instructor: Ask for students' justifications first. One justification starts with the first 2 vertical ones, and then notes that each additional 5 *t*-picks give a shape: $2 + 5n$.)

     c. $f(n) = 2n + 1$ (Instructor: Ask for students' justifications first. One justification starts with the 3 for the first shape, and then notes that the remaining $n − 1$ triangles each requires 2 more *t*-picks: $3 + (n − 1)2$.)

d. $f(n) = 3n + 4$ (Instructor: Ask for students' justifications first. One justification notes that shape n involves $n + 1$ squares. These, independently, would require $4(n + 1)$ t-picks. But that would count the n inside vertical t-picks twice: $4(n + 1) - n$).

e. $f(n) = 5n + 6$ (Instructor: Ask for students' justifications first. One justification counts the $(n + 1)2$ for the roofs, the $n + 1$ for the ceilings, the $n + 1$ for the floors, and the $n + 2$ for the walls: $(n + 1)2 + (n + 1) + (n + 1) + (n + 2)$.)

13. a. $n(n + 1)$, or you may have seen $n^2 + n$

   b.   Factor 2 from each term in $2 + 4 + \ldots + 2n$, and use part (a).

   c.   Factoring 6 from each term gives $6(1 + 2 + \cdots + n) = 3n(n + 1)$, using part (a).

   d. $1 + 3 + 5 + 7 + \cdots + (2n - 1) = n^2$.

14. Sum of first n numbers in the arithmetic sequence $= na + \frac{(n-1)n}{2}d$. Notice the adjustment needed in Learning Exercise 13(b) here because the sequence 1, 3, 6, and so on, starts with $n = 2$ rather than $n = 1$. So to use Exercise 13(b) you have to subtract 1 from how many numbers are being added.

15. Since the n-step stairway involves $1 + 2 + \cdots + n$ small squares, it will have $\frac{n(n+1)}{2}$ small squares, from Learning Exercise 13(b).

16. a.   100°C, 0°C, 37°C, and about 21°C. (These values are worth memorizing.)

   b. $F = \frac{9}{5}C + 32$

17. The digit is 9. There are 250 full 0-4-2-9 blocks to get to the 1000th decimal place, so the digit in that place will be the last one in the last 0-4-2-9 block.

18. a.   2. There are 249 full 8-4-2-6 blocks, plus three places into the next 8-4-2-6 block: ($999 \div 4 = 249$ R 3).

   b.   6

   c.   8

19. a. $\frac{8}{7}$, or $1\frac{1}{7}$, packages per pound

   b. $\frac{7}{8}$ pounds in one package

   c. $10 \times \frac{8}{7} = 11\frac{3}{7}$ packages

20. Each of the function rules gives the same values; they just represent different ways of thinking.

Supplementary Learning Exercises for Section 12.4

1. a.   Function: Every passenger is matched with exactly one seat.

   b.   Not a function: Not every seat is always matched with a passenger.

   c.   Function: A, B, and C in the first set are each matched with exactly one element in the second set.

d. Not a function: One element for the first set, namely A, is matched with not one but three elements in the second set.

e. Not a function: 4 can be matched with both 2 and ⁻2.

f. Function: Every number has exactly one square.

g. Function: Every number (the first in each ordered pair) is matched with exactly one number.

h. Not a function: For example, 3 (the first number in an ordered pair) is matched with both 6 and 8.

2. a. $y = 5x + 7$, $m = 507$, $n = 400$

b. $f(x) = 157 - 4x$, $m = 13$, $n = 50$

c. $output = 2^{input} + 3$, $m = 1027$, $n = 11$

d. $output = 3 \times input + 5$; $m = 305$, $n = 212$

e. $g(x) = x^3 + 1$, $m = 1001$, $n = 20$

f. Notice that the lines for the x-$h(x)$ values need to be put in order. $h(x) = 7x - 3$, $m = 172$, $n = 351$.

3. a. $f(n) = 7n + 1$. One justification: In the nth shape, going sideways one "layer" at a time, there are $n + 2n + (n+1) + 2n + n$, or $7n + 1$, toothpicks required.

b. $f(n) = 3n + 8$. One justification: In the nth shape, across the top takes $n + 1$ toothpicks; the vertical pieces take $n + 2$; and the bottoms of the squares take another $n + 1$. The slanted sides of the triangles take 4 toothpicks. The total is $(n + 1) + (n + 2) + (n + 1) + 4 = 3n + 8$ toothpicks.

c. $f(n) = 8n + 1$. One justification: In the nth shape, the bottoms of the hexagons take $2n$ toothpicks, the vertical segments take $n + 1$ toothpicks, the tops of the hexagons take $2n$ more, and each of the rest of the n squares requires 3, or $3n$ in all. The grand total is $2n + (n + 1) + 2n + 3n = 8n + 1$ toothpicks.

4. The two types are alike in that each entry in the sequence, after the first one, is related to the previous one in the same way. For an arithmetic sequence, the relationship is adding (or subtracting) the same number each time, but for a geometric sequence, the relationship is multiplying by the same number each time.

5. a. 12, 39, 66, 93, 120, 147, 174

b. 3, $9\frac{3}{4}$, $16\frac{1}{2}$, $23\frac{1}{4}$, 30, $36\frac{3}{4}$, $43\frac{1}{2}$

c. 3, 15, 75, 375, 1875, 9375, 46875

d. 8, $5\frac{1}{3}$, $3\frac{5}{9}$, $2\frac{10}{27}$, $1\frac{47}{81}$, $1\frac{13}{243}$, $\frac{512}{729}$ (Why do the entries keep getting smaller?)

6.   200 chirps; $C = 4T - 160$ (Below what temperature is the cricket not chirping?)

12.5 Algebra in Reasoning About Quantities

1.   Dan, \$7.80; Lincoln, \$15.60; and Miguel, \$23.40 (Instructor: If d = the amount of Dan's cash in dollars, then $d + 2d + 3d = 46.80$.)

2.   65 students (Instructor: If s = the number of students at the dance, then $2s + 6 \cdot 3 = 148$.)

3.   Letting x = the number of miles driven the first day, Lee might write an equation such as $x + 316 + 280 + 156 + 2x = 1112$. The equation gives 120 miles for the first day and 240 miles for the fifth day.

4.   a. 4 dimes and 7 nickels. If n = the number of dimes, then $16 + 5(n + 3) + 10n + 2 \cdot 25 = 141$.

   b. 12 nickels, 6 dimes, and 3 quarters (besides the 18 pennies) (Instructor: If q = the number of quarters she has, then $18 + 5(2q + 6) + 10 \cdot 2q + 25q = 213$.)

   c. \$8.41 (Instructor: If d = the number of dimes she has, then $51 + \frac{85}{5} + d + \frac{1}{2}d + 6 = 101$ gives the number of dimes [18] and quarters [9].)

5.   29 feet by $14\frac{1}{2}$ feet (Instructor: Letting w = the width of the room in feet, $w + 2w + w + 2w = 87$.)

6.   First year, 11,000 tons; second year, 13,750 tons; and third year, 16,500 tons (Instructor: If f = the number of tons the first year, then $f + 1.25f + 1.20(1.25f) = 41,250$.)

7. $3\frac{3}{7}$ h

8.   Both arrive at school at 8:10.

9.   \$64,000,000 (Bestburg, this year). A diagram may be very helpful.

10. 3 cans (Instructor: If a = the number of cans drunk after noon, then $120 + 2 \cdot 42 + a \cdot 42 = 330$.)

11. 6 hours (Instructor: If n = the number of hours of labor, then $338.95 + 35n = 548.95$.)

12. 3 months (Instructor: If m = the number of months paid for, then $50 + 30m + 100 = 240$.)

13. a. 687 lb, 15 ½ oz (Instructor: From 22 lb 4 oz + (47 ½ – 7) 16 lb 7 oz)

   b. 19 (Instructor: From $5 + (n - 1)5 = 95$)

14. a. Monday, 15 min; Tuesday, 20 min; Wednesday, 40 min; Thursday, 30 min; and Friday, 15 min. (Instructor: If m = the number of minutes on Monday, then $m + (m + 5) + 2(m + 5) + 2m + m = 120$.)

b. Monday, 4 mi; Tuesday, 7 mi; Wednesday, 6 mi; Thursday, 21 mi; and Friday, 12 mi. (Instructor: If t = the number of miles biked on Tuesday, then

$$4 + t + (t-1) + 3t + 2(t-1) = 50.)$$

15. $15 million; $16.5 million (Instructor: If p = the first year's budget, then

$$19.8M = 1.20(1.10p).)$$

Supplementary Learning Exercises for Section 12.5

A drawing is usually a good idea. Be certain that you write clearly what any variable represents, including its unit. For each problem, the answer is given first and then an example of an equation that could be written. Other ways of thinking might lead to different equations, but the answer to the question should be the same. It is a good idea to check your solution by seeing whether it fits the story statement. If you miss a problem, was it because of your algebraic expressions, your algebraic equation, or your solving of the equation?

1. a. Each allowance was $8 a week. Let a = the amount of the weekly allowance ($). Then

   $$a - 5 = \tfrac{1}{2}(a - 2).$$

   b. Each paid $2800 for his car originally. Let p = the initial cost of each car ($). Then

   $$p + 200 = \tfrac{5}{6}(p + 800).$$

   c. Each outfit cost $120 originally. Let x = the original cost of each outfit ($). Then

   $$x - 45 = \tfrac{3}{4}(x - 20).$$

2. a. First runner, 58.5 s; second runner, 60.5 s; third runner, 63.5 s; and fourth runner, 56.5 s (The information about the second runner refers to the first runner, so let f = the number of seconds for the first runner; then the other runners' times are $f + 2$, $(f + 2) + 3$, and $(f + 2) - 4$. Because 3:59 = 239 seconds, we have

   $$f + (f + 2) + [(f + 2) + 3] + [(f + 2) - 4] = 239 \text{ (you may have simplified early, getting}$$
   $$f + (f + 2) + (f + 5) + (f - 2) = 239.)$$

   b. First swimmer, 102 s (or 1:42 min), and second swimmer, 104.5 s (or 1:44.5 min). Let f = the time for the first swimmer (seconds). Then $f + (f + 2.5) + [f + (f + 2.5)] = 413$.

   c. First run, 50.87 s, and second run, 49.81 s. Let x = time for the first run in seconds. Then $x + (x - 1.06) = 100.68$ because 1:40.68 minutes = 100.68 seconds.

3. a. Danetta $75, Elaine $50, and Jan $40. Let d = amount Danetta spent ($). Then $d + (d - 25) + (d - 35) = 165$. Or, if e = amount Elaine spent ($), then $e + (e + 25) + [(e + 25) - 35] = 165$.

b.   Danetta $18.50, Elaine $37, and Jan $30.50. Let J = amount Jan spent ($). Then $(J-12)+2(J-12)+J=86$.

4. a.   First store $125.85, second $25.20, and third $16.75. Let t = amount spent at the third store ($). Then $t+(t+8.45)+3(2t+8.45)=167.80$.

b.   First store $14.15, second $0, third $30.10, and fourth $5.40. Let x = amount spent at the first store ($). Then $x+0+(x+15.95)+(x-8.75)=49.65$.

5. a.   Alima $\frac{1}{4}$ mile, Noor $\frac{3}{4}$ mile, Noor's husband $1\frac{1}{2}$ miles. Let N = the number of miles Noor carried the baby. Then $\frac{1}{3}N+N+2N=2\frac{1}{2}$.

b.   Dien 200 min (3 h, 20 min); Gia 105 min (1 h, 45 min); Minh 210 min (3 h, 30 min). Let G = the number of minutes Gia drove. Then $2G+G+(2G-10)=515$. If you let G = the number of *hours* Gia drove, then an equation would be $2G+G+(2G-\frac{1}{6})=8\frac{7}{12}$.

c.   Dien 120 miles, Gia 240 miles, and Minh 115 miles. Let D = the number of miles Dien drove. Then $D+2D+115=475$.

6. a. $672,000. A drawing may help. (Let x = the number of dollars in sales for the previous year. Then $1.25x=840,000$.)

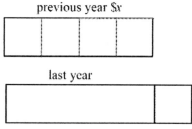

previous year $x

last year

b.   First year $75,000, and second year $105,000. (Let f = first year sales ($). Then $f+(f+.40f)=180,000$.)

c.   First year $300,000; second year $360,000; third year $540,000 (Let x = first year sales in dollars. Then $x+1.2x+1.8x=1,200,000$.)

7. a.   Susan 25 cookies, Rachel 20 cookies, and Steve 27 cookies. Let r = the number of cookies Rachel ate. Then $r+(r+0.25r)+(1.25r+2)=6\cdot12=72$.

b.   Rayann 3 eggs, Nell 9 eggs, and Bell 4 eggs. Let N = the number of eggs eaten by Nell. Then $\frac{1}{3}N+N+(\frac{1}{3}N+1)=\frac{2}{3}\cdot2\cdot12=16$.

c.   4 inches per minute. Be sure that all the values are in the same unit. Let r = Amy's rate of eating, in inches per minute. Then $(2\cdot4)+(1\frac{1}{3}\cdot12)+r\cdot3=36$.

d.   Steve $1\frac{3}{4}$ pints (or $\frac{7}{8}$ quart), and Susan $2\frac{1}{4}$ pints (or $1\frac{1}{8}$ quarts). (Keep the units in mind. If x = the number of pints Steve drank, then $x+(x+\frac{1}{2})=4$. If x = the number of *quarts* Steve drank, then $x+(x+\frac{1}{4})=2$.)

8. $7\frac{1}{2}$ minutes. Keep in mind the units used. Let t = the time in hours they had walked. Then $6t - 4t = \frac{1}{4}$. If you let the time m be in minutes, then Carita's speed is $\frac{6}{60} = \frac{1}{10}$ mile per minute, and Jorge's is $\frac{4}{60} = \frac{1}{15}$ mile per minute. Then the equation would be $\frac{1}{10}m - \frac{1}{15}m = \frac{1}{4}$, giving the final answer directly with somewhat more difficult arithmetic.

Answers for Chapter 13: A Quantitative Approach to Algebra and Graphing

13.1 Using Graphs and Algebra to Show Quantitative Relationships

1. a. Samples: The amount of fuel in the tank decreases as the number of minutes increases. The amount of fuel leaked out increases as the number of minutes increases.

    b. The amount of water in the tank decreases as the number of showers taken increases. The amount of water used increases as the number of showers taken increases.

    c. The amount of money left decreases as you buy more candy bars. The amount of money spent increases as you buy more candy bars.

    d. The number of students in the class decreases as the number of weeks increases (until all the students are gone). The number of students who drop out increases as the number of weeks increases (until all the students are gone).

2. Student answers will vary

3. a. As the perimeter of a square increases, its area increases.

    b. It could happen that the height of the triangle is decreasing in such a way that the product of the base and height (which is twice the area) remains constant. Or, it might happen that the height is constant, in which case the area increases as the base increases. Or, it might be the case that the height is decreasing in such a manner that the product of the base and height is decreasing, in which case the area decreases.

    c. As the numerator gets larger, the value of the fraction increases.

    d. As the denominator gets larger, the value of the fraction decreases.

4. Experimental results should show that the number of swings in 10 seconds depends only on the length of the string. If the angle at which the pendulum is released is small (less than 15° from vertical, say), that has no detectable effect on the number of swings. (FYI, the time for one swing back and forth is given by $T = 2\pi\sqrt{\frac{L}{g}}$, where L is the length of the pendulum and g is the gravitational constant.)

5. Samples:

    a. Distance run—money raised. The money raised by Joella from her company is unaffected by the number of miles she runs.

    b. Distance this year—distance last year. The distance run last year is the same as the distance run this year.

    c. Miles run—minutes reduced. The reduction in Bianca's practice time increases as the number of miles run increases.

d. Number of people in group—cost per person. The cost per person decreases as the number of people in the group increases.

e. Number of commercials—cost. The cost increases as the number of commercials increases.

6. a. It decreases.

b. For 2 minutes, 60 gallons; for 3, 50; etc.

c. Multiply the number of minutes by 10 and subtract that result from 80 gallons.

d. $G = 80 - 10T$

e. Compare the table results with those predicted by the equation.

f. $T = 8$ minutes. When the tank is empty, $G = 0$, so $0 = 80 - 10T$, and $T = 8$.

g. Straight-line graph for $G = 80 - 10T$ (y-intercept at 80, and slope ⁻10).

h. The total of the fuel in the tank and the fuel leaked should equal 80 gallons. That equation is algebraically equivalent to the one in part (d).

7. a. As time increases, the amount of fuel that has leaked out increases.

b.
Time (min)	0	1	2	3	4	...
Fuel leaked (gal)	0	10	20	30	40	...

c. $g = 10t$, where g represents the number of gallons leaked out and t represents the number of minutes that have elapsed.

d.

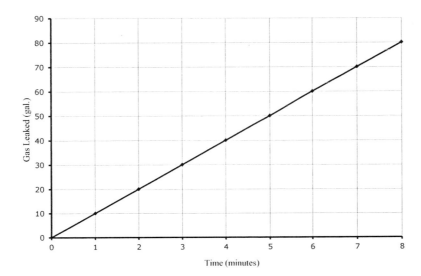

Gas Leaked over Time

e. The graph in Learning Exercise 1(g) is decreasing, whereas the graph in 2(g) is increasing. Both graphs are straight lines, but the graph in 1(g) has a negative slope (goes down from left to right), and the graph in 2(d) has a positive slope (goes up from left to right). These slopes mean that in 1(g), the amount of fuel is decreasing over time, whereas the opposite is true in 2(d).

f. 10 gallons per minute. The change—10 gallons less in part 1(g), 10 gallons more in part 2(d)—per minute is 10 gallons.

8. a. Graph of perimeter versus length: Straight line through origin, slope 4. (Vice versa: slope $\frac{1}{4}$)

b. Part of parabola (students may/may not know). Watch for joining points with line segments as opposed to a smooth curve. Using some fractions in lengths helps make the curve clearer.

c. Part (a) graph is straight; part (b) is curved.

d. $p = 4s$ (check against table or graph); $A = s^2$. Each equation shows a relationship to the number of length units in the side of the square; the second equation involves a second power, which apparently makes the graph curved.

10. a. Table should show 2, $\frac{1}{2}$ as entries, for example.

b. Graph is part of hyperbola, size $= \frac{1}{\text{number of people}}$. It approaches the number-of-people axis.

c. No. Connecting the dots would imply that in-between values make sense for a number of people.

d. Decreases

e. The change in size varies as you add another person at different numbers of people.

f. The sizes would be 2 (or 6 or $\frac{3}{4}$) times as much, but the graph would have the same general shape.

11. a. Answers will vary.

b. Circumferences increase.

c. Answers will vary.

d. The graphs should be roughly linear, through the origin (if extended that far down), slope about π.

e. "About 3" or "A little more than 3" is acceptable.

f. Answers will vary.

g. Yes, because measurements between those actually made are possible for other circles.

h. Perhaps roughly a line.

i. Anything in the $c = \pi d$ territory is acceptable.

12. a. After the first year, there are $30 + (12 \times 5) = 90$ employees. So it will take 21 more months at the 10-per-month rate to reach 300 employees—33 months total.

b. A number-of-employees versus time in months graph should have two linear pieces, the first from (0, 30) to (12, 90), and the second from (12, 90) to (33, 300).

Supplementary Learning Exercises 13.1

1. a. The amount of money that Joella raises from her sister is related to the number of miles that she runs.

   b. The total amount that Joella raises from pledges is related to the number of miles that she runs. Her grand total is twice the amount that she raises from actual pledges.

   c. The number of lemons, or the amount of sugar, or the amount of water needed each depends on the number of gallons of lemonade you make.

2. a. As the cost of an airline ticket increases, the number of miles increases. This is not strictly true because of specials or lack of competition.

   b. As the number of party guests increases, the number of cans of soda bought increases.

   c. Except possibly for large amounts, the cost per pound does not depend on the number of pounds bought.

   d. As the diameter of a circle increases, so does the radius.

   e. The base and the height of a rectangle do not depend on each other As one increases, the other can increase, stay the same, or decrease.

   f. As the width of a rectangle from the set increases, the height of the rectangle decreases.

   g. As the number of miles driven increases, the amount of gasoline used increases.

3. a. Because the light from the lightning is so fast, you sense it almost instantly. So the time for the sound is essentially the whole 5 seconds. $5 \times 343 = 1715$ meters.

   b. $d = 343 \times t$, where d is the distance in meters and t is the time between seeing the flash and hearing the thunder, in seconds.

4. a. (1) The number of people attending and the money raised through concert tickets sold; $T = 40P$ where T is the total dollars raised and P is the number of people attending.

      (2) The number of raffle tickets sold (N) and money raised by the raffle (R); $R = 10N - 300$.

      (3) No, because even if we know the number of people at the party we have no idea of the amount raised by the raffle.

   b. (1) the total amount of money taken in was $10a + 5c$ where a stands for the number of adults and c stands for the number of children who attended. There are no additional quantitative relationships that can be illustrated with an algebraic expression.

5. a. A table helps clarify this situation.

Month	Built	Sold	Total Sold
1	20	0	0
2	30	20	20
3	30	30	50
4	30	30	80
5	40	30	110
6	40	40	150

After 6 months he will have built and sold 150 units. He still has 600 units to build and sell. It will take $600 \div 40$, or 15, additional months for all units to be built and sold, for a total of 21 months.

b. See the graph below.

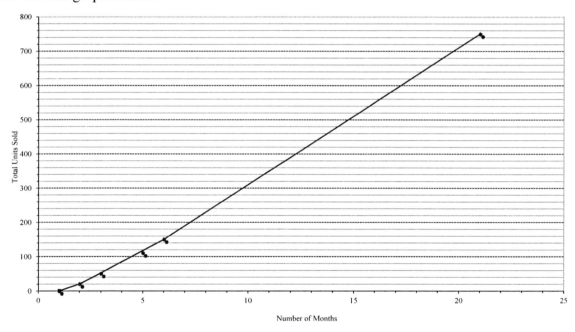

13.2 Understanding Slope: Making Connections Across Quantitative Situations, Graphs, and Algebraic Equations

1. a. 3

    b. The cost is $3 for each game.

    c. There would be a different up-front charge, rather than the $2 illustrated.

    d. $2. The *y*-intercept is (0, 2).

    e. You pay for bowling by the whole number of games, so strictly speaking, only points for 0, 1, 2, 3, etc., games should be given.

2. a. The slope is $^-\frac{10}{1}$, or $^-10$.

b. This slope tells us the amount of fuel the airplane is losing per minute.

c. The slope is $\frac{10}{1}$, or 10.

d. This slope tells me the amount of fuel that is leaking out per minute. (We could think of this as fuel being gained into the atmosphere.)

e. The slopes are alike except for the sign. That is, the first slope is negative, and the second is positive. The negative slope indicates the amount of fuel being lost by the plane per minute, whereas the positive slope indicates the amount of fuel being leaked (gained) into the atmosphere per minute. In conventional graphs, a negative slope indicates that values from the vertical axis *decrease* as values from the horizontal axis increase.

3. a. The line should go through (0, 15) through or to (20, 5). A solid line is appropriate because fractional values of a minute make sense.

   b. $-\frac{1}{2}$

   c. The candle burns at the rate of $\frac{1}{2}$ cm per minute.

4. a. 3 cm, 4 cm, and 7 cm (from bottom)

   b. Each graph: $\frac{1}{2}$ cm per minute (from calculating, say, the 1 cm decrease in height in 2 minutes for the bottom graph)

   c. $-\frac{1}{2}$

   d. Group 3 because . . . (*Hint*: The heights tell only part of the story.)

   e. From bottom: $y = 3 - \frac{1}{2}x$; $y = 4 - \frac{1}{2}x$; $y = 7 - \frac{1}{2}x$

   f. Slopes are the same, but the graphs have different values at $t = 0$.

   g. and h. Any linear equation with slope $-\frac{1}{2}$. The y-intercept gives initial height of the candle.

   i. Its height will be different from those of the others, but specifiable, and it will burn at the same rate.

5. a. 8 cm

   b. From bottom: 1 cm/min; 2/3 cm/min; 1/2 cm/min

   c. From bottom: ⁻1; ⁻2/3; ⁻1/2

   d. Group 1 because . . . the order of the candles is . . .

   e. $y = 8 - x$; $y = 8 - \frac{2}{3}x$; $y = 8 - \frac{1}{2}x$

   f. The equations all have the same constant term, 8, but the coefficients of x are different (and equal to the slopes).

   g.– i. The equation and graph should follow the $y = 8 - \#x$ form, with the description being accurate *vis a vis* the given candles.

6. a. Cindy. She did not pick any more strawberries after 10 AM.

b. $19\frac{1}{5}$ quarts per hour

c. 9 AM; 28 quarts per hour

d. Barb. The slope of her line is greatest of the three. Alternatively, Barb picks 28 quarts per hour, Annette picks $19\frac{1}{5}$ quarts per hour [part (b)], and Cindy picked 24 quarts per hour while she was picking.

7. The graph for Annette's second day starts at (8, 0) and stops at (11, 30), with slope 10.

8. a. The store opens at 7.

   b. The numbers of customers increase steadily during each time period.

   c. F (15 customers)

   d. No increase in customers, perhaps because the number leaving = the number entering.

   e. There were 5 additional shoppers per hour.

   f. 6 to 8, or possibly 5:40 to 8.

9. a. Your table should have one column (or row) for the number of roses, and a second column (or row) for the total cost.

   b. The total cost depends on the number of roses purchased.

   c. If r = the number of roses purchased and C = the total cost (in $), then $C = 20 + 5r$.

   d. Your graph should have the number of roses on the horizontal axis. The graph should include (1, 25) and have a slope = 5.

10. If j = the number of jars sold and N = her net income (in dollars), then $N = 7.50j - 175$.

11. a. $F = \frac{9}{5}C + 32$

    b. 86° F

Supplementary Learning Exercises 13.2

1. a. Missing temperature: 78°; missing number of cricket chirps: 11

    b. $T = C + 39$, where T is the Fahrenheit temperature and C is the number of cricket chirps in 15 seconds.

    c. Because chirp counts will be whole numbers, strictly speaking, the points in the graph should not be joined, but they often are in order to communicate the straight-line nature of the relationship.

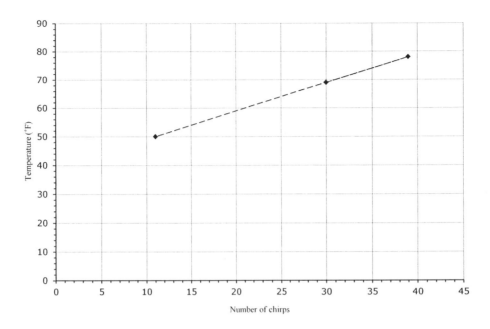

Temperature vs Number of Chirps

d. The slope is 1.

2.   a. $L = 2W$, where L is the length and W is the width of the rectangle (same units).

b. The equation Area = (length) × (width) applies to rectangles, so taking part a into account, $A = (2W) \times W = 2W^2$.

c. and d. If the length is on the vertical axis, your graph should go through (0, 0) and have slope of 2.

3.   a. Additively: The wingspan is 23 feet longer than the length (or the length is 23 shorter than the wingspan). Multiplicatively: The wingspan is $\frac{262}{239} \approx 1.1$ times as long as the length (or the length is $\frac{239}{262} \approx 0.9$ times as long as the wingspan).

b. $81890 \div 8000 \approx 10.2$ gallons per nautical mile (sharing-equally division)

c. The graph that follows assumes a steady use of fuel, which is unrealistic because of take-offs and high-altitude cruising.

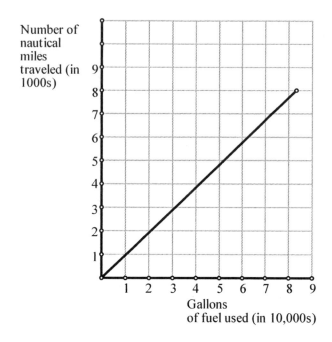

Number of nautical miles traveled (in 1000s)

Gallons of fuel used (in 10,000s)

d. $\frac{81890}{8000} \approx 10.2$

4. One possibility, with the equal slopes implying the same thickness of candle, and the steeper slope (= faster burning) implying less thickness:

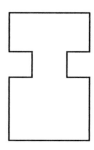

5.   a. About 1.6 kilometers
   b. About 62 miles per hour
   c. About 6.2 miles
   d. (See the graph below.)
   e. Not as steep

13.3 Linear Functions and Proportional Relationships

1. If m = the number of miles and k = the number of kilometers, then $m = \frac{k}{1.6}$ or $k = 1.6m$. Your graph should include (0, 0) and have slope $\frac{1}{1.6} \approx 0.6$ or 1.6, depending on which unit you have on the horizontal axis. The number of miles and the corresponding number of kilometers are proportionally related.

2. a. With P = the air pressure in pounds per square inch and h = height above sea level in feet, the slope is $\frac{12.1-14.7}{5280-0} \approx {}^{-}0.0005$ and $P = {}^{-}0.0005h+14.7$. The relationship between P and h is not proportional.

   b. As distance below sea level increases by 33 feet, pressure increases 14.7 pounds per square inch. Not proportional.

3. If D = the number of Dinars and F = the number of Florins, then $F = \frac{23.25}{5}D$, or $F = 4.65D$, a proportional relationship.

4. a.   120 birds

      b. $N = 4C$

5. a. $1\frac{5}{6}$ cups per container. Because 11 cups come from 6 containers, each container must contain $\frac{1}{6}$ of the 11 cups.

   b. $\frac{6}{11}$ container per cup. Similarly, because 11 cups come from 6 containers, 1 cup must contain $\frac{1}{11}$ of the 6 containers.

   c. $\frac{2}{3}$ is Special Formula. Four containers of Special Formula are mixed with 2 containers of water, giving 6 containers in all, so $\frac{4}{6}$ of the mixture must be Special Formula.

   d. $\frac{1}{3}$ is water, reasoning as in part (c).

   e. The ratio 4:2 for formula to water will apply to other mixtures. Alternately, the equation $f = 2w$ relating the number of containers of formula, f, and the number of containers of water, w, shows a proportional relationship.

6. a. Both graphs are lines and should go through (0, 0). Chris's line should have slope 12, and Sam's line should have slope 10.

   b. Chris: $d = 12h$.   Sam: $d = 10h$, where d stands for the distance traveled in h hours.

   c. The slope of the line representing Chris's ride is 12. The slope of the line representing Sam's ride is 10.

   d. For Abby: $d = 10h + 10$.

   e. Only the equations for Chris's and Sam's rides are of the form $y = mx$ and so show proportional relationships.

7. a. For A: $p = 13h$ (where p is the number of parts and h is the number of hours).
      For B: $p = 14h$ (Note that $\frac{243-(9\times13)}{9}$ is 14. Or, $243 \div 9 = 27$, and $27 - 13 = 14$.)

   b. Both expressions have the form $y = mx$ and so both are proportional relationships.

   c. Both graphs start at (0, 0); the graph for A has slope 13, and the graph for B has slope 14. The slopes tell you how fast each worker works, 13 parts/h for A, 14 parts/h for B.

8. Only graphs b and c. They are linear and go through (0, 0).

9. Only b, c, and d. In part (a), the equation is not of the correct form. In part (c), the variables are the number of crackers and the number of calories. In part (d), the variables are the number of tickets and the total dollar cost.

Supplementary Learning Exercises for Section 13.3

1. a. $y = 3x$, $m = 300$, $n = 120$

   b. $f(x) = 157 - 4x$, $m = 13$, $n = 50$

   c. $output = 2^{input} + 3$, $m = 1027$, $n = 11$

   d. $output = {}^-6 \cdot input$; $m = {}^-72$, $n = 100$

   e. $g(x) = x^3 + 1$, $m = 1001$, $n = 20$

   f. Notice that the lines for the x-$h(x)$ values need to be put in order. $h(x) = 4x$, $m = 100$,

      $n = 201$

Each of parts (a), (d), and (f) has a rule of the form $y = mx$, with m a fixed number, so each represents a proportional relationship between x and y.

2. Only a, b, c, and d give proportional relationships between y and x. That is, only those parts give an equation that is, or can be changed to, an equation of the form $y = mx$, with m a fixed number.

3. a. Janet drove 210 miles at 50 mi/h, which took 4.2 hours, or 4 hours 12 minutes. Sylvia drove 240 miles at 60 mi/h, which took 4 hours. She stopped for 15 minutes, so the total time was 4 hours 15 minutes. So Janet arrived first, but the times are very close.

   b. The lighter line represent Janet's trip. The heavy line represents Sylvia's trip.

   c. The tent-like portion at the very beginning of her drive. The flat part on the x-axis between 30 minutes and 45 minutes.

   d. The line should begin at (0, 210) and cross over the two lines representing the trips. The line representing Janet's trip should cross it slightly before the line representing Sylvia's trip.

   e. Carlene drove 65 mi/h for 210 miles, so her trip took 3.23 hours, or about 3 hours and 14 minutes. But she left an hour later, so she will arrive about 2 minutes after Janet and about 1 minute before Sylvia. Practically speaking, the times are so close one would probably say they all arrived at the same time.

13.4 Nonlinear Functions

1. In the nonlinear cases and with enough points, your graphs should not be straight lines.

a. Nonlinear. The equation cannot be written in the $y = mx + b$ form.

b. Nonlinear. The equation cannot be written in the $y = mx + b$ form. $x(x+5) = x^2 + 5x$, so the given equation is actually a quadratic.

c. Nonlinear. The equation cannot be written in the $y = mx + b$ form.

d. Nonlinear The equation cannot be written in the $y = mx + b$ form. (Instructor: The pieces of its graph follow parts of the graphs of two linear functions: $y = {}^-3x$ for $x \geq 0$, and $y = 3x$ for $x < 0$).

2. In the nonlinear cases and with enough points, your graphs should not be straight lines.

a. Nonlinear. $y = 5x(x - 2) = 5x^2 - 10x$, which cannot be written in the $y = mx + b$ form.

b. Linear. The given equation can be simplified to $y = \frac{-7}{2}$ or $y = 0x + \frac{-7}{2}$.

c. Linear. The variables do not have to be x and y, and π is a definite number.

d. Linear. (Instructor: $y = {}^-2x + \frac{52}{3}$)

3. Samples:

a. The number of gallons remaining in the tub decreases as the number of minutes the drain is open increases. If the outflow rate is steady, the relationship would be linear, perhaps of the form: (number of gal remaining) = (number of gal originally) – (outflow rate)x

b. The area increases as the length increases. $A = (\frac{1}{2}w)w$, or $A = \frac{1}{2}w^2$, a nonlinear equation.

c. The amount in your checking account will increase as the number of years increases. $A = 2500(1 + 0.0125)^y$, a nonlinear relationship between A and y. So after one year, you will have $2500(1 + 0.0125) = 2531.25$ dollars.

4.   a. $N = (1 + 0.03)^3 S$, where N is your new salary for a starting salary of S. Linear.

b. As the distance on the map increases, the actual distance increases. $a = 2000n$ with a being the actual distance in miles and n being the distance on the map in inches. Linear.

c. As the length of the side of the square increases, so does the area of the shaded region.

(Instructor: $A = s^2 - \pi(\frac{s}{2})^2 = (1 - \frac{\pi}{4})s^2$, a nonlinear relationship.)

5. Each of the function rules is linear.

6. If there are n students and f is the fraction of the pizza each gets, then $f = \frac{1}{n}$.

Supplementary Learning Exercises for Section 13.4

1.   a. $y = x$ b. $y = 3$ c. $y = x^2$ d. $y = 2x^2 + 2x$

x	y
0	0
2	2
5	5
8	8
9	9

x	y
0	3
1	3
2	3
6	3
10	3

x	y
0	0
1	1
2	4
3	9
4	16

x	y
0	0
1	4
2	12
3	24
6	84

Linear   Linear   Not linear   Not linear

2. Here are some possible input-output tables.

   a. $x = 3y$ b. $h = 4v^3$ c. $2y = 3x$ d. $P = 5s$

                                                     is $y = \frac{3}{2}x$

y	x
0	0
2	6
4	12
6	18
8	24

v	h
0	0
1	4
2	32
3	108
10	4000

x	y
0	0
1	$\frac{3}{2}$ or $1\frac{1}{2}$
2	3
3	$4\frac{1}{2}$
4	6

s	P
0	0
1	5
2	10
3	15
6	30

Parts (a), (c), and (d) are linear because for each there is a constant rate of change. Part (b) does not have a constant rate of change and is not linear.

3. a. Let c stand for the number of cupcakes and d stand for the cost in dollars. Then $5d = c$ or $d = 0.20c$ This is a linear function. For each increase in c, d is increased by 20¢.

   b. Let c stand for the amount of punch concentrate and w stand for the amount of water. Then $2c = w$, or $c = \frac{1}{2}w$. This is a linear function. For any amount of concentrate used the amount of water used is twice that amount.

4. Using an input-output table, at the beginning of the 5th year she will earn $1756.92.

Beginning of year	Salary
1	$1200
2	$1320
3	$1452
4	$1597.20
5	$1756.92

The change from year-to-year is not the same, so this would not be a linear function.

5. 1023 grains. ($2^0 + 2^1 + 2^2 + \ldots 2^9 = 1023$) The change from day-to-day is not the same, so this would not be a linear function.

Answers for Chapter 14: Understanding Change: Relationships Among Time, Distance, and Rate

14.1 Distance-Time and Position-Time Graphs

1. a. Graph should show the different segments of the trip: first a steady increase from 0 (to the cliff), then a continuation at the same rate (more distance back to the cave), then a flat piece (in the cave), then a steeper-than-before increase for about half the distance in the first two segments, then a still greater increase for another half-distance. The overall graph should be nondecreasing, with excellent graphs showing the slopes consistently with the speeds cited and with the *y*-axis pieces related properly.

   b. Again, the segments should show the different parts of the trip: first a steady increase from 0, then a steady decrease (at the same rate) to 0, a flat piece at $y = 0$, a greater slope to half the *y* that represented the earlier peak, finally an even sharper decline to 0.

   c. Comments should relate the slopes.

2. a. Sample: Wile E. was out of his cave, looking for Road Runner. He trotted back to his cave to get his binoculars and immediately trotted a little faster to where he was at the start. He stood there for a while, looking around unsuccessfully, and then walked back toward the cave. When he was about two-thirds of the way, he realized that it was time for his favorite cartoon show, so he ran back to the cave.

   b. The graph should be nondecreasing, with the slopes reflecting the paces at which Wile E. went.

3. a. He has to travel 140 ft, at the rate of 5 ft/s, so it takes him 28 s to return home.

   b.

t	0	5	10	15	20	25	30	35	40	43
d (from cave)	0	40	80	140	115	90	65	40	15	0

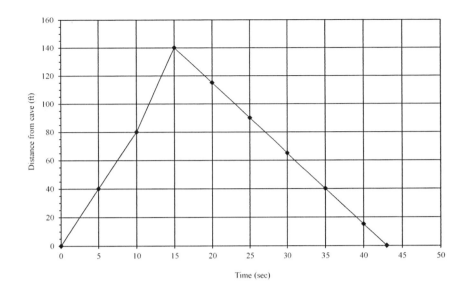

c.

t	0	5	10	15	20	25	30	35	40	43
Total distance	0	40	80	140	165	190	215	240	265	280

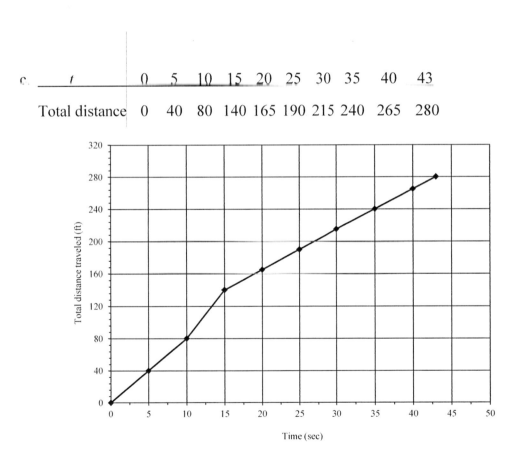

d. The slopes can be compared with the speeds; in the first graph, the negative slope in the last segment can be compared to the slope in the last segment of the second graph. (Better comparisons are possible when the graphs use the same scales.)

e. Calculate the slopes in the different segments.

4.   a.

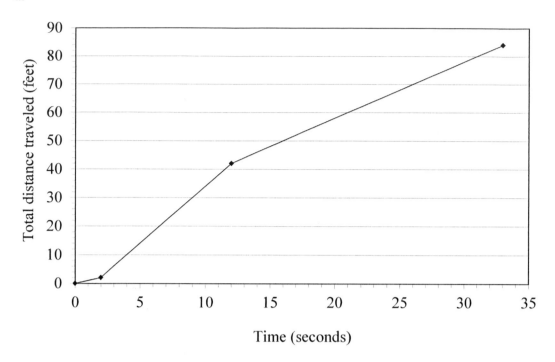

b. In order of segments: 1 ft/s, 4 ft/s, and 2 ft/s

c.

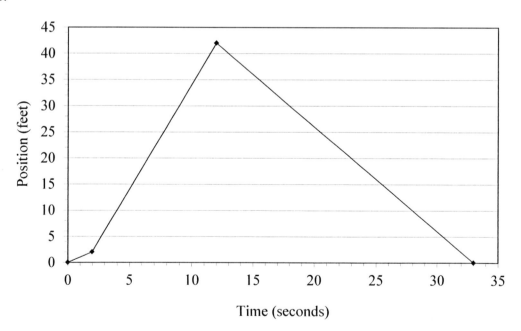

d. In order of segments: 1 ft/s, 4 ft/s, ⁻2 ft/s

5.   a. Your graph should start at (0, 0) and have slope 4. $d = 4t$

b. Your graph should start at (0, 20) and have slope 4. $d = 4t + 20$

c. Your graph should start at (0, 56) and have slope ⁻4. $d = 56 - 4t = 56 + {}^{-}4t$

d. The slopes have the same absolute values, but the graphs hit the *y*-axis at different points.

e. The slope is 4. Wile E. travels 4 feet every second. The 4 appears as the multiplier (coefficient) of *t*.

f. The slope is 4. It tells us that Wile E. is walking at a rate of 4 ft/s. The slope is the coefficient of the time (the multiplier of *t*).

g. The slope is ⁻4. It tells us that Wile E. is walking at a rate of 4 ft/s, but so as to decrease his distance from the cave. The slope is the coefficient of the time (the multiplier of *t*).

6. a.

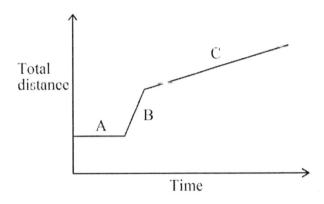

b. 0 ft/s

c. 8 ft/s

d. 0.72 ft/s

e.

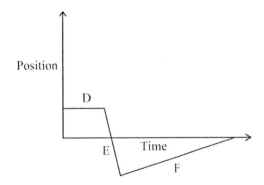

f. D, 0 ft/s; E, ⁻8 ft/s; F, 0.72 ft/s

g. The corresponding slopes are the same in size (absolute value), with E's slope being the negative of B's slope.

7. $\dfrac{68 \times (365 \times 24 \times 60 \times 60 \times 1.86 \times 10^5) \text{ miles}}{(2 \times 10^6)(365 \times 24) \text{ hours}} \approx 22,766 \text{ mi/h, on average}$

8. Road 1 h, 15 min + canoe 36 min + jungle 16 h + path 3 h, 15 min = (in all) 21 h, 6 min. Was your explanation the same for each part?

9. a. $4.47 + $9.60 + $3.84 = $17.91

b. 64 miles

c. 24 x (60 x 70) = 100,800 beats per day; 1,000,000,000 ÷ 100,800 is about 9920.6 days, or more than 27 years.

Supplementary Learning Exercises for Section 14.1

1. The dashed segments are to help in comparing the two graphs.

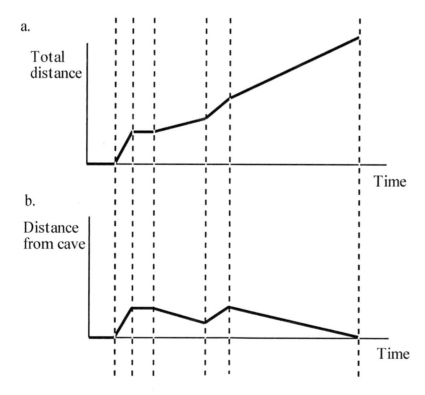

c. Alike: The first three pieces are the same because total-distance and distance-from-cave are the same. Some pieces should have the same slopes. Either graph is flat when the distance is not changing. Different: The total-distance graph never goes down, but

the distance-from-cave graph can. When Wile E. heads toward the cave, the total-
distance still increases but the distance-from-cave decreases.

2. a. There are many possibilities. Try to have the slopes indicate something about the speed.
   For example, Wile E.'s running should lead to a greater tilt than when he is walking or
   trotting.

   b.

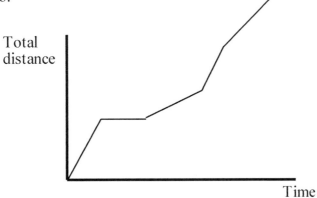

3. Your scales may be different, but your equations should be the same, of course.

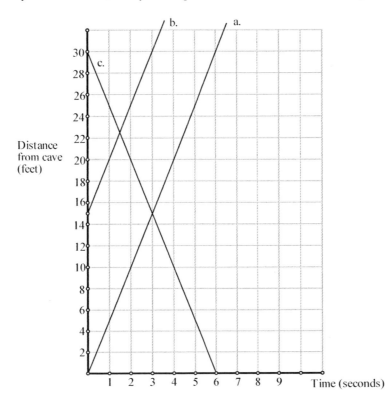

Equations: a. $d = 5t$ b. $d = 5t + 15$ c. $d = 30 - 5t$, or $d = 30 +\ ^-5t$

d. Graphs a and b are parallel but meet the *d*-axis at different points. In graph c, the *d* values decrease as *t* increases. The graphs have different starting points on the *y*-axis.

e. The slopes in equations a and b the slopes are the same, and the slope in equation c appears to have the same absolute value.

4. a. The slope, 5, tells that Wile E.'s distance from the cave is increasing at 5 feet per second. The slope, 5, is the multiplier of *t* in the equation.

   b. The slope, 5, tells that Wile E.'s distance from the cave is increasing at 5 feet per second. The slope, 5, is the multiplier of *t* in the equation.

   c. The slope, ⁻5, tells that Wile E.'s distance from the cave is decreasing at 5 feet per second. The slope, ⁻5, is the multiplier of *t* in the equation.

5. There are many possibilities, but the story should start with Wile E. in the cave and then walking/strolling/running away from the cave at 10 feet per second.

6. There are many possibilities, but the story should start with Wile E. 50 feet from the cave and then moving toward the cave at 5 feet per second.

7. There are many possibilities, but your story should have Sam's speeds the same during the first and last segments, and have Sam stopped during the middle segment.

8. a. See below. b. 5. For part (c), $\frac{100}{18} \approx 5.56$.

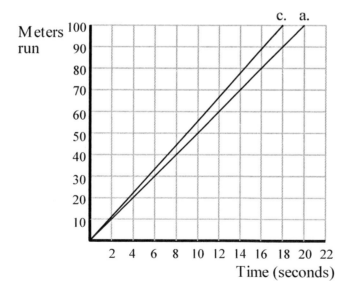

d. Any line starting at (0, 0) but going below the line for part (a)

e. It takes a little time to get to full speed and, for longer races, a runner may tire or may strategize and slow down to save strength for the end of the race.

14.2 Using Motion Detectors

1 and 2.a. The walker started 2 ft away from the motion detector and then walked away from the motion detector at a constant speed for 6 s. (The speed was $\frac{2}{3}$ ft/s.)

    b. The walker started 2 ft away from the motion detector and then walked away from the motion detector at a constant speed for 3 s. The walker in part (b) walked faster than did the walker in part (a). Walker (b)'s speed was $\frac{4}{3}$ ft/s.

    c. The walker started 6 ft away from the motion detector. The walker walked to the motion detector in 6 s at a constant speed. The speed was 1 ft/s.

    d. The walker started 6 ft away from the motion detector. The walker walked to the motion detector in 3 s at a constant speed. The walker in part 1(d) walked at a faster constant speed than the walker in part 1(c). The speed in part (d) was 2 ft/s.

    e. The walker was 4 ft away from the motion detector and stood there for 6 s. The speed was 0 ft/s.

3.   Answers will vary.

4.   a. Sample: The walker started a short distance from the motion detector. He/she started walking away from the motion detector very slowly and then gradually increased speed until he/she was walking very quickly.

Supplementary Learning Exercises for Section 14.2

1.   a. The walker started at the motion detector and walked away from it at $\frac{1}{3}$ foot per second for 6 seconds. $d = \frac{1}{3}t$

    b. The walker started at the motion detector and walked away from it at $\frac{7}{5}$ ft/s for 5 seconds. $d = \frac{7}{5}t$

    c. The walker started 3 feet from the motion detector and walked farther away at $\frac{1}{3}$ ft/s for 6 seconds. $d = 3 + \frac{1}{3}t$

    d. The walker started 7 feet away from the motion detector and walked toward it at $2\frac{1}{3}$ ft/s for 3 seconds. $d = 7 - 2\frac{1}{3}t$ or $d = 7 + {}^{-}2\frac{1}{3}t$

    e. The walker started 5 feet away from the motion detector and walked toward it at 1 ft/s for 5 seconds. $d = 5 - 1t$ or $d = 5 + {}^{-}1t$

    f. The walker started 3 feet from the motion detector and stood there for 6 seconds. $d = 3$

2.   Each of the walkers would be the same distance from his or her motion detector after a little less than 3 seconds.

3.   a. The graphs with the greatest tilts (b and d) would belong to the fastest walker away from the detector (b) and toward the detector (d).

b. The equation with the greatest positive slope ($d = \frac{7}{5}t$) would belong to the fastest walker away from the detector, and the equation with the negative slope with the greatest absolute value ($d = 7 + {}^-2\frac{1}{3}t$) would belong to the fastest walker toward the detector.

4.   (Equations only are given.)

a. $d = 4 + 2t$ or an algebraic variation, like $d = 2t + 4$ or even $d - 2t = 4$, because they describe the same relationship between the variables, algebraically.

b. $d = 4 - 1t$ or $d = 4 - t$ or $d = 4 + {}^-1t$

c. $d = 6 - 2t$ or an algebraic equivalent

14.3 Graphs of Speed Against Time

1.   a. The graph should be a horizontal straight line from (0, 4).
      b. The graph should be a horizontal straight line from (0, 10).
      c. The graph should be a horizontal straight line from (0, 15).

2.   The graph should have the first segment be a horizontal segment and the next piece be a horizontal segment of the same length with the same y-intercept (or its negative if you are encouraging the distinction). The next segment would be horizontal and on the horizontal axis. Next would be a horizontal segment higher than the first, for some extent of the time less than that for the first segment, and then another, higher horizontal segment for still less time (possibly on the negative side).

3.

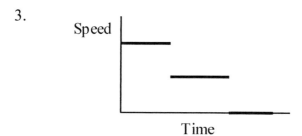

All three parts of the graph are straight horizontal line segments, each indicating constant speed. They differ by their positions on the vertical axis; the height signifies the speed in each of the cases. If you made this graph as a companion to that of the given graph, the times for the different pieces should match.

4.

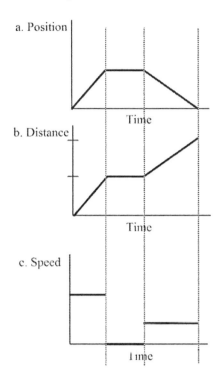

a. Position

Time

b. Distance

Time

c. Speed

Time

5. Height-time: The graphs should reflect the starting height, a straight line with small slope, then a continuation at a greater slope until the height is 3 times that of the original, and finally a horizontal segment. Rate-time: Horizontal segments, the second higher, the last on the time axis.

6. a. Sample: Bart trotted evenly to the corner. There he saw some friends stopped ahead, so he sped up at a steady pace to catch them. When he did, they chatted a little while. But then they realized they might be late to the game so they decided to run as fast as they could.

   b. Notice the negative speed. This should be reflected in the story by heading back toward the starting place in the story.

   c. This graph is not possible, because at the time of the vertical segment, it is not possible to tell what speed is occurring (even in a cartoon).

   d. Watch that the story does not end with the person standing still (that would give a horizontal piece).

7. No answers are provided. Check that the graph for part (d) does not look like a hill and that the one for part (e) does not have a circular part (mimicking the orbit).

8. Parts (a) and (b) should be made of line segments. Check for some sensitivity to differences in slopes for parts (a) and (b), with a greater slope when the neck is reached. The first part of the graph for part (c) is curved, with slower increases in height at the start and at the neck becomes a line segment. Each graph eventually becomes horizontal when the container is filled.

9. a. C. The change in height per unit of horizontal distance is greater during C than in B.

b. G. During H, the speed of the roller coaster is about 0, but during G, the speed is positive although decreasing.

c. Very roughly…

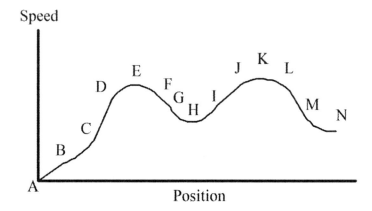

Supplementary Learning Exercises for Section 14.3

1.

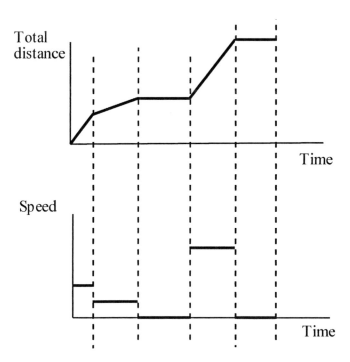

2. a.

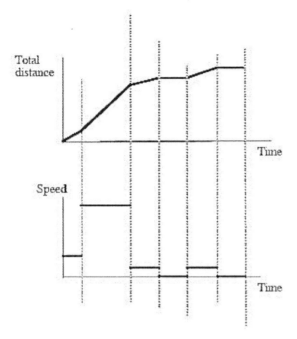

b.

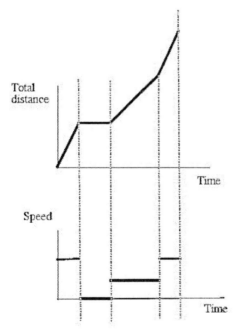

c.

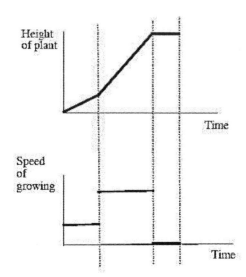

3. a.   The distance stays the same while Wile E. is stopped, so the corresponding piece of the graph is horizontal.

   b.   The speed should be zero, so the corresponding piece of the graph is on the time axis.

   c.   The position stays the same while Wile E. is stopped, so the corresponding piece of the graph is horizontal.

4. a.

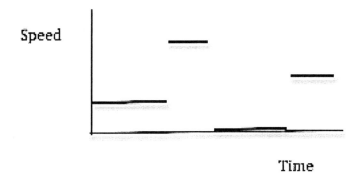

b.

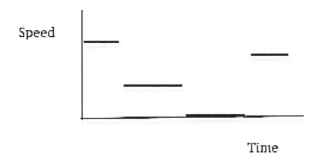

Speed

Time

5. Here are some (rough) samples.

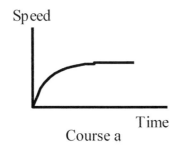

Speed

Time

Course a

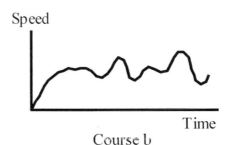

Speed

Time

Course b

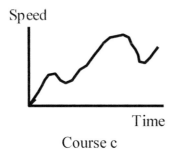

Speed

Time

Course c

14.4 Interpreting Graphs

1.   a. The fifth graph is most reasonable. The first part shows her speed increasing until she gets to the comfortable pace, at which she runs until she slows to a stop (the decrease of speed to 0). Then the increasing speed as she runs downhill fits the last part of the fifth graph.

     b. Notice that the graph involves *distance traveled.* (Instructor: second graph)

     c. Notice that some graphs are for distance-time and others speed-time. (Instructor: third graph)

2.   No answers provided. Look for descriptions that fit the lettered segments.

3.   C, because her speed is decreasing to 0.

4.   a. Boat 1: John was sitting on his boat in the middle of the lake, fishing. He began to row farther from shore, then stopped and fished for a while. He saw a storm cloud, so he rowed quickly back to shore.

     Boat 2: Steve was riding around the lake when he "goosed" the motor on his boat and accelerated up to a nice cruising speed. He stayed at this speed for a while, then cut the motor and drifted until the boat stopped moving.

     b. No, unless the horizontal segment in the speed-time graph occurs from running at that speed parallel to shore

     c. There could be many possible stories for the boat graphs.

5.   Student 1 may be falling victim to a graph-as-picture misconception. Even then, the "half the time" to get to the bottom is not reflected in the graph because the times are the same (4 hours). The last, "less steep" hill must have been the same   height as the others, but "less steep" and the same height as the first hill would suggest a greater speed and therefore a greater slope.

     Student 2 writes an imaginative story and seems well aware of distance-time-speed relationships. He/she uses the scale in the given coordinate system to give accurate values for the speeds, distances, and times.

6.   a. Segment A took the longest time because the section on the time line beneath A is longer that the sections for B and C.

     b. Trip segment A covered a greater distance than segment C did. The change on the distance axis is greater for A than for C.

     c. Segment C, because the slope, and therefore the speed, is greatest.

     d. The distance does not change, even though time increases.

7.   a. A, because its height on the graph is greater than B's at $t = 0$.

     b. B, because its height is 0 before A's is at 0.

     c. B, because its height decreases more than A's height does for an equivalent unit of time.

8.   The oven is turned on at B, and heats up to 350°. It cools and warms up to keep the temperature about 350°.

Supplementary Learning Exercises for Section 14.4

1. There are many possible stories, but yours should reflect a high rate of speed for the first piece, then a stop, then a resumption of the high speed, then a slowing down, and finally a further slowing down.

2. The speed increases steadily and then stays constant.

3. There are many possibilities, but your story should indicate that Diane sped up steadily for 20 minutes until she was biking 0.1 mile per minute, then she biked at that speed for 20 minutes, and then she again speeded up until she was biking 0.2 mile per minute.

4. a. There should be a flat piece after P while she ate/drank something at the snack shop, but there is none.

   b. S. From the vertical scale, the distance walked during S is greater than those for P and Q (and R).

   c. P. From the horizontal scale, the time taken for P is greater than those for Q, R, and S.

   d. Q. The differences in distances for Q is relatively great for the short time span that Q took.

   e. Not for certain, although the first part of the walk took a goodly amount of time for not a great distance. In particular, Q very likely did not involve any steep hills because it was her fastest piece [part (d)].

5. Type a goes with graph ii; it will fill up fast at the start, then slow down, and then speed up as it goes past the middle of the vase. Type b goes with graph i because it fills steadily all the way to the top. Type c goes with graph iv because it will fill up faster at the start and then less fast later. Type d goes with graph iii because it will fill up slowly at first but gradually speed up.

6. Your choice of proportions should reflect that because the vase fills faster and faster during the first 5 seconds, it is getting narrower and narrower. Then the vase gets slightly wider and wider.

Answers for Chapter 15: Further Topics in Algebra and Change

15.1 Finding Linear Equations

1. a. 2   b. $\frac{y-7}{x-4}$ or $\frac{y-17}{x-9}$

     c. $y = 2x - 1$

2. a. $\frac{y-9}{x-5}$ b. $y = 6x - 21$

     c. On a line, the slope is the same everywhere.

3. $y = 4x - 42$

4. $y = {}^-2x + 5$

5. $y = {}^-3x + 9.5$

6. $y = 7x - 595$

7. $y = \frac{3}{4}x - 10$

8. $y = \frac{8}{9}x - \frac{92}{9}$

9. $y = \frac{2}{3}x - \frac{5}{3}$

10. $y = \frac{1}{7}x + \frac{33}{7}$

11. $y = \frac{6}{7}x + \frac{33}{7}$

12. $y = 2x - 11$

13. $y = {}^-\frac{5}{3}x + \frac{15}{2}$

14. $y = {}^-\frac{5}{8}x + \frac{73}{12}$

15. $y = 3$, $y = x - 3$, and $y = {}^-\frac{1}{3}x + 3\frac{2}{3}$

16. $s = \frac{1}{4}w$ or $w = 4s$, depending on which variable you treat as the independent one.

17. With $T =$ the Celsius temperature and $h =$ the height in km, $T = {}^-6.5h + 22.2$.

18. a. p: ${}^-\frac{3}{2}$, and q: $\frac{2}{3}$ b. ${}^-1$

19. a. Perpendicular (slopes are 2 and ${}^-\frac{1}{2}$)

     b. Perpendicular (slopes are $\frac{-3}{4}$ and $\frac{4}{3}$)

     c. Perpendicular (slopes are $\frac{1}{3}$ and ${}^-3$)

20. a. Any equation giving a line with slope 7 but not passing through the point (0, –4). For example, $y = 7x + 10$.

b. Any equation giving a line with slope $^-\frac{5}{3}$ but not passing through the point (0, $\frac{7}{3}$)

c. $y = {}^-\frac{1}{4}x +$ (your choice of a number)

d. $y = {}^-\frac{2}{7}x +$ (your choice of a number)

21. 0, undefined. The product is not $^-1$. Any horizontal line and any vertical line are perpendicular, but the product of their slopes is not $^-1$.

22. a. $y = \frac{1}{5}x + 6\frac{2}{5}$

b. $y = {}^-5x + 22$

c. $y = {}^-\frac{1}{3}x + \frac{58}{3}$

d. $y = {}^-3x + 13$

Supplementary Learning Exercises for Section 15.1

1. $y = 2x + 1$, from $\frac{y-5}{x-2} = \frac{9-5}{4-2}$

2. $y = 3x + 4$, from $\frac{y-7}{x-1} = \frac{22-7}{6-1}$

3. $y = {}^-x + 10$, from $\frac{y-9}{x-1} = \frac{14-9}{-4-1}$

4. $y = \frac{1}{3}x + \frac{1}{2}$, from $\frac{y-2\frac{1}{2}}{x-6} = \frac{2-2\frac{1}{2}}{4\frac{1}{2}-6}$

5. $y = 8x - 5$, from $\frac{y-3}{x-1} = 8$

6. $y = \frac{3}{4}x + 2$, from $\frac{y-5}{x-4} = \frac{3}{4}$

7. $y = {}^-4x - 7$, from $\frac{y-{}^-11}{x-1} = {}^-4$

8. $y = {}^-2x - 9$, from $\frac{y-{}^-7}{x-{}^-1} = {}^-2$

9. $y = 6x - 3$, because it will have the same slope: $6 = \frac{y-3}{x-1}$

10. $y = {}^-2x + 9$, because it will have the same slope: $^-2 = \frac{y-7}{x-1}$

11. The slopes using every pair of the points should be equal, but they are not: 2, 3, and $2\frac{1}{3}$.

12. The equation of the line through the two points is $y = 5x + 2$, so the line is parallel to the line $y - 5x = 7$, or $y = 5x + 7$.

13. The equation for his descent is $h = {}^-700t + 5300$, from $\frac{h-3200}{t-3} = \frac{400-3200}{7-3}$.

    a. 700 ft/min downward

    b. 5300 ft

    c. $\frac{53}{7} \approx 7.6$ min after jumping (from $0 = {}^-700t + 5300$)

14. 230 ft, from $t = 0$ in $\frac{d-500}{t-6} = 45$

15.2 Solving Two Linear Equations in Two Variables

1.   When the time is 2.5 hours, their distances will be the same: 7 miles.

2. $x = 3, y = 7$

3. $x = 5, y = 10$

4. $x = 2, y = 2\frac{1}{2}$

5. $x = {}^-2, y = 3$

6. $x = 1, y = {}^-5$

7.   No common solution (the two equations are inconsistent)

8. $x = 3, y = 3$

9. $x = 1, y = 6$

10. $x = 100, y = 75$

11. $x = 9, y = 7$

12. $x = 1, y = 5$

13. $x = 2\frac{1}{4}, y = 4\frac{1}{2}$

14. $x = 10, y = 7$

15. $x = 12, y = 5$

16. $x = 43, y = 31$

17. No common solution (the two equations are inconsistent)

18. $x = 7\frac{1}{6}, y = 3$

19. $x = {}^-2, y = 4$

20. a. The slopes of the two distinct lines are the same (4), so the lines are parallel.

b. Joe's equations are dependent (one is a multiple of the other), so the graphs coincide.

21. a. Any linear equation with slope 3 but y-intercept not $(0, {}^-10)$

    b. Any linear equation obtained from the given one by multiplying both sides by the same nonzero number

22. a. Many possible answers, but $(5, 7)$ should satisfy each one.

    b. Any linear equation with slope ${}^-4$ but y-intercept different from $(0, 6)$

23. a. $1\frac{2}{7}$ minutes, or about 1 minute, 17 seconds. (Instructor: $h = 100t + 200$ and $h = {}^-75t + 425$)

    b. Passenger, 100 ft/min; freight, 75 ft/min (going down this trip)

    c. 425 ft

24. a. After $3\frac{2}{7}$ minutes, both elevators are at $164\frac{2}{7}$ feet. (Instructor: $h = 575 - 125t$ and $h = 50t$)

    b. Passenger, 125 ft/min (headed down); freight, 50 ft/min

    c. Passenger, 575 ft, freight, 0 ft

25. a. After $4\frac{11}{19}$ minutes, both elevators are at $189\frac{9}{19}$ feet. (Instructor: $h = 120t - 360$ and $h = 25t + 75$. Some alert student may notice that the passenger elevator was at -360 when $t = 0$; explain that time must have been given in terms of the freight elevator clock.)

    b. Passenger, 120 ft/min; freight, 25 ft/min

26. a. After $1\frac{3}{8}$ minutes, both elevators are at 152.5 feet. (Instructor: $h = {}^-180t + 400$ and $h = 60t + 70$)

    b. Passenger, 180 ft/min; freight, 60 ft/min

27. a. The passenger elevator starts out above the freight elevator and keeps getting farther above (140 ft/min vs 25 ft/min) because both are headed up.

    b. The person likely found two equations and solved them, getting a negative value for the time. The negative value for time indicates that the two elevators would have been at the same height in the past *if* this trip had not started with time = 0. (Instructor: $h = 140t + 80$ and $h = 25t + 50$ intersect at $t = {}^-\frac{6}{23}$)

28. Sketching the elevator trip on the graph indicates that the two elevators were at the same height during the passenger elevator's trip between 3 and 4 minutes. With $(3, 240)$ and $(4, 360)$ for the passenger elevator and $(1, 500)$ and $(6, 200)$ for the freight elevator, we find

that the elevators are at the same height ($333\frac{1}{3}$ ft, or 333 ft, 4 in.) after a trip time of $3\frac{7}{9}$ seconds. (Instructor: $h = 120t - 120$ and $h = {}^-60t + 560$)

29. The two elevators are at the same height at 12:03 $\frac{21}{44}$ and 12:08 $\frac{1}{4}$. (Instructor: First leg, passenger: $h = 60t + 30$; last leg, passenger: $h = 600 - 60t$; freight: $h = 336 - 28t$)

30. a. Gayle: $I = 30000 + 0.024S$ Helena: $I = 25000 + 0.04S$

 b. Sales of \$312,500 for each would give each an income of \$37,500.

Supplementary Learning Exercises for Section 15.2

1. a. Each equation will be true if you substitute $x = 5$ and $y = 4$ into them.

 b. Yes. The substitution leads to 22 = 22 and 4 = 5 – 1, both true.

 c. Their graphs will have the point (2, 7) in common.

2. a. The equations in the system do not have a common solution. Graphically, it means their graphs never meet or cross.

 b. One of the equations can be obtained from the other by multiplying both sides of the other by the same nonzero number. Graphically, it means that their graphs are the same sets of points.

3. $x = 5, y = 8$, or more compactly, (5, 8)

4. (10, 3)

5. (1, $^-2$)

6. The system is inconsistent.

7. $s = 4, t = 2\frac{1}{2}$

8. (3, 1)

9. ($^-2$, $^-3$)

10. (25, 21)

11. The equations are dependent (multiply the second equation by 2 and reorganize the equation).

12. ($^-5$, $^-6$)

13. a. Any linear equation with slope 5 but not passing through (0, 0)

b. Any equation obtained by multiplying both sides of $y - 5x = 19$ by the same nonzero number

14. a. Any equation that gives a slope of $\frac{20}{42} = \frac{10}{21}$ but does not have a y-intercept at $^-\frac{163}{42}$.

b. Check that (2, 3) is a solution of each of your equations. At the start, work gradually—for example, starting with $2x - y$, you could finish by seeing what $2x - y$ equals when $x = 2$ and $y = 3$. $2x - y = 2 \cdot 2 - 3$, so $2x - y = 1$ would be one equation.

15. Jones $75, Smith $250, and Quan $225

16. Misha and Lavonne each scored 16 points, and Sue scored 8.

17. Misha, 16 points; Sue, 10 points; and Lavonne, 5 points

18. Angela, $13.20; Marcy; $4.40; and Lucia, $39.60

19. The two elevators were at the same height after $1\frac{1}{4}$ min. The problem did not ask what the height was then, but you could calculate it by substituting $t = 1\frac{1}{4}$ into either of your equations.

20. The first time after $\frac{2}{3}$ min, the second time (when A is stopped) $2\frac{1}{3}$ min after the start of the trips, and the third time $5\frac{2}{3}$ min after the start of the trips.

15.3 Different Approaches to Problems

1. a. How far Rita goes in t seconds

   b. $d = 50 + 10t$

   c. $d = 15t$

   d. The time when Rita's and Tony's distances are equal

   e. After 10 seconds

   f. Tony will have run 100 ft (so he is 150 ft from the starting line); Rita will have run 150 ft.

   g. 125 ft

   h. Tony's graph: Through (0, 50), with slope 10; Rita's graph: Through (0, 0), slope 15.

2. Kien cannot catch Leo before the race is over. When Leo finishes the 10K run (after 37.3 minutes), Kien will be 115.5 meters behind.

3. 4 minutes

4.   a. Bobby: $d = 21 + 7t$, and Jaime: $d = 10t$

   b. Jaime catches up after 7 seconds (70-ft mark) and pulls ahead and wins Lily's heart.

5.   a. A: $d = 45t$, and B: $d = 65t$

   b. 3.2 hours; A: 144 mi; B: 208 mi

   c. A: $\frac{9}{22}$ of the distance, and B: $\frac{13}{22}$ of the distance

6.   a. No. It takes Brother 40 minutes to get to school, so with her 15-minute head start, Sister would already be at school.

   b. Sister will have traveled 35 more minutes after Brother starts, so Brother will be $\frac{35}{40}$, or $\frac{7}{8}$, of the way to school.

7.   16 seconds, counting the head-start time

8. $607\frac{1}{11}$ ft (including the 126 ft head start)

9.   11 hours, 46 minutes

10. The plans give the same profit at sales of 200,000 CDs. Before that point, Option B gives more profit. After 200,000 CDs are sold, Option A gives more profit.

11. a. A: 0.05   B: 0.4

   b. Plan A costs less if you make more than 30 calls per month.

   c. Plan B costs less if you make fewer than 30 calls per month.

12. $200,000 in sales

13. a. Tables are understandable, and if a particular value of interest appears in the table, they are easy. If a value does not appear in the table, either because it is between values or would require a lengthy table, tables are not accurate or efficient.

   b. Graphs give a visual sense for some questions (as in Exercises 10, 11, and 12), but they require at least a few table-like calculations, and it may be difficult to read exact answers.

   c. Algebra is very efficient, but the solver has to have some skill at translating situations into algebra and with algebraic manipulations. Questions like some of those in Exercises 7–13 are not so easy to answer with algebra, because other factors may enter in.

Supplementary Learning Exercises for Section 15.3

1.   a. A-One starts out 30¢ behind but gains 3¢ each $\frac{1}{18}$ mile, so in $10\frac{1}{18}$-mile pieces (= $\frac{5}{9}$ mile), A-One's fare will be the same as Speedy's: $2.70.

b. The scale for the distance is best expressed as $\frac{1}{18}$-mile pieces. Because the fare jumps at each $\frac{1}{18}$-mile segment, joining points to get the cost isn't actually proper but is often done. If the graphs crossed at some distance that is not an exact multiple of $\frac{1}{18}$, one could read an incorrect answer from the graph.

c. You may have used other letters for the variables, of course. Speedy: $c = 1.50 + 0.12d$, with c being the cost of the fare in dollars and d being the number of $\frac{1}{18}$-mile distances, or $c = 150 + 12d$, with c being the cost of the fare in cents. For A-One: $c = 1.20 + 0.15d$ (or $c = 120 + 15d$). Equating the two costs gives $1.50 + 0.12d = 1.20 + 0.15d$, or $0.30 = 0.03d$, or $10 = d$. $10 \times \frac{1}{18} = \frac{10}{18} = \frac{5}{9}$ mile, with each company's fare being $2.70.

2. a. Perfecto starts out $10 behind but gains $2 every 15 minutes, so until five 15-minute periods of work have been done, Perfecto would be less expensive than Pronto. Longer times (more than 75 minutes or 1.25 hours) would favor Pronto.

   b. The scale for time is best expressed in terms of 15-minute pieces. As in Exercise 1, because the charge jumps at the 15-minute marks, the points should not actually be joined (but often are) because reading the graph for, say, a 20-minute job could give an incorrect cost.

   c. Perfecto: $c = 30 + 20p$, where c = the cost for a job that takes p 15-minute periods. Pronto: $c = 40 + 18p$. From $30 + 20p = 40 + 18p$, one gets $p = 5$, so the costs are equal then. Trying a value less than 5 for p shows that Perfecto is less expensive than Pronto. (Notice that this finding is clear from the graph.)

3. a. The male starts out 210 calories ahead, in calories used, but for every hour of walking, the female uses 30 calories more. So in 7 hours of walking at 3 miles per hour (21 miles!), the two would use the same number of calories, 3970.

   b. Deciding on the scales may be a key part. Expressing the calories used scale in terms of 100s and the "distance" in terms of the number of hours (= 3 miles) might be best. Joining the points here is correct because there is no requirement to walk for a whole number of hours.

   c. Female: $C = 1520 + 350h$, where C = the number of calories and h the number of hours walked. Male: $C = 1730 + 320h$. $1520 + 350h = 1730 + 320h$ gives $h = 7$, so 7 hours of walking, or 21 miles, will result in the two using the same number of calories.

4. It can be interesting to share your reactions with those of others.

5. The graphs should intersect at $(^-40, {}^-40)$, so when either temperature is $^-40$, so is the other one.

15.4 Average Speed and Weighted Averages

1. a. $96

    b. $12/hour (Ask, "why does the plain average of $8 and $16 work here?")

    c. $(96 + 16) \div 8 = 112 \div 8 = 14$. $14.00/h

2. a. $120   ($56 + $36 + $28)

    b. $4 per mile

3. 12 mi/h (He has to cover the 18 miles in $1\frac{1}{2}$ hours.)

4. The key is graphing total cost versus miles for part (a) and total distance versus time in part (b). Part (b) involves putting in the last segment from (5.5, 21) to (7, 39) and calculating the slope of that segment: 12 mi/h.

5. Be careful—the number of credits at each place matters! (Instructor: Allowing for rounding to get the initial GPAs, 2.95; if treated as exact GPAs, 2.96. Ask why it is higher than the average of 3.2 and 2.6, or 2.9.)

6. 60 words per minute

7. Predictions and rankings may vary. In order, Turtle's speeds to tie are 3.2 m/s; 0.95 m/s; and 4.95 m/s.

8. It is almost essential to draw a picture of the race track.

    a. Turtle will be ahead by 1.5 m.

    b. Rabbit will have forged ahead by 2 m. At the 20 m mark, when they head back, R will have traveled for 4 s, and T for $3\frac{1}{3}$ s. So on the way back, R will travel for 1.5 s, and thus go 15 m. T, on the other hand, will travel $5\frac{1}{2} - 3\frac{1}{3}$ s on the way back, or $2\frac{1}{6}$ s, and thus go 13 m. So R is ahead by 2 m after 5.5 s. When R heads back (after 4 s), T has been heading back for $\frac{2}{3}$ s, or 4 m. Because R catches up by 4 m each second (on the way back), it will take 1 more second for R to catch T, at the 10-m mark from either end, when both have traveled 5 s.

    c. It takes R $4 + 2 = 6$ seconds to finish. After 6 seconds, T has gone 36 m, 20 m over and 16 back. So T is 4 meters behind when the race is over.

    d. The part (b) answers will change (R will be 4.5 m ahead, and after the start was always ahead of T), but the part (c) answers will stay the same because it will take R the same amount of time to win.

9. a. Xenia has a good sense for weighted averages, even at age 7! It would be interesting to know whether she loses that sense as she associates "average" with the computational procedure.

   b. 140 total miles ÷ 3 total hours = $46\frac{2}{3}$ miles per hour

   c. If traffic had allowed, they would have covered the same distance if they had traveled at $46\frac{2}{3}$ mi/h all the way.

10. a. $\frac{12}{60} = \frac{1}{5}$ of the way over

    b. 10 m/s (Rabbit ran for 36 seconds, total.)

    c. Turtle, because 3.173 m/s is a faster speed than the speed giving a tie.

11. a. 6 m/s

    b. 4 m/s

    c. Rabbit was 12 m from the turn-around point, or 18 m from the finish line. Turtle was 18 m from the turn-around point, or 12 m from the finish line.

    Notice how important it is to have the quantities involved clearly in mind.

12. a. The graph coordinates are (0, 0), (0.5, 3), (1.5, 15). Speeds are 6 m/h and 12 m/h.

    b. 10 m/h. If Carly's speed did not vary, the graph would be a line from (0, 0) to (1.5, 15).

    c. 10 m/h

    d. 10 m/h

    e. Their averages are the same because they traveled the same distance in the same amount of time.

13. a. The coordinates of the graph's legs should be (0, 0), (15, 4), (20, 6), (35, 13), (50, 28), (60, 32), with time in minutes and distance in miles.

    b. 16 mi/h; 24 mi/h; 28 mi/h; 60 mi/h; 24 mi/h

    c. 32 mi/h

    d. The coordinates of the graph are (0, 0) and (60, 32).

    e. Both traveled the same distance in the same amount of time. For both, the average speed was 32 mi/h.

Supplementary Learning Exercises for Section 15.4

1. No. She has $2.8 \times 108 =$ about 302.4 grade points, and with a 4.0 for the last 12 semester hours, she will earn 48 more grade points, for a total of about 350. But for a 3.0 average for all 120 hours, she needs 360 grade points. The best she can get is about $350.4 \div 120 = 2.92$.

2. a. The total time for the trip is $7\frac{1}{3}$ hours, so the average speed for the whole 400 miles is $400 \div 7\frac{1}{3} = 54\frac{6}{11} \approx 54.5$ mph.

   b. This time the total time for the trip is $9\frac{5}{7}$ hours, giving an average for the whole trip of $400 \div 9\frac{5}{7} = 41\frac{3}{17} \approx 41.2$ mph.

   c. The 65 mph for the whole 400 miles would take $6\frac{2}{13}$ hours. The 50 mph trip going takes 4 hours, so that leaves only $2\frac{2}{13}$ hours for the return 200 miles, requiring a speed of $200 \div 2\frac{2}{13} = 92\frac{6}{7}$, or about 93 mph!

3. Needed is information about either the number of classes at each school, enabling one to find the total enrollment for both schools and the total number of classes. Alternatively, if there are assurances that there is the same number of classes at each school, then the given 27 as an average is correct.

4. Without knowing whether the same number of tickets was sold in each city, it is risky to use the $54 figure. If, say, there were 200 tickets sold in the first city (yielding $9600) and 1000 tickets in the second city (yielding $60,000), the average for the two cities is $(9600 + 60000) \div (200 + 1000) = 69600 \div 1200 = 58$ dollars, not $54.

5. a. There is no information about how many weeks the two people dieted.

   b. The 2.5 figure would be accurate if the two people dieted for the same number of weeks.

6. a. Turtle must run at 8 m/s to tie. (Rabbit takes $[30 \div 20] + [30 \div 5] = 7.5$ seconds in all, so Turtle must run the 60 meters in 7.5 seconds to tie. $60 \div 7.5 = 8$.)

   b. Turtle must run at $60 \div 11 = 5\frac{5}{11}$ m/s to tie.

   c. Turtle must run at 16 m/s to tie.

   d. Turtle must run at $60 \div 30\frac{1}{2} = 1\frac{59}{61} \approx 2$ m/s.

7. a. In each part, Rabbit's average speed is the same as Turtle's speed because that steady speed gives the same distance as the Rabbit trips over and back.

   b. None would be changed. (Think of the 120 as two 60 m races.)

8. Rabbit takes $(40 \div 10) + (40 \div 16) = 6.5$ seconds to go over and back. Turtle must cover only 60 m, having a 20-m head start, so Turtle must go $60 \div 6.5 = 9\frac{3}{13} \approx 9.2$ m/s, to tie.

15.5 More About Functions

1. a. If a singer's popularity could be assigned a value, then there would be a correspondence between that value and the number of CDs sold.

    b. If success could be assigned a value, then knowing the number of hours worked could predict the success value.

    c. For a given person, knowing his/her blood alcohol content could enable one to predict his/her reaction time.

2. Check that the students' justifications (there may be more than one) deal with the general case.

    a. $p(n) = 4n + 2$, perhaps from $6 + (n-1)4$. Check that the students' justifications (there may be more than one) deal with the general case.

    b. $p(n) = 3n + 5$, perhaps from $8 + (n-1)3$.

    c. $p(n) = 6n + 2$, perhaps from $8 + (n-1)6$.

3. a. 56   b. 206   c. $2(x^2 + 3)$, or $2x^2 + 6$

    d. 256   e. 676   f. $[2(x+3)]^2$, or $4(x+3)^2$, or...

4. $y = x^2 - 1$

5. $y = \frac{1}{2}x^2$

6. $f(x) = x^2 + x$, or you may have noticed $f(x) = x(x+1)$

7. $y = x^3$

8. $y = 2x^3$

9. $f(x) = 5x - 3$

10. Students may have algebraic equivalents.

    \# with 3 squares painted $= 8$ (the corner cubes)

    \# with 2 squares painted $= 4(m-2) + 4(n-2) + 4(p-2)$ (the cubes along the edges but not at the vertices)

    \# with 1 square painted $= 2(m-2)(n-2) + 2(n-2)(p-2) + 2(m-2)(p-2)$ (the other cubes in the faces)

    \# with 0 squares painted $= (m-2)(n-2)(p-2)$ (the cubes inside)

Supplementary Learning Exercises for Section 15.5

1. a. Given a value for sales, one can predict the profit (in large part).

   b. Given the speed, the stopping distance is predictable.

   c. Given the amount of rainfall, the agricultural yield is predictable.

   d. Given a measure of the care for the product, its life can be predicted.

2. a. $p(n) = 6n + 2$.   One justification: The first shape has perimeter 8 units. Each of the $n-1$ additional ones adds only 6 units because the two that overlap disappear. All together that gives $8 + 6(n-1)$, or $6n + 2$, units.

   b. $c(n) = 2.98n + 0.06(2.98n)$, or $1.06(2.98n)$, or $3.1588n$. Justification: Each box costs $2.98, so n boxes cost $2.98n$, and then the sales tax is added on.

   c. $p(n) = 8n + 2$.   One justification: The top four of the first shape are repeated n times for $4n$ units, as are the bottom four for $4n$ more, plus the two at the ends. Total: $4n + 4n + 2$. Try a justification similar to that for part (a).

   d. $p(n) = 10n + 2$.   One justification: The top five in Shape 1 are repeated n times, as are the bottom five, plus the two at the ends. Total: $5n + 5n + 2$. Again, try a justification similar to that in part (a).

   e. $c(n) = 3.95n + 12n(0.05)$, or $4.55n$.   Justification: The packs cost $3.95 each, and because each of the 12 cans in a pack requires a 5¢ deposit, that adds $12(0.05)$ to the cost for each pack.

3. a. 17   b. 51

   c. 7   d. 21

4. a. 2025   b. 144   c. $56\frac{1}{4}$ d. 547.56

5. a. No. For an input of x, Machine 1 gives $2x + 8$, but Machine 2 gives $2(x + 8)$.

   b. 142.8. Machine 1 gives $2(27.7) + 8 = 63.4$, and then Machine 2 doubles $63.4 + 8 = 71.4$, giving 142.8.

   c. 150.8. Machine 2 doubles $27.7 + 8 = 35.7$, giving 71.4, and then Machine 1 doubles 71.4, giving 142.8, and adds 8: 150.8.

6. $f(x) = x^2 + 4$

7. $g(x) = x^3 - 1$

8. $y = 15x - 4$

9. $y = 2x^2$

15.6 Issues for Learning: Topics in Algebra

1. Not only could different quantities be associated with each animal (time traveled, speed, distance traveled, distance from other animal,…), but "T = turtle" suggests that the T is a label for the animal rather than some quantity associated with the animal.

2. a. 0 (Joke: "All that work for nothing.")

    b. $45\frac{5}{8}$

3. a. $^-8$ b. 55   c. $^-8\frac{7}{9}$ d. -1

4. Samples:

    a. After Peter Rabbit nibbled 7 carrots more, Farmer Jones said, "You have nibbled 13 carrots!" How many carrots had Peter nibbled earlier?

    b. Peter nibbled 7 carrots for lunch, and then nibbled some more for dinner. In all, Peter nibbled 13 carrots. How many carrots did Peter nibble for dinner?

    c. Junior had $9 left after he spent $6 on food. How much did he have before he bought food?

    d. Junior had $14 and spent some on food. Then he had $6. How much did he spend on food?

    e. Donita bought two tablets and a mechanical pencil. The pencil cost $1.95. How much did each tablet cost, if she paid $4.15 for all the items?

    f. Lee got 76% on a 25-item T-F quiz. How many did Lee get correct?

5. The distributive property (of multiplication over addition):

    $A \times (B + C)$ initially, then splitting the two rectangular regions apart gives $A \times B$ and $A \times C$. Because the same area quantity is involved each time,
    $$A \times (B + C) = (A \times B) + (A \times C).$$

6. A drawing would no doubt show a larger share for the number of students than for the number of professors. But then 6 times the number of students would clearly not equal the number of professors.

Part III: Reasoning About Shapes and Measurement

Answers for Chapter 16: Polygons

16.1 Review of Polygon Vocabulary

1. a. Scalene right triangle

    b. Trapezoid

    c. Equilateral triangle (or regular triangle)

    d. Parallelogram

    e. Regular pentagon

    f. Parallelogram

    g. Square

    h. (Equiangular) hexagon

    i. Equilateral 12-gon, or concave equilateral 12-gon (see Learning Exercise 6 in this section). Using less-well known prefixes, it is also an equilateral dodecagon.

    j. Rhombus

2. Only parts (g), (l), and (q) are impossible.

3. a. Each vertex is on two sides, so the way of counting given will count each vertex twice.

    b. Each side actually makes two angles, one at each endpoint; the way of counting given does not take that fact into account.

4. a.–d. Answers will vary, but rectangles and rectangular regions should be common.

5. a. Most of them are isosceles right triangles, but there are also a square and a parallelogram.

    b. There are 7 isosceles right triangles, 2 (overlapping) isosceles trapezoids (not counting special ones), 3 nonisosceles trapezoids (not counting special ones), and 1 parallelogram region (not counting special ones).

    c. The different sizes are $\frac{1}{4}$ (I, II), $\frac{1}{8}$ (IV, VI, VII), and $\frac{1}{16}$ (III, V). Rather than trust one's eyes, copying and cutting out the pieces and comparing then them gives a convincing justification. You might also justify the results by using area formulas.

6. a. Answers will vary.

    b. Informally, one might say: "A polygon that does not have any dents," or "One that does not pooch in." A common technical definition is "A polygon is convex if, whenever two of its points are joined, the line segment never goes outside the polygonal region." The idea extends to nonpolygonal shapes.

   c. Answers will vary.

   d. A kite is a quadrilateral that has two consecutive sides the same length, with the other two sides also having equal lengths.

7.   a. The "fat" rhombuses in Pattern Blocks; join the center of the hexagon to every other vertex of the hexagon.

   b. The equilateral triangles in Pattern Blocks; join the center of the hexagon to each vertex of the hexagon.

   c. The isosceles trapezoids in Pattern Blocks; cut the hexagon through its center.

   d.    e.    f.

8.   Polygon: Number of sides, number of angles, length of each side, size of each angle, total of the lengths of the sides (the perimeter), total of the sizes of the angles, and so on. (See Learning Exercise 9.) Polygonal region: Same as polygon, plus the area of the region.

9.   A table helps to see a pattern that may be less obvious if the results are just written. The pattern can then often be extended from one line to the next (for a 12-gon, 54 diagonals; for a 20-gon, 170 diagonals), but without seeing the general result for n vertices. *Hint* 1: Add a column for twice the number of diagonals. Can you relate that column to the column for the number of vertices? A pattern suggests an educated guess, but, as you will see, patterns cannot always be trusted! Hence, now that you have a conjecture, try to reason why it must be true. Better *Hint*, because it gives a general argument: Each vertex in an n-gon is joined to all but 3 of the vertices to give $n - 3$ diagonals at each vertex, but doing this at each of the n vertices will count each diagonal twice. (Instructor: For an n-gon, there will be $\frac{n(n-3)}{2}$ diagonals.)

10.   The sum of the sizes of the angles in each of the triangles is 180°. When you add all of those up, you are also adding the sizes of the angles of the quadrilateral.

11.   a. 95°   b. 102°   c. $360 - (85 + 78 + 90) = 107°$ d. 73°   e. 90°

      f. 130°   g. $360 - (130 + 109 + 52) = 69°$ h. 111°   i. 71°   j. 128°

    k. The sum of the sizes of the exterior angles, one at each vertex, will be 360° for a quadrilateral.

    l. The sizes of the 4 straight angles, one at each vertex, add up to 720°. But the interior angles add to 360°. So 720 – 360 = 360.

12. a. 162   b. $168\frac{3}{4}$ c. $176\frac{8}{17}$

13. a. $\frac{(5-2)180}{5} = 108°$ b. 72°   c. 135°   d. 45°   e. $\frac{(n-2)180}{n}$
    f. $180 - \frac{(n-2)180}{n} = \cdots = \frac{360}{n}$

14. a. 90°   b. 67°   c. 61°   d. 84°   e. All five angle sizes should add up to $(5-2)180 = 540$, so $540 = 90 + 113 + 119 + 96 + e$, or $e = 122°$
    f. 58°   g. 72°   h. 59°   i. 52°   j. 101°   k. 79°   m. 62°
    n. The sum of the exterior angles, one at a vertex, for a pentagon is 360°.
    o. $5(180) - (5-2)180 = 360$

15. Each is true. What is your reasoning? (Instructor: (a) The right angle uses 90° of the 180° for all three angles, so the sizes of the other two angles must be 90. That is, the acute angles are complementary. (b) If a triangle had more than one right angle, then sum of the sizes of its angles would be more than 180°. Students may not be comfortable with the indirect reasoning in part (b). (c) $x + (180 - x) = 180$)

16. a. Five rows, with five dots (probably) in each row
    b. n^2, $(n+1)^2$
    c. *Hint*: It may be helpful to add a new column, 2 × # dots, and see how the entries in that column are related to the number in the first column, or to consider the differences between successive numbers of dots. Once you have a conjecture based on a pattern, see whether you can give an argument that justifies the conjecture. Instructor: Making an *n*-by-(*n* + 1) "rectangle" with two copies of the right-triangle version helps to see the $\frac{n(n+1)}{2}$ result for the nth triangular number.

17. Methods will vary.

18. a. Rectangular region
    b. Triangle
    c. Triangular region
    d. Parallelogram region
    e. Nearly a triangular region (since the corners are rounded)

    f. Rectangle, most commonly

    g. Hexagon

    h. Hexagonal region

19. The trials should support the conjecture because it is true in general.

20.

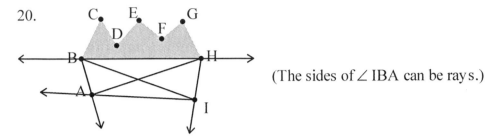

                              (The sides of ∠ IBA can be rays.)

(The points need italics, as does IBA.)

21. There are many possibilities. Check to make sure the rays start at the correct points and that *D* is the vertex of angle *FDE*. *TUV* should be shaded in, but *PQRS* should not.

Supplementary Learning Exercises for Section 16.1

1.   a. Trapezoid   b. Heptagonal region

    c. Equilateral triangle or regular triangle (These are the best answers, but isosceles triangle also applies.)

    d. Square (This is the best answer, but rectangle, rhombus, kite, parallelogram also apply.)

    e. Rhombus (This is the best answer, but parallelogram and kite also apply—*diamond* is not commonly used in geometry.)

    f. Right-triangle region

    g. Isosceles trapezoid

    h. Hexagon region

2.   a. Your shape should have 5 sides, with at least two of different lengths.

    b. Do you have 12 sides?

    c. Not possible; a square is both equilateral and equiangular and therefore regular.

    d. Any rectangle, even a square, will do.

    e. Not possible; you probably know that a rectangle has four 90° angles.

f. Not possible, for then the angle sum would be greater than 180°.

g. Any equilateral triangle will do.

h. The right angles should be at the "sides" of a kite in the common kite drawing.

3. a. 90°   b. 80°   c. $360-(90+80+76)=114°$ d. 66°   e. 104°

    f. 110°   g. 64°   h. 120°   j. $360-60-110-64=126°$

    k. 145°   m. 104°

    n. The interior angle by n has $720-(90+145+104+118+119)=144°$, so 36°.

4. a. $(9-2)\cdot180=1260°$ b. $(12-2)\cdot180=1800°$ c. $(m-2)\cdot180$

5. Samples:

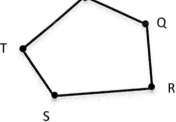

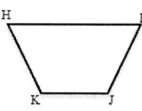

6. Here are some samples.

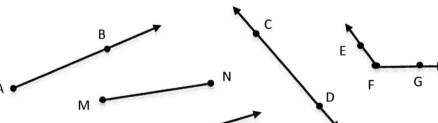

16.2 Organizing Shapes

1. The classification has each type of quadrilateral in a separate category, even though they share many characteristics besides having four sides. (The circles are a common way of showing the categories, and are not to be viewed as quadrilaterals themselves.)

2. a. AT   b. ST (Sketch a nonsquare rectangle.)   c. ST (Sketch a parallelogram that has no right angles.) d. AT e. ST f. ST g. ST

   h. AT i. AT j. ST k. ST l. ST m. ST n. ST

3. Samples:
   a. *Shared*: Opposite sides parallel and equal in length; opposite angles the same size, and so on. *Different*: Possible for angle sizes to differ, lengths of diagonal can differ, and so on.

   b. *Shared*: Have pairs of adjacent sides the same length, diagonals make right angles, pairs of opposite angles have the same size, and so on. *Different*: Possible for angle sizes to differ, possible for some sides to be different lengths, and so on.

   c. *Shared*: Have 4 sides, 4 angles, 2 diagonals, angle sum is 360°, and so on. *Different*: Trapezoids have parallel sides, quadrilaterals may not, and so on.

   d. *Shared*: Two sides parallel, four sides. *Different*: Other pair of sides may not be parallel, sides (or angles) may all be different sizes, and so on.

   e. *Shared*: Both pairs of opposite sides parallel and equal in length, opposite angles are the same size, diagonals bisect each other, and so on. *Different*: Sides may not all have the same length, diagonals may not be perpendicular, and so on.

4. Three, parts (c), (e), and (f), are not possible.

5.
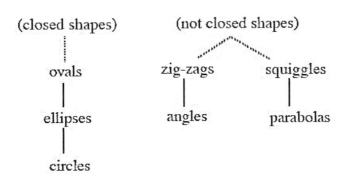

6. a. That the parallel sides are horizontal, with one shorter than the other and above it

    b

    (i). Perhaps the student thinks a parallelogram's angles cannot be right angles—that a parallelogram's sides must be "tilted."

    (ii). Perhaps the student thinks a rectangle must have unequal dimensions.

    (iii). Perhaps the student thinks that the angles of a rhombus cannot be equal in size.

    (iv). Perhaps the student thinks that the sides of a kite cannot all be the same length.

Supplementary Learning Exercises for Section 16.2

1. a. Yes   b. Yes   c. No   d. Yes   e. No
    f. No   g. Yes   h. No   i. No
2. a. Yes   b. No   c. Yes   d. No   e. Yes (squares)

16.3 Triangles and Quadrilaterals

1. Kites and isosceles trapezoids do not fit easily into this Venn diagram.

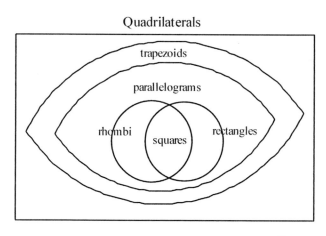

2. "Opposite sides/angles are equal" means both pairs. For the conjectures listed, there are counterexamples for each conjecture for quadrilaterals and trapezoids and kites, for all but the third conjecture for isosceles trapezoids, for the third and fourth for parallelograms, for the fourth for rectangles. All the conjectures are true for squares, and all but the third is true for rhombuses. Following is a summary compiled with one class; the conjectures are numbered and only the number is given when the conjecture is automatically true from the hierarchy.

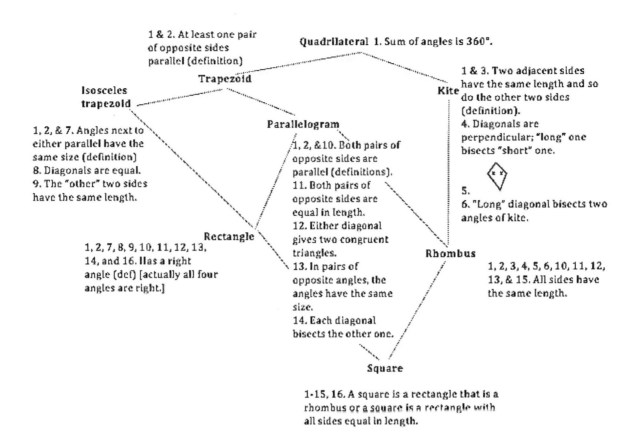

1 & 2. At least one pair of opposite sides parallel (definition)

Trapezoid

Quadrilateral 1. Sum of angles is 360°.

1 & 3. Two adjacent sides have the same length and so do the other two sides (definition).

Kite

4. Diagonals are perpendicular; "long" one bisects "short" one.

Isosceles trapezoid

1, 2, & 7. Angles next to either parallel have the same size (definition)
8. Diagonals are equal.
9. The "other" two sides have the same length.

Parallelogram

1, 2, &10. Both pairs of opposite sides are parallel (definitions).
11. Both pairs of opposite sides are equal in length.
12. Either diagonal gives two congruent triangles.
13. In pairs of opposite angles, the angles have the same size.
14. Each diagonal bisects the other one.

5.
6. "Long" diagonal bisects two angles of kite.

Rectangle

1, 2, 7, 8, 9, 10, 11, 12, 13, 14, and 16. Has a right angle (def) [actually all four angles are right.]

Rhombus

1, 2, 3, 4, 5, 6, 10, 11, 12, 13, & 15. All sides have the same length.

Square

1-15, 16. A square is a rectangle that is a rhombus or a square is a rectangle with all sides equal in length.

3. In each case, the properties should apply to the more special polygon.

4. Stuck? Measure segments and angles—are there any possible relationships?

   a. The segment joining the midpoints is parallel to, and half the length, of the third side.
   b. The part (a) results hold, of course, and the four triangles are "exactly the same shape" (congruent); hence, each has one-fourth the area of the large triangle.

5. a. The angles can be placed next to each other so that the two outside sides appear to lie along a straight line, and their sum is therefore 180°.
   b. The new "placements" of the three angles again appear to lie along a straight line. The method does work with obtuse and right triangles, by folding down the vertex with the largest angle size.

6. a. $x = 72°$; $y = 142°$

   b. $n = 112°$; $p = 36°$; $q = 144°$

   c. $s = 75°$; $r = 95°$ (using the fact that the sum of the sizes of the four angles of the quadrilateral is 360°)

7. a. After the last clue, the shape must be a parallelogram.

8.   a. Pat could have been thinking $a - \frac{b}{c} = a \times \frac{b}{c}$, or perhaps $a - \frac{a}{a+1} = a \times \frac{a}{a+1}$ (or perhaps something else).

   b. The first conjecture is not true in general; find a counterexample. But the second one is correct; try different values for a, and they will strengthen your belief in it. Use your algebra knowledge to show that $a - \frac{a}{a+1}$ is indeed always equal to $a \times \frac{a}{a+1}$.

   (Instructor: A similar situation can be built on an example or two suggesting correctly that $a + \frac{a}{a-1}$ is also equal to the product, $a \times \frac{a}{a-1}$, but an attractive $a + \frac{b}{c} = a \times \frac{b}{c}$

   conjecture is not true in general. The problems are from Usiskin.)

Supplementary Learning Exercises for Section 16.3

1. a.

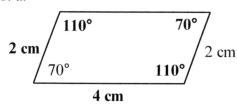

b.

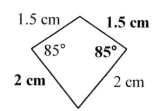

   c.

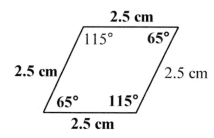

2.   a. A trapezoid that is not at all an isosceles trapezoid should give a counterexample.

   b. Use a rectangle that is much, much longer than it is wide.

   c. Your trapezoid for part (a) should give a counterexample.

   d. Any rectangle gives a counterexample.

3.   a. Your measurements should support the conjecture.

   b. Again, your measurements should support the conjecture.

   c. The evidence is based on only one example of a rectangle. Results might potentially be different for some other rectangle(s).

16.4 Issues for Learning: Some Research on 2D Shapes

1. Relevant: 4 sides, 2 sides parallel but not necessarily the "top" and "bottom." Your drawings should include the parallel sides not at the top and bottom, top longer than bottom, 2 or 3 sides equal in length, a very small one, one with 2 right angles, and one not "cut off" (perhaps like the one with 2 right angles, but with the right angles at the top).

2. It is likely that the examples that the child had seen did not have any angles small in size.

3. The child likely is focusing on the lengths of the visible parts of the sides of the angle.

4. Does your collection include rhombuses with 1, 2, or 4 right angles and with different orientations of the parallel sides?

5. a. Except for the choice of 6, the child seems to be looking for right angles at all the vertices.

    b. Perhaps the child is looking for four sides of about the same length for square, and shapes evenly "stretched out" for rectangle.

Answers for Chapter 17: Polyhedra

17.1 Shoeboxes Have Faces and Nets!

1. Your "box" should be taller than it is wide or deep.

2. Did you start at the top and take advantage of the last cube drawn when adding later cubes?

3. a. 5 faces, 5 vertices, 8 edges   b. 5 faces, 6 vertices, 9 edges

4. The net shows only 5 faces, and a cube has 6 faces.

5. a.
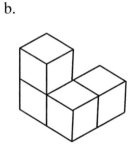

    Front   Right   Top view
    view   side   (from front)

    b. Do you see *two* possible answers for the top view, depending on what might or might not be hidden in the back left corner?

    c. They are like views from the reverse (or mirror images).

6. a.   b.   c.

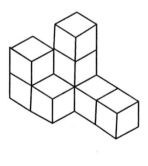

   The shape in the example (Ex. 5)   (one   (one
                                             possibility   possibility

Supplementary Learning Exercises for Section 17.1

1. a. 8 faces, 12 vertices, 18 edges

    b. 5 faces, 6 vertices, 9 edges

    c. 6 faces, 8 vertices, 12 edges

    d. 6 lateral edges; 3 lateral edges

2. b. 6 faces (Count each flat surface of the whole shape, not the individual square regions.), 12 edges

3.

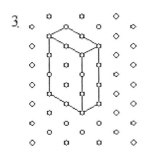

4.   Front view   Right view   Top view

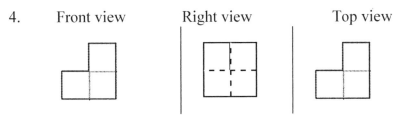

17.2 Introduction to Polyhedra

1. a. B, E (squares are special parallelograms), F

    b. G

    c. A, C, H (and M, if used)

    d. D, G, I, J

    e. H, J, K (and L and M, if used)

    f. K (What about C, E, F, and J? Some people regard a rectangle as a special isosceles trapezoid, as we will see later.)

    g. A, E, H (and L and M, if used)

    h. A, G

2. a. Lateral edges of a prism are equal in length and parallel to each other. The lateral faces of a prism are parallelogram regions (or special parallelogram regions, such as rectangular regions).

    b. 50 edges, one edge from each vertex of the base to the vertex not on the base; 50 faces, one face for each side of the base

3. a. A hexagonal pyramid

4. There is a polyhedron with the fewest number of vertices: a triangular pyramid (4 vertices); if there were only 3 vertices, they would all lie in the same flat surface (plane) and not give a polyhedron. But a polyhedron may have any large number of edges; consider a prism or pyramid with a base with a large number of vertices. So there is not a polyhedron with the greatest number of vertices.

5. a. Unless you have a weird polyhedron such as a polyhedron with a square hole in it, the relationship will hold.

    b. 7

    c. 12

    d. No, because $F + V$ would then be even, but $E + 2$ would be odd.

6. a. Right rectangular prism

    b. Right hexagonal prism (the common kind of pencil)

    c. Right rectangular prism

    d. There are different possibilities, including a right rectangular prism and a parallelogram right prism for the most common ones.

7. a. The 4 edges on the base were counted twice, as were the 4 lateral edges.

    b. Each vertex is on 3 faces, so it is counted 3 times in the argument that looks at the vertices on the 6 faces separately.

8. a. For an n-gonal pyramid, there are $3n$ angles at the n vertices on the base, plus n angles at the other vertex, for a total of $4n$ angles.

    b. Similarly, with 3 angles at each of the $2n$ vertices, there are $6n$ angles for an n-gonal prism.

9. a. C, E, F

    b. Rectangular regions

    c. A and G

10. a. 14 (12 usually, but if the bases are….)

    b. 24 (16 usually, but if the bases are….)

11–13. Answers will vary.

14. Their lateral faces are not parallelograms (or special parallelograms).

Supplementary Learning Exercises for Section 17.2

1.	a. C, D, E, F	b. A	c. A, C	d. A, G e. F
2.	a. 100	b. 50	c. 51	d. 51
3.	a. 20	b. 20	c. 40	d. 22
4.	No			
5.	a. 45	b. 45	c. 46	d. 46
6.	No			
7.	a. 12	b. 60	c. 120	

8. a. 14   b. 26   c. 14
9. a. 150   b. 60   c. 48

17.3 Representing and Visualizing Polyhedra

1. a. Looking straight at the midpoint of an edge with the cube turned so the same amount seems to be above the edge as below the edge

    b. Looking from above and in front of an upper-right vertex from the right

    c. Looking straight on at one face of the cube

2. a. Maximum number of faces: 3; minimum: 1

    b. Maximum number of vertices: 7

    c. Maximum number of edges: 9

3. *Hint*: Add three hidden edges to the base and the two hidden lateral edges.

4. a. *Hint*: See Figure 1.

    b. *Hint*: Be sure that your lateral edges appear to be parallel and perpendicular to the edges of the base that they meet.

    c. *Hint*: Adjust the quadrilateral pyramid in Figure 8.

    d. *Hint*: Sketch the top base first, remembering that you are to look at the prism obliquely. Then, sketch the lateral edges, keeping them parallel and of the same length. Finally, put in the edges of the bottom base, keeping in mind which edges are hidden.

    e. *Hint*: See Learning Exercise 3.

    f. See Figure 7.

    g. *Hint*: Learning Exercise 10 in Section 17.2.

    h. One possibility is a quadrilateral pyramid. Why isn't it possible with a prism?

5. a. 1-6, 2-4, 3-5

    b. 1-3, 4-6, 2-5

    c. 3-5, 1-4, 2-6

    d. 2-4, 3-6, 1-5

6. Answers will vary.

7. Nets (a) and (c) only (Did you notice that (b) and (d) are really the same net?)

8. The view is from above and in front of but to the right. Although equal or parallel lengths in the actual polyhedron will also be equal or parallel in the isometric sketch, right angles in the actual polyhedron are not right angles in the isometric drawing (they only appear to be because our minds can process the drawing).

    b. Yes

c. Right hexagonal prism

e. Volume: 4 cube regions; surface area: 18 square regions

9. a.

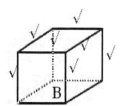   b. 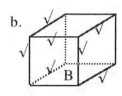   c.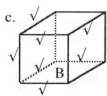

There might be other possibilities; compare yours with someone else's. This task is often difficult—what strategies did you use (e.g., focusing on edges that are *not* cut? Holding a cube as you imagined the cuts? Turning the net to make it easier to visualize where the base is? Working backward from a cutout net to the cube?).

10.

a.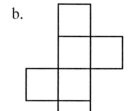

b.

c. Same as part (b). Do you see why?

In each case, your version might be turned or even flipped from the answer here.

11. Answers will vary.

12. *Hint*: There are 5 differently shaped tetrominoes.

Instructor:

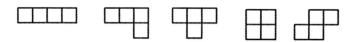

13.   a. There are 12 pentominoes. Did you find them all? How can you be sure?

Instructor (the darker squares may suggest how to build on the tetrominoes):

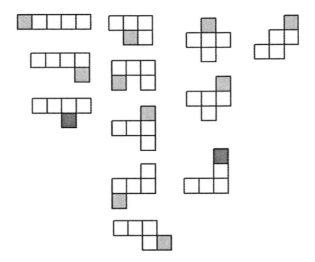

Solomon Golomb (*Polynominoes*, rev. ed., 1994, Princeton University Press) suggests this mnemonic: The last part of the alphabet, TUVWXYZ, and the capitalized parts of FILiPiNo, turning the above and using a little license.

b. Each has area – 5 square regions, but the perimeters...

c. No, for example... (Instructor: Use some of the pentominoes.)

d. No, for example... (Try some rectangular regions with the same perimeters.)

(Instructor: For example, a 2-by-4 rectangular region and a 1-by-5 one.)

e.

Instructor:

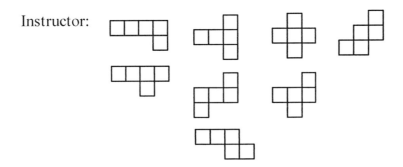

14. a. A rectangular region, not square

b. A rhombus region

15. There are different possibilities for each part. One somewhat laborious way to check is to cut out your net and fold it. Another (recommended) way is to have a classmate or two look at yours.

16. a. Triangular right prism

b. Cube

17. a. 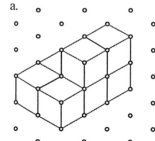   b.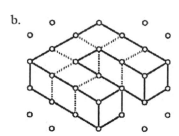

18. a. $\overline{FE}$, $\overline{AE}$, $\overline{AB}$, $\overline{FH}$ b. BC, GH, and FE

19.

a.   b.   c.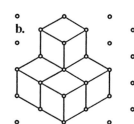

Supplementary Learning Exercises for Section 17.3

1. You should have a pentagonal prism.

2. a. You should have a hexagonal pyramid, with the top vertex off-center with the base.

   b. You should have a quadrilateral pyramid, with the top vertex off-center with the base.

   c. Your drawing for part (a) should suffice.

3. a. Your net should have 6 triangles and a hexagon. The side of a triangle that matches the "next" triangle should be the same length. At least one triangle should not be isosceles.

   b. Your net should have 4 triangles and a quadrilateral. The side of a triangle that matches the "next" triangle should be the same length. At least one triangle should not be isosceles.

   c. Your net for part (a) should work.

4.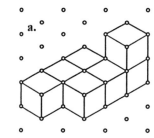

b.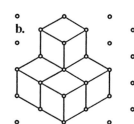

5. Only shape (d) can be obtained from the starting shape. Notice in the starting shape where the square corner is.

6. a. A regular hexagonal region and isosceles triangular regions.

    b. Rectangular regions

    c. A rectangular region and triangular regions, probably isosceles

    d. Rectangular regions and isosceles trapezoidal regions

7. The diagram will look like the one for quadrilaterals, but with "prisms" attached to each type of quadrilateral.

8. Think hierarchically (every rhombus is a special trapezoid, so the result should be the same). Or, each of the faces in each case is a quadrilateral, so the sum of all the angles in all the faces will be the same for any quadrilateral prism, 2160°.

17.4 Congruent Polyhedra

1. Answers will vary.

2. No—none can be moved to match another exactly.

3. The hidden shape will have the same-sized faces and (as a result) the same areas as the given shape, so 108 cm².

4. a. Yes. A rotation of 360° (or 0°) will make it match itself.
    b. Yes. Just reverse the motions that showed that P was congruent to Q.
    c. Yes. Do all the motions that show that R is congruent to S and then continue with the motions that show S is congruent to T.

5. There are the 5 suggested by the 5 2D tetrominoes (see below), plus another couple pictured below to the right (for us, the mirror image of the next-to-last one would be considered to be congruent).

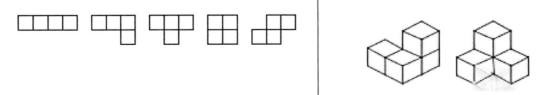

6. Answers will vary.

7. a.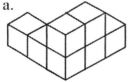

b.–d. Answers will vary.

8. Answers will vary.

9. Possibility: Two polygons are congruent if one polygon can be moved (by rotating, reflecting, or sliding, or a combination of such motions) so that it would fit on the other polygon exactly.

Supplementary Learning Exercises for Section 17.4

1. It is not possible for any prism to be congruent to a given pyramid because it would be impossible to make the figures match exactly. A prism has at least 3 faces that are parallelogram regions, and a pyramid can have at most one such face.

2. Congruent shapes can be matched exactly, so each face in one prism must correspond to a face in the other prism.

3. Yes. Some edge in prism Y must match the 4-in. edge in prism X exactly.

4. The matching edges will have the same lengths (2 cm, 6 cm, or 3 cm), as will the matching angles. Matching faces will be the same size.

5. One possibility is the following prism. Be sure that your version is oblique and that the hidden edges are shown.

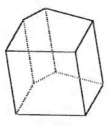

17.5 Some Special Polyhedra

1. always true (AT) or sometimes true (ST)
    a. AT   b. ST   c. ST   d. AT   e. ST   f. ST   g. AT   h. ST   i. ST
    j. ST   k. ST   l. AT

2. Knowing how many types (and what the types are) can enable you to ask, "Why are these the only ones?" and perhaps reveal something important about them. If only regular

polyhedra can appear in some context for some theoretical reason, then you will know ahead of time what the possibilities are.

3. a. A 20-faced polyhedron (icosahedron), perhaps regular, made up of 20 triangular regions

    b. A 12-faced polyhedron (dodecahedron), perhaps regular, made up of 12 pentagonal regions

    c. An 8-faced polyhedron (octahedron), perhaps regular, made up of 8 triangular regions.

4. a. Check to see whether there is the same arrangement of faces at every vertex.

    b. Try any quadrilateral prism that is not a cube.

    c. Some of the triangles in your net should *not* be equilateral triangles.

5. a. The tetrahedron may be more easily seen with an actual cube, especially if the cube is transparent.

    b. The other four vertices also give a regular tetrahedron.

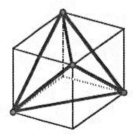

6. Euler's formula, $V + F = E + 2$, does hold. It is curious that some of the same numbers occur with the cube-octahedron and the dodecahedron-icosahedron.

7. a. First polyhedron: Equilateral triangles, regular hexagons; second polyhedron: squares, regular hexagons

    b. Euler's formula (see answer to Exercise 6) does hold, as it does for both polyhedra, although without the hidden edges in the second, it is likely impossible to count V, F, and E.

    c. Instructor: A natural question is: "How many types of semiregular polyhedra are there?"

8. Answers will vary; look for a reason.

9. a. Yes, because adjacent faces share edges, and all the edges of a given face are the same length.

    b. Yes, because each face is the same type of regular polygonal region.

    c. Yes, for the same reason as for part (a).

    d. No. The regular polygons may be different types, as a square and a hexagon.

10. Answers will vary.

Supplementary Learning Exercises for Section 17.5

1. a. The student counted all the visible edges and vertices, not realizing that the unfolding of the polyhedron would give duplicate edges and multiple copies of some vertices in many places in the net.

    b. Take into account that the unfolding of the polyhedron will use some edges twice and some vertices more than once. Try to anticipate which ones are counted more than once.

2. The base of the Great Pyramid is a square region, not an equilateral triangle region like the other faces.

3. Answers will vary.

4. Try to be systematic. For example, with 4 squares in a row, how can you add the other 2 squares to get a net for a cube? With 3 squares in a row? If you get stuck, try Cube Nets at http://illuminations.nctm.org.

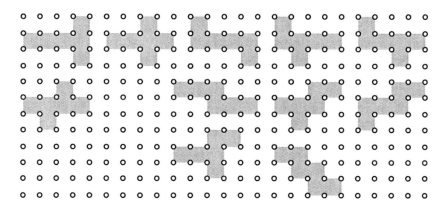

Answers for Chapter 18: Symmetry

18.1 Symmetry of Shapes in a Plane

1. Having reflection symmetry: ABCDEH(2)I(2)MO(2)TUVWX(2)Y

    Having (nontrivial) rotational symmetry: HINOSXZ

2. For example, for reflection symmetry: some leaves of trees or blades of grass or flower blossoms, some shells that are nearly flat,...; for rotational symmetry: the moon as it appears to us, some flower blossoms,...

3. For example, for reflection symmetry: a clock face (without numbers), a door (ignoring knob and hinges), most walls,...; for rotational symmetry: a pizza pan, the clock face and door again,...

4. a. 1 reflection symmetry only (Don't count a 360° rotation unless there are other rotational symmetries.)

    b. 2 reflection symmetries; 2 rotational symmetries

    c. 2 rotational symmetries (180° and 360°—2 reflection symmetries if rhombus)

    d. One reflection symmetry (unless it is a rectangle, in which case it has 2 reflection symmetries and 2 rotational symmetries, or a square, in which case it has 4 reflection symmetries and 4 rotational symmetries)

    e. Zero symmetries

    f. 2 reflection symmetries; 2 rotational symmetries

    g. One reflection symmetry (unless the kite is a rhombus, which has 2 reflection symmetries)

5. a. The bisector of the angle

    b. Don't overlook the lines themselves.

    c. There are actually infinitely many—do you see that?

    d. Any line through the center of the circle is a line of symmetry for the circle, so there are infinitely many lines of symmetry for a circle.

    e. 2 reflection symmetries (Do you also see 2 rotational symmetries?)

6. A rotation of *any* number of degrees, say 3.6° or 4 2/3°, will be a rotational symmetry.

7. Samples b. c. d. e.
   a.

8. a. 1 reflection symmetry

   b. 1 reflection symmetry

   c. 2 rotational symmetries

   d. 1 reflection symmetry

   e. 17 rotational symmetries ($\frac{360}{17} = 21\frac{3}{17}$, $42\frac{6}{17}$, $63\frac{9}{17}$, and so on)

   f. 1 reflection symmetry

9. Answers will vary.

10. a. The segments must have the same length, so the triangle must be isosceles.
    b. The two angles must have the same size.

    c. *M* must be the midpoint of segment *BC*.

    d. The two angles must have the same size.

11. a. They must have the same length, because one would fit on the other exactly if the dashed line is a line of symmetry.

    b. They must have the same length.

    c. Nothing relates the lengths of these two segments.

    d. These two angles must have the same size because one would fit on the other exactly if the dashed line is a line of symmetry.

    e. Because *A* would fit on *B*, the dashed line goes through the midpoint of segment *AB*. Similarly for segment *ED*. The angles at *E* and *D* will have the same size, as will the angles at *A* and *B*.

12. Segment *GH* will have the same size as segment *KJ*, as will segments *LG* and *JI* and as segments *LK* and *HI*. Angles *G* and *J* will have the same size, as will angles *K* and *H*, and angles *L* and *I*.

13. a. The reflection symmetry shows that the two diagonals would fit on each other, so they must have the same length. (Notice that this is not true for ordinary trapezoids.)
    b. The result should apply to rectangles because they can be regarded as special isosceles trapezoids. It is not true for nonrectangular parallelograms.

14. a. Stuck? Try *rotational* symmetry.

b. The result should apply to special parallelograms, but it is not true for all kites.

15. a and b. Use the "long" diagonal as a line of symmetry. What if the kite is concave?

c. Use the 180° rotational symmetry of a rhombus (or a possible fact about parallelograms and the hierarchy) and a reflection symmetry.

d. Use two reflection symmetries. (There may be other arguments.)

Supplementary Learning Exercises for Section 18.1

1. a. Only one reflection symmetry, with the line of symmetry going through the midpoints of the top and bottom of the polygon.

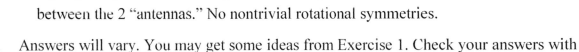

b. 2 reflection symmetries (in the dotted lines) and 2 rotational symmetries (180° and 360°, center at highlighted point).

c. Only one reflection symmetry, in a line along the horizontal segment midway between the two other horizontal segments.

d. 3 reflection symmetries (see drawing for the reflection lines) and 3 rotational symmetries (120°, 240°, and 360°, center at highlighted point.

e. One reflection symmetry in a line through the highlighted point and the midpoint of the segment between the 2 "antennas." No nontrivial rotational symmetries.

2. Answers will vary. You may get some ideas from Exercise 1. Check your answers with someone else.

3. Your argument can use a 60° rotational symmetry or use reflections in 2 lines of symmetry that are not diagonals.

4. Answers vary by individual.

5. The arrangement of the two halves is also important.

18.2 Symmetry of Polyhedra

1. No, it is not possible. This right- versus left-handedness requires a reflection.

2. a. 6 different planes of symmetry, one through each edge

b. Only 3 (Why don't the other "inviting" planes work?)

c. 5

d. 2

3. Remember that for a given axis, there may be more than one rotational symmetry possible, using different numbers of degrees.

   a. 4 axes of rotational symmetry, each has a 120° and 240° rotation, plus the 360° rotation that gives the same result for each axis, so there are 9 total rotational symmetries for shape A. (Instructor: That the 360° rotation counts just once may need discussion; as you know, the different descriptions entail the same beginning-end results, so they are describing just one function from the mathematical view.)

   b. Each of the 3 axes of rotational symmetry can involve a 180° rotation, or the 360° one. The latter would give the same result for each axis, so it is counted just once (shape F).

   c. One axis of symmetry, with 72°, 144°, 216°, 288°, 360° rotations (shape G)

   d. One axis of symmetry with 180° and 360° rotational symmetries (shape K)

4. There are 3 through pairs of opposite edges, plus 6 planes (through vertex, perpendicular to edge) for reflection symmetries, and 3 axes of rotational symmetry, each allowing 90°, 180°, and 270° rotations (plus the 360° one), plus 4 axes allowing 120° and 240° rotations (plus the 360° one), plus 6 axes allowing only 180° (and 360°) rotations. Amazing! The 360° rotation is usually counted just once.

5. a. There are 2 planes giving reflection symmetries; they are.... There is one (nontrivial) rotational symmetry of 180°. (What is the axis?)
   b. No symmetries exist.

   c. There are 2 planes giving reflection symmetries and 2 rotational symmetries, counting the 360° rotational symmetry.

6. There are different possibilities. Compare with others. Do any require fewer than twice the original number of cubes?

7. *Hint*: The base must be a square.

8. 9 reflection symmetries and 16 rotational symmetries (8 from one axis, and 2 for 8 other axes, but each of the latter counts the 360° rotational symmetry counted with the first axis)

9. $A \to F$, $B \to G$, $C \to C$, $D \to D$, $E \to E$, $F \to A$, $G \to B$, $H \to H$.

10. Does each have the same final effect, regardless of any difference in motion along the way?

11. Regular octahedron (shape H): 9 planes of reflection symmetry; 13 axes of rotational symmetry (giving 36 different rotational symmetries!)

   Regular dodecahedron (shape L) and regular icosahedron (shape M): 15 planes of reflection symmetry; 31 axes of rotational symmetry (giving 90 rotational symmetries!).

Supplementary Learning Exercise for Section 18.2

1 and 2.

   a. There are two reflection symmetries and two rotational symmetries (180° and 360°). See the drawing below for parts of the cross-sections and the (heavy) axis of rotation sticking out toward you.

   b. Same as for part (a) except the axis of rotation is vertical. See the drawing below.

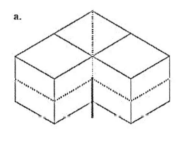
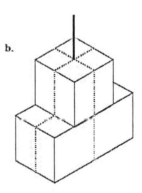

3.   There are 7 reflection symmetries, with 6 of the planes of symmetry suggested by the lines of symmetry in the hexagonal bases and with the 7th plane of symmetry cutting through the lateral faces, halfway down from the top base and perpendicular to the lateral edges.

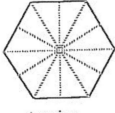

top view

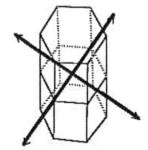

   There is a grand total of 12 rotational symmetries. There are 6 rotational symmetries using an axis joining the centers of the two hexagonal bases (60°, 120°, 180°, 240°, 300°, and 360°). There are an additional 6 rotational symmetries from axes that are lines of symmetry for the hexagonal cross-section from the 7th plane of symmetry; each has 180° (the trivial 360° symmetry has already been counted).

4. Did you actually find four planes of symmetry?

5. No axis of symmetry exists, nor does any plane of symmetry. The slanted nature of shape B and the non-rhombus nature of the parallelogram faces keep pieces from matching when rotated in possible axes or reflected in possible planes of symmetry.

Answers for Chapter 19: Tessellations

19.1 Tessellating the Plane

1. What causes the difficulty?

2. Answers will vary.

3. Answers will vary.

4. If you have trouble, rotate the shape 180° about the midpoint of each side.

5. Each type of Pattern Block will tessellate the plane.

6. Examples

   a.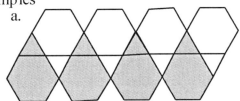

   b.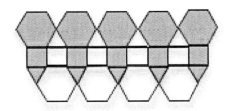

7. After experimenting a bit, you will believe *Yes*.

8.   c. The area of the larger triangle is 4 times the area of the smaller one. (Note that the *lengths* of the sides of the larger one are only twice the lengths of the sides of the smaller.)

9. Parts (a), (c), and (d) have many rotational symmetries (different centers) and translation symmetries (different distances), if shadings are to match. If shadings are to match, part (b) has many translation symmetries (different lines). Translations come up in Chapter 22, so students' language may be different. Each figure also has glide-reflection symmetries, but students have not yet been exposed to glide-reflections.

Supplementary Learning Exercises for Section 19.1

1. For the triangles and the trapezoid, notice that if you can get a parallelogram region you can clearly tessellate the plane with the polygon.

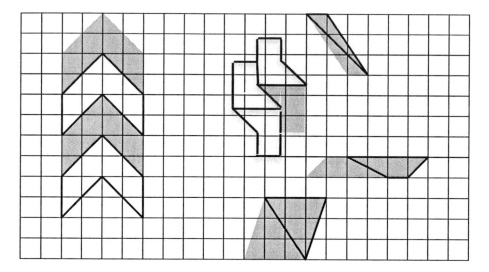

2. Probably. For example, for the chevron shape a reflection in a line down the middle of the part of the tessellation that is shown gives a symmetry; although there do not appear to be any rotational symmetries for the chevron in the one given (yours might have some 180° rotational symmetries).

3. Another regular pentagon would have to fit into either question-marked space. But there is not room for two more (216°) in the first case and not enough (108° + 180° = 288°, leaving 360° − 288° = 72°) in the second case.

4. $x + x + x = 360$, so $x = 120$ degrees.

5. Yes, each of the five tetrominoes can tessellate the plane.

6. Yes. See, for example, the tessellation in Learning Exercise 9(a), or this shape:

19.2 Tessellating Space

1. Yes, there are many.... (Instructor: Abutting two bricks at right angles at the end of one brick, making an L shape, is fairly common. Sliding one brick along another, but not halfway, gives lots of other possibilities.)

2. Parts (b) and (d)

3. a, d, e; in (a), the curved spine could fill in the curved-in space, but in (b) the shape could not fill in the curved space. In (c), the piece(s) will not fit the inward-going spaces.

4. Volume is most often based on the number of cubical regions that fill a space; this space-filling by cubical regions is a tessellation.

5. Three pyramids I can be arranged to make a cube, so shape I can tessellate space.

6. Neither J nor K will tessellate space (even though it looks as though they should).

Supplementary Learning Exercises for Section 19.2

1. Can   2. Cannot (the cylinder-shaped kind)   3. Cannot   4. Can

5. Cannot   6. Can   7. Can   8. Cannot

Answers for Chapter 20: Similarity

20.1 Similarity and Dilations in Planar Figures

1. a. Corresponding lengths: New length = scale factor × old length. Or, the ratios $\frac{\text{new length}}{\text{old length}}$ are all equal to the same value, the scale factor.
    Corresponding angles: New angle size = old angle size

    b. The ratio of the perimeters is equal to the scale factor. The length of each side of the original is multiplied by the scale factor, so the sum of the new lengths is also (using the distributive property, symbolically).

2. a. Not similar. Even though the corresponding angles are all the same size, the given sides would involve different scale factors, 2 and $1\frac{6}{7}$: $12 = 2 \times 6$, but $13 = 1\frac{6}{7} \times 7$.

    b. Not similar. Even though all the sides are related by the same scale factor ($\frac{2}{3}$ or $1\frac{1}{2}$, depending on your view), the corresponding angles are not the same size.

3–6.   Usually, you can tell by looking at your result whether you have carried out the size transformation correctly; sides should be parallel to their images.

7. b. A side and its image appear to be parallel. (This gives a visual check for accuracy.)

    c. Allow for slight measurement discrepancies. The intended scale factor is in the 1.7 to 1.8 range. The intended angle sizes are 88°, 34°, and 58° in each triangle. Again, a side and its image appear to be parallel.

8. a. One pair of parallel sides have lengths 30.5 m; the other pair 12.2 m. The angle sizes are 115° and 65°.

    b. $3\frac{1}{3}$ m, $1\frac{1}{3}$ m (students may have decimals); 115°, 65°

    c. Each image is a parallelogram.

9. a. $a = 50°$, $b = 60°$, scale factor is 2/3 or 1 ½; $x = 7.2$ km, $y = 5\frac{1}{3}$ or $5.\overline{3}$ km if measurements are perfect.

    b. The primes (A', B', C') tell what correspond. $p = 40°$, $r = 60°$, $q = s = 80°$, scale factor is 3 or $\frac{1}{3}$; $x = 6$ cm, $y = 2\frac{2}{3}$ cm.

    c. $p = 12°$, $q = 120°$, $y = 2.5 \times 129 = 322.5$ yd, $x = 36$ yd

    d. $r = 75°$, $s = 75°$. So x and 28 correspond, as do y and 28.3, and 24 and 30. The 24 and 30 give the scale factor. $x = 22\frac{2}{5} = 22.4$ cm, $y = 35\frac{3}{8} = 35.375$ cm.

10. Yes, in both cases. If the center is on the figure, there are segments that overlap with rays, so it is visually different from the other cases.

11. The image is the same size but in a different place.

12. A change in only the scale factor will result in a change in the size and location of the image.

13. The image will be just like the original (although it may have moved if a rotation, and so on, is involved). The two will be congruent.

14. a. Just one point!

    b. After multiplying by ⁻2, measure in the opposite direction through the center.

15. Two are incorrect. Instructor: Sample corrections—a. 200% should be 100%, or 60 should be 90; b. 150% should be 50%, or 12 should be 20 (or 8 should be 4.8).

16. a. 1.6, or 160%

    b. 7.5 cm and 22.5 cm; 125% (the original is the other 100%)

17. a. The new segment should be 3 copies of the original.

    b. The new segment should be 2.5 copies of the original.

    c. The new segment should be 4 copies of the original.

    d. The new region should have 9 squares.

    e. The new region should have 4.5 squares.

    f. The new region should have 12 squares.

18. a. The first and third express the same relationship. (Your example?)

    b. The first and third express the same relationship. (Your example?)

    c. The first and third express the same relationship, and the second and fourth express the same relationship (but different from the first relationship).

19. a. 56 cm   b. 80 cm   c. 18 cm

    d. 42 cm   e. 54 cm   f. 30 cm

    g. 150 cm   h. 210 cm

20. One way would be to use the ruler method. Another way would be to draw a 60° angle, mark off on its sides length 4 times the lengths of the given 60° angle, and then draw parallels to finish the shape.

21. In (a)–(c), angle sizes are the same as in the original, and each length in the original is multiplied by the scale factor to get the length in the image.

    d. Say P dollars are invested at an interest rate of 5% per year. After one year, the original P dollars would become $1.05P$ dollars, as though the original is scaled up by a factor of 1.05.

22. Map scales are usually expressed as ratios or equations, so this one might be written 28 mi:1 in., or 1 in.:28 mi, or 1 inch = 28 miles. Many times the units are the same, so the scale here could be written 1,774,080:1 without any need to mention units. (There are 5280 feet in a mile and 12 inches in a foot.)

23. 150 km. *Hint*: You will have to measure the distances on the maps.

24. A scale of 1 cm = 100 years allows all of the likely dates to be shown, up to 2000. With that scale and starting with year 0 at 0 cm, the Magna Carta would be 12.1(5) cm from the start; Columbus, 14.9 cm; Declaration of Independence, 17.8 cm; French Revolution, 17.9 cm; Civil War 18.6 cm; Wright brothers 19.0 cm; WW II 19.4 cm; atomic bomb 19.5; TV 19.5+ cm; computers 19.7 cm; and so on.

25. a. Here, it is reasonable to have 1 cm = 30 million years. Then, starting with the Cambrian at 0 cm, Carboniferous would be at about 10.7 cm, Triassic at about 13.3 cm, Cretaceous at about 17.8 cm, Oligocene at 19 cm, Pleistocene at essentially the 20-cm mark.

    b. About 66.7 cm!

26. The original and the final image are similar; the scale factor is not 7, however. (Instructor: 12)

27. a. Answers will vary.

    b. About 2, because the dimensions of the smaller squares are roughly doubled to get the larger squares.

    c. Yes, by…. (Instructor: Use smaller squares than those in the given grid.)

28. a. Yes. All the angles in each triangle have 60°, so corresponding angles are the same size. And, even though for these triangles we need not check, every ratio of the lengths of corresponding sides is 7:12 (or 12:7).

    b. Yes. Again, the pairs of 60° angles assure that the triangles will be similar. How would you determine the scale factor for the chosen triangles?

    c. No. One triangle might have angles 90°, 45°, 45°; the other could have 90°, 30°, 60°.

    d. Yes. Every pair of corresponding angles has 90°, and because all the sides of each square have the same length, the equal ratios for similarity will be assured.

    e. No, even though the corresponding angles all have the same size. Give an example to show that the ratios of corresponding sides will not necessarily all be equal.

    f. No. Sketch a couple, avoiding regular hexagons.

    g. Yes. Corresponding angles will have the same sizes, and because all the sides of each *n*-gon have the same length, the ratios of lengths of corresponding sides will all be equal.

29. Measure your drawings. For example, the woolly mammoth is about 8.5 m (from $170 \times 5 = 850$ cm) from tip of tail to tusks' end, and about 5.1 m tall (from $170 \times 3 = 510$ cm). This termite is about 0.6 cm long (from $4.2 \div 7.3 \approx 0.575$ cm).

30. a. For example, $\frac{x'}{y'} = \frac{rx}{ry} = \frac{x}{y}$ and $\frac{x''}{y''} = \frac{sx}{sy} = \frac{x}{y}$.

    b. These ratios are all equal.

    c. These ratios are also all equal. In trigonometry, the ratios are related to the angle C in the right triangle and given names like "sine $\angle C$."

Supplementary Learning Exercises for Section 20.1

1. The sizes of each pair of corresponding angles are the same. The ratios of the lengths of corresponding sides all have the same value (the scale factor).

2. In each part, the image is a line segment 2.5 times as long as the original segment.

3. Only the location of the images would be different.

4. a. The angles in the image will all be 90°, so the image is a rectangle. The scale factor is $\frac{7}{4} = 1\frac{3}{4}$ (remember to use measurements from the center), so the new dimensions are $\frac{7}{4} \times 28 = 49$ cm and $\frac{7}{4} \times 56 = 98$ cm.
    b. The image will still be a rectangle, but the scale factor is now $\frac{4}{7}$, giving new dimensions for the rectangle of $\frac{4}{7} \times 28 = 16$ cm and $\frac{4}{7} \times 56 = 32$ cm.

5. $a, b = 118°$ $c = 45°$ $d = 17°$ (scale factor = 1.5) $y = 22.5$ cm $x = 12$ cm

6. $c = a = 98°$ $b = 60°$ $d = 22°$ (s.f. = 3.5) $x = 6$ m $y = 14$ m

7. $a = 83° = c$ $b = e = 41°$ $d = 139°$ (s.f. = 1.2) $x = 24 - 20 = 4$ ft $y = 25$ ft

8. $a, c, f = 70°$ $b, d, e, g = 110°$ $v = 24$ cm (s.f. = $\frac{2}{3}$) $z, y = 36$ cm

    $x = 12$ cm $w = 8$ cm

9. a. \$18   b. \$30   c. \$18   d. \$30
    e. 40 lb   f. 32 lb   g. 40 lb   h. 32 lb

20.2 More About Similar Figures

1. Corresponding lengths: New length = scale factor × old length. Or, the ratios $\frac{\text{new length}}{\text{old length}}$ are all equal to the same value, the scale factor.

    Corresponding angles: New angle size = old angle size.

    Corresponding areas: New area = (scale factor)^2 × old area.

The ratio of the perimeters is equal to the scale factor, because...

The ratio of the areas is equal to the scale factor, squared.

2.   A size change like that in the section shows the relative sizes.

3.   The triangles in one pair are *not* similar (pair c).

4.   a. $x = 22.5$ km; $y = 16$ km. The triangles are similar because there are two pairs of corresponding angles that have the same sizes.

   b. A "tricky" part is seeing the correspondence after you have established similarity because the two triangles share an angle, giving a second pair of the same size along with the 114° angles. It may be helpful to redraw the triangles separately, with one triangle reoriented and the shared angles marked. $k = 5.6$ cm, and $n = 5.4 - 5.1 = 0.3$ cm.

   c. The right triangles also have same-sized angles where the lines cross, so they are similar. $p \approx 6.4$ mi; $q \approx 6.4$ mi. (The given 10.2 is rounded.)

   d. 30 ft

   e. Part (a), $(1.5)^2 = 2.25$; part (c), $(1.6)^2 = 2.56$

   f. Treat the pond like the tree in part (d). From some location a convenient distance from one side of the pond (and perpendicular to the line segment showing the distance across the pond), sight to see the other side of the pond, and make a convenient right triangle like the small one in part (d).

5.   a. $2\frac{1}{4}$

   b. A rectangle, because size changes keep angles the same size

   c. 4 cm by $6\frac{2}{3}$ cm

   d. $26\frac{2}{3}$ cm² and 135 cm². The second is $\left(2\frac{1}{4}\right)^2$ times the first.

   e. Each could have been answered differently, because the 4 cm might have referred to the longer side and hence correspond to the 15 cm side rather than the 9-cm one.

6. $x = 45$ cm, using a scale factor of 1.5 (or $\frac{2}{3}$, depending on your viewpoint)

7.   a. Ask about the sizes of two angles in the remote triangle, and check them against the angle sizes in your triangle.

   b. Unless the quadrilaterals are special, you would have to find out about the sizes of 3 of the angles (why not 4?) and the lengths of the four sides, for each quadrilateral. If the angles can be paired so that their sizes are equal, then you would have to check the ratios of the lengths of the paired sides.

Supplementary Learning Exercises for Section 20.2

1. The pairs of triangles in each of parts (a), (c), and (d) are similar.

2. $b = 125°$ $a, c, d = 90°$ $e = 55°$ (s.f. $= 0.6$) $y = 7.2$ m $x = 4.8$ m $z = 9$ m

3. $a = 111°$ $b = c = 93°$ $d = 75°$ $e = 81°$ (s.f. $= 1.2$) $y = 10.8$ in. $z = 9.6$ in. $x = 4.1$ in.

4. Ratio of areas ($=$ s.f.^{2}) and ratio of perimeters ($=$ s.f.), so #2, 0.36 and 0.6; #3, 1.44 and 1.2.

5. a. Regular pentagon

    b. The perimeter of the second polygon, which has 5 sides of the same length, is given to be 45 in., so each side is 9 in. Then the scale factor from larger to smaller is $\frac{9}{12} = \frac{3}{4}$.

    c. So, using part (b), the scale factor from larger to smaller is $\frac{9}{12} = \frac{3}{4}$.

20.3 Similarity in Space Figures

1. This exercise is important because it requires that you summarize some of the major relationships for similar polyhedra, and they reinforce the relationships for similar 2D shapes.

    Corresponding lengths: New length = scale factor × old length. Or, the ratios $\frac{\text{new length}}{\text{old length}}$ are all equal to the same value, the scale factor.

    Corresponding angles: New angle size = old angle size

    Corresponding areas: New area = (scale factor)^2 × old area

    Corresponding volumes: New volume = (scale factor)^3 × old volume

2. a. Drawings may vary. b. 1.5

3. Shapes (b) and (d) are similar, with scale factor 2 (or $\frac{1}{2}$, depending on your view of the original); shapes (b) and (e) are similar (allowing a reflection in a plane and a rotation as well as a size change), with scale factor $1\frac{1}{2}$ (or $\frac{2}{3}$); and (in the same way) shapes (d) and (e) are similar, with scale factor $\frac{3}{4}$ (or $1\frac{1}{3}$).

4. Shapes (b), (d), (f), and (g) are congruent (and therefore similar), and shapes (b), (d), (f), and (g) are similar to shape (a). b. $2^3 = 8$, because the shapes are similar.

5. b. Because $36 = 12 \times 3$, $84 = 12 \times 7$, and $96 = 12 \times 8$ and all the corresponding angles are right angles, the prism in (b) is similar to the given one. Alternatively, we could say that each of the ratios 36:3, 84:7, and 96:8 is equal to 12:1 or 12 (and the corresponding angles are all equal), so the prisms are similar.

There are three other definite "Yes" answers and one "Well, probably, taking rounding into account." (Besides (b), the ones similar to the 3-7-8 prism are in (c) (s.f. = 2.9), e (s.f. = 2.54, because 1 inch = 2.54 cm), (f) (s.f. = $1\frac{2}{3}$ probably), and (i) (s.f = 0.5).)

    j. Yes. The scale factor is about 4.14.

6.   a. 12 feet × 12 inches per foot = (scale factor) × 8 inches, ... , scale factor = 18. You might also get $\frac{1}{18}$ by using a different viewpoint as to the original figure, and the latter way is probably more common: "A $\frac{1}{18}$ scale model."

    b. $2\frac{2}{35}$ inches, which is more meaningful to people than $\frac{6}{35}$ feet.

7.   a. The matching angles will be the same size; several edges in P will be 2 cm or 3 cm or 4 cm, and their matches in Q will be about 5.3 cm, 8 cm, and about 10.7 cm.

    b. The scale factor is 8:3, or $2\frac{2}{3}$.

    c. $\frac{3}{8}$

    d. 3.6 cm

8.   With a scale factor of $\frac{1}{30}$, the height in the scale model should be $\frac{1}{30}$ × 40 inches, so the son is correct (the roommate probably subtracted 30 inches). The other dimensions should be $1\frac{1}{5}$ inches for the length and $\frac{2}{3}$ inch for the width.

9.   a. 8

    b. 27

    c. Yes, because...

    d. From the theory, one is $\left(1\frac{1}{2}\right)^2 = 2\frac{1}{4}$ times as large as the other.

    e. The ratio of the volumes is 27:8, but $\frac{27}{8} = \frac{3^3}{2^3} = \left(\frac{3}{2}\right)^3$, the cube of the scale factor.

10.   a. Yes, with scale factor... (Instructor: Scale factor = 1)

    b. Yes. The two scale factors are reciprocals, or multiplicative inverses.

    c. Yes, X and Z are similar. It is tricky to keep track of new and original, but using Z as the original and X as the final, the scale factor is (s.f. from Z to Y) × (s.f. from Y to X).

    Try a specific example to see how the product of the two scale factors enters in.

11.   a–b. Answers will vary.

    c. The ratio of the two should be the square of your scale factor.

    d. The ratio of the two should be the cube of your scale factor.

12.   a. 20*r* cm, 20*r* cm, and 25*r* cm

    b. *r*

    c. Original: 2800 cm^2, new one 2800r^2 cm^2, so the ratio is r^2.

    d. Original: 10,000 cm^3, new one 10,000r^3 cm^3, so the ratio is r^3.

13.   *Twice as large* could refer to lengths, or to areas, or to volumes, and the three of these are related by different powers of 2.

14. a. 8.8 cm by 13.2 cm by 22 cm

b. 3 cm by 4.5 cm by 7.5 cm

c. $\frac{16}{7}$ cm by $\frac{24}{7}$ cm by $\frac{40}{7}$ cm, or approximately 2.3 cm by 3.4 cm by 5.7 cm

d. $14\frac{2}{3}$ cm by 22 cm by $36\frac{2}{3}$ cm

e. 4 cm by 6 cm by 10 cm

f. 8.8 cm by 13.2 cm by 22 cm

15. The new surface area is 803.5 cm² (the surface area of the original is 62 cm²).
The new volume is 1399.68 cm³ (the volume of the original is 30 cm³); the new
dimensions are 7.2 cm by 10.8 cm by 18 cm.

16. It is *not* 40; recall how *volumes* of similar figures are related. (Instructor: 1000)

17. No. If the scale factor were 0, then the image of every point would be the center.

18. a. Yes. All the angles are 90° and every ratio of the lengths of edges is 5:8.

b. Yes. All the angles are 90° and every ratio of the lengths of edges is m:n.

c. No. Their angles need not be equal, nor do the ratios of lengths have to be the same.

d. No. Give an example.

e. No. Although the ratios of the lengths of edges are all equal to 1:3, there is no
assurance that the angles in the rhomboidal prism are 90°, as in the cube.

19. It is not possible to set up a correspondence so that corresponding angles are the same
size.

20. Use the same pattern as the given net so that the angles are the same, but multiply each
segment in the net by your scale factor.

21. "Each cubic centimeter becomes a 4 cm by 4 cm by 4 cm cube in the enlargement, so
each original cubic centimeter is now 4^3 cubic centimeters."

22. a. 25,600 cm²

b. 204,800 cm³

23. a. 3 (or $\frac{1}{3}$) The ratio of the volumes, 810:30, is 27, and that is the cube of the scale
factor.

b. $3^2 = 9$ (or $(\frac{1}{3})^2 = \frac{1}{9}$ or 9 to 1 or 1 to 9)

24. The new cube was actually 8 times as large in volume as the previous one, so the
magician felt that the people had not followed her instruction. She should have been
pleased, however, because the new cube had much more gold than she asked for.

25. The nets should be nets for cubes, of course, with sides/edges for the larger one twice the
lengths for the smaller one. So the volume of the larger cube will be $2^3 = 8$ times that of
the smaller.

26. Under the assumption that your shape is similar to that of the Statue of Liberty, your answers might be about 4 ft 6 in. for the statue's nose and 3 ft for its width of mouth.

Supplementary Learning Exercises for Section 20.3

1. The points of the three pyramids can be matched so that corresponding angles have the same size and so that the ratio of the lengths of every pair of corresponding sides is the same.

2. No. The lengths may not have the same ratio, and the angles need not be the same size.

3. a. No. The ratios $\frac{4}{6} = \frac{2}{3}$ and $\frac{3}{5}$ are not equal.

   b. Yes. The angles are all right angles, so their sizes are equal, and each of $\frac{12}{9}$, $\frac{20}{15}$, and $\frac{8}{6}$ equals $\frac{4}{3}$.

   c. No. Although $\frac{10}{20}$ and $\frac{12}{24}$ each equals $\frac{1}{2}$, $\frac{14}{21} \neq \frac{1}{2}$.

   d. Yes. The angles are all right angles, so their sizes are equal, and putting the lengths in order for each prism, $\frac{6}{9} = \frac{8}{12} = \frac{10}{15}$ because each equals $\frac{2}{3}$.

4. a. 2200 in. ≈ 184 ft, the actual length of the shuttle, although $2200 \div 12$ gives 183 ft. 4 in.

   b. 1 : 1,000,000

5. a. 22 cm by 33 cm by 44 cm

   b. 37 cm by 55.5 cm by 74 cm

   c. 12.5 cm by 18.75 cm by 25 cm

6. a. Areas (larger compared to smaller), $(2\frac{1}{5})^2 = 4\frac{21}{25}$, so the larger shape has $4\frac{21}{25}$ times the area of the smaller shape; volumes, $(2\frac{1}{5})^3 = 10\frac{81}{125}$

   b. Areas, 13.69, volumes, 50.653

   c. Areas, 156.25%; volumes, 195.3125%

7. a. The triangles' sides: 57.6 cm, 50.4 cm, and 64.8 cm; height 21.6 cm

   b. Sides of triangles: 6.8 cm, 5.95 cm, and 7.65 cm; height 2.55 cm

   c. Sides of triangles: 12.8 cm, 11.2 cm, and 14.4 cm; height 4.8 cm

8. a. Areas, $7.2^2 = 51.84$, so the larger shape has 51.84 times the area of the smaller shape; volumes, $7.2^3 = 373.248$

   b. Areas, 0.7225; volumes, 0.614125

   c. Areas, 256%; volumes, 409.6%

9. a. $\frac{320}{5} = 64 = 4^3$, so the scale factor is 4.

   b. Using the scale factor from part (a), the ratio of the areas is $4^2 = 16$. Polyhedron Y has 16 times as much area as polyhedron X has.

20.4 Issues for Learning: Similarity and Proportional Reasoning

1. Part (a) involves a whole number (2) in comparing the numbers of boxes or in calculating the cost per box ($3); part (b) does not.

2. Problem 2, with its non-whole-number relationships, looks more difficult. But the easier relationships in Problem 1 seemed to invite hasty, incorrect solutions.

Answers for Chapter 21: Curves, Constructions, and Curved Surfaces

21.1 Planar Curves and Constructions

1. a. NT   b. AT   c. ST   d. AT   e. AT

    f. AT   g. AT   h. AT

2. Answers will vary.

3. Drawings will vary; check for tessellations.

4. a. Any line through the center will give a reflection symmetry, and any size rotation with its center of rotation at the center of the circle will give a rotational symmetry.

    b. There are many reflection symmetries (all the lines of reflection will be parallel) and many rotational symmetries (all 180°, but with different centers).

5. Your sketches should show the appropriate part of the circle or the circular region.

    a. $\frac{1}{4}$ b. $\frac{3}{4}$ c. $\frac{1}{3}$

    d. Because the whole circle has 360°, 80° would be $\frac{80}{360}$, or $\frac{2}{9}$, of the circumference.

    e. $\frac{1}{2}$ f. $\frac{1}{8}$ g. $\frac{3}{8}$ h. $\frac{1}{6}$

6. a. 84°   b. 42°   c. 42°   d. 42°   e. 96°   f. 180°   g. 90°   h. 90°   i. 90°

7. The angle at A is the inscribed angle, intercepting the $d°$ arc. Triangle ABC is isosceles because of the radii, so the angles at A and B are equal. The size of the central angle = 2 × the size of the inscribed angle. Or, the size of the inscribed angle is half that of the central angle. Instructor: The sketches below suggest how to extend the argument to other cases.

Use result
above and add.

Use result
above and
subtract.

8. You may check your work by measuring.

9. a. You can get the midpoint of a segment by constructing the perpendicular bisector of the segment.

    b. The segments should pass through the same point (the center of gravity, or centroid, of the triangular region).

10. Look for the construction marks. Parts (c) and (d) and perhaps (f) involve extending the given segment. Parts (e) and (f) are not literally illustrated in the text description.

11. Your eyes can usually tell you whether your work is all right.

12. a. Because the two distances are from the same radius, they are equal.

    b. All the points should lie on the perpendicular bisector of segment *AB*.

    c. The center will be where two perpendicular bisectors of chords intersect. The radius can then be found by measuring from the center to any point on the arc (about 4 cm here). Notice that you can use any three points of the arc to find the center of the circle.

    d. Because concentric circles share the same center, the perpendicular bisectors of chords from the different arcs will meet at the common center of the circles.

13. a. *Hint*: 45 = half of 90

    b. *Hint*: 135 = 90 + 45

    c. and d. *Hint*: $\frac{3}{4} = \frac{1}{2} + \frac{1}{4}$, and $\frac{1}{4}$ is half of a half. $\frac{3}{4} = \frac{1}{2} + \frac{1}{4}$

    e. Bisect the given segment to get half of the segment. Bisect one of the half segments to obtain quarters. Bisect the quarter closest to the half mark to get eighths. Then a half segment with an eighth segment will be $\frac{5}{8}$ of the original segment.

14. a. Suppose a vandal or a malicious drunk came by. (Instructor: A curve of constant width is needed, to prevent the vandal from dropping the cover down the hole.)

    b. Yes. The same idea works with any regular polygon.

15. The designs are self-checking.

16. *Hint*: See Learning Exercise 5. You may check your accuracy by measuring the central angle and comparing that to the 360° for the whole circular region.

17. Various cycles—the lunar cycle, the cycle of the seasons, the apparent shape of the moon,…

18. a. Usually just a visual check will do.

    b. Answers will vary; check for work.

19. Using *A* as center, draw a circle with radius *AB*. Using *B* as center, draw a circle with radius *AB*. Either of the two points in which the circles intersect can be used for *C*.

20. You will recognize the (a) ASA, (b) SAS, and (c) SSS situations. Part (d) allows you to review these, if you wish.

21. a. Yes (SAS or side-angle-side)

b. Not necessarily, but they are similar.

c. Yes (SSS, or side-side-side)

d. Yes, the third angle in GHI makes ASA (angle-side-angle) with Triangle 7.

Supplementary Learning Exercises for Section 21.1

1. a. A segment of the circle   b. A sector of the circle

c. A central angle   d. An inscribed angle

e. A (minor) arc

2. Your diameter, a line segment, should go through the center of the circle and have its endpoints on the circle. Your radius, a line segment, should have endpoints at the center of the circle and at a point on the circle. For parts (c) and (d), compare Exercise 1(a) and (b). Your chord, a line segment, should have endpoints on the circle and (in this case) not go through the center of the circle. Your central angle can be any angle with its vertex at the center of the circle. Your inscribed angle should have its vertex on the circle, with chords as its sides. Your minor arc should be any (connected) piece of the circle that is less than half the circle.

3. a. 70° (It is a central angle intercepting an arc of 70°.)
    b–d. 35° (They are inscribed angles intercepting an arc of 70°.)

    e–g. 90° (They are inscribed angles intercepting half the circle because of the diameter and thus intercepting an arc of 180°.)

4. a. and b. You can check the accuracy of your work with a protractor.
    c. and d. The angle should be 90° or close to it. So a reasonable conjecture is that if you bisect two angles with outside sides making a straight line, the two bisectors make an angle of 90°.

    e. *Hint:* A straight angle has 180°.

5. Your quadrilateral should look like a rhombus. Use the rotational symmetry of the rectangle and a line of symmetry to justify your conjecture.

6. You may have bisected any angle of the pentagon and argued that the bisector will be a line of symmetry (how can you be sure that the other parts do coincide when reflected? The last step in the argument is difficult.). Or you might have constructed the

perpendicular bisector of a side of the pentagon and argued that it is a line of symmetry. (How can you be sure that the other parts do coincide when reflected? The last step in the argument is difficult.) You could also construct the perpendicular to a side from the opposite vertex, but it is more difficult to argue that this perpendicular is a line of symmetry.

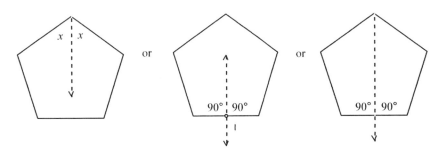

In any case, your argument should be about the properties your constructed line and the regular pentagon have rather than an argument based on direct measurements or folding the shape on the line.

21.2 Curved Surfaces

1. a. NT   b. AT   c. AT   d. AT (but sometimes just 1 nontrivial one)
    e. AT   f. AT   g. AT

2. a. Right circular cylinder   b. Right circular cylinders
    c. Right circular cone   d. Right circular cone
    e. Oblique cone   f. Right circular cylinder

3. a. Using the line through the centers of the bases as axis, there are infinitely many rotational symmetries. With every line along a diameter of a cross section halfway down as axis, there are 180° and 360° rotational symmetries as well. Any plane perpendicular to the bases and passing through the centers of the bases will give a reflection symmetry, along with the plane parallel to the bases and halfway down the cylinder.

    b. Do you see infinitely many rotational symmetries and infinitely many reflection symmetries? If not, reread the answer for part (a).

    c. Any line (or plane) through the center of the sphere will give a rotational (or reflection) symmetry.

4. See nets for shapes N and O.

5. a. Soda or soup can, hot dog with ends cut off squarely, and so on
    b. Some ice-cream cones or drinking cups or snow-cone containers, dunce hat, and so on

     c. Smooth balls (not footballs), meatballs, jawbreakers, the Earth (roughly) and other planets and their moons, and so on

     d. The equator, or any circle that passes through both the North and South Poles, and so on

6.   e. Not possible—every two great circles on a sphere will intersect.

7.   Cone

8.   a. If the layers are the same thickness, the whole cylinder would hold $22\frac{2}{3}$ cups.

     b. 66 ml (*Hint*: How much will $\frac{1}{4}$ of the cylinder hold? $\frac{4}{4}$?)

9.   a. The larger sphere has a diameter with a length twice the diameter of the smaller sphere.

     b. These are not intuitive results. Because the spheres are similar, the volume of the larger is $2^3 = 8$ times as large as that of the smaller, and the surface of the larger is $2^2 = 4$ times as large as that of the smaller.

10. a. Circles or ellipses, if the resulting cylinder is a circular cylinder

     b. Two of the open curves may be of different types if the cutting plane is or is not parallel to some position of the generating lines.

11. a. Right circular cylinder

     b. They are.

12. one long connected piece with two loops like a figure eight.

Supplementary Learning Exercises for Section 21.2

1.   a. Your great circles should appear to meet each other at the ends of a diameter.

     b. Your cone should be a right circular cone.

     c. The vertex of your cone should not be right over the center of the base.

     d. Start with a curve such as the one in Figure 1 in Section 21.2.

2.   For example, look at your hand (as well as things outside your body).

3.   Something like the drawing in Learning Exercise 18(a) in Section 25.2, although you may have put in the hidden edge of the base and some other curves or line segments.

4.   a. To fill the rest of the container requires another $\frac{1}{4}$ of the container. Because $2\frac{1}{2}$ cups fill $\frac{3}{4}$ of the container, $\frac{1}{3}$ of $2\frac{1}{2}$ cups would fill the other $\frac{1}{4}$ of the container. $\frac{1}{3} \times 2\frac{1}{2} = \frac{5}{6}$ cup to fill the rest of the container. (A drawing might help.)

     b. $2\frac{1}{2} + \frac{5}{6} = 3\frac{1}{3}$ cups for the whole container (or from another way of thinking, $4 \times \frac{5}{6} = 3\frac{1}{3}$ cups), so $\frac{1}{2} \times 3\frac{1}{3} = 1\frac{2}{3}$ cups for half the container.

Answers for Chapter 22: Transformation Geometry

22.1 Some Types of Rigid Motions

1. Mirror image = reflection image; slide = translation; flip = reflection in a line; turn = rotation about a point.

2. a. *B* reflection, *C* translation, *D* rotation, *E* rotation, *F* translation, *G* glide-reflection

    b. Each is congruent to shape *A* because it is the image of *A* for a rigid motion.

3. a. Translation (unless you focus on the wheels only)

    b. Rotation   c. Translation (if the slide is straight)

    d. Rotation   e. Rotation

    f. Rotation   g. Glide-reflection

4.

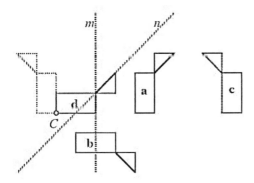

    e. Each is congruent to the original because each is the image of the original for some rigid motion.

5. a. Translations leave the orientation unchanged.

    b. Rotations leave the orientation unchanged.

    c. Reflections change the orientation.

    d. Glide reflections change the orientation.

6. All make sense for 3D shapes.

7. There are at least 14. Decision making likely involves all the rigid motions. (Instructor: Following is an attempt to be systematic, building all 2-triangle ones and 3-triangle ones and then using the 3-triangle ones to build the 4-triangle ones.)

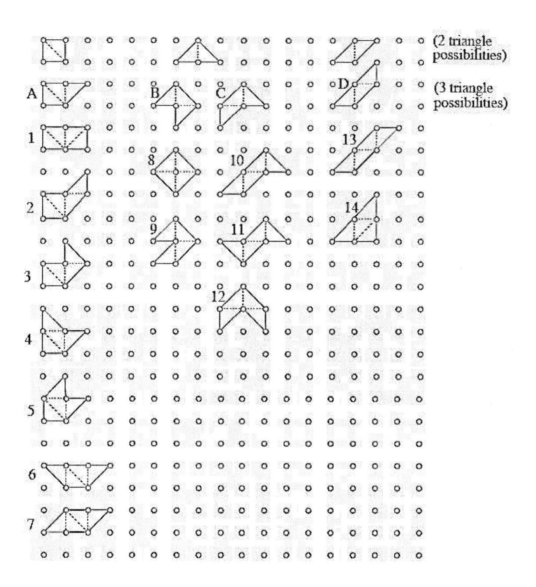

Supplementary Learning Exercises for Section 22.1

1. a. Translation, rotation, reflection, glide-reflection (Could you name them without referring elsewhere?)

    b. ...is a movement that does not change lengths or angle sizes.

2. The lengths of the sides of the image will be the same as those in the original (2 cm, 2.5 cm, 4.45 cm, and 3 cm), and the angle sizes will be the same also (90°, 148°, 54°, and the 68° size not given in the original).

3. Decisions might be based on eye-sight, key ideas, or orientation as an aid.

    original → A, reflection   original → B, reflection

    original → C, rotation   original → D, translation

original → E, rotation   original → F, glide-reflection

4. The same orientation for original and each of images (C), (D), and (E). The opposite orientation for original and each of images (A), (B), and (F).

5. Parts (a)–(d) below. (e) Each image is congruent to the original, because they are related by a rigid motion.

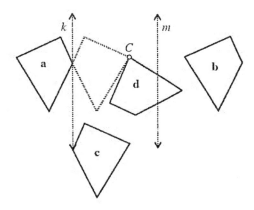

6. B. 180 degree rotation of A; C. Translation; D. Reflection of A; E. Glide-reflection; F. Translation; G. Reflection; H. Translation

22.2 Finding Images for Rigid Motions

1 and 2. Visual checks usually reveal whether images have been located correctly. Rotation images are the most difficult for many people.

3. Answers will vary.

4.

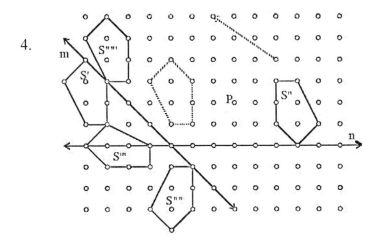

5.

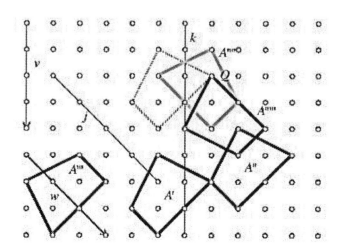

6.

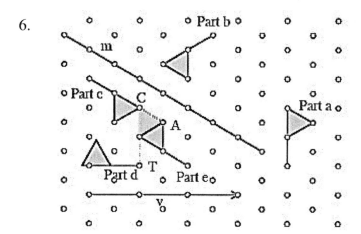

7.

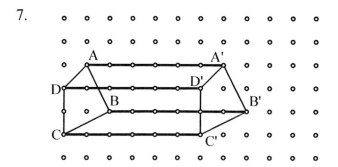

Each of the segments is 6 spaces long. (And each is directed toward the east.)

8.   a. The segments are not all the same length. Points farther from the center have to "travel" farther than do points closer to the center.

b.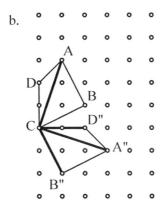

$\overline{CA}$ and $\overline{CA}''$ have the same length, as do $\overline{CB}$ and $\overline{CB}''$, and $\overline{CD}$ and $\overline{CD}''$. This makes sense for a rotation because each point should stay its distance from the center, C.

c. Each of the angles is 90°. This result makes sense for a rotation, because each point "travels" through the same angle.

9.   The segments can have different lengths, but each is perpendicular to the line of reflection.

10.   Choices (a), (d), and (g) all give the same translation. Choices (c), (e), (f), and (i) all describe another translation.

11.   Parts (c) and (d) will have the same effect on every point of the plane; turning 180° one clock direction will cause a shape to end up in exactly the same place as going 180° in the other clock direction.

12. a. Horizontal, vertical, and diagonal lines through points allow for easy reflection.
    b. 90°,180°,270°

13. a. How far it is moving and in what direction (formally, vector)
    b. Distance from a line of reflection
    c. Degree (and agreed direction) of rotation about which point

Supplementary Learning Exercises for Section 22.2

1.   Usually, you can tell from your work whether the image looks correct and is in the correct place.

2.   Only the first two points of the images are labeled.

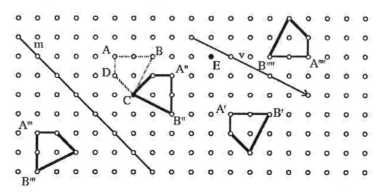

3.   Here is a sample exercise with answers. None of the vertices in the images are labeled. Can you label them with confidence?

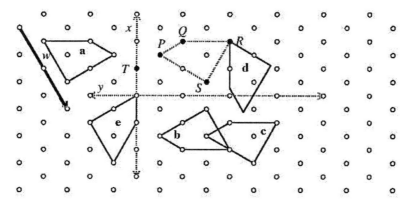

4.   Yes. Each has the effect of leaving the point where it was initially, no matter what the intermediate movement was.

5.   Each describes the same movement: move 3 cm straight to the right.

22.3 A Closer Look at Some Rigid Motions

1.   Again, your eyes usually tell you whether the result is all right, keeping in mind that most people have more trouble with rotations.

2.   a. The vector should *end* at the figure to the left. Which shape is the original does matter because the direction of the vector is opposite if the other figure is chosen as the original.

    b. For a reflection, either shape as the original gives the same line of reflection.

    c. The clock direction of the angle depends on which shape is the original.

    d. Notice that this reflection is one of the lines of symmetry.

3.   a. Reflection in line m (see the following diagram; construction marks not shown)

b. Translation with vector v

c. Reflection in line n

d. Rotation, center D, angle about 120° counterclockwise

e. Rotation, center E, angle 180°

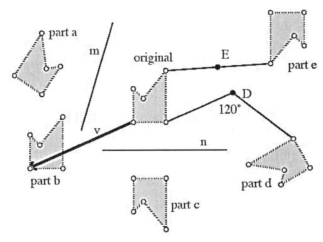

4. a. Every point on line *k* is a fixed point.

b. There are no fixed points.

c. and d. There is one fixed point, namely...

e. Every point is a fixed point, for the 360° rotation.

5. a. and b.

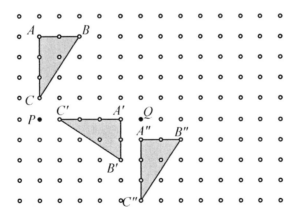

c. A translation...

6. a. Line *n*   b. $\overrightarrow{BC}$ is the reflection in line *k* of $\overrightarrow{BA}$ and vice versa.

Supplementary Learning Exercises for Section 22.3

1. If you have doubts about your results, have someone else look at them.

2.

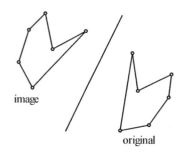

3.

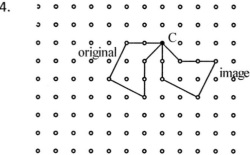

4.

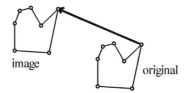

Center C, 90° counterclockwise

5. Rotation with center at the common vertex, angle 120° counterclockwise (or 240° clockwise).

6. a. and b.

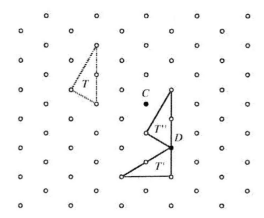

c. A translation, 3 diagonal spaces in a roughly south-easterly direction

22.4 Composition of Rigid Motions

1. Lines k and m are perpendicular to the direction of the translation (and therefore are parallel) and are 1 cm apart. Note that 1 cm is one-half the 2 cm.

2. a. Translation, 1.2 cm east

   b. Translation, 3 cm southwest

   c. Translation.... (Instructor: The vector has length twice the distance between the parallels, and direction perpendicular to the parallels, from first line of reflection toward second.)

   d. Rotation.... (Instructor: The center of the rotation is the intersection of the lines of reflection; the angle size is twice the angle made by the intersecting lines, from the first line toward the second.)

   e. Rotation... (unless $x = y$) (Instructor: Center P, angle size $(x + y)$ degrees, clockwise.)

   f. Rotation... (Instructor: Center P, angle size $|a - b|$ degrees, with the direction depending on which of a and b is greater.)

   g. Rotation.... (Instructor: Without more theory, the center can be located only visually or by using the original and final shapes, but the angle of the rotation will be 110° clockwise. As in Exercise 5(b) of Section 22.3, with different centers and sum of angles algebraically = 0, the composition is a translation.)

   h. Reflection in a different line through T (Instructor: More theory would enable us to describe the location of the line of reflection exactly, without using the original and final shapes.)

   i. Glide-reflection (Instructor: More theory would enable us to describe the location of the glide-reflection exactly, without using the original and final shapes.)

3. a. A glide-reflection changes the orientation of a figure.

   b. Translations and rotations do not change the orientation of a figure, but reflections and glide-reflections do.

   c. The image will be congruent to the original because each of the motions making up a glide-reflection gives a figure congruent to its original.

4. a. A translation or a rotation (Each of the originals keeps the orientation the same, so their composition will also.)

   b. A translation or a rotation

   c. A translation or a rotation

    d. A single reflection or a glide-reflection

    e. Even: translation or rotation; odd: reflection or glide-reflection

    f. A reflection or a glide-reflection, because...

5.   a.

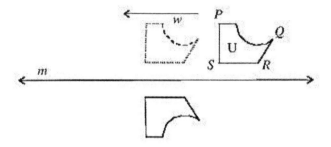

    b. The line of reflection appears to pass through the midpoints of the segments.

6.   a. In general, yes. For example, ... (try two reflections)

    b. Order does not matter for two motions defining a glide-reflection. (That is why the definition demands that the line of reflection and the vector of the translation be parallel.)

7.   a. Rotation, because the orientations are the same, and a translation won't work. (You may also have just "eyeballed" it.)

    b. Reflection, because...

    c. Translation, because...

    d. Reflection, because...

    e. Glide-reflection, because...

8. $Q'R'S'T'$ by a glide-reflection; $Q''R''S''T''$ by a rotation.

9.   a. Your two lines of reflection should be perpendicular to the line of the vector, and half the vector's length apart.

    b. Your two lines of reflection should intersect at the center of the rotation; the angle they make will be half the size of the angle of the rotation.

    c. Perhaps surprisingly, there are many possibilities in each case.

11.   Any rigid motion is one of these: reflection, translation, rotation, or glide-reflection. Each of translation/rotation can be achieved by the composition of two reflections

(Exercises 9 and 10), and a glide-reflection can be achieved by the composition of three reflections (two for the translation, plus the separate reflection of the glide-reflection).

12. a. 1 or 3 reflections   b. 2 reflections

13. a. Glide-reflection   b. Translation   c. Glide-reflection

    d. Rotation

    e. Rotation or translation, depending on the type of tuner (dial or lever)

    f. Rotation or translation, depending on the type of thermostat

14. No. (For our purposes, the translation has a nonzero vector, so reflections and glide-reflections are different.)

15. The rigid "motion" that leaves every point in the same place; this is legitimate, even though no net motion results. (Instructor: You may have introduced the idea of the identity transformation.)

16. The composition will be a single reflection. The line of reflection will be parallel to the other lines. If the original lines are, from the left, x units and y units apart, with $x > y$ and the composition is done starting at the right, then the composition line will be y units to the right of the third line of reflection (or x units to the left of the first line of reflection).

Supplementary Learning Exercises for Section 22.4

1. Translation, rotation, reflection, and glide-reflection (Did you answer without referring elsewhere?)

2. The translation

3. a. Translation 2 in. north

    b. Translation 2 in. north   Notice that order does not matter with translations.

    c. Rotation 10° counterclockwise, center C

    d. Rotation 10° counterclockwise, center C (Notice that order does not matter with rotations that have the same center.)

4. a. Given → (A) by a translation (Can you draw the vector?)

    b. Given → (B) by a rotation

    c. Given → (C) by a rotation

    d. Given → (D) by a glide-reflection

    e. Given → (E) by a reflection (Can you locate the line of reflection?)

5.   a. Did you do the translation first?

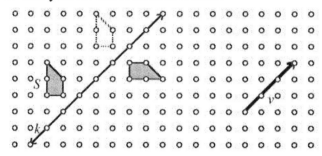

b. A glide-reflection

c. Even though the intermediate step (from the reflection) would give a different location for the image, the final image would be exactly the same.

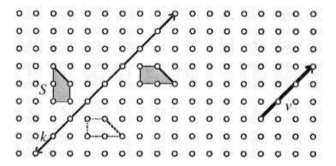

6.   Each leaves every point in its same location. (They describe the same *function*.)

22.5 Transformations and Earlier Topics

1.   a. There are many translation symmetries, as well as many reflection symmetries. Describe several of the translation symmetries.

b. There are many translation symmetries, as well as many rotational, reflection, and glide-reflection symmetries.

2.   The first statement in each part is the only true one.

3.   a. (Two, yes, two) reflection symmetries, (two) rotational symmetries (counting the 360° rotation)

b. (Only one) reflection symmetry

c. Reflection, rotational, translation, glide-reflection

d. (One) reflection symmetry

5.   a. There are several different translation symmetries, as well as reflection and rotational symmetries. There are also glide-reflection symmetries.

b. Several translation symmetries

c. Several translation symmetries

d. Several translation symmetries; several 180° rotational symmetries

6. *Hint*: What is the size of the third angle in each triangle? (Instructor: (a) and (d) are similar, as are (b) and (c).)

7. The image will be congruent to the original shape.

8. a. Yes, just use the reverse of the rigid motion.

b. Yes, use a 360° rotation.

c. Yes, use the composition of the two rigid motions.

9. a. Yes,…

b. Yes, use a scale factor of 1.

c. Yes,…

10. For example, two equilateral triangles with sides of different lengths. The triangles will be similar.

11. a. Each of the triangles is similar to each of the others. Any will tessellate the plane.

b. The shape has 6 reflection symmetries and 6 rotational symmetries. It will tessellate the plane.

c. The shape has 6 rotational symmetries, but no reflection symmetries.

d. It is likely to have translation symmetries, and perhaps other sorts. It will tessellate the plane.

12. Two rectangles with dimensions not related by the same ratios

Supplementary Learning Exercises for Section 22.5

1. a. Translation symmetries, by moving the shape to the right or left by (multiples of) the distance from the left-hand start of a semicircle to the right-hand end of a triangle. Reflection symmetries with lines of reflection perpendicular to the line the figures are resting on and through the top of a semicircle or a bottom vertex of a triangle. (There are no rotational or glide-reflection symmetries.)

b. Translation symmetries, by moving the shape to the right or left by (multiples of) the length of the side of the triangle. Reflection symmetries with lines of reflection perpendicular to the line the triangles are resting on and through a vertex of a triangle. Reflection symmetries with lines of reflection perpendicular to the line the triangles are resting on and through the point of intersection at the base of the triangles. (There are no rotational or glide-reflection symmetries.)

c. Translation and reflection symmetries as in part (b). Rotational symmetries of 180° with centers at either vertex of the triangle on the line the triangles are resting on. Glide-reflection symmetries from reflecting in the line the triangles are resting on and translating by (multiples of) the side of the triangle to the right or left.

2.   Answers will vary.

3.   The final image will be a rectangle, 15 cm by 20 cm. We can't say anything about its location or orientation without knowing more about its original orientation and the location of point *C*.

4.   Did you see rotational and reflection symmetries? Did you see a possible tessellation with the shape? Each of these involves transformations.

22.6 Issues for Learning: Promoting Visualization in the Curriculum

1.   a. Circles or, more precisely, circular regions. An occasional orange may give some elliptical cross-sections as well.

   b. Circles (circular regions), 2D pear shapes, and a flatter pear shape with a slanted cut

2.

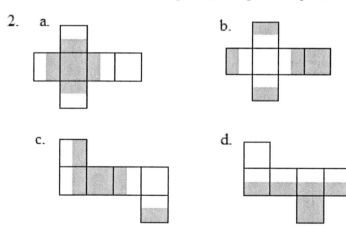

3.   The top part of the second drawing is off. Like the original play area, the child's drawing is symmetric about a vertical line; unlike the original, it is not symmetric about a horizontal line. Holding the shape in memory while changing its location was apparently difficult.

4.   All three shapes are the same. It might be interesting to compare how others approached the exercise.

5 and 6. Answers will vary.

7. Here are two possible core squares. Are they different from each other? If you found another possible core square, are you certain it is different?

Answers for Chapter 23: Measurement Basics

23.1 Key Ideas of Measurement

1. a. Length   b. Volume, although weight could conceivably be used

    c. Temperature   d. Weight   e. Area

    f. Speed   g. Time   h. Area

    i. Area   j. Your ideas, besides student achievement?

2. (Other correct answers are possible.)

    a. Yards, feet, inches, centimeters (!), millimeters (!!)

    b. Milliliters, or ounces if weight is used

    c. Degrees Fahrenheit or degrees Celsius

    d. Grams or ounces

    e. Square centimeters or square inches

    f. Meters per second or yards per second

    g. Minutes

    h. Square meters or square yards

    i. Square meters or square yards

    j. Students' scores on tests or students' later success rate or…

3. a. Temperature, height (by using the thermometer as a length unit)

    b. Height, weight, mathematics achievement

    c. Running speed, walking speed, respiration rate—all of which involve measuring other quantities as well

4. a. Barometric pressure   b. Population density   c. Area

    d. 24 (sometimes 25) sheets of paper   e. Area (used for land)   f. Length (about 18 inches)   g. Luminous intensity   h. Weight   i. Electrical charge

    j. Viewership   k. Intensity of sound   l. Hotness of peppers   m. General fitness

    n. Area (640 acres, or 1 square mile)

5. a. The stretchiness of a rubber band might lead to an inconsistent unit, in repeating it.

    b. The ice cube would melt, leaving no permanent unit for later use.

    c. "One person's junk is another person's treasure," so the unit would have different values depending on who was using it.

      d. You have perhaps read about perception experiments in which people's judgments of relative temperature were vastly influenced when one finger was in hot water, as compared to when the same finger was in cold water.

      e. The actual amount in a pinch likely varies from person to person.

      f. Different people, or even the same person at a more thirsty time, likely would have differently sized sips.

6.   a. Real-life length measurements cannot be 100% exact.

      b. The fish could weigh as little as $122\frac{1}{2}$ pounds and up to $123\frac{1}{2}$ pounds.

7.   a. Show segments as short as $6\frac{1}{2}$ units and up to $7\frac{1}{2}$ units.

      b. Show segments as short as $7\frac{1}{4}$ units and up to $7\frac{3}{4}$ units in length.

8.   a. Most likely not, because a measurement of 151.0 to the nearest half-pound covers a range of possible values (as light as 150.75 or as heavy as up to 151.25).

      b. 161.75 pounds $\le$ a possible weight $<$ 162.25 pounds

      c. 128.25 pounds $\le$ a possible weight $<$ 128.75 pounds

      d. Both 116.0 pounds and 223.5 pounds could be as much as 0.25 pounds off.

9.   a. $x > 2000$ because it would take more than 2000 raisins to weigh 2000 pounds.

      b. $x > 2000$ because a raisin's weight is smaller than a pound.

      c. $x > 2000$ because…

      d. $x < 2000$ because…

      e. $x < 2000$ because…

      f. $x > 2000$ because…

      g. $x < 2000$ because…

      h. $x > 2000$ because…

10. a. The ap unit is larger than the ag because it takes fewer aps to equal 150 ags.

      b. The ba unit is larger than the bo because… (*Hint:* Recall that $1.31 \times 10^3 = 1310$.)

      c. The cin unit is larger than the con because…

11. Weigh yourself holding the puppy, and then...

12. a. $8\frac{1}{2}$ units, by counting repetitions of the unit; "cutting" the region into individual and part units and totaling them

      b. 8 units, by...   *Hint* for exact reasoning:

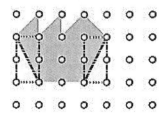

c. $6\frac{1}{2}$ units, by...

d. 4 units, by…

e. $2\frac{1}{8}$ new units, because...; 2 new units because...; $1\frac{5}{8}$ new units because...

13. Probably 8 × \$2.89 = \$23.12, because some leftover pieces from a section would be too short to be useful elsewhere.

14. a. $17\frac{1}{8}$ inches

    c. $5\frac{5}{8} + 7\frac{13}{16} + 3\frac{1}{4} = 16\frac{11}{16}$ inches

    d. Just under $5\frac{7}{8} + 7\frac{15}{16} + 3\frac{3}{4} = 17\frac{9}{16}$ inches

    e. From $16\frac{11}{16}$ inches to just under $17\frac{9}{16}$ inches (whereas the part (a) length would incorrectly imply the more narrow range of possible lengths between $17\frac{1}{16}$ inches and $17\frac{3}{16}$ inches).

15. The individual scores given could have been as low as 81.5, 72.5, and 86.5, giving a sum of 240.5. The 240.5 would have been shown as 241.

16. a. 0.763   b. 270   c. 1.9   d. 46.2

    e. 620   f. 0.108   g. 87   h. 2.9

    i. 1.55

17. a. 1300 ms

    b. 143×10^{-9} s = 1.43×10^{-7} s

    c. 0.500 s or 0.5 s

    d. 2.5×10^{-3} s

18. a. 0.1532 kg

    b. 3400 mg

    c. 2170 g

    d. 0.056 g

19. a. 80 km   b. 15 cm

20. 1

21. Even within one country at that time, from community to community there were likely to be different systems of measurement. Hence, the idea of a single system would involve an almost incredible changing of established practices.

22. *Correct*: Only parts (a) and (d). *Hints*: The calculations are done as though the relationships are base-ten relationships, but 1 hour = 60 minutes, not 100; 1 pound = 16 ounces, not 10; 1 gallon = 4 quarts, not 10.

23. Rather than what appears to be a random collection of terms, as in the given list, the metric system uses prefixes with a basic term for all of its units of a particular type.

24. a. 16
    b. In order, starting with mouthful: $\frac{1}{64}, \frac{1}{32}, \frac{1}{16}, \frac{1}{8}, \frac{1}{4}, \frac{1}{2}, 1, 2, 4, 8, 16, 32, 64, 128, 256, 512, 1024$

    c. Units are related by powers of the same number. 2 is used instead of 10.

25. About $0.9144018 - 0.9144 \approx 0.0000018$ meter shorter

26. Web assignment

Supplementary Learning Exercises for Section 23.1

1. More than 7 units. It takes more of a smaller unit to equal a certain number of a larger unit.

2. You do not know whether the "glasses" for you and your friend were the same size.

3. a. and b. Measurements, except for counts, are only approximations. Eyesight and especially limits of the measuring tool mean measurements should not be considered "exact."

4. a. Shortest: $2\frac{1}{2}$ units; longest: just under $3\frac{1}{2}$ units
   b. Shortest: $3\frac{1}{4}$ units; longest: just under $3\frac{3}{4}$ units

5. a. Greater than 100. A meter is shorter than a kilometer, so it will take more meters to make a given number of kilometers.

   b. Less than 100. A kilometer is longer than a meter, so it will take fewer kilometers to make a given number of meters.

   c. Greater than 100. An ounce is smaller than a pound, so it will take more ounces to make a given number of pounds.

d. Less than 100. A pound is greater than an ounce, so it will take fewer pounds to make a given number of ounces.

6. a. 4   b. 30   c. $\frac{5}{8}$ (0.6 is sometimes used)   d. 8

7. a. 0.49   b. 120   c. 49 000   d. 0.049

    e. 520   f. 5.2

8. a. 512 megabytes = 512 000 000 bytes

    b. 4 gigabytes = 4 000 000 000 bytes

    c. 2 terabytes = 2 000 000 000 000 bytes

9. a. 3 lb 13 oz (because 1 pound = 16 ounces)

    b. 3.7 kg (Notice that the basic relationships in SI mesh well with decimal arithmetic.)

    c. 2 yd 2 ft 7 in (because 1 yd = 3 ft and 1 ft = 12 in.)

    d. 3.58 m (Again, notice how easy the arithmetic is with metric units.)

    e. 1 gal 3 qt (because 1 gallon = 4 quarts)

    f. 2 hours and 45 minutes

23.2 Length and Angle Size

1. Recall that measurements are not exact, so answers close to those given likely reflect a correct approach. (Production processes also can change lengths slightly.)

    a. ≈ 31.4 cm   b. ≈ 10.6 cm   c. ≈ 10.8 cm

    d. A: about 20 cm; B: 2 faces each—about 14.4 cm, 18.2 cm, 15.4 cm

2. Measurements are approximate.

3. Any segment with length ≥ 6.25 cm but < 6.5 cm would fit the conditions.

4. Try doing these mentally, if you did them with paper and pencil.

    a. $3\frac{3}{4}$ inches   b. $3\frac{3}{8}$ inches   c. $3\frac{9}{16}$ inches

5. Answers will vary.

6. a. 9 cm   b. 6 cm   c. 0.5 cm   d. 2 cm

    h. Just under 2.5 cm, if you do not have a quarter handy

    i. Almost 28 cm

    j. About 99 cm, or about 1 m

7. Remember that the sides have to fit together to make a polygon: 1 cm, 1 cm, 1 cm, and 21 cm would be impossible. The complete answers are not given here.

   a. Try to be systematic, possibly this way: 6-6-6-6; 5-6-6-7; 4-6-6-8; 3-6-6-9; 2-6-6-10; 1-6-6-11.

   b. 1, 11, 1, 11 cm; 2, 10, 2, 10 cm; 3, 9, 3, 9 cm; 4, 8, 4, 8 cm; 5, 7, 5, 7 cm; 6, 6, 6, 6 cm. Notice how much easier the problem is with a rectangle because the opposite sides must be the same length.

8. Experiment, gathering and organizing the data from several simpler, specific values for n (e.g., $n = 1$, $n = 2$, $n = 3$, etc.), and look for a pattern. Instructor: For n square regions, the maximum perimeter will be $2n + 2$, possibly justifying the general result by "seeing" the $2n + 2$ (n across the top and bottom, plus the 2 ends) for a long strip, or by thinking $2 \cdot 3 + 2(n - 2)$, or $1 + 2n + 1$.

9. a. By measuring the distance of the line segment perpendicular to the line(s) from the point to the line or from one parallel line to the other

   b. No, so long as the distance is measured along a perpendicular

10. The distance between the top and bottom parallel sides.

11. The ancient Greeks used this idea: The perimeter (and area) of the circle should be between the perimeters (and areas) of the outer and inner polygons.

12. a. 1200 m   b. 530 cm   c. 6.2 cm   d. 32.5 cm

    e. 3.35 cm + 4.25 cm = 7.6 cm. Remember that "3.4 cm" implies the measurement is accurate to the nearest tenth-centimeter.

13. 6 cm and a little more (perhaps 7 cm), using a 2-cm segment to measure with; 7 cm and a little more, using a 1-cm segment; just under 7 cm, using a 0.5-cm segment. The 0.5 cm segments fit very closely, so an estimate of just under 7 cm should be a good estimate.

14. a. About 90°   b. About 60°   c. About 145°

    d. Right angle a (or close to it), acute angle b, obtuse angle c. No straight angle is shown; are you clear about what a straight angle would look like?

15. Answers will vary and students will check their estimates.

16. a. 270°   b. 35/60, or 7/12, of 360° is 210°   c. 30°

    d. 174°   e. 360°   f. 540°   g. 618°   h. 8640°

17. 21,600 minutes, so 1,296,000 seconds. One second would then be $\frac{1}{1296000}$ of a full turn. (Instructor: 1 minute = 1 nautical mile, useful for ocean distances. Cf. Exercise 20.)

18. a. 17° 43' 37"   b. 46° 28' 43"   c. 54° 40'

19. *Hint*: 360 ÷ 15 =...

20. 25,000 ÷ 360 = about 69.4 mi per degree; 1.16 mi (a nautical mile) per min...; about 0.02 mi per s

21. Remember to check your drawings by measuring with a protractor.

22. a. $y = 180 - x$, so then ? = $180 - y = 180 - (180 - x) = 180 - 180 + x = x$.

b.

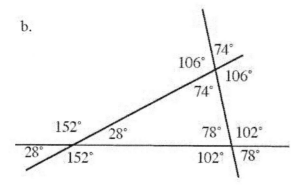

23. a. *a,e; b, f; c,g; d,h*

    b. No

    c. Corresponding angles of parallel lines appear to be the same size.

    d. The two pairs of alternate interior angles are *c, e* and *d, f.* If lines are parallel, the alternate interior angles are the same size.

24. (From vertical angles and the 180° for a straight angle) *e, g*: 128°; *f*: 52°; *h, j*: 75°; *i*: 105°. (From the parallel lines and vertical angles) *k, r*: 75°; *p, q*: 105°; *a, d*: 128°; *b, c*: 52°. (Using inscribed angles and alternate interior angles of parallels) *s* = 40°, *t* = 40°, *v* = 40°. Angle *u* intercepts the rest of the half-circle, or 100°, so *u* = 50°.

25. a. *Hint*: What are the sizes of the other angles at vertex *A*, in terms of *z* and *y*?

    b. 69°   c. 49°   d. 60° 38'

    e. 80° and 80°; 20° and 140°   f. 90°

26. *a* = *y; b* = *z; c* = *x*   *d* = *z; e* = *w; f* = *y; g* = *x*

27. a. Because the *n* angles total ... and they are all equal in size, each is ...

b. Your table should show these results: $3 \rightarrow 60°$; $4 \rightarrow 90°$; $5 \rightarrow 108°$; $6 \rightarrow 120°$; $7 \rightarrow 128$ $\frac{4}{7}°$; $8 \rightarrow 135°$; $9 \rightarrow 140°$; $10 \rightarrow 144°$; $11 \rightarrow 147\frac{3}{11}°$; $12 \rightarrow 150°$. Notice that the angle sizes are getting larger. How do you know that they will never equal $180°$?

c. The sizes get larger and larger, but they are less than $180°$. Instructor: If you have time, consider looking at a graph and/or the angle size expression, $\frac{(n-2)180}{n} = (1 - \frac{2}{n})180$.

d. *Hint*: $(n - 2)180 = 4500$ (Instructor: $n = 27$)

e. 16

28. a. and b. Focus on what must happen at a given vertex, and apply Learning Exercise 27(b).

29. a. If it were $360°$, it would be flat. (If it were more than $360°$, it would not be convex.)

b. What polygons give (same-sized) angles that will total less than $360°$ at a vertex? See Learning Exercise 27(b) and be sure to see whether there is more than one possibility for a given polygon.

c. *Hint*: See Learning Exercise 27(b) again.

30. The 1080 refers to the number of degrees in the turn the athlete can make when he or she is in air. So a 1080 refers to 3 full turns. Excellent athletes can do 720s and 900s as well.

31. $65° 35'$ (*Hint*: $120.25° = 120° +$ how many minutes?)

32. Look at $90°$ arcs on circles of quite different sizes.

33. For example, three consecutive angles at the blue point will give the result.

34. a. $120°, 90°, 72°, \dots$ b. *Hint*: See part (a).

35. a. $120°$ b. $55°$ c. $p + q$ degrees

36. The conventional way is to measure the angle formed by the two perpendiculars to the edge of the dihedral angle, at the same point on the edge, and with one in each plane making the dihedral angle.

37. *Hint*: Look at lots of multiples of 19. (Instructor: $14 \times 19 = 266$, $360 - 266 = 94$. Someone may notice $7 \times 19 = 133$, $180 - 133 = 47$, and ask about doubling that.)

38. a. Additive comparison: The 100-yd dash is 8.56 m (or 9.36 yd) shorter than the 100-m dash.

Multiplicative comparison: 100 yd:100 m = 0.9144:1, or

100 m:100 yd = 1:0.9144 = 1.0936:1

b. The mile run is about 109 meters (or about 120 yd) longer than the 1500-m run. The ratio 1760 yd:1500 m would most likely be given with the units the same. 1760 yd:1640 yd = ..., or 1609:1500.

39. a. 7040   b. $\frac{3}{4}$ c. $\frac{1}{4}$ d. 7920   e. 432   f. $2\frac{1}{3}$

40. a. College degree, temperature degree, extent ("to a degree"),...

b. Areas around a house,... c. Gas meter, parking meter,...

d. Usual or ordinary   e. Left angle

41. b. Although you can make definite assertions about the angles, you can say only that the ratios of lengths of corresponding sides will be equal; you do not know the value of that ratio.

42. a. 400

b. 0.009° (This is not a temperature, even though you may know that the Celsius temperature scale was once called the centigrade scale.)

43. 117 cm

44. a. The endpoints give a square. Each angle intercepts half the circle and so has size 90°. Rotate 90° to see that the sides have the same length.

b. A regular hexagon. Joining the points to the center of the circle shows 6 connected equilateral triangles, so each side of the hexagon has the same length, and the angle at each vertex is 120°.

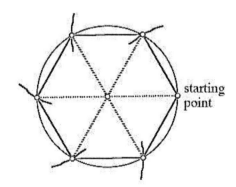

c. Octagon: Bisect the central angles in part (a); 12-gon: Bisect the central angles in part (b).

Supplementary Learning Exercises for Section 23.2

1.   Answers will vary.

2.   a. About 5 cm   b. About 10 cm or 1 dm   c. About 3 cm

3. The measurements appear to have been made to the nearest half inch. So the $3\frac{1}{2}$ in. could be as small as $3\frac{1}{4}$ in. or as long as up to $3\frac{3}{4}$ in., and the $4\frac{1}{2}$ in. could be as small as $4\frac{1}{4}$ in. or as long as up to $4\frac{3}{4}$ in. So the sum of the lengths might actually be as small as $3\frac{1}{4}+4\frac{1}{4}=7\frac{1}{2}$ in. or as long as up to $3\frac{3}{4}+4\frac{3}{4}=8\frac{1}{2}$ in. Notice that the potential "errors" add up.

4. a. 0.056   b. 560   c. 8.4   d. 0.084   e. 4500   f. $1\frac{1}{4}$

5. a. 5' 6" or 66"   b. 5.5 m   c. 14.28 cm   d. 25.48 cm   e. $34\frac{2}{3}$ yd

6. Good estimates would be in the vicinity of 135°, 75°, 170°, and 30°. "Good" might mean within 10° or 5°, depending on your experience.

7. Answers will vary.

8. a. 69°   b. 39° 43'   c. 66° 46' 48"   d. 169°   e. 75°, 105°, 105°
   f. 104°, 76°, 76°   g. 70°, 96.5°   h. 135° each   i. 156° each   j. 40°, 40°

9. $a, b, e, f = 139°$ $c, d, g = 41°$ $h, k, l, o = 69°$ $j, i, m, n = 111°$

10. $b = 104°$ $a = 360 - (104 + 136) = 120°$ $c = 68°$ $d = 60°$
    $e = 180°$ $f = 40°$ $g = 180°$ $h = 90°$ $i = 50°$ $j = 100°$
    $k = 64°$ $l = 168 - 52 = 116°$ $m = 116°$ $n = 96°$ $p = 116°$
    $q = 2 \cdot 50 - 56 = 44°$ $r = 2 \cdot 88 - 56 = 120°$ $s = 140°$ $t = 92°$ $u = 130°$

11. A whole (such as the circle) can be measured by cutting it into parts, measuring each of those, and adding those measures. For example, $360 = 136 + 104 + a$, so you could calculate a.

12. a. 42   b. 28

Answers for Chapter 24: Area, Surface Area, and Volume

24.1 Area and Surface Area

1.   a. $3\frac{1}{6}$ hexagonal regions, $6\frac{1}{3}$ trapezoidal regions; $9\frac{1}{2}$ rhombus regions

    b. $3\frac{1}{3}$ hexagonal regions; $6\frac{2}{3}$ trapezoidal regions; 10 rhombus regions

2.   a. 24 rhombus regions, because...

    b. $31\frac{1}{2}$ rhombus regions, because...

3.   Here are possibilities, if you cannot think of any: nail of little finger for square centimeter, VW Beetle door for square meter, floor of an ordinary classroom (10 m by 10 m, or roughly 30^+ ft by 30^+ ft).

4.   a. $6\,\mathrm{dm}^2$ b. Varies, perhaps $4\,\mathrm{cm}^2$

    c. Varies, perhaps 1 are, more likely in square meters

    d. Varies, square meters likely unit

    e. Varies, might be in dm^2 or m^2, depending on size

5.   a. $20 > x$, because if the measurements are equal, then it will take more of the smaller units to give an area equal to x of the larger units (or, ...it will take fewer of the larger units to make an area equal to 20 of the smaller units).

    b. $20 > x$, because…

    c. $20 > x$, because…

    d. $x > 20$, because…

    e. $y > x$, because...

    f. $x > y$, because…

    g. $\frac{24}{7}$ or $3\frac{3}{7}$ unit P's make 1 Q. $\frac{7}{24}$ Q makes 1 P.

    h. $\frac{8}{3}$ Q makes 1 R. $\frac{3}{8}$ R makes 1 Q.

    i. $\frac{3.7}{2.4}$, or $\frac{37}{24}$, or $1\frac{13}{24}$ blobs make 1 glob. $\frac{24}{37}$ glob makes 1 blob.

6.   a. 64 of Beth's unit, $10\frac{2}{3}$ of Cai's unit

    b. $2\frac{3}{8}$ of Al's unit, $1\frac{7}{12}$ of Cai's unit

    c. $9\frac{1}{2}$ of Al's unit, 38 of Beth's unit

7.   a. Your sketch should confirm, for example, that there are 144 square inches in 1 square foot. Hence, 1 square inch is $\frac{1}{144}$ of a square foot.

    b. 9 sq ft in a square yard; $\frac{1}{9}$ sq yd makes a square foot

c. *Hint*: There are 1760 yards in 1 mile.

Instructor: $1760 \times 1760 = 3,097,600$ square yards in a square mile

8. 640 acres in a square mile, perhaps from a dictionary or from $\frac{5280 \times 5280}{43,560}$

9. a. 230   b. 0.45   c. 0.196   d. 400

10. 10 m

11. a. ≈ 26 units   b. ≈ 13 units   c. ≈ 19 units   d. ≈ 24 units

12. a. 19 units   b. *Hint*: "Surround" the triangle with a rectangle. 10.5 units

   c. "Cut off" a slice from the left end and put it on the right end. 25 units

   d. 21 units   e. 26 units   f. 195 units

   g. 11 units   h. 8 units   i. $5\frac{1}{2}$ units   j. 15 units

13. a. Find the area of a lateral face, multiply by 8, and add twice the area of a base. (How did you find the area of the base?)

   b. Find the area of a lateral face, multiply by 6, and add the area of the base. (How did you find the area of the base?)

   c. Find the area of a face and multiply that by 8.

14. a. 104 units   b. 82 units

15. See Exercise 4 in Section 21.2, or nets N and O in the appendix.

16. No. The second one has area 16 square meters.

17. Answers will vary.

18. First region: around 8.8 cm^2; second region: around 6.2 cm^2

19. a. The different sizes are $\frac{1}{4}$ (regions I), $\frac{1}{8}$ (III, IV, V), and $\frac{1}{16}$ (regions II). Copying, cutting out the pieces, and moving them around should convince you.

   b. $11\frac{3}{4}$ area units (I), $5\frac{7}{8}$ area units (III, IV, V), and $2\frac{15}{16}$ area units (II)

   c. $1\frac{1}{6}$ area units (I), $\frac{7}{12}$ area unit (III, IV, V), and $\frac{7}{24}$ area unit (II)

20. ≈ 20 units. "Cutting" the region into pieces, getting an approximate measurement of each piece, and then totaling is one method.

21. a. Ollie is incorrect because… (*Hint*: See Learning Exercise 7(b).)

   b. 270 dm^2, 27000 cm^2, 2.7 m^2…

22. The original 64 squares now seem to fill 65 squares! This strange result would violate the cutting-up key idea. The secret is that the apparent diagonal of the rectangle is really a very thin but long region, with area 1 square region.

23. Your sketch should show that the original square centimeter now occupies 25 square centimeters.

24. a. 24,010 cm^2, because areas are related by the square of the scale factor.
    SA(larger) $= 7^2 \cdot 490$

    b. 10 cm^2, because...

    c. Not necessarily, because the pyramids are not similar (4:6 $\neq$ 6:8).

25. The scale factor is either 2 or $\frac{1}{2}$, depending on which region is the original, because the ratio of the two areas, 4 or $\frac{1}{4}$, is the square of the scale factor.

26. a. Add the lengths of the three sides of the rectangle, and half the circumference of the circle.

    b. Subtract half the area of the circular region from the area of the rectangular region.

27. Your work should show that figures with the same perimeter may not have the same area. (Instructor: Consider 1 by 3 and 2 by 2 rectangles.)

28. Each is incorrect, usually because of the inappropriateness of the unit for the quantity.

29. a. Double each answer in Learning Exercise 12: a-38, b-21, c-50, d-42, e-52, f-390, g-22, h-16, i-11, j-30.

    b. Divide each answer in Learning Exercise by 15: a-$1\frac{4}{15}$, b-0.7, c-$1\frac{2}{3}$, d-$1\frac{2}{5}$, e-$1\frac{11}{15}$, f-13, g-$\frac{11}{15}$, h-$\frac{8}{15}$, i-$\frac{11}{30}$, j-1

Supplementary Learning Exercises for Section 24.1

1. An $8\frac{1}{2}$ in. by 11 in. sheet has area about 6 dm^2 (using metric sense and envisioning dm^2 on the sheet), so 200 pages would have an area of about 1200 dm^2.

2. a. One J is $\frac{3}{4}$ as large as a K, so 30 J = $22\frac{1}{2}$ K. One J is $\frac{3}{5}$ as large as an L, so 30 J = 18 L.

   b. Similarly, 1 K = $1\frac{1}{3}$ J and 1 K = $\frac{4}{5}$ L. Hence, 30 K = 40 J = 24 L.

   c. As before, 1 L = $1\frac{2}{3}$ J and 1 L = $1\frac{1}{4}$ K, giving 30 L = 50 J = $37\frac{1}{2}$ K.

   d. From the above relationships, 17 J = $12\frac{3}{4}$ K = $10\frac{1}{5}$ L.

   e. As before, 17 K = $22\frac{2}{3}$ J = $13\frac{3}{5}$ L.

   f. 17 L = $28\frac{1}{3}$ J = $21\frac{1}{4}$ K

   g. m J = $\frac{3}{4}m$ K = $\frac{3}{5}m$ L

   h. n K = $\frac{4}{3}n$ J = $\frac{4}{5}n$ L

i. $p\,L = \frac{5}{3}p\ J = \frac{5}{4}p\ K$

3. A drawing suggests that 1760 rows with 1760 yd^2 in each row make a square mile, so $1760 \times 1760 = 3{,}097{,}600$ yd^2.

4. 1 $mm^2 = 0.01$ cm^2 (10 rows, with 10 mm^2 in each row make 1 cm^2)

5. a. 0.78   b. 1500

   c. 140   d. 14 000 (or 14,000)

   e. 1.28   f. 260

6. "Surrounding" the polygon or a part of its region with a rectangle may help.

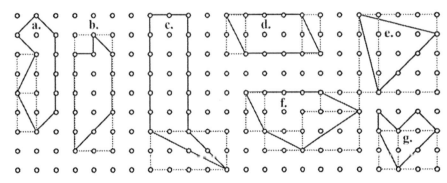

   a. 8 units   b. $8\frac{1}{2}$ units   c. 14 units   d. 8 units

   e. $16 - (2 + 2 + 4\frac{1}{2}) = 7\frac{1}{2}$ units   f. 11 units   g. $4\frac{1}{2}$ units

7. a. One way: top-bottom views, 2 units each; right-left faces, 6 units each, front-back, 4 units each. Total: 24 units

   b. One way: top-bottom views, 13 units each; right-left views, 9 units each; front-back views, 11 units each. Total: 66 units

8. a. $1.2^2 \cdot 72 = 103.68$ cm^2

   b. $\frac{72}{\text{smaller area}} = 1.2^2$, and so smaller area $= 72 \div (1.2)^2 = 50$ cm^2

9. The ratio of the areas is 1:9, so the scale factor could be 1:3 (or, if the original and final were switched, 3:1).

10. a. $(\frac{36}{4})^2 = 81$ (or 81:1)

    b. There are many values that have an 81 to 1 ratio (for example, 162 and 2, 243 and 3, 810 and 10, 90 and $1\frac{1}{9}$, 180 and $2\frac{2}{9}$, and so forth).

11. a. Double each answer in Supplementary Learning Exercise 6: a-16, b-17, c-28, d-16, e-15, f-22, g-9

b. Divide each answer in Supplementary Learning Exercise 6 by 8: a-1, b-$1\frac{1}{16}$, c-$1\frac{3}{4}$, d-1,

e-$\frac{15}{16}$, f-$1\frac{3}{8}$, g-$\frac{9}{16}$

24.2 Volume

1. The units given here are possible, but others can be defended. The important thing is that the units be of the correct kind and not too large or small. Units like km or cm^2 for the area of a lake are either not appropriate (km is for length) or sensible (cm^2 is too small).

    a. Volume, km^3 (possibly m^3)   b. Area, km^2 c. Length, m or dam

    d. Length, km   e. Area, m^2 or dam^2 or km^2

    f. Volume, m^3 g. Angle size, degrees   h. Volume, m^3

    i. Length, m   j. Volume, m^3 k. Volume, km^3

    l. Area, m^2 or dam^2 m. Length, m   n. Area, m^2

2. If you are stuck, here are some ideas: a portion of your little finger (1 cm^3, 1 mL), some plastic soda containers (1 dm^3, 1 L), a box for a large washing machine (1 m^3).

3. a. cm^3 b. mL, or cm^3 c. mm^3, possibly cm^3
    d. L or kL or m^3 e. dm^3 or cm^3 f. L

4. a. About 250 mL or 250 cm^3 b. About a liter (slightly less)
    c. About $\frac{1}{3}$ liter   d. Perhaps about 300 m^3

5. The usual piece of paper is about 28 cm by 21.5 cm, allowing only 2 dm across and 2 dm down. So the net would not fit. (Note that the area is 602 cm^2, but any arrangement of the squares in a net would not fit on the paper.)

6. a. $x > y$ b. $x < y$

7. These are important for classroom work.

    For part (a), to see the 1000 cubic centimeters in a cubic decimeter, show the 10 cubic centimeters in 1 row, then the 100 in the 10 rows in one layer, then the 1000 in the 10 layers.

    b. 1000   c. 1000 (1 L = 1 dm^3)   d. 1 000 000

8. a. 0.001   b. 0.000001   c. 0.001 (Think metric.)

9. a. 10 times, 100 times, 1000 times
    b. 100 times, 10 000 times, 1 000 000 times

10. a. 3280   b. 32.8   c. 0.2257   d. 2.257

11. a. Your drawings should suggest that 1 cubic foot = 1728 cubic inches; 1 cubic yard = 27 cubic feet; OR 1 cubic inch = $\frac{1}{1728}$ cubic feet; 1 cubic foot = $\frac{1}{27}$ cubic yard.

b. 7.48 (often rounded to 7.5)

12. $\frac{7}{12}$ cup. The key idea is the thinking of the measurement of a whole amount in terms of measurements of its parts.

13. *Key to the second question*: Your answer to "Does *anything* include idealizations that exist just in the mind?"

14. a. Surface area = 150 square regions; volume = 108 cubic regions

   b. S.A. = 238 square regions; volume = 222 cubic regions

   c. S.A. = 160 square regions; volume = 105 cubic regions

   d. 108 mL, 222 mL, 105 mL, respectively (1 mL = 1 cm^3)

   e. No (1 L = 1000 mL or 1000 cm^3)

15. 1 gram, 1 gram

16. Most have surface area 18 square regions. (A 2 by 2 arrangement of cubes has a surface area = 16 square regions.)

17. a. Count by rows. 42 cubic regions; 40 cubic regions

   b. 42 square regions; 40 square regions (Instructor: As a preliminary to the $V = Bh$ formula later, point out that the answers in parts (a) and (b) are *numerically* the same.)

   c. The first (30 stories, each 42 cubic regions – 1260 cubic regions vs. 31 stories, each 40 cubic regions = 1240 cubic regions)

18. Six cubic regions in each layer, 5 layers = 30 cubic regions. Some additional partial cubic regions would be needed to fill in the rest—estimate 2 per layer. 40 cubic regions. Key ideas: measurements are approximate—thinking of a region in pieces, getting the measurement of each piece, and then adding those measurements to get the measurement of the whole thing.

19. a. $13\frac{1}{2}$ b. $1\frac{2}{3}$ c. $\frac{1}{2}$ d. $10\frac{2}{3}$

   e. 6   f. 8, 16   g. $\frac{7}{8}$ h. $9\frac{1}{3}$

   i. $\frac{3}{4}$ j. $\frac{2}{3}$ k. 48   l. $\frac{3}{16}$

20. a. Congruent shapes have the same measurements, so S.A. = 32 square regions and volume = 12 cubic regions for the first shape, and S.A. = 34 square regions, volume = 9 cubic regions for the second shape.

   b. Surface area of the hidden, larger version of the first shape = 800 square regions; volume = 1500 cubes. For the hidden, larger shape for the second one, S.A. = 850 square regions and volume = 1125 cubic regions.

21. a. 20 800 cm^2; 192 000 cm^3

   b. 2925 cm^2; 10 125 cm^3

   c. 53 248 cm^2; 786 432 cm^3

d. 6292 cm^2; 31 944 cm^3

Supplementary Learning Exercises for Section 24.2

1. a. 2000   b. 2000   c. 49
    d. 1300   e. 4 000 000 (or 4,000,000)   f. 1000

2. a. $4 \times 12^3 = 6912$ b. 1   c. 81

3. a. $x > y$. The dm^3 unit is smaller than the m^3 unit, so it takes more of them to equal a certain number of the larger unit.

    b. $x < y$. The dm^3 unit is larger than the cm^3 unit, so it takes fewer of them to equal a certain number of the smaller unit.

    c. $x < y$. The ft^3 unit is larger than the in^3 unit, so it takes fewer of them to equal a certain number of the smaller unit.

    d. $x > y$. The ft^3 unit is smaller than the yd^3 unit, so it takes more of them to equal a certain number of the larger unit.

4. a. 7 cubes   b. 31 cubes

    c. 7 mL and 31 mL, because 1 cm^3 = 1 mL

    d. 7 ft^3 and 31 ft^3. Because 1 yd^3 = 27 ft^3, the part (b) polyhedron has volume greater than 1 yd^3.

5. With luck, you would have some cubes of the same size at hand (and perhaps a small empty box). You might say, "The volume of something is the number of these cubes that it would take to fill it, or to make a shape just like it. Let's see what the volume of this box is."

6. a. First shape: S.A. = 20 units, V = 5 cubes

    Second shape: S.A. = 68 units, V = 24 cubes

    b. Image of first: S.A. = $6^2 \times 20 = 720$ units, V = $6^3 \times 5 = 1080$ cubes

    Image of second: S.A. = $6^2 \times 68 = 2448$ units, V = $6^3 \times 24 = 5184$ cubes

7. a. S.A. = $2^2 \times 856 = 3424$ cm^2, V = $2^3 \times 1.68 = 13.44$ L
    b. S.A. = $(\frac{2}{3})^2 \times 856 = 380\frac{4}{9}$ cm^2, V = $(\frac{2}{3})^3 \times 1.68 = \frac{8}{27} \times 1.68 = \frac{8}{9} \times 0.56 = \frac{4.48}{9} \approx 0.498$ L

    c. S.A. = $10^2 \times 856 = 85\ 600$ cm^2 (or 85,600 cm^2), V = $10^3 \times 1.68 = 1680$ L

    d. S.A. = $0.1^2 \times 856 = 8.56$ cm^2, V = $0.1^3 \times 1.68 = 0.00168$ L (or 1.68 mL)

24.3 Issues for Learning: Measurement of Area and Volume

1. a. They might have counted the visible square regions.

    b. *One possibility*: Double the count as in part (a), for the hidden parts. Or, count the 4 in front, double for the back, giving 8. Do the same for the right and left sides, for another 8. Finally, get another 8 for the top 4, plus 4 for the bottom.

    c. The counts for the right and left are counting cubes that have been counted already.

2. a. For example, the 9 in the front and the 12 on the right both count the 3 cubes at the front right corner.

    b. The student is overlooking the cubes in the inner, middle columns.

Answers for Chapter 25: Counting Units Fast: Measurement Formulas

25.1 Circumference, Area, and Surface Area Formulas

1. Answers will vary.

2. a. 5π cm, or 15.7 cm

    b. 320π km, or 1004.8 km, or 1005 km. (So this is about $1005 \times 1000 \times 100$ cm, or about 1.005×10^8 cm.)

    Instructor: If the reproducing process has altered the dimensions, these answers for (c) and (d) may not be correct. No answers for (b) and (d).

    c. The radius is about 3 cm, so $C = 6\pi$ cm, or 18.8 cm, or about 19 cm.

    d. 10 cm + 2π cm, or 16.3 cm

3. 3981 miles; 7962 miles (often referred to as 4000 miles and 8000 miles). *Note:* Earth is not a perfect sphere but is often treated as such.

4. a. $\frac{22}{7} \approx 3.1428571$, so...   b. 0.038 cm

    c. The radius of the orbit is 200 miles more than Earth's radius, or about 4181 miles. Then the difference from the calculations with the two approximations of π is 13.3 miles, which might be important if there are people on the satellite. (How does the answer differ if you use 4000 miles as the radius? Are you surprised?)

5. c (The others are only approximations.)

6. 31.8 cm, or 32 cm

7. Perhaps surprisingly, all but humans taller than about 6′ 4" could walk under the rope, and the same result would apply on larger or many smaller spheres. The problem involves comparing the two radii: $\frac{C+40}{2\pi} - \frac{C}{2\pi} = \frac{40}{2\pi} \approx 6.37'$.

8. a. "Let's draw a parallelogram on graph paper. Check it out."

    b. "Remember how we put two triangles together to make a parallelogram? Then to find the area of one triangle, we had to take half the area of the parallelogram."

9. a. 12.16 cm^2

    b. 76.5 cm^2

    c. 54 cm^2

    d. 40 cm^2

    e. 20 cm^2 each, even though their areas may look different

10. Create a parallelogram region, and see how it is related to the triangular region.

11. Make sure that your heights make right angles with the sides. In the right triangle, *d* is the altitude for side *e*, and vice versa. Two of the heights for the obtuse triangle are outside the triangle, and the sides *i* and *g* must be extended to see the heights (but one would use just *g* and *i* as the bases, not the extensions).

12. It should not matter, but actual measurements may be off enough to make the calculated areas seem to be different. You should get the same area no matter which side you choose as base.

13. Each way should give an area of 24 square regions.

14. Each of the triangles has the same area, $7\frac{1}{2}$ units, even though the triangles may appear to the eye to have different areas. Because parallel lines are the same distance apart no matter where you measure it, the heights of all the triangles are the same (and the base is the same for each of them).

15. So long as the height is measured between the lines the bases are on, it does not matter where, as long as it is measured along a perpendicular.

16. Instructor: If the reproducing process has altered the dimensions, these answers may not be correct.

    a. 8.99 cm^2 b. 12.18 cm^2

    c. Cut each of the bases into 4 equal segments, and join them. (It will not be visually obvious; check with the formula.)

17. a. 62 square inches   b. The area is multiplied by 9: 558 in^2.

18. i. Shape a: 15 cm^2, Shape b: 30 cm^2, Shape c: 29.75 cm^2

    Shape d: 12.08 cm^2, Shape e: $4.5\pi + 9$, or about 23.1 cm^2

    Shape f: also 23.1 cm^2, Shape g: $12 + 4.5\pi$, or about 26.13 cm^2

    Shape h: $28 + 2\pi$, or about 34.28 cm^2

    ii. Shape i: Area $= mj + \frac{1}{2}(m + n)(k - j)$

    Shape j: Area $= \frac{1}{2}(pq + rs)$

    Shape k: *Hint*: Sketch in the rest of two opposite semicircles; then the radius $= \frac{1}{4}t$.

    Area = Area (two whole circular regions) + square region $= \cdots = \frac{\pi+2}{8}t^2$.

    Shape l: Area $= vw + \frac{1}{2}\pi\left(\frac{v}{2}\right)^2 = \frac{\pi v^2}{8}$

iii. For shapes a, b, and i, the "slant" sides cannot be predicted at this time. (If you remember the Pythagorean theorem and if the shape is symmetric, as it appears to be, you can make progress.)

Perimeters: c—22.3 cm; d—14 cm; e and f—6π cm; g—$10 + 3\pi$ cm; h—$18 + 2\pi$ cm

Shape j: Perimeter $= p + q + r + s$

Shape k: Perimeter $= \pi t$

Shape l: Perimeter $= v + 2w + \pi\dfrac{v}{2}$

19. a. What are the areas of the two pizzas? (Assume that they have the same thickness.) The larger pizza is cheaper by the square inch. If you were surprised by the answer, put the smaller pizza on top of the larger one and look at a slice of each with the same central angle.

Instructor: Prices per square inch: smaller—13.9¢; larger—12.3¢. Surprised students may be focusing on just the difference in the diameters.

   b. No, the larger one costs about 15.1¢ per square inch, but the smaller costs only about 13.7¢ per square inch.

20. a. 12.56 cm^2

   b. 1 cm^2 for the first grid; 0.25 cm^2 for the second

   c. The second grid should give a better estimate, unless you are a fantastic estimator!

21. a. 48π or about 150.8 cm^2

   b. 13.824π or about 43.43 cm^2

   c. 80π or about 251.33 cm^2

   d. Look at the fraction $\frac{\text{size of central angle}}{360}$; that will tell you what part of the whole circular region the sector is. Multiply that fraction by the area of the whole circle, πr^2.

   e. This time, consider $\frac{\text{actual length of arc}}{\text{whole circumference}}$, or $\frac{\text{actual length of arc}}{2\pi r}$. Multiply that fraction by the area of the whole circle. Continuing, you get
   $\frac{\text{actual length of arc}}{2\pi r} \times \pi r^2 = \frac{\text{actual length of arc}}{2} \cdot r$, or $\frac{1}{2}(\text{length of arc}) \cdot r$. If the length of the arc is labeled s, $A(\text{sector}) = \frac{1}{2}sr$, with a pleasing resemblance to the formula for the area of a triangle.

   f. $24 + 8\pi$ or about 49.13 cm

g. 20 + 16π or about 70.27 cm (for part (c))

22. In the first figure, assuming that the side of the square is *s* units long (= the diameter of the circular region), the percent uncovered = 100% – the percent covered = 100% – $\frac{(\frac{s}{2})^2 \pi}{s^2}$ = 100% – $\frac{\pi}{4}$ ≈ 21.5%. In the second figure, ...

Instructor: A more elegant way is to cut the second and third regions into miniature versions of the first, and see that the percent uncovered is the same in each.

23. a. S.A. ≈ 200,000,000 or 2×10^8 sq. miles.

b. *One way*: The land area is about 30% of the total area, so find 30% of the S.A. from part (a): about 6×10^7 sq miles.

c. 10^8 sq. miles

24. a. Because the globes are similar, the ratio of their surface areas will be the square of the scale factor: $\left(\frac{16}{12}\right)^2 = \left(\frac{4}{3}\right)^2 = \frac{16}{9} \approx 1.78$. The larger globe has 1.78 times as much area as the smaller one does.

b. Smaller: 144π sq. in.; larger: 256π sq. in. (Does this agree with part (a)?)

25. a. 592 cm²

b. 35,200 cm², or 3.52 m²

c. $22\frac{1}{3}$ ft², or 3216 in.²

d. $2xy + 2xz + 2yz$, or $2(xy + xz + yz)$

26. 2880 cm²

27. The estimate could be improved by using narrower rectangles.

28. Look at the units that would result; neither the product nor the sum of four lengths would give square units.

29. a. 22.5 cm²   b. 156.25%   c. 56.25% (Why not 25%?)

30. Recall that the scale factor affects each length measurement. See what happens to the old length *and* the old width, so when you multiply the two new lengths, each involves a scale factor, giving (scale factor)² times the product of the old lengths. The areas of triangular regions are multiplied by k^2 also because each of the two length measurements in the formula introduces a factor of *k*.

31. a. See the right triangles?   b. Rhombuses and squares, because...

32. If you get stuck, look at $\frac{\text{No. of dots on}}{2}$ + no. of dots inside, which is close to the correct number. The final result that does give the area is called Pick's formula.
Instructor: $A = \frac{\#\text{ dots on}}{2} + \#\text{ dots inside} - 1$.

33. a. See the parallelogram region? How is its area related to the area of the triangle?

b. See the "short" rectangular region? What is its area?

34. b. The new parallelogram has the same area as the trapezoid; its base is $a + b$ and its height is $\frac{1}{2}h$.

c. The midline is the segment joining the midpoints of the sides that are not necessarily parallel; its length is half the sum of the lengths of the two parallel sides (that is, it is the average of the two).

35. a. A triangle
    b. $A(\text{triangle as special "trapezoid"}) = \frac{1}{2}(0+b)h = \frac{1}{2}bh$

36. a. The rectangle will have sides the lengths of the legs of the right triangle.
    b. "Cut" the general triangle into two right triangles.
    c. $(\frac{1}{2}bh) + (\frac{1}{2}ah) = \frac{1}{2}h(a+b)$

37. $A(\text{sphere})$ = area of the cylinder's curved surface (without the two bases of the cylinder)

Supplementary Learning Exercises for Section 25.1

1. The statement means that pi (π) cannot be expressed exactly as a terminating or repeating decimal, or equivalently, in the form $\frac{\text{integer}}{\text{nonzero integer}}$.

2. The date March 14 is often 3/14, resembling 3.14, an approximation for π.

3. For a rectangle, $A(\text{trapezoid}) = \frac{1}{2}h(a+b)$ becomes $A(\text{rectangle}) = \frac{1}{2}w(l+l) = lw$.

   For a rhombus, $A(\text{trapezoid}) = \frac{1}{2}h(a+b)$ becomes $A(\text{rhombus}) = \frac{1}{2}h(b+b) = bh$.

4. With 3.14 as an approximation for π, the diameter of the ball is given by $28.5 \approx 3.14d$, or $d \approx 28.5 \div 3.14 \approx 9.08$ in., so two balls at one time would take more than the 18 in. available.

5. a. 38.936 m　　　　b. 132 in.　　　　c. $12\pi + 24$, or about 61.7 cm
   d. 15.4π, or about 48.38 cm (*semi*-circles)　　e. $33 + 16.5\pi$, about 84.84 cm

6. a. $\pi 6.2^2$, about 120.8 m^2　　b. 1386 in^2　c. $144 + 36\pi$, or about 257.1 cm^2
   d. $\frac{1}{2}\pi 4^2 + \frac{1}{2}\pi 5^2 + \frac{1}{2}\pi 6.4^2 + \frac{1}{2} 8 \cdot 10 =$ about 80.98 cm^2

7. 49π is about two times 25π. Your cut-out circular region should make the result reasonable.

8. a. $220 + 73\pi$, or about 449.3 cm^2　　b. $240 - 144 = 96$ cm^2　c. $360 - 180 = 180$ cm^2
9. a. 7.2 m　　　　　　　b. 16 in.　　　　　　c. 3 cm
10. a. 2537.16 cm^2　　　　　b. 208 m^2

11. 950.4 cm^2 (The lateral faces are rectangular regions.)

12. a. 266π, or about 835.7 in^2 b. 1120π, or about 3518.6 cm^2

    c. (radius = 4 cm) 88π, or about 276.5 cm^2 d. (radius = 9 cm) 342π, or about 1074.4 cm^2

13. 2(220 + 73π) + (11π + 5π + 32)5, or 600 + 226π, or 1310 cm^2

14. From the description, the two boxes are similar with scale factor 1.5. So, *S.A.* of larger box = 1.5^2 · 236 = 531 in^2. *V* = 1.5^3 · 240 = 810 in^3.

15. Either $A = \pi a^2$ or $A = \pi b^2$. As the two values change to the same number, the ellipse becomes a circle, so the "new" formula is no surprise.

16. a. $\dfrac{12 \times 18}{9} = 24$ sq. yd; 24 ☐ $15.60 = $374.40

    b. $\dfrac{216}{13.1} \times 1.05 \approx 17.3$ bundles, so must buy 18 bundles at 13.1 × $2.99 = $39.17 per bundle or $705.06

    c. Allowing for door, window, and closet openings, the area of the walls is $416\frac{8}{9}$ sq. ft, so a gallon might not be enough. If you buy 2 gallons, $66.

25.2 Volume Formulas

1. In which ones are all the layers identical in volume?

2. a. 840   b. 105, if the 2-cm cubes can be cut

    c. 548 cm^2

3. Measurements can vary somewhat, and the production process may have changed measurements used in calculating the answers. If your answer is in the neighborhood of the listed answers, you were likely correct in your reasoning.

    a. For *B* = about 3.1 cm^2, 1000 such pieces would need about 1860 cm^3 of plastic.

    b. With *B* = 2.9 cm^2 (or thereabouts—don't forget the holes), the volume of plastic needed for 1000 such pieces would be 1740 cm^3.

    c. With *B* = about 9.3 cm^2, 1000 pieces would need 5580 cm^3 of plastic.

    d. The key idea about the measurement of the whole equaling the sum of the measurements of its parts

4. a. The same

    b. The top-bottom way gives a radius of $\frac{11}{2\pi}$ and a volume about 81.8 cubic inches, whereas the side-side way gives a radius of $\frac{8.5}{2\pi}$ and a volume about 63.2 cubic inches. So the top-bottom way gives 18.6 cubic inches more, or is about 129% as large as the side-side.

    c. You can find another example of shapes having the same surface area but different volumes, but it takes some work. *Hint*: Examine the surface area of a 1 by 1 by 5 right rectangular prism and find a shape made with 6 cubes having the same surface area. (Instructor: The $1 \times 1 \times 5$ right rectangular prism and a right prism made of 2 layers of 3 cubes in an L-shape have the same surface area, 22 units, but different volumes, 5 and 6 units, respectively.)

5. a. 336 cm^3 b. 112 cm^3 c. 292 cm^2

6. Again, measurements can vary somewhat and the production process may alter the original dimensions, so if your answers are somewhat close to the ones here, your measurements were probably correct.

    a. 13.4 cm^3 b. about 4.5 cm^3 (one-third of the part (a) value)

7. 2,592,276.5 m^3

8. a. 8" ball, volume $= \frac{256\pi}{3} \approx 268.1$ in.^{3};   16" ball, volume $= \frac{2048\pi}{3} \approx 2144.7$ in.^{3}

    b. The areas are 64π in.^{2} and 256π in.^{2}, so the costs of the plastic are about $0.39 and $1.56 (don't forget to change the square inches into square feet).

    c. Because the spheres are similar, the ratio of the volumes is $(\frac{1}{2})^3$ or 1:8, and the ratio of the areas is $(\frac{1}{2})^2$ or 1:4.

9. a. $\pi 8^2 \cdot 12 + \frac{1}{3}\pi 8^2 \cdot 3 \approx 2613.8$ ft^3

    b. Because 2150.42 cu. in. ÷ 1728 cu. in. per cu. ft, 1 bushel ≈ 1.24 cu. ft. So the silo will hold about 2613.8 ÷ 1.24, or 2108 bushels. Notice that the calculations would be simpler in the metric system.

10. a. S.A. $= 4\pi$ m^2; $V = \frac{4\pi}{3}$ m^3

    b. $V \approx 270,000,000,000$ or 2.7×10^{11} cubic miles

    c. $\approx 3.45 \times 10^{17}$ cubic miles

    d. About 1,278,000, using the rounded answers in parts (b) and (c)

11. a. 2 to 1   b. 2 to 3

12. a. and b. No, they are not congruent, but they have the same volume.

c. $\sqrt[3]{\frac{6}{\pi}} \approx 1.24$, so about $1\frac{1}{4}$ inches

13. a. $\frac{2}{3}$ (Compare with Learning Exercise 11(b).)   b. $1 - \frac{\pi}{6} \approx 47.6\%$

14. The sphere, by about 2.4 cm (its radius is about 6.2 cm).

15. $r = 3$ cm for the original sphere. $r = 0.005$ cm for the small spheres. The number x of small spheres can be found from $36\pi = x \cdot \frac{4}{3}\pi(0.005)^3$, which gives that there are 2.16×10^8 small spheres. These will have a total surface area of $2.16 \cdot 10^8 \cdot 4\pi(0.005)^2$, or 21600π cm^2. The ratio of the surface areas, all smaller spheres to original sphere, is $\frac{21600\pi}{36\pi} = \frac{600}{1}$, giving considerably more surface for burning. (A similar principle holds for melting ice: Broken-up ice from a block will melt faster than the block would.)

16. a. $\frac{4}{3}\pi\left(\frac{1}{6}\right)^3 \approx 0.019$ cubic miles

    b. $\dfrac{\text{later volume}}{\text{earlier volume}} \approx 0.027$, so the later volume is only 2.7% of the earlier volume, which is quite an error. (But even the smaller asteroid could cause immense damage.)

17. a. Answers will vary.

    b. "Cut" shape K into rectangular and triangular prisms and pyramids. Find the volume of each of those, and add them.

18. a. $V = 72\pi + 18\pi = 90\pi$, about 282.7 cm^3; S.A. $= 9\pi$ (the bottom) $+ (\pi 6)8 + 18\pi$, about 235.6 cm^2

    b. $V = 75\pi + \frac{250\pi}{3} \approx$ about 497.4 cm^3; S.A. $= 25\pi + (10\pi)3 + 50\pi = 105\pi$, about 329.9 cm^2

    c. $V = \pi r^2(h - r) + \frac{2}{3}\pi r^3$

    d. $V = kmn + \frac{1}{3}mnh$

    e. $V = \pi r^2 h$, and S.A. $= 2\pi r^2 + 2\pi r h$. For the surface area, did you account for both bases, and did you notice that a net for a right circular cylinder includes a rectangle?

19. The volume of a cube with edges x units long is x^3 cubic units.

20. a. 384 cm^2

    b. S.A.(cube) $= 6s^2$

    c. 512 cm^3

    d. V(cube) $= s^3$

    e. As measurements, the area and volume cannot be equal, of course, because area and volume are completely different characteristics. The second question comes down to whether $6s^2 = s^3$ has any *numerical* solutions, and it does: $s = 6$ and the trivial (for here) $s = 0$.

21. Recall that the scale factor multiplies each length measurement, so in the formulas...

22. a. $V = \frac{\pi}{6}d^3$ (The relationship between the diameter and the radius is so simple that most people do not memorize this formula.)

   b. $V = \frac{2}{3}\pi r^3$

   c. $A = \pi d^2$

   d. $A = \frac{1}{2}\pi d^2$ (for just the curved part; add $\pi(\frac{d}{2})^2$ if you included the planar part)

23. Without more restrictions on the shape of the dog house, there is no definite answer.

24. a. $x^2 + 2xy + y^2$ c. $...x^2 + xy$ d. $... x^2 + 5x + 6$

25. There are no "right" answers, but it is surprising that some progress can be made, using estimations.

Supplementary Learning Exercises for Section 25.2

1. In your sketch, the two bases should be congruent, and their area, B, should be indicated. The height, h, should be the distance between the bases, not the length on a slant.

2. An area formula should give units in, say, cm^2, but $A = 4\pi r^3$ would give cm^3. Similarly, a volume formula should give units in cm^3, but $V = \frac{4}{3}\pi r^2$ would give cm^2.

3. a. 448 ft^3 b. 400 m^3 c. 3600 cm^3 d. 600 ft^3 e. 216 in^3
   f. $33\frac{1}{3}$ cm^3 g. 1620π, or about 5089.4 cm^3 h. 67.5π, or about 212.1 in^3

   i. The volume of each cone would be one-third that of the cylinder.

4. The new volume is the old volume multiplied by the cube of the scale factor. Here, then, (a) new $V = 4^3 \cdot 448 = 28672$ ft^3; (c) new $V = 4^3 \cdot 3600 = 230400$ cm^3; and (h) new $V = 4^3 \cdot 67.5\pi = 4320\pi \approx 13572$ in^3.

5. If you are using the usual cubic units, then each length should be expressed in the same unit. Here, the 1.1 m should be replaced by 110 cm, if the answer is to be in cm^3. Notice that paying attention to units might have helped this student avoid the error.

6. a. $V = 2304\pi$, about 7238.2 in^3; S.A. = 576π, about 1809.6 in^2

   b. V about 8.2 cm^3; S.A. about 19.6 cm^2

   c. V about 2094.4 m^3; S.A. = 300π, or about 942.5 m^2

   d. $V = 2250\pi$, about 7068.6 ft^3; S.A. = 675π, about 2120.6 ft^2

   e. $V = \frac{2}{3}\pi r^3$; S.A. = $3\pi r^2$

7. Volume, $571666\frac{2}{3}\pi$, or about 1 795 943.8 ft^3; S.A. (not including the bases of the cylinder) 19600π, or about 61 575.2 ft^2

8. a. 23 cm   b. 88 cm   c. 24 in.^{2} d. ($r = 2$) 12π, or 37.7 cm^2

9. The small b is for the length of a side of the parallelogram, whereas the capital B is for the area of the base of the prism or cylinder.

10. a. 325,851.429

    b. About 815

    c. Metric calculations (using liters and ares or even hectares) would involve dealing only with powers of 10.

Answers for Chapter 26: Special Topics in Measurement

26.1 The Pythagorean Theorem

1. a. $p^2 + q^2 = r^2$

   b. $z^2 + x^2 = y^2$

   c. $b^2 + c^2 = a^2$ (Notice that what is important is what the variables represent.)

2. Do not have either a or b equal to 0, and you will have a counterexample.

3. a. Perimeter = 60 cm, area = 150 cm^2

   b. $35 + \sqrt{175}$ cm, or 48.2 cm; $7.5\sqrt{175}$ cm^2, or 99.2 cm^2

   c. 5.6 cm; 0.84 cm^2 d. $10 + \sqrt{50}$ cm, or 17.1 cm; 12.5 cm^2

   e. 14.4 m; 5.04 m^2 f. 7 cm; 2.1 cm^2

   g. 90 in.; 270 in^2 h. 20 m; 15 m^2

4. a. 14.1 cm   b. $\sqrt{2s^2}$, or $s\sqrt{2}$, cm

   c. 26 cm   d. $\sqrt{m^2 + n^2}$ cm

5. 10 cm, $\sqrt{117} \approx 10.8$ cm, and $\sqrt{145} \approx 12$ cm are the lengths of the diagonals of the faces, and $\sqrt{181} \approx 13.5$ cm for each of the "inside" diagonals. How do you know that the triangle inside the prism *is* a right triangle?

6. a. $\sqrt{x^2 + y^2 + z^2}$ b. No, but a 4-foot one would, just barely.

   c. $e\sqrt{3}$ units

   d. The diagonal of the cube is a diameter of the sphere, so . . . ($d = 10\sqrt{3}$ and $r = 5\sqrt{3} \approx 8.7$).

7. Consider a right triangle with legs 22 ft and $\frac{x}{4}$ ft, and hypotenuse x. (Instructor: Any of the ladders will do, because only 22.7 feet are needed to reach the top.)

8. More than $70 (Instructor: $70.68)

9. Volume = $28\sqrt{42} \approx 181$ cm^3; surface area = $84 + 6\sqrt{91} + 14\sqrt{51} \approx 241.2$ cm^2

10. a. 4.5π cm^2, 8π cm^2, 12.5π cm^2. The sum of the areas on the legs equals the area on the hypotenuse, just as in the Pythagorean theorem!

    b. The area of the semicircular region on the hypotenuse is equal to the sum of the areas of the semicircular regions on the legs. Because $a^2 + b^2 = c^2$ from the right triangle, $\frac{1}{2}\pi(\frac{a}{2})^2 + \frac{1}{2}\pi(\frac{b}{2})^2 = \frac{\pi}{8}(a^2 + b^2) = \frac{\pi}{8}c^2$, and $\frac{\pi}{8}c^2$ is also what you get from $\frac{1}{2}\pi(\frac{c}{2})^2$.

11. a. The height of an equilateral triangle in terms of the length s of its sides is derived in the narrative, $h = \frac{s\sqrt{3}}{2}$.

    b. 10.83 cm², 62.35 cm², 73.18 cm². Once again, the sum of the areas on the legs (10.83 + 62.35) is equal to the area on the hypotenuse.

    c. The justification is like that in Learning Exercise 10 (but with the triangle area formula, of course).

12. How do you know that $\angle PVQ$ is a right angle? If you are stuck, it may be because you need $(a+b)(a+b) = a^2 + 2ab + b^2$.

13. Parts (b) through (d) give Pythagorean triples. Do you see how they are related to the triple 3, 4, 5?

    e. Yes, with an algebraic justification. This fact is useful for a teacher, as in part (f).

14. a. $\sqrt{20}$ units

    b. $\overline{QR}$, 2 units; $\overline{ST}$, $\sqrt{20}$ units; $\overline{UV}$, $\sqrt{32}$ units; $\overline{WX}$, $\sqrt{20}$ units; $\overline{YZ}$, 10 units

    c. Find the algebraic difference in the first coordinates and in the second coordinates; then...

15. One statement in each pair is false. (Instructor: In part (a), the second statement is false, and in parts (b), (c), and (d), the first statements are false. A counterexample for the first statement in part (d) comes from, for example, $p = 4$, $q = 6$, and $r = 10$.)

16. a. $A = 270$ sq units

    b. Because $15^2 + 36^2 = 225 + 1296 = 1521$, and because $39^2 = 1521$ also, the measurements give a right triangle. The area, from $A = \frac{1}{2}bh = \frac{1}{2} \cdot 36 \cdot 15 = 270$, agrees with the result from part (a).

17. For the 6 rows with 6 dots in each row, 20 is not correct; there are only 19! Which one is missing? This problem is another example to show that patterns cannot be trusted 100%. Instructor: At the time of the 5 × 5, a 3–4–5 right triangle is possible, so one of the hypotenuses is 5. The 5 usually *thought* to be new in the 6 × 6 is not new.

18. a. $p = 10 + 2\sqrt{10}$ units $A = 15$ square units

    b. $p = 9 + \sqrt{18} + \sqrt{13}$ units $A = 13.5$ square units

    c. $p = \sqrt{8} + \sqrt{18} + \sqrt{26}$ units $A = 6$ square units ("surround" the triangle with a rectangle, and use a key idea)

    d. $p = 4\sqrt{5}$ units $A = 4$ square units

19. *Suggestion*: Use the Pythagorean theorem for the heights of the triangles and of the pyramid.

    a. A drawing helps to see that the altitude of each triangle is 2 cm ($1.5^2 + h^2 = 2.5^2$) and the height x for the pyramid is about 1.3 cm ($1.5^2 + x^2 = 2^2$). So, S.A. $= 3^2 + 4(\frac{1}{2} \cdot 3 \cdot 2) = 21$ cm^2, and $V = \frac{1}{3} Bh \approx \frac{1}{3} \cdot 3^2 \cdot 1.3 = 3.9$ cm^3.

    b. Complication: The triangles are not all congruent. As in part (a), the altitudes of the base-14 triangles are $\sqrt{120}$, or about 11 m, and of the base-10 triangles, 12 m. The height of the pyramid is $\sqrt{95}$ m. So, S.A. $\approx 14 \cdot 10 + 2(\frac{1}{2} \cdot 14 \cdot 11) + 2(\frac{1}{2} \cdot 10 \cdot 12)$, or about 414 m^2, and $V = \frac{1}{3} Bh = \frac{1}{3}(14 \cdot 10) \cdot \sqrt{95} \approx 455$ m^3.

20. a. Assume that the ground covered is a circular region, that the pile has lots of rotational symmetries, and that the pile will be shaped like a cone.

    b. 16π, or about 50.3 m^3

    c. Filling one sandbox to the top will take 0.675 m^3, so the pile will fill $16\pi \div 0.675$ sandboxes, or about 74.

21. a. Make a drawing. Where is a right triangle? (Instructor: $\sqrt{160} \approx 12.6$ cm)

    b. An 80° angle cuts off what part of the whole circumference? That length is the circumference of the base of the cone; now what is the radius? The height? The volume? (Instructor: Radius of base of cone $= \frac{16}{9}$ in. Height of cone ≈ 7.8 in. $V \approx 25.8$ in^3.)

22. One way: How are areas of similar shapes related? (Instructor: $A = 3360$ cm^2; second way—find sides of larger triangle, then its area.)

23. Values are in feet. P to A: $\sqrt{300} + 1 \approx 18.3$; P to B: $\sqrt{200} + 1 \approx 15.1$; P to C: $\sqrt{2100} + 1 \approx 46.8$; P to D: $\sqrt{1400} + 1 \approx 38.4$. Total ≈ 118.6 ft

24. Use a key idea of measurement and Learning Exercise 11(a). (Instructor: $\frac{1}{6}$ of area of whole circular region – area of equilateral triangle ≈ 9.1 cm^2.)

25. The volumes of cubes with edges equal to legs a and b and hypotenuse c of a right triangle are related by the given equation.

26. *Hint*: Place one of the boards across the corner of the canal to make an isosceles right triangle.

27. Issue: Is the inner quadrilateral a square? Examine the acute angles in the right triangles. Because the large squares are the same size, $c^2 + 4(\frac{1}{2} ab) = a^2 + b^2 + 4(\frac{1}{2} ab)$.

28. Stuck? Does the Pythagorean theorem help? (Instructor: (a) 31° in each triangle, 1.8 cm in the larger, with 1.9 cm and 1.7 cm sides in the smaller one. (b) Larger: 58°, vertical leg 230 cm, other leg x cm, plus $\frac{15}{23}x$ for the corresponding leg $= 600$ cm, so $x = 368.2$, hypotenuse 430.0 cm; smaller, 32° and 58°, leg 236.8 cm, hypotenuse 280.3 cm.)

29. In order: $\sqrt{2}, \sqrt{3}, \sqrt{4}, \sqrt{5}, ...$

Supplementary Learning Exercises for Section 26.1

1. a. 90 cm   b. $18 + \sqrt{164}$, about 30.8 cm   c. 112 m   d. $28 + \sqrt{224}$, about 43 cm
2. a. 56" or 4' 8"   b. 40 cm   c. $14 + \sqrt{98}$, about 23.9 cm   d. About 40 m
   e. $8 + 8\pi$, about 33.13 cm
3. a. 192 in^2 b. 96 cm^2 c. 24.5 cm^2 d. 100 m^2
4. $\sqrt{16 + 100} = \sqrt{116} \approx 10.8$ You might ask the student to check his/her answer to see whether $14^2 = 116$ (it doesn't, of course).
5. The triangles in parts (a) and (c) are right triangles. For part (a), $40^2 + 42^2 = 1600 + 1764 = 3364 = 58^2$. For part (c), $28^2 + 96^2 = 784 + 9216 = 10000 = 100^2$, and 100 cm = 1 m.
6. Design A: volume $= 1600$ m^3;

   outside S.A (not including floor) $= 550 + 5\sqrt{244} + 6\sqrt{200} \approx 713$ m^2

   Design B: volume = about 467 m^3

   outside SA (not including floor) $= 270 + 2.5\sqrt{674} + 3.5\sqrt{650} \approx 424$ m^2

7. S.A.: $h^2 + 2^2 = 2.9^2$ gives $h = 2.1$ m. So the area of each of the two bases of the right triangular prism is $\frac{1}{2} \cdot 4 \cdot 2.1 = 4.2$ m^2. The area of the floor is 24 m^2, and the area of each rectangular slanted side is 17.4 m^2. The total is $4.2 + 4.2 + 24 + 17.4 + 17.4 = 67.2$ m^2.

   Volume: With the area from above, $V = 4.2 \times 6 = 25.2$ m^3.

8. a. 7   b. 5   c. 2a   d. 3d   e. 5   f. $\sqrt{41} \approx 6.4$ g. 13   h. 5
   i. $\sqrt{(m-p)^2 + (n-q)^2}$
9. $4 + 5 + \sqrt{58} + 7 = 16 + \sqrt{58} \approx 23.6$

26.2 Some Other Kinds of Measurements

1. Answers will vary.
2. Answers will vary.

3. Answers will vary.

4. a. 97.5 ms, up to 98.5 ms (ms = milliseconds not meters)

   b. 149.5 m, up to 150.5 m

   c. 1.415 L, up to 1.425 L

5. If, say, your measuring container is smaller than a container of liquid, you can remove amounts with your measuring container, keeping a record of each amount and then adding these amounts when the large container is empty.

6. These might give examples: costs of lettuce, breathing rates, gasoline mileage rates, and so on.

7. Answers will vary.

8. Rather than what appears to be a random collection of terms, the metric system uses prefixes with a basic term for all of its units of a particular type.

9. Answers will vary.

10. a. Slightly under 3.3   b. About 3.2

    c. About 41 mph   d. About .328

11. a. Slightly under 26.1   b. About 24.8

    c. About 22.2   d. About 81 kg or 178 lb

    e. About 8.7 kg or 19 lb, at least

12. a. *One way*: Showing on the drug number line that $\frac{1}{4}$ is $\frac{1}{3}$ of $\frac{3}{4}$, so $\frac{1}{4}$ g should use $\frac{1}{3}$ of 12 mL, or 4 mL, on the water number line.

    b. So 1 g, or 4 one-fourths, should take 4 times as much, or 16 mL.

    c. $1\frac{1}{2}$ g

    d. Each 4 mL uses $\frac{1}{4}$ g, so 20 mL would use $\frac{5}{4}$, or $1\frac{1}{4}$, g.

    e. $\frac{3}{8}$ g   (Instructor: It is more likely that decimals would be used in Learning Exercise 12 because the measurements are metric. If someone mentions this likelihood, acknowledge that they are correct but that the authors like to keep fraction ideas fresh.)

13. a. Because 100 Celsius degrees match 180 Fahrenheit degrees, the Celsius degree is larger: 1 C° = 1.8 F°

    b. 20° C would be $\frac{20}{100}$, or $\frac{1}{5}$ of the way from 0° C to 100° C. The corresponding Fahrenheit temperature should then be $\frac{1}{5}$ of the way from 32° F to 212° F, or $\frac{1}{5}$ of 180, or 36°. Starting from 32° gives a temperature of 68° F.

c. Reasoning as in part (b), –40° C corresponds to a temperature $\frac{2}{5}$ of 180, or 72°, below 32° F. –40° F. (This is the only temperature at which the two scales give the same reading.)

14. a. km/s, because a kilometer is longer than a meter

   b. km/s, because 1 km per sec = 3600 km per hour

   c. m/s, because 1 m/s = 3600 m/h = 3.6 km/h

   d. yard/s, because 1 yd/s = 3600 yd/h and there are only 1760 yards in a mile

15. a. $\frac{1}{25}$ gallon per mile (The 25 miles per gallon means 25 miles per 1 gallon.)
   b. About 9.1 kilometers per liter

16. a. 10 m/s   b. 36 km/h (if the runner could run that fast for an hour)
   c. The runner's rate is 10 meters for every second.

   d. The runner's rate is 36 km for every hour (if …)

17. a. 10 yd/s   b. About 20.45 mi/h
   c. Metric (Learning Exercise 16) is easier because the calculations are easier.

18. a. With the cost per pound as a criterion, rather than the total cost, Danyell's was most expensive ($7.20 versus $6.99 per lb for Amy's, $6.79 per lb for Bea's, $6.40 per lb for Conchita's).

   b. The average for the amounts actually bought is about $6.863 ($42.72 for 6.225 lb), but the average of the four costs per pound is $6.845 ($27.38 ÷ 4).

19. a. The total cost was $130, or $32.50/blouse.

   b. Splitting the $70 evenly would mean you would pay $14.

   c. Although $2.29 is the average of the $1.99 and $2.59, you bought more of the $2.59 bags, giving a total cost of $29.88 for the 12 bags, or an average of $2.49 per bag.

20. For example, the cost per pound, the rate of eating, the cost per day per cow.
   a. $22\frac{3}{4}$ ¢ per day per cow

   b. 24¢ per day per cow

21.

$$\frac{20}{3\times10^{5}\text{km/s} \cdot 3600 \text{ s/h} \cdot 24 \text{ h/day} \cdot 365 \text{ day/yr} \cdot 1500 \text{ yr}} \times 360° \approx$$

$5.07 \times 10^{-13} = 0.000000000000507°$

22. With 8000 miles as the diameter of Earth and a world population of 6 billion,

$$\frac{6 \times 10^9}{.29 \times 4\pi(4000)^2} \approx 103 \text{ people per square mile.}$$

23. a. For example, ounces/serving size, # servings/container, calories/serving

    b. 495 calories

    c. 10,000 mg (because 1% must have 100 mg)

    d. No, there are 3 grams of each. Comparing the 5% and 10% rates does not make sense because they are based on different values.

    e. $6\frac{1}{4}$ servings ÷ 4.5 servings/box, or $1\frac{7}{18}$ boxes

24. a. $6\frac{1}{4}$ cups powdered sugar, $6\frac{1}{4}$ cups molasses, $2\frac{11}{32}$ (about $2\frac{1}{3}$) teaspoons each of salt and soda, $16\frac{13}{32}$ cups flour,... 1200 square inches, or $8\frac{1}{3}$ square feet

    b. $\frac{1}{4}$ cup sugar, $\frac{1}{4}$ cup molasses, $\frac{3}{32}$ tsp. each of salt and soda, $\frac{21}{32}$ cup flour,... (What would be approximations for the latter two?)

    c. For example, 16 bars per recipe, different amounts of ingredients per recipe or per 16 bars

25. About 55.9 miles per hour (475 miles traveled in 8.5 hours) (Why is the average larger than 55 mi/h?)

26. If the number of children were distributed evenly over all the families, each family would have 2.6 children (a sharing-equally division of the total number of children by the number of families).

27. a. $1\frac{1}{2}$ days

    b. 6 days. There are different analyses possible. Here is one, using the compound unit, painter-day: It takes 6 painter-days to paint 1 house, so it will take 120 painter-days to paint 20 houses, which will take 20 painters 6 days.

    c. $14\frac{7}{12}$ days

Supplementary Learning Exercises for Section 26.2

1. Most people recognize that building larger and smaller units by powers of 10 and communicating the different sizes by the same prefixes are two strong features. That their definitions are scientifically based is another strong feature. Disadvantages might be lack of familiarity for many in the United States and the existence of many everyday objects that are not based on the metric system but need repair in a metric world.

2. One way of thinking is $\frac{100\ \text{years}}{\text{century}} \cdot \frac{365\ \text{days}}{\text{year}} \cdot \frac{24\ \text{hours}}{\text{day}} \cdot \frac{50\ \text{miles}}{\text{hour}} = 43{,}800{,}000\ \frac{\text{miles}}{\text{century}}$.

3. a. 400 mg (1 carat is 200 mg)   b. 75% (24 karat gold is pure gold)

4. Ignoring a difference in taxes and possible differences in cost from the suppliers, we know that the Canadian (Imperial) gallon is larger than the U.S. gallon.

5. The area of the room is 180 ft^2, or 20 yd^2. So the carpet cost would be 20×12.99, or about $260.

6. One way of thinking is to note that $\frac{\text{number of births}}{\text{population in 1000s}} =$ the birth rate. Hence,

   $\frac{\text{population in 1000s}}{\text{number of births}} = \frac{1}{\text{birth rate}}$, or population in 1000s $= \frac{\text{number of births}}{\text{birth rate}}$. This equation gives:

   a. Population in 1000s in 2005 $= \frac{4138349}{14.0} \approx 295{,}596$, so the 2005 population was about 295,596,000 (or just 260 million).

   b. About 250,240,000   c. About 202,790,000

Part IV: Reasoning About Chance and Data

Answers for Chapter 27: Quantifying Uncertainty

27.1 Understanding Chance Events

1. Remember that a probabilistic situation involves a certain process repeated a large number of times, *under the same circumstances.*

    a. Not probabilistic, because the secretary of state either is or is not a woman. Reformulation: The probability of a woman over the next several U.S. secretaries of state. However, the fact that this choice is not made each time under essentially the same circumstances means that it is not actually a probabilistic situation under any change in wording.

    b. Probabilistic (assuming that the class is not too small)

    c. Not probabilistic, because the gender is determined. Reformulation: See part (d).

    d. Probabilistic, because there will be many cases that have not happened yet.

    e. Probabilistic as usually conceived: Out of several days with conditions like those expected tomorrow in this city, the probability of snow.

    f. Not probabilistic, because Joe either did or did not eat pizza yesterday. Reformulation: The probability that Joe will eat pizza sometime during the next several days.

2. 0%, 100%. With probability, 100% is the maximum, unlike many percent situations. Zero percent means that there are zero ways that an event can occur. 100% means that every possible outcome is included.

3. In an uncertain situation, you do not know what happened or is going to happen, or even whether the circumstances might differ in the future. In a probabilistic situation, some process will (in the future) be repeated in the same way a large number of times.

4. a. Toss the penny, nickel, and dime together, the same way, a large number of times, and note which of heads or tails is on top for each coin.

    b. One outcome might be the penny showing heads, the nickel showing tails, and the dime showing heads.

    c. The event of getting exactly two heads can happen in three ways:

    The penny and nickel show heads and the dime shows tails.
    The penny shows heads, the nickel tails, and the dime heads.

The penny shows tails, and the nickel and the dime show heads. *all* five other outcomes would *not* be in this event.

5. a. One possibility is to toss all three dice at the same time, many times, and note each time the sum of the numbers of dots showing. For ease, consider the dice to be different colors; blue, red, and black.

    b. One outcome might be 3 on blue, 2 on red, and 6 on black.

    c. An event might be tossing a 13. One outcome in this event would be 6 on red, 4 on blue, and 3 on black.

    d. Let the first number represent the number of dots showing on the blue, the second number the dots showing on the red, and the third the dots showing on the black. Then the outcomes in the event of a sum of 5 would be (1, 1, 3), (1, 2, 2), (1, 3, 1), (2, 1, 2), (2, 2, 1), (3, 1, 1). (Notice the manner in which the outcomes are listed: All possibilities with 1 in the first place, all with 2 in the first place, and all with 3 in the first place.)

6. a. One experiment might be to draw three cards, many times, each time noting the sum of the numbers showing on the three cards.

    b. This is an outcome, unless the event is specified to be this particular draw, in which case the event has only one element in it.

    c. This is an event because it is a set of outcomes specifically described. One outcome that would be in the set would be a draw of 2 of hearts, 2 of spades, and 6 of clubs. Can you name others?

Supplementary Learning Exercises for Section 27.1

1. a. Not probabilistic. This has happened and is either true or false. One rephrasing is, "The probability that a person born next year will grow up in the same town that he or she was born in."

    b. Probabilistic, if read as referring to a future situation.

    c. Not probabilistic, because it has already happened. One rephrasing is, "The probability you will go to the grocery store on some Friday in the future, given circumstances like the ones you are now in."

    d. Probabilistic, if it refers to a future situation with the same kind of deck of cards.

2. a. 0.5   b. 0   c. 1.0   d. 0.03   e. 0.85

3. a. There are 12 outcomes: H1, H2, H3, H4, H5, H6, T1, T2, T3, T4, T5, and T6.

    b. H1, H3, H5

    c. Outcomes are the simplest things that can result with an experiment (as in part (a)), whereas an event is *any* collection of outcomes (as in part (b)), even a collection with only one outcome or even none. Hence, a single outcome can be considered an event.

4. The probability derives from the large number of tickets purchased. This is the fraction of tickets that would win.

5. Possible outcomes for 2 cards drawn from a regular deck of 52 cards consist of any two cards: jack of diamonds & queen of spades; 3 of clubs and 10 of hearts.

    Examples of possible events for 2 cards drawn from a regular deck of 52 cards: drawing two black cards; drawing two face cards; drawing a pair.

27.2 Methods of Assigning Probabilities

1.   a. The sex of a child is a two-outcome situation (male/female), as is the toss of a coin (heads/tails).

    b. The choice of answer is a two-outcome situation (true/false), as is the toss of a coin (heads/tails).

    c. The choice of winner is a two-outcome situation (Team 1/Team 2), as is the toss of a coin (heads/tails).

    d. The choice of winner is a two-outcome situation (Person 1/Person 2), as is the toss of a coin (heads/tails).

2.   a. Is each sex equally likely? Some data collected at one time suggested that the probability of a male birth was 0.53 and that of a female was 0.47. (Does nature know that males have a more difficult time living to maturity?)

    b. Each of the choices may not be equally likely.

    c–d. Each of the choices may not be equally likely.

3.   a. In a large number of similar patients with those symptoms, 90% had the disease.

    b. On a large number of days with the same conditions, it rained during 80% of the days.

    c. No. It just means that, over the long run, with conditions like those expected when the forecast was made, it would rain on half of the occurrences of such conditions.

4.   Yes. A zero probability means that none of the outcomes are examples of the event—for example, getting a 7 on a toss of a die.

5.   Yes. A probability of one means that all of the outcomes are examples of the event—for example, getting 12 or fewer on a toss of two dice.

6. No, because the maximum possible probability is 1, when the event is certain to occur on every outcome.

7. "Are your answers equal? How can you tell?"

8. Not really, unless the couple plans to have many children and lots of them will be sons, with the possibility of receiving the same name!

    There would be six outcomes, namely Abraham-Aidan, A-B, B-A, B-B, C-A, and C-B.

    "At random" and the nature of the outcomes means that it would be reasonable to regard them as equally likely, each with probability $\frac{1}{6}$.

9. a. The outcomes making up the sample space are Q, R, S, T, U, and V. Each has theoretical probability $\frac{1}{6}$.

    b. The outcomes making up the sample space (and their probabilities) are W($\frac{1}{2}$), X($\frac{1}{4}$), Y($\frac{1}{8}$), and Z($\frac{1}{8}$).

    c. The outcomes, with their probabilities, are E: 0.5; F: 0.25; and G: 0.25. (Notice that it is the angle, not the area, that is significant with a spinner. Which would be more important if the region were a dartboard?)

    d. Sample space (and probabilities): H($\frac{1}{6}$), I($\frac{1}{3}$), J($\frac{1}{2}$)

10. You could spin the spinner 100 times (or any large number of times), find the frequency for each outcome and divide by 100 (or the total number of spins). It is important that you be able to answer this question. If you cannot, review and contrast "experimental probability" and "theoretical probability."

11. Yes, it is possible to get 8 *J*'s with 12 spins. With many, many spins, however, you would expect very close to half of them being *J*'s. That is, you would expect the experimental probability to be close to the theoretical probability.

12. a. $\frac{1}{3}$ b. $\frac{2}{3}$ (either from $\frac{1}{6}+\frac{1}{2}$, or from $1-\frac{1}{3}$)

    c. $\frac{5}{6}$ d. 0   e. $\frac{1}{6}$ f. $\frac{5}{6}$

13. a. The event not-E and the event E would involve all of the outcomes, so $P(E) + P(\text{not-E})$ must = 1, or $P(\text{not-E}) = 1 - P(E)$.

    b. $\frac{48}{52}$, or $\frac{12}{13}$

    c. 1 – your probability for a thumbtack landing point up from Activity 2

    d. $\frac{3}{4}$ (There are 4 equally likely outcomes: HH, HT, TH, TT.)

    e. $\frac{5}{6}$

f. $\frac{4}{5}$, assuming that the keys are so alike that each is equally likely to be chosen.

14. a. A $\frac{5}{18}$ B $\frac{1}{18}$ C and D $\frac{1}{3}$ each

   b. Outcomes C and D are equally likely.

   c. $1 - \frac{1}{18} = \frac{17}{18}$ is more efficient than $\frac{5}{18} + \frac{1}{3} + \frac{1}{3} = \frac{17}{18}$.

15. a. The spinner should be cut into five $360 \div 5 = 72°$ sectors.

   b. Start with 6 equal sectors of 60° each, and omit one of the dividing radii.

   c. A drawing should show that the sectors have $x, x, x, 3x,$ and $3x$ degrees, or a total of $9x$ degrees. So, 40°, 40°, 40°, 120°, and 120° sectors work.

   d. Each spinner: ten probably equal sectors of 36°, labeled 0–9. The same-factor facts would be practiced more, assuming the child is not sensitive to commutativity of multiplication. In other words, the a x a facts would only be represented once, while the others are each represented twice: a x b and b x a.

   e. Each spinner could be marked into five equal sectors, labeled 5–9.

16. Examples: a. Probability = 1—getting a red ball in drawing from a bag containing only red balls; getting a one- or two-digit sum on a toss of 2 dice;…

   b. Probability = 0—getting a green ball in drawing from a bag containing only red balls; getting a three-digit sum on a toss of 3 (or 4 or 5 or…or 16) dice;…

17. a. Experimentally. Draw a sample of 20, say, and determine the fraction that is red.

   b. Theoretically.   Of the 6 outcomes, one favors getting a two, so $\frac{1}{6}$.

   c. Theoretically, if the data on out-of-state students and total enrollment are available. or, experimentally, by choosing a fairly large sample of students and determining the fraction that are from out of state.

   d. Theoretically. Of the 52 cards, 13 are hearts, so the probability is $\frac{13}{52}$ or $\frac{1}{4}$.

18. a. About 900

   b. About 300

   c. Yes, ... (The explanation is important.)

   d. Yes, because...

   e. About 150 Ss and 50 Ts.

   f. Perhaps something like, 3 out of 4 = how many out of 1200, or $\frac{3}{4}$ of the time you should get S, so $\frac{3}{4}$ x 1200 times.

19. a. 6 reds and 7 blues, because in the long run you expect respective probabilities of $\frac{2}{5}$ and $\frac{6}{13}$, and $\frac{6}{13} > \frac{2}{5}$.

   b. The chances are the same, because...

c. 3 reds and 5 blues, because...

d. 623 reds and 623 blues, because…

20. For example, what if some balls were covered with fabric and others with leather? What if the balls were different sizes or weights? What if the container was not shaken before each draw? There should be nothing that makes the balls feel of different weights. And of course, no looking!

22. Very small. Four-tenths percent.

23. For both situations the probability is found using a ratio, either area of section to whole area for the area model, or degrees in angle of the region to 360° for the spinner model. On a spinner the shape and area of the region are not important; only the measure of the angle for the region, in degrees, matters.

24. a. The probability of the Mammoths winning is $\frac{3}{13}$.

b. The probability of the Dinosaurs losing is $\frac{67}{77}$.

25. a. $x < y$

b. You would expect Team A to lose $\frac{x}{x+y}$ of the games. Or, out of $x + y$ games, we expect Team A to lose x times.

26. a. The odds of making the field goal are 2 to 1.

b. The odds of drawing a red ball are 7 to 5.

c. The odds of not getting a winning card are 7 to 23. (Or, the odds of getting a winning card are 23 to 7.)

Supplementary Learning Exercises for Section 27.2

1. a. $120° + 120° + 90° = 330°$, so B must have an angle $360° - 330°$, or $30°$. Hence, $P(A) = P(D) = \frac{120}{360} = \frac{1}{3}$, $P(C) = \frac{90}{360} = \frac{1}{4}$, and $P(B) = \frac{30}{360} = \frac{1}{12}$.
Alternatively, $P(B) = 1 -$ sum of the other probabilities, or
$P(B) = 1 - (\frac{1}{3} + \frac{1}{3} + \frac{1}{4}) = 1 - \frac{11}{12} = \frac{1}{12}$.

b. $P(B) = \frac{1}{12}$ means that if you spin the spinner a large number of times, you would get B on about $\frac{1}{12}$ of the spins.

2. No, a probability cannot be negative. As the fraction $\frac{\text{number of outcomes in event}}{\text{total number of trials}}$, a probability cannot be less than 0 or greater than 1. Events cannot happen a negative number of times.

3. a. $P(J) = \frac{90}{360} = \frac{1}{4}$. $360° - 90° = 270°$, so the angle size for each of K and L is $270° \div 2 = 135°$. Hence, $P(K) = P(L) = \frac{135}{360} = \frac{3}{8}$. Alternatively, $P(K)$ and $P(L)$ must share equally the $1 - \frac{1}{4} = \frac{3}{4}$ left from $P(J)$, and $\frac{3}{4} \div 2 = \frac{3}{8}$.

b. $P(L) = \frac{3}{8}$ means that if you spin the spinner a large number of times, you would get L on about $\frac{3}{8}$ of the spins.

4. a. Letting p be the probability of one of the first three outcomes, $p + p + p + \frac{1}{2}p = 1$, so $\frac{7}{2}p = 1$, and $p = \frac{2}{7}$. The first three have probability of $\frac{2}{7}$ and the last is $\frac{1}{7}$. To find the sizes of the angles, multiple $360°$ by each probability (getting $102\frac{6}{7}°$ for each of the largest three angles and $51\frac{3}{7}°$ for the fourth).

   b. Let $P(A) = x$. Then $P(B) = \frac{1}{2}x$, and $P(C) = \frac{1}{4}x$. The sum of the three probabilities must be 1, so $x + \frac{1}{2}x + \frac{1}{4}x = 1$. Then $\frac{7}{4}x = 1$, or $x = \frac{4}{7}$. That is, $P(A) = \frac{4}{7}$, $P(B) = \frac{2}{7}$, and $P(C) = \frac{1}{7}$. To find the sizes of the angles, multiply $360°$ by each probability (getting $205\frac{5}{7}°$, $102\frac{6}{7}°$, and $51\frac{3}{7}°$).

   c. Letting x and y be the two probability values, we have $3x + 2y = 1$ from the sum of all five probabilities and $x + y = \frac{3}{8}$ from the information about the two values. Solving those two equations (double each term in the second equation and subtract the result from the first equation), we get $x = \frac{1}{4}$ and $y = \frac{1}{8}$. Your spinner should have three $90°$ sectors (for A, B, and C) and two $45°$ ones (for D and E).

   d. Letting x and y be the two probability values, we again have $3x + 2y = 1$ from the sum of all five probabilities but $3x = 2y$ from the information about the two values. Substituting for $2y$ in the first equation gives $3x + 3x = 1$, or $x = \frac{1}{6}$. From $3 \cdot \frac{1}{6} = 2y$, we get $y = \frac{1}{4}$. (Alternatively, substitute $2y$ for $3x$ in the first equation, giving $y = \frac{1}{4}$ and then $x = \frac{1}{6}$.) The sectors for A, B, and C should have $60°$ and the two for D and E should have $90°$.

5. a. Since each part is the same size the probability for each is part is $\frac{1}{4}$. The probability of winning a prize is $\frac{3}{4}$.

   b. $P(\text{large prize}) = \frac{1}{4}$

   c. $P(\text{no prize}) = \frac{1}{4}$

   d. The area of each section is $\frac{1}{4} \cdot 120 = 30$ in^2.

   e. The probability can be found by dividing the area of the section by the total area.

6. a. $\dfrac{\sqrt{3}}{60}$ b. $1 - \dfrac{\sqrt{3}}{60}$

7. It may be helpful to complete the division lines.
   a. $P(X) = \frac{1}{9}$ b. $P(Y) = \frac{3}{9} = \frac{1}{3}$ c. $P(Z) = \frac{5}{9}$

8. Drawings can vary greatly. For part (a) the regions for *A* and *B* should each be the same size, and the region for *C* twice that size. For part (b), the region for *E* should be half the size of each of the other four regions. Here are two ways for part (b); notice that the probabilities are relatively easy to see from the drawings:

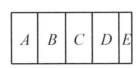

9. a. If the list of students is known for the class or if the class is visible, this probability would be theoretical. One would calculate the number of females compared to the total number in the class.

   b. Theoretically. Find all of the ways that two dice can come up (36) and count how many of those sum to seven (6 ways—1, 6; 6, 1; 2, 5; 5, 2;.3, 4; and 4, 3). The (theoretical) probability is $\frac{6}{36} = \frac{1}{6}$.

10. a. Expect to spin R 750 times, from $\frac{150}{360} \cdot 1800$. The 150 comes from $360 - (90 + 120)$.

    b. Expect to spin S 450 times.

    c. Expect to spin T 600 times.

    d. Yes, it is possible.

11. It depends. Suppose there are *x* red marbles and *y* blue marbles. The probability of drawing a red is then $\frac{x}{x+y}$. Putting in one more of each color changes the probability to $\frac{x+1}{x+y+2}$. How do these two fractions compare? Rewrite with a common denominator:

    $\frac{x(x+y+2)}{(x+y)(x+y+2)}$ and $\frac{(x+1)(x+y)}{(x+y)(x+y+2)}$, or $\frac{x^2+xy+2x}{\text{denominator}}$ and $\frac{x^2+xy+x+y}{\text{same denominator}}$. Comparing the numerators leads to comparing $2x$ and $x + y$, or just *x* and *y*. If $x = y$, the probabilities are the same. If $x > y$, then the first fraction (from before the marbles are added) is greater than the second fraction, so the probability has decreased when the marbles were added. If $x < y$, then the first fraction (from before the marbles are added) is smaller, so the probability has increased when the marbles were added. If you considered examples, be sure that you included all the cases: $x = y$, $x > y$, and $x < y$.

12. a. This event has already occurred, so either it was a boy or not. Can you rephrase the situation to make it probabilistic?

    b. This question does not refer to probability. You either have a dog or do not. This could also be rephrased to ask a probability question.

13. a. The odds of drawing a red queen are 1 to 25.

b. The odds of that chicken laying an egg with a double yolk are 125 to 875 or 1 to 7.

c. The odds of Jim hitting the bull's eye are 2 to 3.

14. a. The probability of Jon making a base hit is $\frac{3}{7}$.

b. The probability of a calico cat being male is $\frac{1}{100,000}$ or 0.00001.

c. The probability of being put on hold when calling the doctor is $\frac{23}{25}$.

15. a. 14/36 or 7/18   b. 8/30 or 4/15   c. $P(YY) = 1/36$ or zero without replacement

27.3 Simulating Probabilistic Situations

1.   The experimental probabilities should be close to the theoretical probabilities of $\frac{1}{6}$ for each outcome. A greater number of repetitions should give a value closer to the $\frac{1}{6}$ value.

2.   a. Any appropriate simulation will do.

b. Green and red should show up the most, because their probabilities are greater than those for blue and yellow.

c. Theoretically, as you will find out later, the probability is $\frac{1}{18} \approx 0.0556$; the experimental results from the simulation for 1000 repetitions should be around that value.

d. In part (c), that the first spin gave the green was specified, whereas in part (d)...

e. Theoretically, $\frac{8}{9} \approx 0.889$, so experimental results for 1000 repetitions should be around that value. The easy way uses P(not green twice in a row) $= 1 - P$(green twice).

3.   Results for curing none of the five should be around 0.237. It is possible that all five could be cured, but unlikely ($\frac{1}{1024} \approx 0.00098$). With 10,000 repetitions, the results should be closer to the theoretical values given earlier in this answer. (One simulation might involve taking five random digits at a time and assigning the values 1 and 2 to cure, 3–8 to not-cure and passing over any 9's or 0's.)

4.   Your answer here is important. Phrase it carefully, and be sure to include a reference to many repetitions, or the "long run."

5.   Experimental probabilities, because they are based on (simulated) data, not theoretical considerations. Experimental probabilities will not (usually) be exactly the same as theoretical ones, but with more and more trials, the two will be very close.

6.   Depends on use of an online simulator. As the number of spins increases, the experimental probability should be closer to the theoretical probability.

Supplementary Learning Exercises for Section 27.3

1.   a. The area of the purple is $\frac{3}{10}$. The simulation could use a random number list with this
        code: 0, 1 = red
                             2, 3, 4 = green
                             5, 6 = yellow
                             7, 8, 9 = purple

     b–e. Your answers to these parts will depend on your data. The experimental
        probabilities may be close to the theoretical, but should vary slightly. The answer to
        part (e) should be 1 – your answer to part (d).

2.   Your simulation might be based on sets of 4 two-digit numbers, with, say, 01–65 being
     effective, and 66–00 being ineffective. Your probability from the simulation should be
     close to 0.179. The more repetitions, the closer the estimate will be to this value.

3.   One way to simulate this is to use five playing cards with consecutive numbers—for
     example, use a 2 (for B), 3(for I), 4 (for N), 5 (for G), and 6 (for O). Then shuffle and
     blindly pull the cards out one at a time. A draw of 23456 would be a B-I-N-G-O.
     Another would be to use a random number list and code the letters carefully. Many
     repetitions will be needed to get a nontrivial answer.

4.   a. Any 35% simulation will do—for example, random numbers.
     b–d. Results will vary. With lots of repetitions, your result for part (c) should be around
        0.005, and your result for part (d) should be around 0.03.

5.   The simulation should indicate snoring 59% of the time and include a group size of four.
     There are assumptions being made in the question itself. For example, there is no
     distinction between males and females snoring, but males do snore more often than
     females. Also, we are not considering whether snoring runs in families. With lots of
     repetitions of your simulation, your result should be around 0.12.

Answers for Chapter 28: Determining More Complicated Probabilities

28.1 Tree Diagrams and Lists for Multistep Experiments

1. Drawing with replacement would occur if a name is chosen at random from the telephone book, without removing the names of those already called. Drawing without replacement would occur if a person's name was penciled out as he/she was called. With a large population and a modest sample size, the methods do not differ by that much.

2. Your tree diagram should show the 12 outcomes (why is it 12?); in a common notation, they are the following: (1, H), (1, T), (2, H), (2, T), (3, H), (3, T), (4, H), (4, T), (5, H), (5, T), (6, H), (6, T). Each has probability $\frac{1}{12}$, because we are assuming an honest die and an honest coin.

3. The "condensed" tree diagrams might look like these:

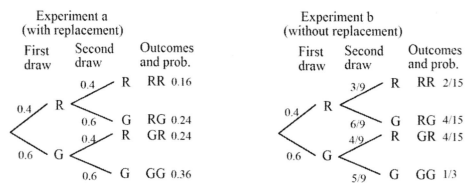

4. a. All outcomes are equally likely.

		Number	on	white	die		
		1	2	3	4	5	6
	1	(1, 1)	(1, 2)	(1, 3)	(1, 4)	(1, 5)	(1, 6)
On	2	(2, 1)	(2, 2)	(2, 3)	(2, 4)	(2, 5)	(2, 6)
red	3	(3, 1)	(3, 2)	(3, 3)	(3, 4)	(3, 5)	(3, 6)
die	4	(4, 1)	(4, 2)	(4, 3)	(4, 4)	(4, 5)	(4, 6)
	5	(5, 1)	(5, 2)	(5, 3)	(5, 4)	(5, 5)	(5, 6)
	6	(6, 1)	(6, 2)	(6, 3)	(6, 4)	(6, 5)	(6, 6)

b. If the dice are "honest," there is no reason to expect one outcome to be more likely than another. $P(\text{sum} = 2) = \frac{1}{36} = P(\text{sum} = 12)$; $P(\text{sum} = 3) = \frac{1}{18}$; $P(\text{sum} = 4) = \frac{1}{12}$; $P(\text{sum} = 5) = \frac{1}{9}$; $P(\text{sum} = 6) = \frac{5}{36}$; $P(\text{sum} = 7) = \frac{1}{6}$; $P(\text{sum} = 8) = \frac{5}{36}$; $P(\text{sum} = 9) = \frac{1}{9}$; $P(\text{sum} = 10) = \frac{1}{12}$; $P(\text{sum} = 11) = \frac{1}{18}$. What are $P(\text{sum} = 1)$ and $P(\text{sum} = 13)$? Young children may focus on the numerical size of the number and often think that larger numbers or larger sums are more likely.

    c. Yes. The two dice are different dice, whether they are colored differently or not. Hence, 2 on die X, 3 on die Y is a different outcome from 2 on die Y, 3 on die X.

5. Literally, 400 outcomes, although you might argue for 100; in either case the outcomes would be equally likely unless the icosahedron were unbalanced in some way. The probability of practicing $0 + 0$ is $\frac{4}{400}$ (the 400-outcome interpretation) or $\frac{1}{100}$ (the 100-outcome interpretation); notice that either interpretation gives 0.01. The probability of a sum of 15 is 4%.

6. a. Your sample space should have 16 equally likely outcomes: HHHH, HHHT, HHTH, and so on.

    b. One simulation could be to use random digits and call the evens heads and the odds tails.

7. a. If we go from left to right in the tree, with the spinners in numerical order, the first level has two branches, each with probability 0.5. The next level has three branches, two labeled 0.25 for red and black and one 0.5 for white. The third level will have three branches, each with probability $\frac{1}{3}$. (Would a tree with a different order of spinners give different results in parts (b–d)?)

    b. Each of RRR, RRB, RRW, RBR, RBB, RBW, BRR, BRB, BRW, BBR, BBB, and BBW has probability $\frac{1}{24}$; each of RWR, RWB, RWW, BWR, BWB, and BWW has probability $\frac{1}{12}$.

    c. $\frac{3}{4}$ (Do you see two ways to find this?)

    d. $\frac{3}{4}$

8. a.   HH1   HH2   HH3   HH4   HH5   HH6

         HT1   HT2   HT3   HT4   HT5   HT6

         TH1   TH2   TH3   TH4   TH5   TH6

         TT1   TT2   TT3   TT4   TT5   TT6

    b. $\frac{6}{24}$ or $\frac{1}{4}$

9. The tree diagram is the same in design as that for a fair coin, but each branch for heads has probability 0.7, and each branch for tails has probability 0.3. For example, $P(HH) =$

0.49 instead of 0.25, so the probability of two heads is 0.24 more with the dishonest coin than with an honest one.

10. a. $\frac{1}{1024}$ b. $\frac{1}{1024}$ c. $\frac{1}{1024}$ d. $\frac{1}{1024}$

 e. $\frac{1}{1024}$ (How can we know the probability, without knowing which outcome you were thinking of?)

Supplementary Learning Exercises for Section 28.1

1.

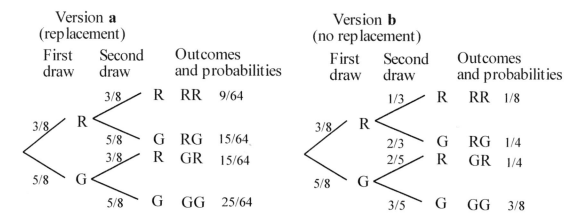

2. a. Your spinner should have $0.6 \times 360 = 216$ degrees for heads.

 b. Your tree diagram should give these outcomes and probabilities:

 HH, 0.36   HT, 0.24   TH, 0.24   TT, 0.16

 c. Here are the corresponding probabilities for an honest coin:

 HH, 0.25   HT, 0.25   TH, 0.25   TT, 0.25

3. a. RRR   WRR   BRR

 RRB   WRB   BRB

 RWR   WWR   BWR

 RWB   WWB   BWB   Each outcome has probability $\frac{1}{12}$.

 b. Only outcome RRR has all the same color, so the probability is $\frac{1}{12}$.

 c. 10 outcomes have one or more reds, so the probability is $\frac{10}{12} = \frac{5}{6}$.

 d. $1 - \frac{5}{6} = \frac{1}{6}$, using part (c), or by directly counting the outcomes with no reds (WWB and BWB).

 e. RWB, WRB, WWR, BRB, and BWR have exactly one red, so the probability is $\frac{5}{12}$.

4. a. $\left(\frac{1}{2}\right)^{12} = \frac{1}{4096}$ (Think of going through the tree diagram.)

b. If you repeated the 12 tosses many, many times, about $\frac{1}{4096}$ of the repetitions would have all tails.

5. a.

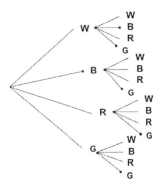

b.

WW	BW	RW	GW
WB	BB	RB	GB
WR	BR	RR	GR
WG	BG	RG	GG

c.

Outcome	Prob	Outcome	Prob	Outcome	Prob	Outcome	Prob
WW	$\frac{1}{36}$	BW	$\frac{1}{36}$	RW	$\frac{1}{18}$	GW	$\frac{1}{18}$
WB	$\frac{1}{36}$	BB	$\frac{1}{36}$	RB	$\frac{1}{18}$	GB	$\frac{1}{18}$
WR	$\frac{1}{18}$	BR	$\frac{1}{18}$	RR	$\frac{1}{9}$	GR	$\frac{1}{9}$
WG	$\frac{1}{18}$	BG	$\frac{1}{18}$	RG	$\frac{1}{9}$	GG	$\frac{1}{9}$

6. a.

1, 1	2, 1	3, 1	4, 1	5, 1
1, 2	2, 2	3, 2	4, 2	5, 2
1, 3	2, 3	3, 3	4, 3	5, 3
1, 4	2, 4	3, 4	4, 4	5, 4
1, 5	2, 5	3, 5	4, 5	5, 5

b. Because each section has the same angle, each outcome has probability $\frac{1}{25}$.

7. a. Spinning a spinner twice is similar to drawing with replacement.

b. Sample space of products of two spins

1	2	3	4	5
2	4	6	8	10
3	6	9	12	15
4	8	12	16	20
5	10	15	20	25

c. $\frac{2}{25}$

d. $\frac{16}{25}$

8. a. Draw 3 balls twice with replacement

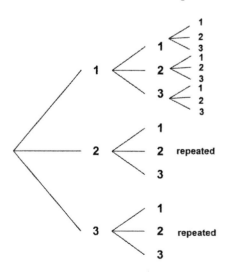

b. Draw 3 balls twice without replacement

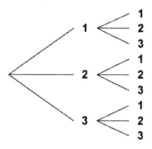

c. Draw 3 balls three times with replacement

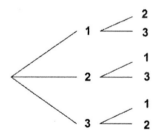

d. Draw 3 balls three times without replacement

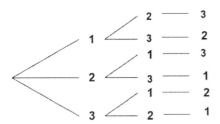

9.   a. Rolling a six-sided die followed by the roll of a four-sided die

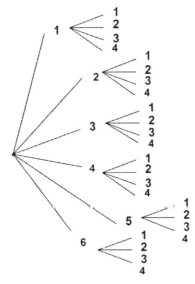

b. Rolling a four-sided die followed by a six-sided die

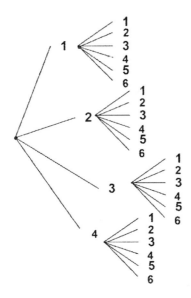

c. The diagrams in parts (a) and (b) illustrate that the first branch has six choices followed by four choices versus four choices followed by six choices. Each has 24 branches at the second step, and the outcomes are the same except for order.

10. a.

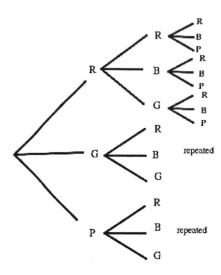

b. Sample space:

RRR	GRR	PRR
RRB	GRB	PRB
RRP	GRP	PRP
RBR	GBR	PBR
RBB	GBB	PBB
RBP	GBP	PBP
RGR	GGR	PGR
RGB	GGB	PGB
RGP	GGP	PGP

c. P(at least one purple) $= \frac{1}{36} + \frac{1}{18} + \frac{1}{12} + \frac{1}{36} + \frac{1}{18} + \frac{1}{12} + P$(last column of sample space).
P(at least one purple) $= \frac{2}{3}$. Alternatively,

$$P\text{(at least one purple)} = 1 - P\text{(no purple)} = 1 - (\tfrac{2}{3} \times 1 \times \tfrac{1}{2}) = \tfrac{2}{3}.$$

d. P(no red) $= P$(GBB) $+ P$(GBP) $+ P$(GGB) $+ P$(GGP) $+ P$(PBB) $+ P$(PBP) $+ P$(PGB) $+$ P(PGP). P(no red) $= \frac{11}{24}$ Alternatively, P(no red) $= \frac{2}{3} \times \frac{11}{12} \times \frac{3}{4} = \frac{11}{24}$.

11. First there are 35 branches, each of these has 34 branches, each of these has 33 branches, each of these has 32 branches, and finally each has 31 branches.

12. Students might have said that if a marble is taken from the bag without looking, it is most likely to be yellow because the fraction $\frac{1}{12}$ might *seem* like the biggest.

28.2 Probability of One Event OR Another Event

1. a. H1 H2 H3 H4 H5 H6
      T1 T2 T3 T4 T5 T6
   b. $\frac{1}{12}$ c. $\frac{2}{12}$ d. $\frac{3}{12}$ or $\frac{1}{4}$

2. a. R1   R2   R3   R4   R5   R6
      B1   B2   B3   B4   B5   B6
      G1   G2   G3   G4   G5   G6

   1/18 for each of the items in the sample space

   b. 2/18   c. 2/3   d. 2/18

3. a.

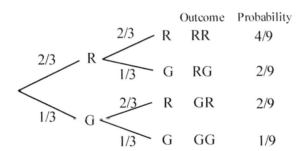

   b. $\frac{4}{9}$ c. $\frac{5}{9}$ d. $\frac{4}{9} + \frac{5}{9} - \frac{4}{9} = \frac{5}{9}$ e. $\frac{5}{9}$

4. a.

   b $\frac{1}{3}$ c. $\frac{1}{3}$ d. $\frac{1}{3}$ e. $\frac{2}{3}$

5. a.

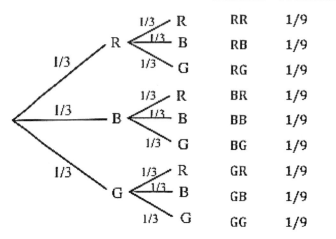

	Outcome	Probability
	RR	1/9
	RB	1/9
	RG	1/9
	BR	1/9
	BB	1/9
	BG	1/9
	GR	1/9
	GB	1/9
	GG	1/9

b. $\frac{1}{9}$ c. $\frac{3}{9}$ or $\frac{1}{3}$ d. $\frac{1}{9}+\frac{3}{9}-\frac{1}{9}=\frac{3}{9}$ or $\frac{1}{3}$ e. $\frac{2}{9}+\frac{1}{9}=\frac{3}{9}$ or $\frac{1}{3}$

6. a.

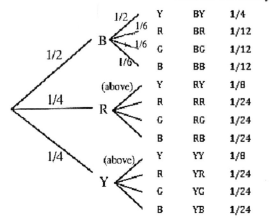

	Outcome	Probability
Y	BY	1/4
R	BR	1/12
G	BG	1/12
B	BB	1/12
Y	RY	1/8
R	RR	1/24
G	RG	1/24
B	RB	1/24
Y	YY	1/8
R	YR	1/24
G	YG	1/24
B	YB	1/24

b. $\dfrac{1}{24}$

c. $\dfrac{1}{12}+\dfrac{1}{24}+\dfrac{1}{8}=\dfrac{6}{24}=\dfrac{1}{4}$

d. $\dfrac{1}{24}+\dfrac{6}{24}-\dfrac{1}{24}=\dfrac{6}{24}=\dfrac{1}{4}$ e. $\dfrac{1}{24}$

f. Red on at least one of the spins is $\dfrac{1}{12}+\dfrac{1}{8}+\dfrac{1}{24}+\dfrac{1}{24}+\dfrac{1}{24}+\dfrac{1}{24}=\dfrac{9}{24}$

Yellow on at least one of the spins is $\dfrac{1}{4}+\dfrac{1}{8}+\dfrac{1}{8}+\dfrac{1}{24}+\dfrac{1}{24}+\dfrac{1}{24}=\dfrac{15}{24}$

The intersection (or overlap) includes the cases RY and YR: $\dfrac{1}{8}+\dfrac{1}{24}=\dfrac{4}{24}$

Therefore *P*(red on one of the two spins or yellow on one of the two spins)

$$= \frac{9}{24} + \frac{15}{24} - \frac{4}{24} = \frac{20}{24} = \frac{5}{6}.$$

Simply adding the probabilities above where there is at least one R or at least one Y or both will also yield $\frac{5}{6}$.

7.   a. BBR   BBY   BGR   BGY   BYR   BYY

        RBR   RBY   RGR   RGY   RYR   RYY

        GBR   GBY   GGR   GGY   GYR   GYY

        YBR   YBY   YGR   YGY   YYR   YYY   Each outcome has probability $\frac{1}{24}$.

   b. *P*(all one color) = *P*(YYY) = $\frac{1}{24}$.   *P*(red on one spinner) = $\frac{1}{2}$ (interpreting "red on one spinner" to mean on *exactly* one). There is no overlap so the probability for part (b) = $\frac{1}{24} + \frac{1}{2} - 0 = \frac{13}{24}$. If you interpreted "red on one spinner" to mean "red on *at least* one spinner," your answer for part (b) would be $\frac{1}{24} + \frac{15}{24} - 0 = \frac{2}{3}$.

   c. *P*(yellow on all three spinners) = $\frac{1}{24}$. *P*(red on all three) = 0. There is no overlap.

     So *P*(yellow on all three spinners or red on all three spinners) = $\frac{1}{24}$.

   d. *P*(blue on at least one spin) = $\frac{12}{24}$ and *P*(yellow on at least one spin) = $\frac{18}{24}$.

     P(blue on at least one spin AND yellow on at least one spin) = $\frac{8}{24}$.

     P(blue on at least one spin or yellow on at least one spin) = $\frac{12}{24} + \frac{18}{24} - \frac{8}{24} = \frac{22}{24}$.

     Note that this answer can be found also by counting all outcomes with at least one blue or at least one yellow. There are 22 such outcomes.

8.   a. B1   B2   B3   B4   B5   B6

        R1   R2   R3   R4   R5   R6

        Y1   Y2   Y3   Y4   Y5   Y6

        G1   G2   G3   G4   G5   G6

   b. $\frac{2}{24}$ c. $\frac{3}{24}$ d. $\frac{4}{24}$

9.   a. 1,1   1,2   1,3   1,4

        2,1   2,2   2,3   2,4

        3,1   3,2   3,3   3,4

        4,1   4,2   4,3   4,4

b. $\frac{4}{16}$ c. $\frac{8}{16} + \frac{1}{16} - \frac{1}{16} = \frac{8}{16}$ d. $\frac{4}{16}$ e. $\frac{3}{16}$

10. a. $\frac{9}{36}$ b. 0   c. $\frac{10}{36}$ d. 1   e. $\frac{33}{36}$ f. $\frac{10}{36}$

g. $\frac{30}{36}$ h. $\frac{32}{36}$ i. $\frac{10}{36}$ j. $\frac{1}{36}$ k. $\frac{11}{36}$

11. a.   Tetrahedron

	1	**2**	**3**	**4**
Red	R1	R2	R3	R4
Yellow (Y_1)	$Y_1 1$	$Y_1 2$	$Y_1 3$	$Y_1 4$
Yellow (Y_2)	$Y_2 1$	$Y_2 2$	$Y_2 3$	$Y_2 4$
Green	G1	G2	G3	G4

b. $P(\text{R3}) = 1/16$; $P(\text{yellow and no.} > 1) = 6/16$; $P(\text{green and no.} > 4) = 0$; $P(\text{yellow and no.} > 2) = 4/16$.

12. a. 6/16   b. 1/16   c. 1/16   d. 2/16 (for BGBG and GBGB)

Answers for the 28.2–28.3 Supplementary Learning Exercises follow the answers for 28.3.

28.3 Probability of One Event AND Another Event

1. See the narrative for the definitions. Try to come up with new examples.

2. No, it applies only when *A* and *B* are independent.

3. a. The tree has two levels with two branches each. Each branch for hitting the bull's-eye should be labeled 0.98, and each branch for a miss should be labeled 0.02.

b. Yes, "nerves of steel" must mean that. The tree diagram assumed independence by using the same probabilities for the second shot as for the first.

c. 96% (assuming nerves of steel)

d. Almost 1 (see part (e))

e. Essentially 0 ($0.02^2 = 0.0004$).

4. a. Exclusive: The person will have exactly one of the two. Inclusive (the mathematics way): The person could have either one or both.

b. Exclusive: The person will wear exactly one type of shoe. Inclusive: This doesn't make sense, unless we allow the person to wear one shoe of each type, as well as either type solely.

5. $P(\text{sun and good surfing}) = 0.7 \times 0.4 = 0.28$, assuming...

$P(\text{sun or good surfing}) = 0.7 + 0.4 - (0.4 \times 0.7) = 0.82$, assuming...

6. The independent events are in parts (a, d), and one other.

7.   a. $\frac{2}{16}$ b. 0   c. $\frac{8}{16}$ d. $\frac{1}{16}$

8.   a. The probability that all three systems work is 0.84645, assuming...Hence, the probability that at least one fails is... (Instructor note: ...assuming independence, $1-(0.95 \times 0.9 \times 0.99) = 1 - 0.84645 = 0.15355$. Then for part (b), about 15%.)

   b. That probability means that with a very large number of launches, _____ will be aborted.

9.   a. $P(A) + P(B)$ b. $P(A) + P(B) - P(A) \times P(B)$ c. $P(A)$, because... (These are not worth memorizing.)

10.   Incorrect. $\frac{8}{28}$, because two blue candies are gone. 18% of the eighth graders were completely correct, although another 30% knew Bill was incorrect but did not give complete explanations.

Supplementary Learning Exercises for Sections 28.2 and 28.3

1.   a.   1H   1T
         2H   2T
         3H   3T
         4H   4T

   b. $P(2\text{H}) = \frac{1}{8}$

   c. $P(\text{an even } and \text{ H}) = \frac{1}{4}$

   d. $P(3) = \frac{1}{4}$

2.   Make a tree diagram if needed.

   a. $P(\text{same color both times}) = P(\text{RR}) + P(\text{GG}) + P(\text{BB}) + P(\text{YY})$.

   $P(\text{same color both times}) = \frac{1}{12} + \frac{1}{12} + \frac{1}{24} + \frac{1}{24} = \frac{6}{24}$

   b. $P(\text{RY}) = \frac{1}{24}$

   c. $P(\text{YR}) = \frac{1}{12}$

   d. $P(\text{they are the same color } or \text{ exactly one is yellow}) = P(\text{same color}) + P(\text{exactly one is yellow})$.
   $P(\text{exactly one is yellow}) = P(\text{RY}) + P(\text{GY}) + P(\text{BY}) + P(\text{YR}) + P(\text{YG}) + P(\text{YB}) = \frac{8}{24}$.
   Therefore, $P(\text{same color } or \text{ exactly one is yellow}) = \frac{6}{24} + \frac{8}{24} = \frac{14}{24}$.

3.   Make a tree diagram if needed. Note that without replacement, the probabilities change in the second set of branches.

   a. YY   BY   GY
      YB   BB   GB
      YG   BG   GG

   b. $P(\text{two different colors}) = 1 - P(\text{same colors})$

$P(\text{same colors}) = P(YY) + P(BB) + P(GG)$

$P(YY) = \frac{4}{9} \cdot \frac{3}{8} = \frac{12}{72}$ $\qquad$ $P(BB) = \frac{2}{9} \cdot \frac{1}{8} = \frac{2}{72}$ $\qquad$ $P(GG) = \frac{3}{9} \cdot \frac{2}{8} = \frac{6}{72} = \frac{1}{12}$

So, $P(\text{same colors}) = \frac{5}{18}$, and $P(\text{two different colors}) = 1 - \frac{5}{18} = \frac{13}{18}$.

c. $P(\text{one ball yellow } and \text{ the other ball blue}) = P(YB) + P(BY)$

$P(YB) = \frac{4}{9} \cdot \frac{2}{8} = \frac{8}{72} = \frac{1}{9}$

$P(BY) = \frac{2}{9} \cdot \frac{4}{8} = \frac{1}{9}$ $\quad$ So, $P(\text{one yellow and one blue}) = \frac{2}{9}$.

d. $P(YB) = \frac{4}{9} \cdot \frac{2}{8} = \frac{8}{72} = \frac{1}{9}$

4.

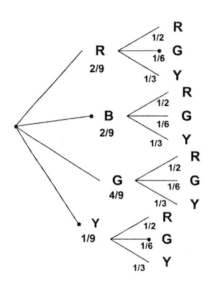

5. a. Without replacement (with a tree diagram you will notice that, surprisingly, the outcomes are equally likely).

RRG   RGR   GRR   YRR
RRY   RYG   GRY   YRG
RGY   RYR   GYR   YGR

b. $P(RRG) = \frac{1}{12}$

c. $P(GYR) = \frac{1}{12}$

d. $P(\text{at least two of the same color}) = \frac{6}{12}$

e. $P(\text{all the same}) = 0$

6.   a. With replacement (with a tree diagram, you will notice that these outcomes are *not* equally likely).

RRR	GRR	YRR
RRG	GRG	YRG
RRY	GRY	YRY
RGR	GGR	YGR
RGG	GGG	YGG
RGY	GGY	YGY
RYR	GYR	YYR
RYG	GYG	YYG
RYY	GYY	YYY

   b. $P(\text{RRG}) = \frac{1}{16}$

   c. $P(\text{GYR}) = \frac{1}{32}$

   d. Perhaps easier than finding probabilities for all the events in the outcome is

   $P(\text{at least two of the same color}) = 1 - P(\text{no two of same color}) = 1 - \frac{6}{32} = 1 - \frac{3}{16} = \frac{13}{16}$,

   by looking at RGY, RYG, GRY, GYR, YRG, YGR, each with probability $\frac{1}{32}$.

   e. $P(\text{all the same}) = \frac{1}{8} + \frac{1}{64} + \frac{1}{64} = \frac{5}{32}$

   f. In this scenario, the probability of choosing a given color does not change from drawing of first ball to drawing of second to drawing of third. The probability of drawing a red is always twice that of drawing a green or a yellow.

7.   a.

	1 on first toss	2 on first toss	3 on first toss	4 on first toss	5 on first toss	6 on first toss	7 on first toss	8 on first toss
1	(1,1)	(2,1)	(3,1)	(4,1)	(5,1)	(6,1)	(7,1)	(8,1)
2	(1,2)	(2,2)	(3,2)	(4,2)	(5,2)	(6,2)	(7,2)	(8,2)
3	(1,3)	(2,3)	(3,3)	(4,3)	(5,3)	(6,3)	(7,3)	(8,3)
4	(1,4)	(2,4)	(3,4)	(4,4)	(5,4)	(6,4)	(7,4)	(8,4)
5	(1,5)	(2,5)	(3,5)	(4,5)	(5,5)	(6,5)	(7,5)	(8,5)
6	(1,6)	(2,6)	(3,6)	(4,6)	(5,6)	(6,6)	(7,6)	(8,6)
7	(1,7)	(2,7)	(3,7)	(4,7)	(5,7)	(6,7)	(7,7)	(8,7)
8	(1,8)	(2,8)	(3,8)	(4,8)	(5,8)	(6,8)	(7,8)	(8,8)

   b. 64

   c. $\frac{32}{64} = \frac{1}{2}$

   d. $\frac{16}{64} = \frac{1}{4}$

8.   a.

	1	2	3	4	5	6	7	8
1	2	3	4	5	6	7	8	9
2	3	4	5	6	7	8	9	10
3	4	5	6	7	8	9	10	11
4	5	6	7	8	9	10	11	12
5	6	7	8	9	10	11	12	13
6	7	8	9	10	11	12	13	14
7	8	9	10	11	12	13	14	15
8	9	10	11	12	13	14	15	16

b. $\frac{5}{64}$

c. $\frac{3}{64}$

d. The sum of 9 has the greatest probability.

9.   a. $P(X \text{ or } Y) = P(X) + P(Y) - P(X \text{ and } Y) = 0.35 + \frac{7}{40} - \frac{2}{40} = 0.475$
b. $P(X \text{ or } Y) = 0.35 + \frac{7}{40} = 0.525$

c. *Disjoint* and *mutually exclusive* mean the same thing, so the probability is the same as in part (b).

d. Because X and Y are independent,
$P(X \text{ and } Y) = P(X) \cdot P(Y) = 0.35 \cdot \frac{7}{40} = \frac{49}{800} = 0.06125$.

10. If one *or both* of the parts separated by the "or" hold, the statement is regarded as true.

11. a. $6 \times 6 \times 6 = 216$
b. $\frac{1}{216}$

c. X can happen in 6 ways (3-4-1, 3-4-2, 3-4-3,…, 3-4-6), and Y can happen in 36 ways, one of which is 3-4-6. So,
$P(X \text{ or } Y) = P(X) + P(Y) - P(X \text{ and } Y) = \frac{6}{216} + \frac{36}{216} - \frac{1}{216} = \frac{41}{216}$.

d. $\frac{1}{216}$ because 3-4-6 is the only outcome in the event X and Y.

e. Yes. The red and white dice must have a total of at least 2 dots. If the green die has 6 dots (Y), that would give a total of at least 8 dots, and hence it is not possible to get 7 dots.

f. $P(Y \text{ and } Z) = 0$

12. a. Not disjoint, because the outcome, king of hearts, would be in both events.

b. Disjoint, because clubs are black and each card is a single color. So it would not be possible for a card to be both red and a club.

   c. Not disjoint, because 2 would favor both events.

   d. Not disjoint, because some pet owners have both a cat and a dog.

   e. Not disjoint, because most states require both forms.

13. a. Not independent, because potentially the first draw could be the king of hearts, thus influencing the probability of a king on the second draw.

   b. We'll say independent, although you could argue that pitchers will bear down more on the second at-bat, or that having made a hit, the batter will be more confident the second time.

   c. Not independent, for most students. Doing homework should help the probability of getting an A on the test.

   d. Not independent, because a square is automatically a quadrilateral.

14. a. These two events are independent: Getting red on the first spinner, and getting blue on the second spinner. (In fact, any choice of two colors on the separate spinners would give independent events).

   b. These two events are not independent: Getting red on first spinner, and getting red-red. (There are other possibilities.)

   c. These two events are disjoint. Getting red on the first spinner, and getting blue on the first spinner. (There are other possibilities.)

   d. The two events, getting red on at least one spinner, and getting blue on at least one spinner, are not disjoint, because the outcome red-blue favors both events. (There are other possibilities.)

15. a. Events A and B are disjoint.

   b. Event A might involve only outcomes that are in B also. Then

$$P(A) + P(B) - P(A \text{ and } B) = 0.2 + 0.35 - 0.2 = 0.35.$$

   c. Not possible. Although $P(A) + P(B) - P(A \text{ and } B) = 0.2 + 0.35 - 0.35 = 0.2$, this would mean that the event (A and B) had *more* outcomes than A itself!

   d. Not possible. Use an argument similar to that of part (c).

   e. Not possible. From $P(A) + P(B) - P(A \text{ and } B) = 0.2 + 0.35 - x = 0.25$, x would equal 0.30, forcing the event (A *and* B) to have more outcomes than A itself does.

   f. From $P(A) + P(B) - P(A \text{ and } B) = 0.2 + 0.35 - y = 0.4$, y would equal 0.15, and this could happen if the event (A *and* B) involved only some of the events in A.

28.4 Conditional Probability

1. Suppose you have a population of 10,000. After you make the contingency table using the information you have (test is 95% accurate, 5% of the general population uses drugs), you should find that 950 of the 10,000 tested positive, and of those 475 (or 50%) do not use drugs. Additional thought questions: Would your conclusions be different if you had started with a population of, say, 5000? Would your conclusions be different if a larger portion of the population of, say, 8% used drugs? Reflection: What if an Olympic athlete tested positive for marijuana use? Does this new understanding affect your perception of the situation?

2. a. One approach is to make a tree diagram to identify the sample space for four children in a family in order of birth (there are 2^4, or 16, possible outcomes). From there, you can determine the sample space for the event that at least one of the children is a girl (the outcome BBBB is eliminated), and with 6 outcomes having two of each gender, the probability of two girls and two boys is $\frac{6}{15} = \frac{2}{5}$. If you did not know that at least one child was a girl, the sample space would have all 16 outcomes, and the probability of two girls and two boys would be $\frac{6}{16} = \frac{3}{8}$. What assumptions have you made? (Think about: independence, theoretical probabilities).

   b. $P(\text{two daughters}) = \frac{1}{3}$; $P(\text{two daughters} \mid \text{older child is a daughter}) = \frac{1}{2}$. (List all the outcomes.)

3. GBBBBB is just as likely as GBGBBG or any other string of 6 Bs and Gs (think of a large tree diagram), so 72 is a good estimate.

4. Choosing from the pool *at random* gives a probability of 0.7 that the person is a lawyer and 0.3 that the person is an engineer.

5. There are three possible scenarios, each with equal probability ($\frac{1}{3}$): (Assume that there are 2 pigs and a car behind the doors.)

   * The player picks pig number 1. The game host picks the other pig. Switching will win the car.

   * The player picks pig number 2. The game host picks the other pig. Switching will win the car.

   * The player picks the car. The game host picks either of the two pigs. Switching will lose.

   Hence, switching gives a $\frac{2}{3}$ probability of winning.

6. The cards can be represented as R/R, R/W, and W/W. When the clown draws one card at random and you see a red side, you know it is not the W/W card. Thus, there are three sides left: two reds and one white. The other side of the card showing could be any one of those three sides, so the probability is not $\frac{1}{2}$. What is it?

7. Each is equally likely. The probability of *any* particular outcome is $\frac{1}{32}$.

8. a. Recall that if events A and B are independent, then $P(A \text{ and } B) = P(A) \times P(B)$. Thus, $P(A \mid B) = \dfrac{P(A \text{ and } B)}{P(B)} = \dfrac{P(A) \times P(B)}{P(B)}$, and the $P(B)$ cancels out, leaving $P(A \mid B) = P(A)$.
   b. No, unless $P(A) = P(B)$.

9. The probability that it was a Blue Cab, given that the witness said it was blue, is $\frac{120}{290} \approx 0.41$. Juries often trust witnesses!

		Cab was Green	Cab was Blue	Totals
Witness says	Green	680	30	710
	Blue	170	**120**	**290**
	Totals	850	150	1000

10. a. The resulting $P(\text{Virus} \mid \text{positive test})$ is the same, $\frac{147}{744} = \frac{49}{248} \approx 20\%$.

	Has the virus	Does not have virus	Totals
Positive	147	597	744
Negative	3	29,253	29,256
Totals	150	29,850	30,000

Since everything is tripled, the probability remains the same. $P(\text{No virus} \mid \text{positive}) = \frac{597}{744} = \frac{199}{248}$ or about 80%.

b. This time the resulting $P(\text{Virus} \mid \text{positive test})$ is $\frac{99}{298} \approx 33\%$. (This result makes sense because the test is more accurate.)

	Has the virus	Does not have virus	Totals
Positive	99	199	298
Negative	1	19,701	19,702
Totals	100	19,900	20,000

$P(\text{No virus} \mid \text{positive}) = \frac{199}{298}$ or about 67%.

c. The resulting $P(\text{Virus} \mid \text{positive test})$ is $\frac{294}{488} \approx 60\%$. Even though the incidence rate is 6 times as great as in the original situation, $P(\text{Virus} \mid \text{positive test})$ is only 3 times as great.

	Has the virus	Does not have virus	Totals
Positive	294	194	488
Negative	6	9506	9512
Totals	300	9700	10,000

11. a.

	High-Income	Low-Income	
Support vouchers	30	160	190
Oppose vouchers	50	160	210
	80	320	400

b. $P(\text{oppose vouchers} \mid \text{high-income}) = \frac{50}{80} = 62.5\%$

c. $P(\text{high-income} \mid \text{oppose vouchers}) = \frac{50}{210} \approx 24\%$

d. $P(\text{high-income or opposes vouchers}) = \frac{80}{400} + \frac{210}{400} - \frac{50}{400} = \frac{240}{400} = 60\%$

12. a. If you prefer whole numbers, use a population of $n = 100{,}000$.

	Has cancer	No cancer	
Test is positive	$0.0072n$	$0.07(0.992n) = 0.06944n$	$0.07664n$
Test is negative			
	$0.008n$	$0.992n$	n

False positives are $0.06994n$, with $0.07664n$ positives in all. So the probability of a false positive is $\frac{0.06944n}{0.07664n} \approx 90.6\%$.

b. "90% accurate" sounds so exact, but the correct statement is, "90% accurate at spotting those who have it and 7% (in)accurate in identifying those who do *not* have it."

Supplementary Learning Exercises for Section 28.4

1. a. The women make up 65% of the 4800 employees, so 3120 of the employees are women. Assuming that the 10% college-diploma rate applies to the women alone, Janine would get 312 from 10% of 3120.

b. No, Janine's assumption was incorrect. As the following contingency table shows, only 228 of the women have a college diploma. (The Roman numerals show one order of making the calculations, using the given data.)

	Women	Men	Totals
College diploma	vi. 228	v. 252	ii. 480
No coll-diploma		iv. 1428	
	i. 3120	iii. 1680	4800

2. a. There is not enough information, unless you assume that a college diploma is necessary for a management position.

   b. 4% of 4800 = 192 management employees. 6.25% of 192 = 12 management employees without a college diploma, so 192 − 12 = 180 management employees do have a college diploma, leaving 480 − 180 = 300 college diploma holders in nonmanagement positions. Because 96% of the employees, or 4608 of them, are in nonmanagement positions, 300 ÷ 4608 = about 6.5% of the nonmanagement employees have college diplomas. (Yes, this is a complicated exercise! Try a contingency table, with diploma/not and management/not the two headings, to see how the table makes it easier to keep track.)

3.

	Snore	Does Not Snore	Totals
Sleep Apnea	33,100	33,100	66,200
No Sleep Apnea	556,900	376,900	933,800
Totals	590,000	410,000	1,000,000

4.

	Snore	Does Not Snore	Totals
Sleep Apnea	100,000	100,000	200,000
No Sleep Apnea	490,000	310,000	800,000
Totals	590,000	410,000	1,000,000

5. For independent events, what has happened in the past has no influence on what happens in the future.

6. a. Answer a

   b. Because the puppy is brown, it is one of the 4 brown puppies.

7. For independent events A and B, (i) $P(A \text{ and } B) = P(A) \times P(B)$ and (ii) $P(A \mid B) = P(A)$.

8. a. The sample space is reduced by the condition to the 130 who favor removal, so $P(\text{male} \mid \text{favors removal}) = \frac{9}{13}$.

   b. The sample space this time is reduced by the condition to the 120 males, so $P(\text{favors removal} \mid \text{male}) = \frac{9}{12} = \frac{3}{4}$.

   c. There are 90 + 30 + 60 = 180 who are male or oppose removal, so the probability is $\frac{180}{220} = \frac{9}{11}$.

   d. $\frac{30}{220} = \frac{3}{22}$

9.   The bold **500** gives rise to the other values, possibly in the order and manner indicated by the Roman numerals.

	Parents	Non-parents	
Favor bridge	iv. 60 (150 – 90)	v. 175 (= 50% of 350)	vii. 60 + 175 = 235
Favor park	iii. 90 (60% of 150)	vi. 175 (= 350 – 175)	viii. 90 + 175 = 265
	i. 150 (= 30% of 500)	ii. 350 (= 500 – 150)	**500**

a. $100\% - 60\% = 40\%$ (or $\frac{60}{150} = \frac{2}{5} = 40\%$)

b. $\frac{60}{235} = \frac{12}{47} \approx 26\%$

c. $\frac{235+90}{500} = \frac{325}{500} = \frac{65}{100} = 65\%$

d. $\frac{90}{500} = \frac{18}{100} = 18\%$

Answers for Chapter 29: Introduction to Statistics and Sampling

29.1 What Are Statistics?

1. The first "statistics" refers to the discipline, the second to the numbers studied.

2. a. Samples: Percent of games won, average weight of players on the team, total number of points scored, total number of yards gained by passing…

   b. Samples: Average age, class average on last test, number of students in the class, number of siblings for the whole class…

   c. Samples: Percent female, average age, number of students in the class, average on the last test, average number of calories consumed at breakfast…

3. a. Baseball performances are rarely so predictably uniform, so such a definite prediction is risky.

   b. The performance for a course is most often based on more than one quiz.

Supplementary Learning Exercises for Section 29.1

1. a. Strictly speaking, a grade of B is not a numerical value. In addition, using just one datum to predict the future is risky.

   b. All right

   c. Assuming that a pattern of statistics will continue is risky.

2. a. Examples: Percent of all students using a computer daily. Percent of all students using a particular website daily. Average number of minutes on a computer per day by computer-using students. Number of students using Macintosh computers.

   b. Examples: Number of beagles in the kennel. Daily number of pounds of food eaten by the dogs in the kennel. Weekly cost of veterinarian care for dogs in the kennel.

   c. Examples: Number of crayons that are not broken. Number of crayons that are shades of red.

3. Answers will vary, of course. Check that your answer refers to the value, perhaps unknown, of a quantity.

29.2 Sampling: The Why and the How

1. You would *not*, for example, stand outside the fine arts building and survey students leaving the building. You might instead randomly select phone numbers from the student telephone directory. The population is the entire student body.

2. It would not be possible to select a completely random sample unless a list of all students could be obtained. If you think that almost all students eat on campus, or use the library,

you could take a convenience sample at one of those places. Otherwise, you might try a stratified sample of dorm students and off-campus students (by selecting students from those who leave the parking lot). The population is the entire student body.

3. He is using systematic sampling. He *could* number eggs in a carton, 001–006 left to right in front, 007–012 left to right in the back, 013–018 for carton 2 in the front, and so on, up through 715–720 for the back row of eggs in the 60th container, then use a table of random digits to obtain a random sample. However, the systematic sampling will probably give him the information he needs in much less time. The population is the entire shipment of cartons of eggs.

4. Probably a mix of convenience sampling (depending on how the polling sites are selected) and cluster sampling (because only some sites are used).

5. a. If the stereotype of fraternities (that excessive drinking is widespread) is true, this sample would be biased.

   b. Stratified (random) sampling. The sample should be unbiased unless the samples from each group are not selected in some unbiased way (e.g., randomly).

   c. If the two groups have about the same number of people, this sample should be all right. If not, the larger group would be underrepresented.

   d. Although a stratified random sample, the choice of religious groups could bias the results about alcohol abuse. There is also the likelihood that the religious groups are of quite different sizes, so a very small group would be overrepresented and a very large group underrepresented.

   e. Convenience sampling. There could be a bias for several reasons: Do students patronize the student center because alcohol is served there? What time of day would the polling be done? What if, say, the sample is drawn right after a large class populated mostly by a group likely to include alcohol abusers?

6. a. Stratified sampling. If the same number is selected from each of the three groups, teachers would be overrepresented and so there would be some bias if all questionnaires are put together as one sample.

   b. Convenience sampling. Which door is used, one by an information booth already there, or one not close to an information booth? The time the sample is collected could possibly give a bias, if it is known that shoppers already familiar with the mall come mostly at that time.

c. This is an example of systematic sampling that is also self-selected. One source of bias is that questionnaires are more likely to be completed by unsatisfied students than by satisfied students.

d. Convenience sampling. When the cars are manufactured may make a difference in the quality. If the sample is collected all at the same time, it may be neglecting to check a machine in the manufacturing process that needs more regular maintenance or a shift with a worker that has inadequate training.

e. Convenience sampling. Bias may be present in that given the timing before Christmas holidays (Dec. 21 – Dec. 23) shoppers may feel too busy to think about stopping for coffee or, off work, more likely.

7. a. If an important decision that affects only a few people is to be made, all the people should be polled. For example, a family is deciding on a vacation locale, or a new drug has been tried on only 12 people.

b. Any assembly-line product, or particularly troublesome parts of an assembly line

c. If you want to know how people in a 15-block neighborhood feel about a new mall being planned for the neighborhood, you could randomly select 3 of the 15 blocks and then interview all the residents of those blocks. The information gathered in this way should not be biased in any particular way.

8. a. 27% refers to all people, and so it is a population parameter. (It may have been arrived at by a sample, but not necessarily. It might have been arrived at through the last census.)

b. 85% refers to the percent of students *polled* in a sample, so 85% is a sample statistic.

c. One fourth-grade class makes up the population referred to, so this is a population parameter.

d. Surveys do not usually reach 100% of the population, nor do they get a 100% return, so this is a sample statistic.

e. It is reasonable to expect that all the prices of the homes sold were examined, so this would be a parameter for the population of homes in Atlanta last year.

f. "The marathon" appears to refer to one particular race, so the 3% is a population parameter.

9. a. Answers will vary

b. The cafeteria is most likely to contain a cross section of the student body. The algebra and French classes might represent just a segment of the student body, as might the students in the guidance office or the faculty room.

10. The people who call in are a self-selected sample. In the case of political respondents, there may be organized responses for particular candidates.

Supplementary Learning Exercises for Section 29.2

In 1–4, other answers might be acceptable. If your answer departs considerably from the one given, you might ask someone else to evaluate your answer.

1. Best (as always) is a simple random sample of the students at the university. The sample must be chosen carefully, of course. For example, randomly sampling students close to a parking area would likely involve a bias toward those who drive, whereas sampling students by a bus stop would likely involve a bias toward those who do not drive.

2. If the winning grade is known, the principal could randomly sample children in that grade, perhaps stratified by gender, or even poll all the children in that grade. If the winning grade is not known, the principal could use a random sample stratified by grade (and perhaps stratified within each grade as well).

3. If the producer has a database of its viewers (unlikely), then a random sample of them would be appropriate. If from some source the number of viewers of the news show is known, then the number of "hits" to the website could be used, even though a single user might visit the website multiple times. In the more likely case that the viewers are not known, then telephone calls to a random sample could be used, with the results for those who watch the news show giving the statistic of interest.

4. A few cluster samples (perhaps just one) as the machine operates might show whether the machine is off-kilter. A systematic sample, say by measuring every 100th container, could be used on an ongoing basis.

5. If the population is quite small and accessible, polling the whole population is reasonable. If the stakes are high, the whole population might be used even if it is large. As an example, the DNA of every inhabitant in an isolated community might be collected to try to identify a serial killer.

6. a. self-selected, or voluntary, sampling from those given the telephone number, even though the initial effort was systematic (the ones who respond)

   b. cluster sampling

   c. systematic sampling

d. self-selected, or voluntary (the ones who respond)

e. self-selected, or voluntary (the ones who respond)

7. a. If only Ms. Allen's class is involved, the 60% would be a population parameter. However, if the 60% result is being used to represent all fourth-graders or even all students, the 60% would be a sample statistic.

   b. The 42% is a population parameter, for the population of all students taking Algebra I for the first time in Jefferson School District.

   c. "Survey" implies a sample, so the 89% is a sample statistic.

29.3 Simulating Random Sampling

1. Yes. Jonathan's numbers could include 01–35 and 36–00, while Maria's breakdown is 00–34 and 35–99.

2. Look at strings of three-digit numbers. For example, suppose you begin with the 4th row of the 4th column of the TRSD. Ignore numbers greater than 500. Moving down, take the first thirty numbers from 001 through 500. (Ignore 614, 909, 750, 672. The first number selected is 340. The second one is 489. The third and fourth are 465 and 082, etc.)

3. Assign each student a two-digit number, 01 through 18. Generate a list of random numbers. Begin any place in the list. Look at pairs of digits. Ignore all of 19–99 and 00. Match the first three pairs that are in the 01–18 range with students. Those three students will be on the committee.

4. Human-made "random" samples usually are not random. For example, although genuinely random numbers will include consecutive repetitions of the same number, humans often avoid such repetitions.

5. a. One way: Use pairs of digits in your random numbers, letting 00–24 represent bass, and 25–99 represent catfish. Then a sample of size 10 would be 20 digits long. For example, the 20 random digits 29504750601883172458 would translate into the sample CCCCCBCBBC.

   b. Usually the percents in the samples will vary. They may vary considerably from the population percent.

6. A master list of the members likely exists, so picking 10 numbers from 001 through 407 with the aid of a table of randomly selected digits would give a sample.

7. First, pick the 5 stores from the 35 stores with more than 50 telephone numbers by assigning a (2-digit) number to each store (01–35, say) and then using a table of random

digits to pick the 5 stores. Then, for each store, assign a number to each telephone number and again use the table to pick 5 telephone numbers.

Supplementary Learning Exercises for Section 29.3

1. One way would be to ignore the digits 0, 7, 8, and 9 and look at consecutive pairs from the table. For example, 184923657 would become 142365, giving "rolls" of (1, 4), (2, 3), and (6, 5).

2. a. One way is to proceed as in Exercise 1 but then to record the sum. For the results in Exercise 1, you have sums 5, 5, and 11. It is important to see that using two-digit numbers to search for the sums 02 through 12 does not take into account the fact that the sums with dice are not equally likely. The sums would incorrectly be equally likely if the table is used to look for sums 02 through 12.

   b. The difference is in the interpretation of the result. For example, (1, 4) is interpreted as 5. Check to see that your method does not give equally likely sums.

   c. With a large number of repetitions, you should get a sum of 7 about $\frac{1}{6}$, or roughly 17%, of the time.

3. Assume that the faces ("sides") of the dice are labeled 1, 2, 3 and 4. The simplest way is to use pairs of digits from the table but ignoring any of the digits 0, 5, 6, 7, 8, and 9, much as in the answer to Exercise 1.

4. a. The list has 12 names. One way would be to put each of the 12 names on identically sized slips of paper, put the slip in an opaque bag (mixing them up), and draw 5 slips (without looking). A TRSD could be used by numbering the 12 names and then using two-digit numbers, ignoring 00, 13 through 99, and any repetitions from 01 through 12 that might occur. Or use five spins of a spinner marked into 12 equal sectors, with the names of the students on the sectors and ignoring repetitions of a name when spinning.

   b. Answers will vary, of course. Were there any surprises in your ten samples? For example, was some one person on a large number of samples?

5. a. Answers will vary.

   b. A TRSD, with even digits being H and odd digits being T, gives one method.

   c. Answer will vary, of course. The interesting thing is that humans usually *avoid* having several H's or T's in a row, but such does happen with random tosses.

29.4 Types of Data

1. a. Categorical

   b. Measurement

c. Categorical

d. Measurement (either in terms of number of programs or number of hours)

e. Categorical

2. Categorical data. The numbers are just codes for computer purposes.

3. a. Possibles: The total score on an attitude questionnaire could give measurement data. A list of descriptions of attitudes, one of which is to be checked, could give categorical data.

b. Possibles: Put the person to work on the task, and see how long the person works to a certain level; this time would give measurement data. Asking the person to check his/her choice in a list of descriptions of willingness to work hard (very willing, somewhat willing, neutral, somewhat reluctant, very reluctant) could give categorical data.

c. Possibles: Measuring the volume of applause at the end would give measurement data. Asking a critic to judge the performance could give categorical data (outstanding, very good, good, and so forth).

d. Possibles: Density of vehicle traffic or the number of pedestrian accidents over a specified time period could give measurement data. The opinion of a traffic guard, if available, could give categorical data (safe, unsafe).

e. Possibles: Using the number of cavities or the depth of the gum-tooth gap would give measurement data. Using the dentist's or dental technician's opinion would give categorical data.

f. Possibles: A gadget that can give varying amounts of electrical shock or pressure until the person complains could give measurement data for beginning pain intensity (it is less clear how the gadget could help measure more intense pain levels). Asking the person to judge "on a scale from 1 to 10, with 10 highest" their reactions to various pain inducers could give categorical data.

g. Possibles: A player's winning percentage against players at one or more standard skill levels would give measurement data. Asking the opinion of a tennis expert could give categorical data.

4. During each heartbeat, blood pressure varies between a maximum (systolic) and a minimum (diastolic) pressure. We express a person's blood pressure in terms of the systolic pressure over diastolic pressure, for example 120/80. Blood pressure expressed in this way can be measurement data. Blood pressure varies throughout the day and is

affected by minor factors but can be characterized as high, normal, or low, for example, if found in particular ranges over a few measurements.

Supplementary Learning Exercises for Section 29.4

1. a. categorical (One might count the number of Tom-Dick-Harry finishes, but T-D-H is just a category.)

    b. categorical (If by some strange chance, someone was thinking "length of favorite movie," then it would be measurement.)

    c. measurement, although if answers are confined to choices such as "lots," "average," "little," and "none," the data would be categorical. Some books would label these categories as *ordinal* data because there is a natural order to the categories.

    d. measurement, if the focus is the number of books; categorical, if the focus is the particular titles

    e. measurement, if the focus is the number of children; categorical, if birth orders like GBG for 3-children families is the focus

2. Samples are given here. There may be other possibilities.

    a. measurement: number of hours or minutes; categorical: types of sports

    b. measurement: number of laps swum, number of competitors, or time for race; categorical: type of stroke, length of race

    c. measurement: amount spent, number of stores visited, or number of items purchased; categorical: types of items sought or types of stores visited

    d. measurement: value of prizes, loudness (singer or audience), or number of votes; categorical: types of songs

3. The numbers just describe the different categories, so they give categorical data.

Answers for Chapter 30: Representing and Interpreting Data with One Variable

30.1 Representing Categorical Data

1. a. Bar chart? Yes. We no longer know who actually walked, rode the bus, and took a car to school. Circle graph? When we use a circle graph, we lose the same information as with the bar chart, and more: We no longer know the actual number of students who took a car, rode a bus, or walked to school. We now know only the percentage of students in the class who took each form of transportation.

    b. A pie chart shows at a glance what part of the whole sample each group is (and most often the percent as well). A disadvantage is that the actual number in each group may not be shown on a pie chart. Which of the two is more effective depends on the story to be told.

2. a. If you required your students to make the graph without software, here are the numbers of degrees for the sectors:

    Nursery and preschool: 22°

    Kindergarten: 18°

    Grades 1–8:   143°

    High School: 75°

    College: 102°

    Enrollment in Schools

    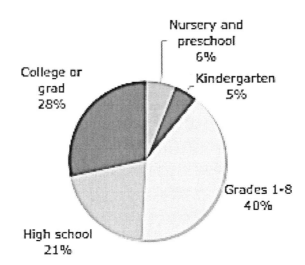

    b. Bar Grapher, from http://illuminations.nctm.org could be used. Unlike below, it does not label the vertical axis. (You may have required your students to make theirs without software.)

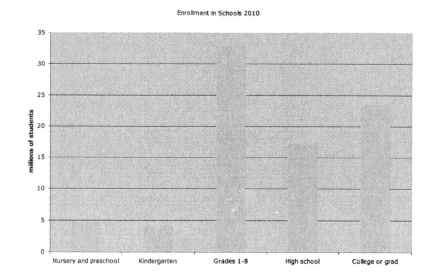

Enrollment in Schools 2010

c. Answers will vary. Many are surprised that there were more students in post–high school than in high school (in 2010).

3. Typically, a graph has a title. What would be a reasonable title for this graph?

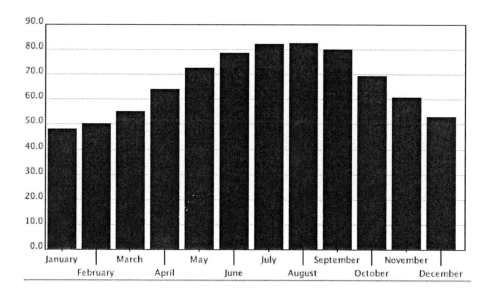

4.   Following is most of the screen (the color coding may not be apparent).

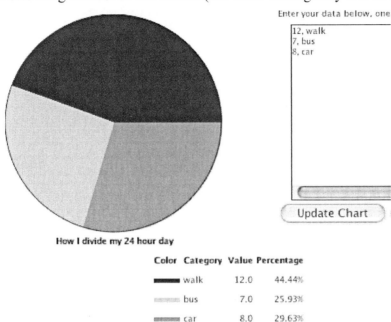

How I divide my 24 hour day

Color	Category	Value	Percentage
walk	walk	12.0	44.44%
bus	bus	7.0	25.93%
car	car	8.0	29.63%
Sum of values =		27.0	

5. Here is most of the display. The color coding may not show up here.

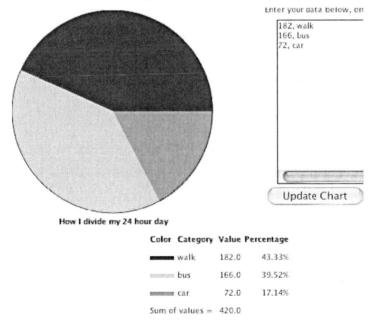

How I divide my 24 hour day

Color	Category	Value	Percentage
walk	walk	182.0	43.33%
bus	bus	166.0	39.52%
car	car	72.0	17.14%
Sum of values =		420.0	

Comparing the graphs for Learning Exercises 4 and 5 suggests that in Jasmine's class, a noticeably greater percent ride the bus and a smaller percent come by car than in the whole school.

6.   Choice b is correct. Is it surprising that 21% of the eighth graders were *not* correct? But to respond correctly, one must recognize that the time spent on mathematics is

represented by about $\frac{1}{4}$ of the circular region, so if that represents 2 hours, then the whole circular region, $\frac{4}{4}$, must represent 8 hours. A correct response required reading the graph and dealing with the resulting fraction, extrapolating the time for the fraction to the time for the whole.

7.   a. Both length and width are doubled for the larger drawing, leaving the visual impression of being 4 times as large as the smaller drawing, when the actual enrollment is only twice as much.

   b. The graph leaves the impression that enrollment changes are much greater than they actually are.

8.   a. The graph triples the three dimensions of the currency, leaving the impression that the "Now" figure is 27 times as great as the "Then" figure, when it is actually only 3 times as great.

   b. Answers will vary.

   c. Nine times as great.

   d. By starting the scale at $20, the graph makes the "Now" amount appear to be much more than 3 times as large as the "Then" amount.

Supplementary Learning Exercises for Section 30.1

1.   a–b. Following are graphs from Excel; compare yours for accuracy. The percents are calculated by dividing the travel mode by the total number of children, 150; angle sizes are calculated in this way:

For bus travel, $\frac{90}{150} \cdot 360 = \frac{3}{5} \cdot 360 = 3 \cdot 72 = 216$ degrees.

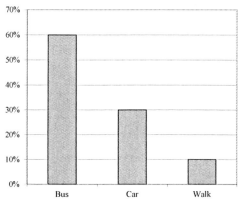

Mode of Travel to Cousin's School (%)

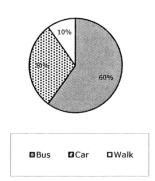

Mode of Travel to Cousin's School

   c. Your pictograph should have 6 of your basic symbols for bus, 3 for car, and 1 for walk.

d. Because of the larger percent by bus and the relatively small percent by walking for the cousin's data than for Jasmine's school, the cousin's school is the one in a rural area.

2. The graphs for Exercise 1 above are from Excel.

3. a. Many of the values are decimals, so showing parts of some basic symbol could be messy.

    b. The sum of the values does not make sense here.

    c. Here is a graph from Excel.

Fertility Rates in Selected Countries

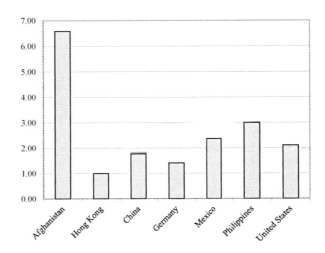

d. Low fertility rates might result in a shrinking population, with an increasing percent of older people. A high fertility rate might result in a high rate of increase in population, with accompanying strains on resources. (Different immigration and emigration figures, as well as child mortality rates, are of course potential influences on population. Hong Kong, for example, might have large numbers of immigrants, and Afghanistan might have a high child mortality rate.)

4.   a. (from Excel)

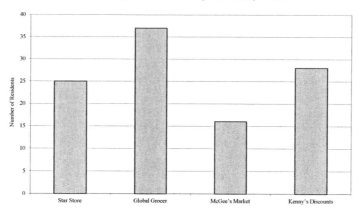

Neighborhood Patronage at Grocery Stores

b. (from Excel)

Neighborhood Patronage at Grocery Stores

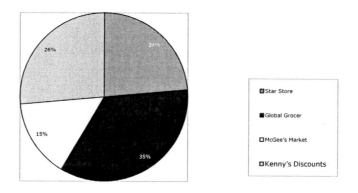

c. In the bar graph it is easy to see a difference in height. Without the percent labels it is difficult to tell the exact portions on the circle graph.

5.   Here is a slightly different style from the one in the answer for Exercise 4.

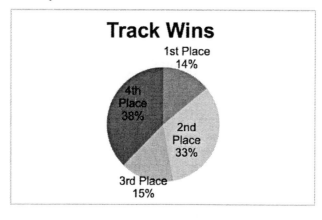

6.

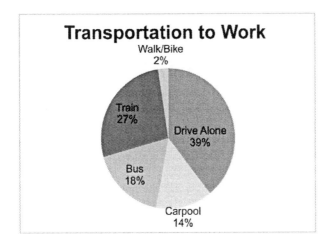

Transportation to Work

Walk/Bike
2%

Train
27%

Drive Alone
39%

Bus
18%

Carpool
14%

7.   Questions will vary. Here is one: What assumptions does this graph make? (A student does only one thing. All students participate.)

30.2 Representing and Interpreting Measurement Data

1.   a.   Stem-and-leaf plot? No. It's just organized differently. Histogram? Yes. The data are now gathered into selected ranges of values, so we no longer know what the individual estimates were.

   b.   Advantage: Counts indicated on the vertical scale. Disadvantage· Cannot tell the original scores because they are lumped together in the cells. If by "telling a story" is meant giving an overall impression of the data, the histogram is so much more common than the stem-and-leaf plot that it might be preferred.

2.   a.   The cells are not of equal size.

   b.   A pie chart might be usable, although there are 10 categories. Alternatively, the data could be put into cells of size $50,000 (but doing that loses lots of information, especially for the low incomes).

3.   a.   Pie chart, or bar chart

   b.   Histogram, or stem-and-leaf plot

   c.   Pie chart, or bar chart

   d.   Pie chart, or bar chart

   e.   Histogram, line graph, or stem-and-leaf plot

   f.   Histogram, or stem-and-leaf plot

   g.   Histogram (if the number of types of candy bars with grams in certain intervals is of concern) or stem-and-leaf plot; bar graph if the focus is on grams versus type of candy bar

h. Histogram, line graph, or stem-and-leaf plot. The first two would be easiest to make as the weights are made.

4. a. *Note*: Excel can order the data for you, if you are able to use it (go to Data in the menu heading at the top).

    ```
    0|00023456668888
    1|000001222224444444566666668
    2|0000022222444668
    3|022
    4|0
    ```

    b. The histogram below was generated by software using the convention that the cell contains scores less than or equal to the upper bound (and greater than the lower bound). Here are the data on the GPAs of the 21 Republican students, ordered:

    0.8 1.9 2.0 2.1 2.2 2.6 2.6 2.7 2.8 3.1 3.1 3.1 3.2 3.2 3.4 3.5

    3.5 3.5 3.6 3.6 4.0

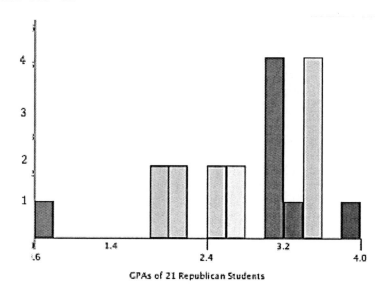

GPAs of 21 Republican Students

5. The color coding may not show up.

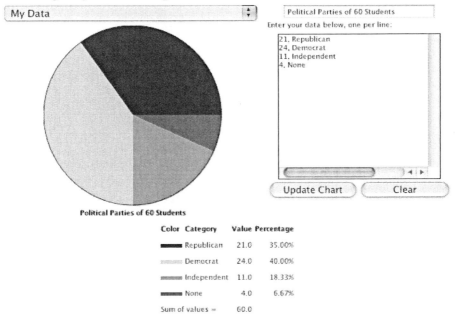

Color	Category	Value	Percentage
	Republican	21.0	35.00%
	Democrat	24.0	40.00%
	Independent	11.0	18.33%
	None	4.0	6.67%
	Sum of values =	60.0	

6. Graphs may differ if the student chose an interval size $\neq$ 4.

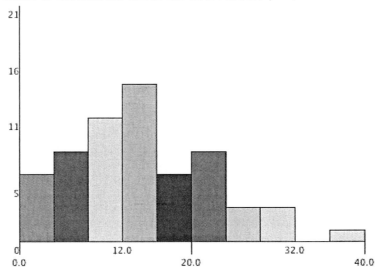

Hours Worked Per Week by 60 Students

7. You may have chosen a different length for the cell width. With a maximum of 8, it is reasonable to have the cell interval of 1 hour. The Histogram Tool includes counts of values at the upper end of the interval in a particular cell.

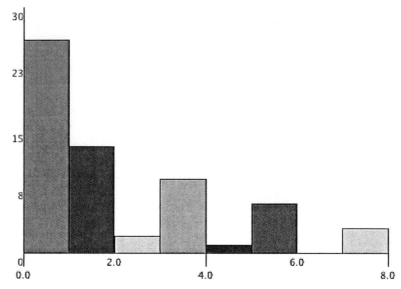

Volunteer Hours Per Week by 60 Students

8.   For example, students work far more than they volunteer each week.

Supplementary Learning Exercises for Section 30.2

1.   a–b. Here are a sample stem-and-leaf plot and (from Fathom) a histogram for the scores.

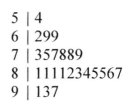

5 | 4
6 | 299
7 | 357889
8 | 11112345567
9 | 137

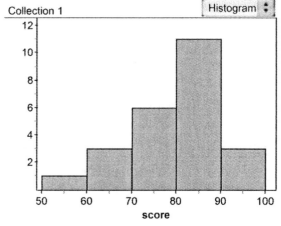

c. The stem-and-leaf plot allows you to tell each individual score, whereas the histogram does not tell where the individual scores are located within the bar.

2.   a. i. 7 rows 3–9   ii. 10 rows (or 11)   iii. 56 rows, 39 through 94
     iv. The last digit does not indicate a significant amount relative to the count.

b. The stem plot could vary depending on your answers in part (a). Truncating (omitting) the ones digit gives the following plot.

The stem is in the hundreds, so 3 | 9 9 represents 390 and 395.

```
3 | 9 9
4 | 0 1 1 2 3 3 4 5 7 8 9
5 | 2 4 4 5 7 8 8 9
6 | 5
7 | 0 5 8
8 |
9 | 1 4
```

c. The data are mostly bunched between 400 and 600.

d. 523

3. a. Circle graph, bar graph

b. Stem-and-leaf plot (histogram, box plot from the next section)

c. Circle graph, bar graph

d. Stem-and-leaf plot (histogram, box plot from the next section)

e. Circle graph, bar graph

f. Circle graph, bar graph

4.

```
2 | 1 2 4 4 4 4 6 6 6 6 6 6 7 7 7 7 8 8 9 9 9
3 | 0 0 0 0 0 1 1 1 2 3 3 3 3 4 4 4 4 4 5 5 5 7 7 7 7 8 8 8 9 9 9
4 | 1 1 1 1 2 2 5 5 7 9 9
5 |
6 | 0 1 1 2
7 | 4
8 | 1
```

5. Your graph should carry the same ideas as the one given here. The colors may be difficult to distinguish in this version. Notice the clutter, even without percents.

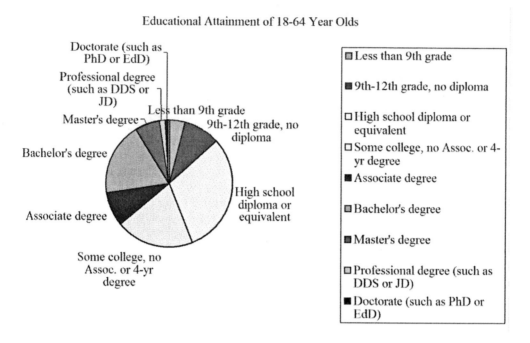

Educational Attainment of 18-64 Year Olds

30.3 Examining the Spread of Data

1.   a. For which of the following data sets does it make sense to talk about quartile scores?

   i.   Quartiles make sense because the data set is numerical and large enough for quartile scores to make sense.

   ii. Quartiles make sense because the data set has a large number of numerical data values.

   iii. Quartiles do not make sense because the data are nonnumerical (categorical).

   iv. Quartiles do not make sense because the data are nonnumerical (categorical).

   v.   Quartiles make sense because the data set is measurement and has a large number of data values.

   It does not make sense to talk about quartile scores for all numerical data sets. In fact, for small numerical data sets, quartile scores are often inappropriate. For example, finding all three quartile scores for a data set containing five numbers is not useful. Therefore, finding the quartile scores for the number of M&M's of each color in a bag is not very meaningful. However, finding the median of these numbers may be meaningful, suggesting a representative number of M&M's for each color.

   b. SAT tests, GPAs for a graduating class, GRE scores, for example

c. Hair color of students in your class, for example

d. A large number of data values that are numerical and can be ordered

2.   In general they are average to above-average readers. Some of the students scored as well as or better than 69% of the students tested, while all of the students in the reading group scored as well as or better than 47% of the students tested.

3.   a. low: 131; 1st quartile: 139.5; 2nd quartile (median): 146; 3rd quartile: 150; high: 164

b. You would still be leaving out the heights of 50% of the girls.

4   a. *Exactly* 50% of the data: 1, 2, 3, 4, 5, 6, 7, 8, 9, 10, 11, 12, for example. Notice that this data set has an even number of values.

b. No. Why not?

c. *More than* 50% of the data: 1, 2, 2, 3, 3, 4, 5, 6, 7, 7, 23, for example. 4 is the median, and 6 of the 11 data values (or about 55% of the data values) are less than or equal to the median. (This data set has an odd number of values. Is this the only way to create a data set with more than 50% of the data less than or equal to the median?)

5.   a. Has no left whisker: 5, 5, 5, 6, 6, 7, 7, 8, 8, 9, 9, for example

b. Has no whiskers at all: 5, 5, 5, 6, 6, 7, 7, 7, 8, 8, 8, for example

c. Has an outlier: 1, 7, 8, 9, 9, 10, 10, 11, 11, 13, 15

d. Has a box made of only one rectangle, not two: 7, 7, 7, 7, 7, 7, 7, 7, 8, 8, 8

e. Has no box: 8, 8, 8, 8, 8, 8, 8, 8, 8, 8, 8

f. The following answers apply to the examples given above:

   a.   The first quartile is the same as the minimum.

   b.   The minimum is the same as the first quartile and the third quartile is the same as the maximum.

   c.   The IQR is $11 - 8 = 3$. $1.5 \times 3 = 4.5$. One value is more than 4.5 from 8.

   d.   The median is the same as the first quartile, but the third quartile is different. (This could be different. How?)

   e.   All the values are the same.

6.   a. It is difficult to judge without knowing more about the nature of the test. But the scores look typical for a test out of 100.

b. The whisker for the first quartile scores does not show exactly where the scores are. The first quartile score itself does appear to be above 70. Thus, the 25% of the 32 scores, or 8, could almost all be in the low 70's, but all *could* be below 70. So we can say that at most 8 of the 32, plus the outlier for a total of 9, could be below 70, or if there is just one low score within the first quartile scores (with the others in the 70's), that score and the outlier would give only 2 scores below 70.

c. About 5

d. Perhaps the aide recorded this test score incorrectly on the computer, and the student actually scored a 95 rather than a 5. Mr. Meyer will probably go back and look at the test scores as they are recorded on each student's test!

7. a. Samples: What is the (1st, 2nd, 3rd) quartile for…? How many women/men…? What are some outliers for the women/men? What is the interquartile range for…?

b. What is the average (mean) weight for women in the study? What is the mean weight for the men? How many men weighed between 150 and 160 pounds?

c. Women's weights are generally less than men's weights, but men's weights are somewhat more spread out.

d. No, because twice as many women as men were surveyed.

8. Without more marks on the scores, the weights are just estimates. With 60 people involved, we will be looking for weights that give four intervals with about 15 people in each. About 10 women (W) weigh less than about 115, plus still no men (M) and more of the W to make 15—1st quartile about 122, say. Similarly, the median might be around 130, because 10 more women and about 2 men are less than 135. The third quartile about 150. The low woman's weight is about 70 pounds, and the high man's weight is about 250 pounds. $1.5 \times (150 - 122) = 42$, so the 70 is an outlier and the low weight is 100, and the 255 is also an outlier, so the high weight is about 215.

9. On examining the box plot of the distribution of the weights of the 20 men in item 7, one could conclude that about 5 men have weights between about 125 and 150 pounds (so not histograms b and c), about 5 men have weights between 150 and 175 pounds, about 5 men have weights between 175 and 190 pounds (so not histogram d), and about 5 men have weights between 190 and 220 pounds. One man has a weight of about 250 pounds. Histogram a looks best.

10. a.

	Form of data (num or cat)	# of Variables	Shows actual data	Shows actual counts	Shows %	Shows shape
Circle graph	cat	1	no	perhaps	usually	no
Histogram	num	1	no	yes	no*	yes
Stem plot	num	1	yes	Can do	no	yes
Bar graph	cat	1	yes	yes	no*	yes
Box plot	num	1	no	no	some	sort of

*Scales can be adjusted.

   b. Each gives a visual representation of the data. Each provides a summary of the data. Some differences are apparent from the chart (type of data, whether or not original data preserved, percents given in some way, "shape" of data shown).

11. The stem-and-leaf isn't shown here.

Five-number summaries:

Females: 0.8 (outlier), 1.8, 2.45, 2.75, 3.15, 3.9

Males: 1.9, 2.45, 3.1, 3.45, 4

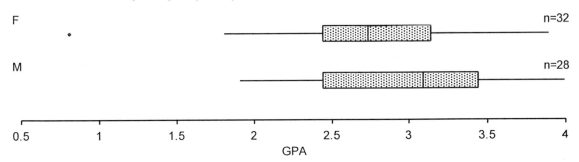

The median for the males is somewhat higher, and the top 50% of the males score about as well as the top 25% of the females. The spreads are about the same for the two genders (ignoring the female outlier).

12. The difficulty with the stem-and-leaf plot here is that the areas are so different, with several values not too far apart but with an extreme value. Here is one way, with the areas in millions of square kilometers.

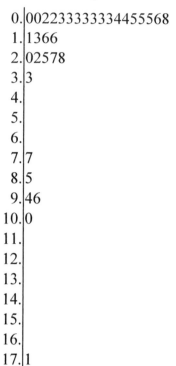

```
 0.|002233333334455568
 1.|1366
 2.|02578
 3.|3
 4.|
 5.|
 6.|
 7.|7
 8.|5
 9.|46
10.|0
11.|
12.|
13.|
14.|
15.|
16.|
17.|1
```

13. Here is most of the display.

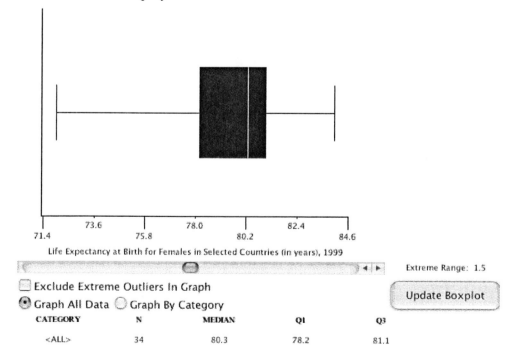

Life Expectancy at Birth for Females in Selected Countries (in years), 1999

CATEGORY	N	MEDIAN	Q1	Q3
<ALL>	34	80.3	78.2	81.1

14. Your paragraph should give not only statistics but also some commentary about what the results might mean for these 60 students.

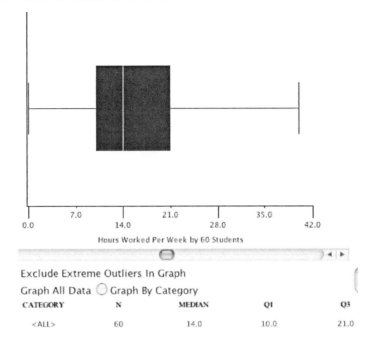

15. Besides the usual numbers, the student's paragraph should include some interpretation of the data, with the discussion of the first quartile of greatest interest and whether a box plot is the best graph to use for these data.

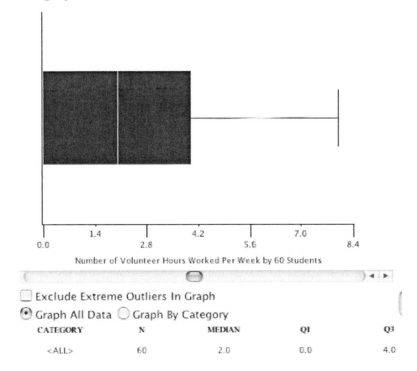

16. Choice d is correct. It is noteworthy that an item about a stem-and-leaf plot is on this national exam (although one could argue that how to read the plot is explained in the item).

17. Choice b is correct. Here are percents choosing the distracters: a, 10%; c, 16%; d, 15%; e, 8%.

Supplementary Learning Exercises for Section 30.3

1. a. The data would be categorical (for example, chocolate, strawberry), so a five-number summary does not make sense.

    b. This situation would give measurement data, so a five-number summary makes sense.

    c. This situation would give measurement data, so a five-number summary makes sense.

    d. The data would be categorical, so a five-number summary does not make sense.

    e. This situation would give measurement data, so a five-number summary makes sense.

2. Neither Arnold's nor Bonnie's parents should be concerned about the child failing, because each scores in the upper half of all the scores. Carl's parents, on the other hand, might worry, because 52% on a semester test is not a good score at all.

3. a. Ignoring the two outliers at 53 and 62, the five-number summary is 68 (low), 78 (first quartile score), about 81 (median), about 88 (third quartile score), 99 (high score). The second quartile involves several scores bunched between 78 and about 81.

    b. This box plot does not contain information about the number of scores, nor about the individual scores. (However, such information is available with the software.)

4. This is not statistically possible. Half of the scores will be below the median by definition. The median is dependent on the scores of the test and is not a value that is predetermined. The district could possibly set a goal for passing, and this could be a specific score that is not dependent on the outcomes.

5. a. Here is a sample box plot (from Fathom).

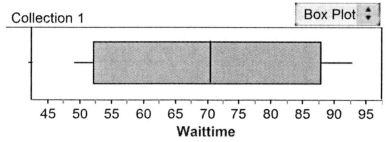

Your box plot should involve (roughly) this five-number summary:

Minimum	Q1	Median	Q3	Maximum
49	52	70.5	88	93

    b. In this case, we no longer have the order in which they occurred, nor any knowledge about their exact values (except for the minimum and maximum).

6.   Your answers may differ from the samples given, of course.

    a. **14**, 15, **18**, 19, 19, 20, 20, **22**, 32, **40**

    b. **82**, 82, 82, 82, **82**, **82**, 94, **94**, 98, **98**

    c. **10**, 10, **19**, 19, **26, 28**, 48, **59**, 60, **75**

7.   Parts of your box plots will depend on your answers, of course. The following Fathom plots are for the data sets given in the answer to Exercise 6.

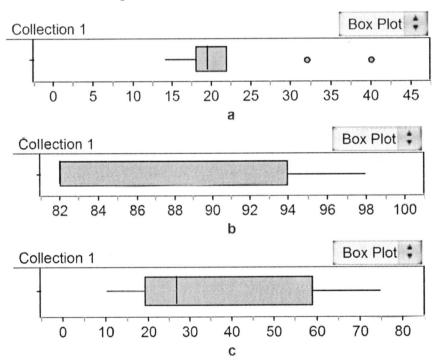

8.   Your box plot should look something like this one from Fathom.

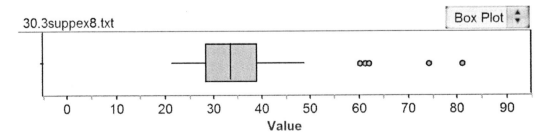

9.   a. Histogram a goes with the third box plot.

      b. Histogram b goes with the middle box plot.

   c. Histogram c goes with the first box plot.

10. a. 58, 72, 76, 86, 95   b. 14, 17.5, 20.5, 25, 32

11. $0.78 \times 485 \approx 378$ students scored equal to or lower than Roger.

12. There are roughly 35% of the cases between the 30th and 65th percentiles. So there are roughly $0.35 \times 750 \approx 262$ students between the 30th and 65th percentiles.

30.4 Measures of Center

1.   a. Yes ($8, $9, $10, $11, $12, e.g.)

     b. Yes ($8, $8, $9, $11, $14, e.g.)

     c. Yes ($1, $2, $3, $6, $38, e.g.)

     d. Yes (Is there more than one set of five prices that meets this condition?)

     e. Yes (see 1(c), e.g.)

     f. No. If one thinks of the mean as a balancing point of the data set, then the mean would have to either be a value in the data set or a value that falls between the largest and smallest value in the data set.

2.   a–e. Yes

     f. No

3.   1, 8, 9, 9, 9, 9, 9, 9. (The mean is 7.875; the first quartile score is 8.5.) The low outlier helps pull the mean down.

4.   a. The mean, because a large percentage of homes may range in price from $100,000–$500,000, but a small percentage of homes may have prices in the millions of dollars. The prices of these more expensive homes may be outliers, which tend to affect the mean (in this case, increase the mean) much more than they affect the median.

     b. The median because... or the mean because...

     c. The mean age of females because, as a group, females probably tend to get married for the first time when they are anywhere from 21–28. A small percentage may get married younger (but only by 1–2 years), and a small percentage may get married older, but this group that marries when they are older could actually be much older than the more typical range (they could be in their late thirties and forties). The older ones then could affect the mean upwards in a more significant way than they would affect the median.

     d. The median, because although there are a few that live a long time, there are many more who die young in accidents.

     e. The mean, because there are relatively few very large families, so these would affect the mean more than they would affect the median.

5.   18, 18, 19, 35, 40, for example. Create your own set.

6.   a. The rectangle's width is about $\frac{6}{10}$ times its height.

     b. No, because the ratio is simply what the Greeks strove for visually. The actual dimensions will have different ratios due to human error in construction, measurement, and measurement tools.

     c. The mean of the ratio of the dimensions of the rectangles is 0.6605, the median is 0.641, and the mode is 0.606. However, without the outliers, the mean is 0.635 and the median is 0.622. It is likely that the Shoshonis also found the shapes of golden rectangles appealing, because the mean, median, and mode are fairly close to the ratio of 0.618034, particularly if outliers are disregarded.

     d. The choice of graph is important. A histogram or box plot will show the spread.

7.   Early coinage: the percents by weight of silver in the coins range from 5.9–7.7; the mean is 6.744 and the median is 6.8

Second coinage: the percents by weight of silver in the coins range from 5.1–6.2; the mean is 5.614, and the median is 5.6

If we assume that the percentages of the silver content of the coins given in the problem are representative of the percentages of the silver contents of the coins for each time period (early and late), then we would probably say that there was a difference in the silver content of the coins, drawing this conclusion because the means and medians both differ greatly between time periods relative to the percent of silver in the coins for either time period.

Of course, in this example we did not actually need to compute means or medians. Because every number in the first set is larger than every number in the second set, we know there is a difference in silver content.

8.   A mean of 79.8 points can be interpreted as meaning that each person would have scored 79.8 points, if all the points for the class had been distributed equally.

9. The means are 11.5 points per game for the Amazons, 12 points per game for the Bears, and about 11.4 points per game for the Cougars. So one could argue that the Bears are best.

10. Because the mean gives a per-person or per-item value, it gives a way to avoid the complication from having groups of different sizes.

11. 10.091 points per player   (Instructor: 111 total points, 11 players)

12. No, because you need to know how many credit hours are represented by each GPA.

13. $83.43 per day

14. The answer is *not* 55 miles per hour; it is 54.55 miles per hour.

15. e. That only 45% were correct suggests that there is little meaning attached to "average weight."

16. (a) and (d) are not possible; (b) and (c) are. Are the results surprising?

17. a. 34

    c. The median, because of the relatively large number at the younger ages

18. Histogram (a) goes with box plot (C); (b) with (B); (c) with (A); and (d) with (D).

Supplementary Learning Exercises for Section 30.4

1. a. Median. There could be outliers of high salaried management.

    b. Mean. Prices tend to be similar in a region.

    c. Mode. Types of car owned give categorical data.

    d. Mean, unless there are some extreme outliers.

    e. Median. Some houses can have extremely high prices compared to others in the area.

    f. Mean, although mode might fit kindergarteners better.

2. a. Mean = 11   median = 7.5

    b. Mean = 8.45   median = 7   The mean is affected more than the median by the relatively large 39 (for 12 cases). When the 39 is removed (now 11 cases) the median is moved by at most one case.

3. a. Mean = 4.85   standard deviation = 0.286 feet (0.279 on some calculators)

    b. Mean = 58.25   standard deviation = 3.432 inches (3.345 on some calculators)

    c. The numbers have increased by a factor of 12, but the actual values (with units) are the same. For example, 0.286 feet = 3.432 inches.

d. Your graphs should have the same shape but different scales.

4. $3 + 4 + 4 + 6 = 17$ dozen, or $17 \times 12 = 204$, cupcakes. With 4 nights involved, that gives an average of 51 cupcakes per night.

5. a. Possible

    b. Possible (if each cat weighed 14 pounds)

    c. Not possible (Why?)

    d. Possible

    e. Not possible (Why?)

    f. Possible (if the third cat weighs enough more than 14 pounds to make up for the lighter cats)

6. $(32 \times 8.50) + (8 \times 12.75) = 374$ dollars for the 40 hours, an average of $9.35 per hour

30.5 Deviations from the Mean as Measures of Spread

1. The average deviation of the Gonzales data is 2 minutes; for the Childress data it is 4.4 minutes. Be sure to point out that the sums of the deviations (20 minutes and 22 minutes) are quite close, but the numbers of deviations are quite different (10 and 5), so the means of the deviations provide a better measure of spread.

2. a. B, because of the one high value

    b. D, because of the very low value at the end

    c. Both B and D have a great deal of variation, so it is hard to tell.

    d. C, because there is very little variation among the numbers

    (Instructor: A has a mean of 63.2 and a standard deviation of 11.1. B has a mean of 63.4 and a standard deviation of 21.7. C has a mean of 69.8 and a standard deviation of 1.7. D has a mean of 59 and a standard deviation of 21.1.)

3. The mean is 5.75 and the standard deviation is 0.8. Most shoe sizes will be within one standard deviation of the mean, which would be between 4.95 and 6.55, that is, shoe sizes 5, 5.5, 6, and 6.5. Most of the shoes should come in these sizes.

    The five-number summary is 4–5–5.75–6.5–7.5. Thus, 50% of the women have shoe sizes between 5 and 6.5.

You may, of course, simply decide to make a tally and use that to decide what percentage of each size to get. With a small sample this is easy to do, and thus the statistics in this case don't give much additional information.

4. The mean is 62.8, and the standard deviation is 12.6. The score 1 deviation below the mean is 50.2, and the score 2 standard deviations below the mean is 37.6. The score 1 standard deviation above the mean is 75.4, and the score 2 standard deviations above the mean is 88. Therefore, the 2 students with scores below 37.6 (62.8–25.2) would receive an F, and the 6 students with scores between 37.6 and 50.2 would receive a D. The 28 students with scores between 50.2 and 75.4 would receive a C. The 9 students with scores between 75.4 and 88 would receive a B. A student with a score 88 or above would receive an A, but there were no such scores.

    There would be 0 A's, 9 B's, 28 C's, 6 D's, and 2 F's.

5. The standard deviation for Mr. Sanders's fire drill data *without* the outlier of 130 seconds is 11.46 seconds. *With* the outlier, the standard deviation is 19.56 seconds. The standard deviation is strongly affected by the outlier because the formula for the standard deviation requires the use of the mean in its derivation. Because the mean increased greatly when including the outlier, the squares of the differences between most of the data values and the mean increased. Thus, the standard deviation increased.

6. a. Mean 2.74, standard deviation 0.65 (or possibly 0.66, depending on the technology)
    b. Mean 2.99, standard deviation 0.60 (or possibly 0.62, depending on the technology). The mean for the males is somewhat higher, and their scores are slightly less spread out.

7. a. The second average deviation would be *numerically* less than the first average deviation because a kilogram is a bigger unit than a pound. The bigger the unit, the smaller the values of the weights. Because the values of the weights will be smaller, the value of the mean and all the other data values will also be *numerically* smaller. Thus, the second average deviation will also be numerically smaller. Taking units into account, the statistics are the same.
    b. The second standard deviation would be numerically less than the first standard deviation for the reasons similar to those described above, but equal if units are taken into account.

8. a. The mean is changed in the same way, but the standard deviation stays the same.
    b. Both the mean and the standard deviation are changed in the same way.

Here is an example, subtracting 5 from the given scores and dividing the given scores by 5. Your investigations should suggest the same results.

Score	Score – 5	Score ÷ 5
75	70	15
80	75	16
85	80	17
90	85	18
95	90	19
means	85	80	17
st. dev.	7.07	7.07	1.41

Supplementary Learning Exercises for Section 30.5

1. a. First reorder the scores: 2, 5, 8, 9, 9, 12, 13, 16, 19, 19, 21, 24. The range is
       $24 - 2 = 22$.

    b. There are 12 values in the set, so the median is the average of the two middle scores,
       12 and 13, which is 12.5. There are 6 values in the bottom half of the set, and the
       median of the bottom half is the average of 8 and 9, which is 8.5. So 8.5 is the first
       quartile. The median of the top half is 19, which is the average of 19 and 19. So 19 is
       the third quartile. The five-number summary is 2, 8.5, 12.5, 19, 24.

    c. The interquartile range is $19 - 8.5 = 10.5$. Outliers would need to be less than
       $8.5 - 15.75 = {}^-7.25$ or greater than $19 + 15.75 = 34.75$. There are no such values
       among the scores ($1.5 \times 10.5 = 15.75$).

    d. This box plot is from *Illuminations*, but you should be able to draw one of your own.
       Remember to keep the units equal in size on the bottom axis.

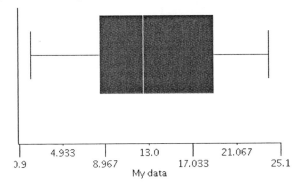

    e. The mean of the scores is slightly more than 13.

    f. The distribution is bimodal. The two modes are 9 and 19.

g. The mean (13) and the median (12.5) are quite close for these data. Because there is not one mode, the mode could not be compared to the mean and the median.

h. The average deviation is 5.6. The calculation is shown below.

Values	Distance from 13	Squared distance from the mean
2	11	121
5	8	64
8	5	25
9	4	16
9	4	16
12	1	1
13	0	0
16	3	9
19	6	36
19	6	36
21	8	64
24	11	121
Sum	**67**	**509**

$67 \div 12 = 5.6$ $509 \div 12 = 42.4$ is the variance, so

$$\sqrt{42.4} \approx 6.5 \text{ is the standard deviation.}$$

i. The standard deviation is 6.5. The calculation is shown above.

j. 5.6 units and 6.5 units are fairly close. Both numbers provide information about the spread of the data. The five-number summary is also an indication of spread, but of a different type.

2. a. The average *yearly* rainfall for New Orleans is 61.88, and for San Diego it is 9.90. (Just add the monthly averages.)

b. The average *monthly* rainfall for New Orleans is 5.16, and for San Diego it is 0.83. (Find the average of the monthly rainfall amounts.)

c. Answers will vary. Recall that the standard deviation is a measure of spread.

d. The standard deviation of monthly rainfall for New Orleans is 0.888 (or 0.928 on some calculators), and for San Diego it is 0.706 (or 0.738 on some calculators). Why are the standard deviations so close while the means are, relatively speaking, so far apart?

30.6 Examining Distributions

1. a. Many students will assume that there are more longer words than shorter words, because it is a college text.

b. Students likely noticed something like this: In my sample, the distribution is light to the right ("skewed right" or has a tail to the right–see Learning Exercise 5). Three-letter words occurred more often than words with any other number of letters.

c. Some students may think that they have chosen an unusual paragraph and create a graph less skewed to the right.

2. a. 3, 4, 4, 5, 5, 5, 5, 6, 6, 7, for example. This data set is *approximately* normally distributed because the mean, median, and mode are all the same, and thus most the data values are equal to or near the mean. Also, it is symmetric. All of these are characteristics of data sets that are normally distributed.

    b. 2, 2, 2, 2, 3, 4, 5, 8, 10, 12, 12, 12, 12, 12, 12, for example. This data set is not normally distributed because the mean is 7.333, the median is 8, and the mode is 12. Because the mode and the mean are relatively spread apart, and because most of the data values are not located relatively close to the mean, this data set is not approximately normally distributed. The data set gives two humps.

3. The mode in Class A was about 90; for Class B, 40; and for Class C, 90. By and large, the students in Class A and C outscored the students in Class B by a wide margin. The students in Class A tended to do better than those in Class C. In Class C the second most common score was 58, while there were only a small number of students who scored 70 or 80 on the exam. The teacher of Class C might wonder whether the students could be grouped into "studied" and "didn't study" categories. What other reasons might lead to such a "bimodal" distribution?

4. a. No, a negative z-score just means that the score was below the mean.
    b. The z-score that corresponds to the mean is 0.

5. a. The number of letters in words in a college text (as in Learning Exercise 1). In texts, we use three letter words such as "and" and "the" often. Other possibilities: Scores on a very difficult test; number of pounds lost on a diet; improvement in strength with an exercise program; times during an open tryout for the swimming team.

    b. Age of women at death, because there may be relatively few women who die young, while most die at an old age, and few live beyond that. Other possibilities: Scores on an easy test; number of pounds gained over the December holidays; points scored in a game by a good basketball player.

6. a. Apparently not. Although the mean (12.87) and median (13) are about the same, the mode (11) differs. The shape of the histogram looks skewed right, rather than being symmetrical.

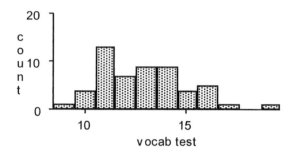

b. The large number of occurrences of 11 makes it difficult to use the rule. With that exception, the rule might be applicable.

7. A data set that has only 90% of the data values within 2 standard deviations of the mean is 1, 1, 1, 1, 1, 1, 1, 1, 1, 10. The mean is 1.9 and the standard deviation is 2.7. Here is one data set that has about 81% of the data values that fall within two standard deviations of the mean: 57 ones and 13 tens.

8. Data sets that are normally distributed have bell shapes that are nearly symmetrical. In this case, half of the values must fall to the right of the mean, and half of the values must fall to the left of the mean. Thus, the mean in a normal distribution is also the median. Also, because the majority of the points are located in the center of the distribution, we can say that the value that occurs most often is the mean. Thus, the mean in a normal distribution is also the mode.

9. Symmetric distributions with two or more "humps" would not be normal. Such a two-humped ("bimodal") distribution might result from scores on a test for which several students studied but several others did not study.

10. The data set 1, 2, 2, 2, 3, 4, 5, 6, 6, 6, 7 has 2 modes: 2 and 6 (it is "bimodal"), yet the median is 4. Bimodal distributions from Exercise 9 would give different values for the median and the (two) modes.

11. a. The six-year-old boy. The z-score for the six-year-old's height is 0.86 and the z-score for the older brother is 0.61. Thus, the six-year-old is taller than a greater percentage of six-year-old boys than his brother is for fourteen-year-old boys.

b. Because the six-year-old's height falls close to the height that is one standard deviation above the mean, he is probably taller than the 50% of the boys whose heights fall below the mean, and also taller than about 34% of the boys who have heights that fall within one standard deviation above the mean. So I would expect 16% of the boys to be taller than he is. In this case 16% of 11 boys is about 2 boys. With such a small sample, however, the actual number taller could differ by quite a lot.

12. 16th percentile

13. This score is almost certainly a passing score. A z-score of $^-0.3$ on a standardized exam means that the student had a score that was three-tenths of one standard deviation below the mean. Therefore, this student scored better than probably 40% of the students. (That is, she scored better than 16% of the students that had z-scores between $^-1$ and $^-3$, and better than those students that had z-scores between $^-0.3$ and $^-1$ (roughly 70% of the 34% or about 24% of all the students).

14. No, because z-scores compare the students' scores with each others', not with some standard.

15. *Advantages of converting raw scores to z-scores*: It's easier to make comparisons across different normal distributions. *Disadvantages of converting to z-scores* (i.e., is any information lost?): As in Exercise 14 above, you lose information about the data, such as the mean score on a test, or the mean height of American women, or some measure of how spread out the heights are in inches.

16. a. Distributions P and Q have the same mean. In graphs of normal distributions, the mean is the score corresponding to the highest point in the graph.

    b. Distribution P has the greatest standard deviation. Distributions Q and R appear to be equally spread out, whereas P is spread out more and that means its standard deviation is greater than that of the other two.

Supplementary Learning Exercises for Section 30.6

1. a. Distribution B. The high point of a normal curve corresponds to the mean on the horizontal axis, and the high point of graph B, corresponding to 90, is farther to the right than is that of graph A, corresponding to 75.

   b. Distribution B. The high point of a normal curve corresponds to the median on the horizontal axis, and the high point of graph B corresponding to 90, is farther to the right than is that of graph A, corresponding to 75.

   c. Distribution B. The high point of a normal curve corresponds to the mode on the horizontal axis, and the high point of graph B, corresponding to 90, is farther to the right than is that of graph A, corresponding to 75.

d. Distribution *B*. The more spread out a normal curve is, the greater the standard deviation, and graph *B* is more spread out.

e. Distribution *B*. The variance is the square of the standard deviation, so the greater standard deviation, part (d), will give the greater variance.

f. Distribution *A*. The *z*-score tells how far you are above or below the mean (in standard deviation units). In distribution *A*, *x* is above the mean (75) and so will give a positive *z*-score, but in distribution *B*, *x* is below the mean (90) and would have a negative *z*-score.

2.   Ann's and Beth's actual scores are the same distance from the mean. Ann's is 0.8 standard deviation below the mean, and Beth's is 0.8 standard deviation above the mean.

3.   a. Answers will vary. Most data will be in the middle and to the left with only a few to the right.

   b. Answers will vary. Most data will be in the middle and to the right with only a few to the left.

4.   a. Mean = 4.85   standard deviation = 0.286 feet (0.279 on some calculators)

   b. Mean = 58.25   standard deviation = 3.432 inches (3.345 on some calculators)

   c. For the height in feet: $z = \frac{5.25-4.85}{0.286} \approx 1.4$. For the height in inches: $z = \frac{63-58.25}{3.432} \approx 1.4$ (No surprise, because all the values involved in the computation are multiplied by 12.)

   d. No, the bar graph is not shaped like a bell curve at all.

5.   You can find the *z* value, but it may not be meaningful in terms of the 68-95-99.7 rule. It might be useful in comparing performance on another test or measurement of some sort.

6.   a. ⁻0.33   b. 1.53   c. 2.4   d. ⁻0.73   e. ⁻2.33

7.   a. Symmetric, normal

   b. Symmetric, non-normal, bimodal

   c. Skewed right, non-normal

8.   a. Not possible. A skewed graph has a different median than mean.

   b. Not possible.

   c. Not possible.

   d. A bimodal distribution is an example.

9.   Locations are approximate.

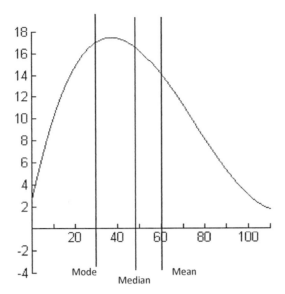

10. The mean would become 89 and the median 83. But the standard deviation would stay the same.

30.7 Issues for Learning: Understanding the Mean

1. $1.80

2. a. Karl is correct.

   b. Tim took the average of $1.60 and $2.20 which is $1.90. Karl took the average of six $1.60s and four $2.20s: ($9.60 + $8.80) ÷10 is $1.84.

3. a. The median is $4.00.

   b. The mean is $3.27.

   c. The mean is lower. There are a greater number of lesser allowances.

4. a. $19; "there are two modes, $12 and $19."

   b. $14.73

   c. The answers might vary, because of different experiences with spending money.

   d. $14 (the median)

   e. Probably something in the $14 to $15 range.

Answers for Chapter 31: Dealing with Multiple Data Sets or with Multiple Variables

31.1 Comparing Data Sets

1.

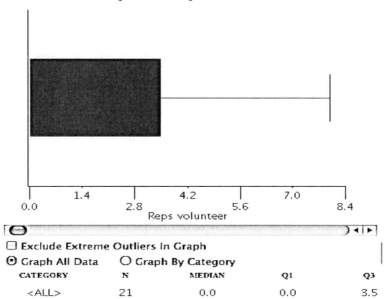

Box plot for Republicans

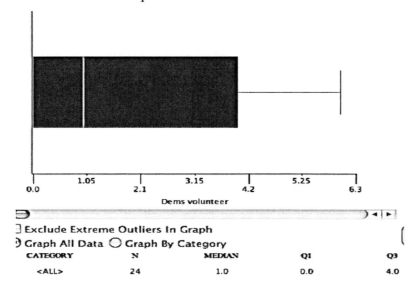

Box plot for Democrats

Box plot for Independents

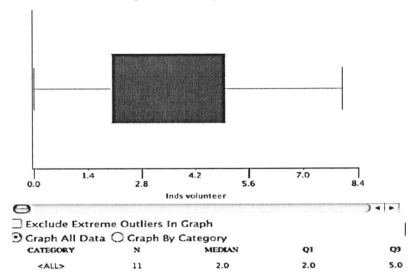

Inds volunteer

Exclude Extreme Outliers In Graph
Graph All Data ○ Graph By Category

CATEGORY	N	MEDIAN	Q1	Q3
<ALL>	11	2.0	2.0	5.0

2. The conjecture seems to be true: Removing that one case changes the mean from 2.74 to 2.80.

3. a–b. Students may offer bar graphs or pie charts. You can also use the table below to make some comparisons. *Tacky the Penguin* (T) and *Kat Kong* (K) appear to be the overall favorites, although Mr. Lopez's class heavily favored *Tacky*. Students may offer the last bar graph below to support T for part (b).

Kindergarten books.txt

		Teacher			Row Summary
		Chen	Lopez	Wilson	
	K	7	4	8	19
	L	2	7	5	14
Favorite	R	3	0	1	4
	S	3	2	2	7
	T	5	10	6	21
Column Summary		20	23	22	65

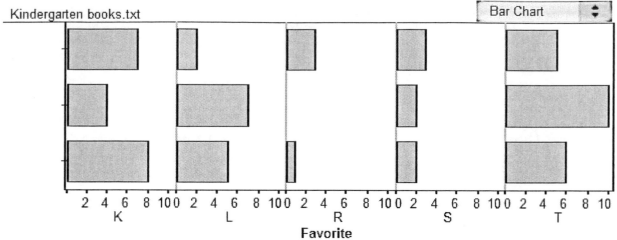

Kindergarten books.txt   Bar Chart

Favorite
Frequency of **Teacher**

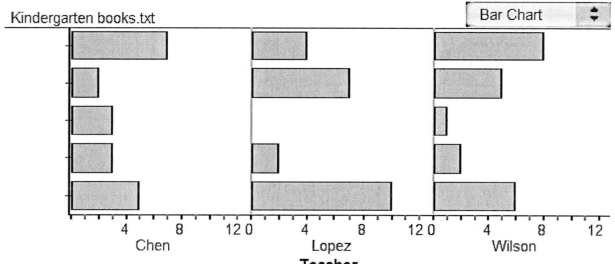

Kindergarten books.txt   Bar Chart

Teacher
Frequency of **Favorite**

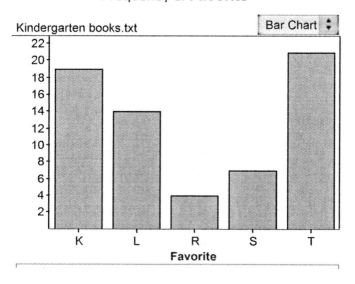

Kindergarten books.txt   Bar Chart

c. A teacher's enthusiasm or some special contribution by a class member may have influenced the class's decisions.

4.   a. Class A appears to have more high-scoring students than does Class B, although it also has more low-scoring ones as well. Occasionally in competitions only the highest scores from a team are counted; even so, the mean for Class A would appear to be higher than the mean for Class B.

b. "That would be one way to do it, although Class A has more high scores. Let's find out whether everyone's score counts for the team, or just the highest ones."

5.   a. Rather than quartiles at the ends of the boxes, the ends are at the 20th and 80th percentiles. (The fact that they are sideways is a difference but not so important.)

b. Number sense: Males are slightly better, and are not so spread out as the females. Measurement: Females and males perform alike, although the males' lowest 20% are more spread out than the females' lowest 20%

Spatial sense: There are no striking differences, although the middle 50% of the females vary less than the middle 50% of the males.

6.   Here is a sample. Cholesterol reading could be on the horizontal axis, but it is usually predicted from weight.

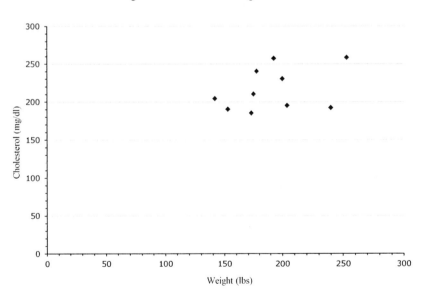

Weight and Cholesterol Readings for 10 Men

7.   a. Box plots for the house prices in the two cities might give Easton enough information. A histogram, with its visual feedback, might be a good second choice.

b. A histogram or box plot of each set of test scores, because both may give her a sense of what a typical score might be and how spread out the test scores were. She could use a scatter plot of the students' two test scores to address the "associated?" question.

c. A scatter plot of the number of assignments turned in versus time would be useful in studying the trend.

d. Unless Stella sees a trend in the April rainfalls in recent years, either a histogram or a box plot, or even a stem-and-leaf plot, for the April rainfalls for the 30 years should be useful in judging whether or not this April is quite unusual.

e. Sanders would probably look at a scatter plot for the two types of costs. If the advertising campaign was in effect only part of the year, he might prefer separate costs-versus-month line graphs.

8. a. One of the couples consists of a woman who is 1590 mm and a man (her husband) who is 1735 mm.

b. Women who are taller tend to marry shorter men, while women who are shorter tend to be married to taller men.

c, e. They are generally positively associated. Women who are taller tend to be married to taller men, while women who are shorter tend to be married to shorter men.

d. The height of a wife would bear little relationship to the height of her husband. For example, knowing that a wife was short would give no information about the likely height of her husband.

f. Here, the general positive association is not distorted by the changes in scale.

9. Here is a sample. Your vertical scale may differ from the one here.

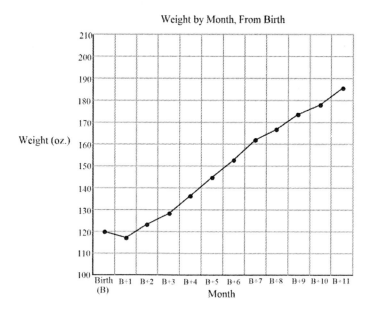

Weight by Month, From Birth

10. a. No association

    b. Positive association (As the first gets larger, so does the second.)

    c. Negative association (As the first gets larger, the second gets smaller.)

    d. Negative association

11. In the second graph, the vertical scale unit starts at 1000 and changes by a factor of 10 each unit up. This factor of 10 disguises the rate of change.

12. Here is a sample.

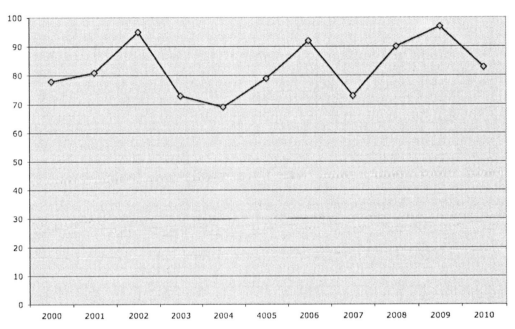

13. a. 5 Look above the 5 on the Number of area codes axis.

    b. One state with 9 area codes has a population between 14 and 15 million.

    c. 18, by doubling the answer for part (b)

    d. Using part (b) again, about 36

    e. Somewhere around 20 to 24 million, doubling the numbers for states with 7 area codes

    f. Grossly, the number of area codes increases as the population increases. Section 31.2 treats finding a "line of best fit" that enables you to make a more precise prediction.

14. a. The dual line graphs enable you to contrast the hours spent from day to day.

    b. The line graphs imply that there is an order to the activities, with in-between values like 1.5 making sense.

Supplementary Learning Exercises for Section 31.1

1. a.

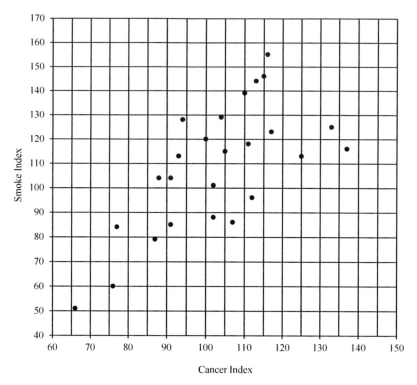

b. The data show a positive association.

c. As the smoking index increases, so does the cancer index. We cannot say that this is a causal relationship without more information, however.

2. a. Type refers to the type of experimental sampling—random in this case.

b. The two variables are size of diamond in carats and price in Singapore dollars.

c. The most expensive diamond cost 1086 Singapore dollars and was 0.35 carats.

d.

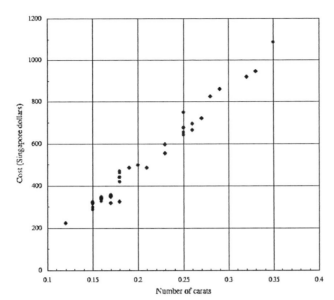

Cost (Singapore dollars) of diamonds

e. The variables are positively associated. This means that the greater the carat size the more the diamond costs.

3. a. Positively associated, at least until the fish is fully grown

   b. Arguments could be made for different answers, but most likely they are positively associated.

   c. No association

   d. No association

31.2 Lines of Best Fit and Correlation

1. a. Positive and strongly associated because as trees age they get larger

   b. Very close to zero because the inside temperature stays about the same, but the outside temperature can vary considerably.

   c. Negative because... (You can also argue "very close to zero" because...)

   d. Negative because the highest-priced cars often do not get good mileage. (An argument of "very close to zero" might be defended by pointing out that special features, like hydrogen fuel cars, are costly, but the correlation would not be −1.)

   e. Perhaps surprisingly, faculty experience suggests a negative correlation coefficient under unlimited time conditions (for exams intended for a set period of time). For speeded tests, with a strict time limit, the correlation coefficient is likely to be positive, although not +1

   f. Positive, although probably not +1.

2. a. Humans (62, 1320), Asian elephants (2547, 4603), and African elephants (6654, 5712)

b. Such a high positive correlation coefficient means that as body weights increase, so do brain weights.

c. Humans are at (62, 1320) and appear not to fit the line of best fit very well, so they can be regarded as outliers (note this is not the same sense as "outlier" for a box plot).

d. Reading the graph will give an estimate, but the equation will give a more exact value: Brain weight = 0.94(2000) + 191.22 = 2071.22 grams, about 2070 grams.

e. There is a strong positive association between the two weights. This is not surprising, because one would expect a larger animal to have a larger brain, in general.

3. a. Many points do not seem as close to the line as before. The equation is a little different, but the "outlier" status of humans is very obvious.

   b. The lower correlation coefficient, $\sqrt{0.29} \approx 0.54$, suggests a lower degree of association, so predictions may be off. (Including the outliers made the correlation seem stronger.)

   c. The regression line should fit the data better.

4. Here is a scatter plot, with time between eruptions vs. duration of eruption, along with the regression line and equation, which are not expected from the students. (Reversing the roles is also natural.) Note that the exercise calls for a write-up.

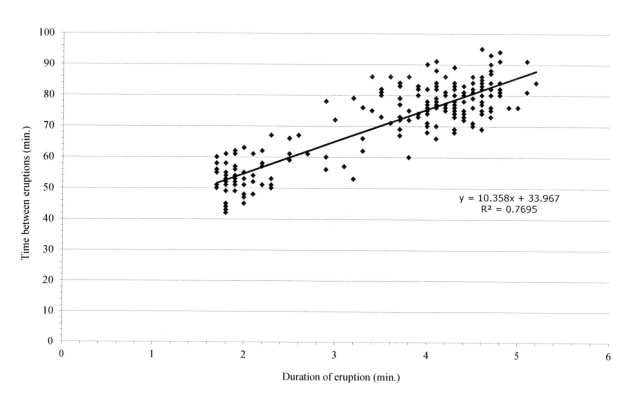

Old Faithful

5. a. $\sqrt{0.81} = 0.9$

    b. About 159; about 185. Why "about"?

    c. 200

    d. No. Correlations do not automatically mean causation.

6. b. The *meanings* of the coordinates are the same, although the scores are interchanged.

    c. The correlations are the same.

Supplementary Learning Exercises for Section 31.2

1. a.

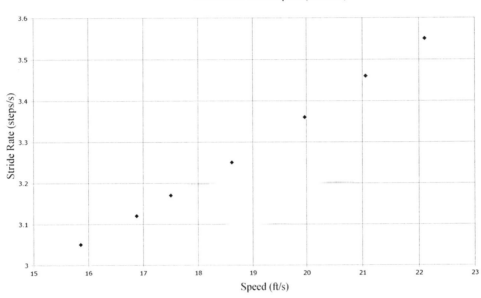

Stride Rate Versus Speed (Females)

    b. These data are very close to being on the line. The *R* value for this graph shows a strong positive association.

    c.

Speed (ft/s)	15.86	16.88	17.5	18.62	19.97	21.06	22.11
Stride rate	3.04	3.12	3.17	3.26	3.37	3.45	3.54

2. a. close to 1   b. close to ¯1

    c. close to 0   d. close to 0

3. a. The graph in 2(c)

    b. The graph in 2(d)

    c. The graph in 2(a)

    d. The graph in 2(b)

4. a. Close to 1   b. Close to 1, but not as close as in part (a)

c. Close to 0   d. Close to ⁻1

5.   The *x*-values from zero to four appear to have a strong negative association. The values from four to ten appear to have a strong positive association. These appear to cancel out, making the overall association closer to 0. This example shows the importance of an awareness of what values of the independent variable are used for a correlation coefficient.

Answers for Chapter 32: Variability in Samples

32.1 Having Confidence in a Sample Statistic

1. The larger sample will give them a smaller confidence interval, so their prediction will be much sharper.

2. This table is worth discussing, because it shows that larger and larger samples may not offer immensely greater precision.

	≤10%	≤5%	≤2%
100	975	775	(421)
500	1000	987	771
1000	1000	1000	885
2000	1000	1000	974
3000	1000	1000	(991)

3. a. $\frac{85}{1000}$, or 8.5%

   b. $\frac{240}{1000}$, or 24%

   c. $\frac{335}{1000}$, or 33.5%

   d. $\frac{421}{1000}$, or 42.1%. Notice that even with a large sample, one cannot expect to "hit" the population parameter exactly.

4. A sample of size 20 cannot be expected to give a good confidence interval. Using the $\frac{1}{\sqrt{n}}$ rule of thumb, the $\pm \frac{1}{\sqrt{20}} \approx \pm 22\%$ gives a confidence interval covering 44%.

5. Low bias and high precision, because both conditions allow one to be more confident of the sample statistics.

6. Using the $\frac{1}{\sqrt{n}}$ rule of thumb, there is a good chance that the population proportion lies in the interval $54\% \pm \frac{1}{\sqrt{400}} = 54\% \pm \frac{1}{20} = 54\% \pm 5\%$, or 49% to 59%.

7. a. Using the thumbnail estimate, $\frac{1}{\sqrt{1631}}$ is about $\frac{1}{40}$, or about 0.025, or 2.5%, so the population parameter should be between 50.5% and 55.5%. Hence, it is very likely that the people will not vote for funding a new library.

   b. But with 100 people, $\frac{1}{10}$ is 0.1, so we can assume that the number of people voting against the library measure will be between 43% and 63%. You should not feel so certain.

   c. However, if the sample statistic is 75%, then the population parameter should be between 65% and 85%, and so in this case 100 randomly selected people should be enough. Of course, pollsters do not just poll until the numbers are right. And using the $\frac{1}{\sqrt{n}}$ rule of thumb is risky, with a population parameter suggested by the 75%.

8.   a. Locating every one, getting them to agree to be questioned, not counting anyone twice, training a large number of conscientious interviewers, developing appropriate questions, completing the census in a timely fashion, keeping track of all the data, and so forth

   b. Homelessness, finding people, language difficulties, for example

   c. Have fewer representatives in Congress, do not get fair share of federal dollars that are distributed according to populations, for example

   d. Mobility (people moving during the census, for example, or being at someone else's home when they were being interviewed), claiming more people in a residence than there were, for example. Overcounts could result in the opposite effects as those in part (c): having more representatives in Congress, getting more than the appropriate share of federal dollars, for example.

   e. *Pro*: Much less expensive; if done carefully, it might even be more accurate.

   Con: People (especially Congress) might not trust the outcomes; tradition; etc.

9.   Greater than. A larger sample should give a statistic closer to the population parameter.

10. With a sample of size 20, the number of browns could vary from, say, 4 to 12 (18% to 62%), or even more. With a sample of size 100, the number of browns should vary less percent-wise, say from 30% to 50%.

11. a. 400 (from $\frac{1}{\sqrt{n}} = 5\% = \frac{1}{20}$)   b. 10,000   c. 40,000

Supplementary Learning Exercises for Section 32.1

1.   a. **36** of the 1000 samples of size 100 gave a percent *against* of 59%; **25** of the 1000 samples of size 500 gave a percent *against* of 59%; **6** of the 1000 samples of size 1000 gave a percent *against* of 59%; and **1** of the 1000 samples of size 2000 gave a percent *against* of 59%.

   b. 1 of the 1000 samples of size 100 gave a percent *against* of 83%.

2.   The column should have fewer entries and be condensed even more around the 63% row.

3.   The $\frac{1}{\sqrt{n}}$ rule of thumb can be used if the (usually unknown) population parameter is around 50%. The *n* refers to the sample size. The rule gives an idea of the margin of error.

4.   88% suggests that the underlying population parameter is not around 50%. The large sample size strengthens that suggestion.

5. a. True

b. False! Sample statistics can vary a lot from sample to sample, as Table 1 shows.

c. True

6.

a.

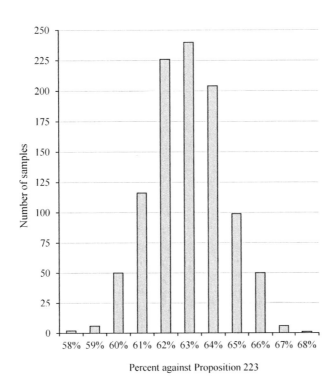

Number of 1000 Samples (size 1000) with Percents

b. To a good degree. "Perfect" data would appear to fit a normal curve.

32.2 Confidence Intervals

1. Yes, he could lose, because the confidence interval contains 49%. He could ask that the pollsters take a larger sample to get a smaller confidence interval, but of course then the poll may show him closer to 50%, so the confidence interval could still contain percents below 50. Besides, it would be very expensive to take another poll on the heels of the one he just requested.

2. The mailings apparently did not give a representative sample, especially with a self-selected 23% returning the sample ballots (23% is not unusual in such a sampling). In 1936 those subscribing to magazines, or owning a car or telephone, may have been a richer part of the population and so gave a biased sample to start with.

3. A 95% confidence interval could be estimated by ± 2 standard deviations from the sample statistic, so it would be the percent you found earlier, ± 10%. (This can be only an approximation, using your sample proportion as the true population proportion.) You might say, "There is a 95% probability that the percent of time a thumbtack lands point up is in (your interval)."

4. With the margin of error in mind, the percent of the population supporting a change would be in the 51% to 55% interval. If the matter were to be voted on, there is a good chance that there would be some changes to Social Security. What those changes might be would affect your reaction.

5. a. $52\% \pm 33\frac{1}{3}\%$, or $18\frac{2}{3}\% - 85\frac{1}{3}\%$

    b. $52\% \pm 10.5\%$, or $41.5\% - 62.5\%$

    c. $52\% \pm 3\frac{1}{3}\%$, or $48\frac{2}{3}\% - 55\frac{1}{3}\%$

    d. $52\% \pm 1\%$, or $51\% - 53\%$

Supplementary Learning Exercises for Section 32.2

1. a. Jeff's polling of the entire student body (if practical) should give no margin of error. From the $\frac{1}{\sqrt{n}}$ rule of thumb, Angie's idea would give a margin of error of $\pm 10\%$, and Jan's would give a margin of error of about $\pm 3\%$.

    b. Strictly speaking, *Yes* did win a majority. But the vote was virtually tied, so the university would have to evaluate which group to offend.

    c. Not with great confidence, because the confidence interval is 46%–66%.

    d. With a confidence interval of 51%–57%, the university should be somewhat safe in proceeding.

2. a. The confidence interval, 48%–56%, does include less than 50%.

    b. From $\frac{1}{\sqrt{n}} \approx 0.04 = \frac{1}{25}$, the sample size was around $25^2 = 625$.

3. a. 96%–100%

    b. 95%

    c. Yes, for a couple of reasons. First, there is only a 95% confidence that repeating such tests would give intervals around the population parameter. Second, the test itself does not appear to be 100% effective.

4. First, the sample of 16 may be biased, because they were all Robin's friends. Second, the confidence interval is large: $54\% \pm 25\%$, or 29%–79%, so the population parameter could well be below 50%.

5. 51% and ± 3%

Answers for Chapter 33: Special Topics in Probability

33.1 Expected Value

1. 3.5. This means that with a large number of tosses, the average number of spaces moved is 3.5.

2. 7. This means...

3. $418,200. You can assume that attractive teams and good weather are independent events. Also, take $P(\text{bad weather}) = 1 - P(\text{good weather})$.

4. Remember that from your viewpoint, when someone makes a basket, you lose 49¢. You would charge 30¢ or more. Suppose you charge c cents. If the person makes a basket, you have gained c cents and lost 49¢. If the person does not make a basket, you have gained c cents. You want the expected value to be $\geq$ 10¢. The expected value is $(c - 49)0.4 + (c)0.6 = 0.4c - 19.6 + 0.6c = c - 19.6$. So if $c - 19.6 \geq 10$, then $c \geq 29.6$.

5. Find the expected values for the two situations. Notice that the free-throw option gives four possible outcomes. Under the given conditions and barring sportsmanship considerations, it would be a good strategy to foul the player because the expected values are 1.2 versus 0.8.

6. a. Assuming that the $1000 does not count in determining expected value except to determine the value of "double your money," the expected value is
    $$\tfrac{1}{16}(800 + 200 + L + 100 + 1000) = \tfrac{7000}{16} = \$437.50$$

    b. With a large number of spins, the contestant can expect to win an average of $437.50 per spin.

    c. $\dfrac{6000 + x}{16}$ dollars

Supplementary Learning Exercises for Section 33.1

1. The expected value is $(0.1 \cdot 1) + (0.1 \cdot 2) + (0.1 \cdot 3) + (0.1 \cdot 4) + (0.1 \cdot 5) + (0.5 \cdot 6) = 4.5$ spaces.

2. You can roll a 7 six different ways, so the probability of rolling a 7 is $\frac{1}{6}$. From your viewpoint, the cost to play is $^{-}1$. Hence, the expected value is $\frac{1}{6} \cdot (5 - 1) + (\frac{5}{6} \cdot {^{-}1}) = {^{-}\frac{1}{6}}$, and in the long run the owner (not you) will average $\$\frac{1}{6}$ per game.

3. $P(\$0.50) = \frac{1}{2}$, $P(\$0.75) = \frac{2}{6}$, and $P(\$2.00) = \frac{1}{6}$. The expected value, without the charge to play, is $(\frac{1}{2} \cdot 0.50) + (\frac{1}{3} \cdot 0.75) + (\frac{1}{6} \cdot 2.00) = 0.83\frac{1}{3}$ dollars or $83\frac{1}{3}$¢. The owner charges $1 so the owner can expect to make money if the game is played many times.

4. a. The expected value is

$$(0.05 \cdot 0) + (0.15 \cdot 1) + (0.25 \cdot 2) + (0.30 \cdot 3) + (0.10 \cdot 4) + (0.15 \cdot 5) = 2.7$$

b. She can expect to get an average of 2.7 calls per day, over the long run.

5. The expected value (from the booth manager's viewpoint) without taking into account the cost to play is $(0.3 \cdot {}^{-}75) + (0.7 \cdot 0) = {}^{-}22.5$. The booth should charge at least one 25¢ ticket to play in order to make money.

33.2 Permutations and Combinations

1. Order is…   a. important.   b. not important.   c. important.

    d. important.   e. not important.

2. a. There are $5 \cdot 4 = 20$. Did you use a system?

    <u>PQ, PR, PS, PT</u>
    QP, <u>QR, QS, QT</u>
    RP, RQ, <u>RS, RT</u>
    SP, SQ, SR, <u>ST</u>
    TP, TQ, TR, TS

    b. There are 10. (The underlined ones in the part (a) answer.)

3. a. *Act 1*: Choose one of the 5 children for the first seat. *Act 2*: Choose one of the remaining 4 children for the second seat, and so on.
    OR *Act 1*: Assign a first child to one of the 5 seats. *Act 2*: Assign a second child to one of the remaining 4 seats, and so on.

    b. *Act 1*: Assign a first child to one of the 7 seats. *Act 2*: Assign a second child to one of the remaining 6 seats, and so on.

    c. Both part (a) and part (b) involve permutations.

4. a. 2520   b. 21 (Order does not matter.)

5. a. $\frac{10 \cdot 9}{2 \cdot 1} = 45$ b. 45
    c. 45   d. 45

    e. Think of part (a) as identifying the ways two "slots" could be picked, out of 10, and filled with H (or T, thus the part (c) answer). Each choice of two slots also gives a choice of (the other) eight slots.

6. a. $\frac{15}{128}$ b. $\frac{45}{1024}$ c. *Hint*: $P(0\ H) + P(1\ H) + P(2\ H) + P(3\ H)$; $\frac{176}{1024} = \frac{11}{64}$

    d. In the long run, with many, many tosses of 10 honest coins, about…

7. $P(\text{all boys}) = P\,(\text{all girls}) = 1 \cdot \left(\frac{1}{2}\right)^4$

P (exactly 1 boy) = P (exactly 1 girl) = $4 \cdot (\frac{1}{2})^4$

P (exactly 2 boys) = $6 \cdot (\frac{1}{2})^4$

In many, many future families of four children…

8. P (all male) = $(\frac{2}{3})^4$; P (all female) = $(\frac{1}{3})^4$;

P (exactly one male) = $4 \cdot \frac{2}{3} \cdot (\frac{1}{3})^3$; P (two of each sex) = $6 \cdot (\frac{2}{3})^2 \cdot (\frac{1}{3})^2$

9.   2,598,960 (The order of the cards in a hand does not matter.)

10. a. 120   b. 20   c. $\frac{20}{120}$, or..   d. 6   e. 252

f. $\frac{20 \cdot 6}{252}$, or… (Why are the 20 and 6 multiplied?)

11. a. There are $\frac{100 \cdot 99 \cdot 98 \cdot 97 \cdot 96 \cdot 95}{6 \cdot 5 \cdot 4 \cdot 3 \cdot 2 \cdot 1} = 1,192,052,400$ combinations, choosing 6 numbers from 00 to

99. Only one of those will be the winner, so the probability of winning is $\frac{1}{1,192,052,400}$.

b. $\frac{1}{1,192,052,400} \cdot 1,000,000 + \frac{1,192,052,399}{1,192,052,400} \cdot 0 \approx 0.0008$ dollar, but the $2 cost means you can

expect to lose all but a smidgen of your $2.

12. *Needed*: The probabilities of hitting exactly 8, exactly 9, and exactly 10 (and then add

those):

$$45 \cdot 0.85^8 \cdot 0.15^2 + 10 \cdot 0.85^9 \cdot 0.15^1 + 1 \cdot 0.85^{10} \approx 27.6\% + 34.7\% + 19.7\% \text{ or about } 82\%.$$

13. a. 5040   b. 3,628,800   c. 6! = 720

d. 720. Note that the common factor 7! allows the fraction to be simplified.

e. 495   f. 28

14–15. When $r = n$, $(n - r)! = 0!$, and what does that mean? So that the expressions make

sense and still apply in cases involving 0!, 0! is defined to be = 1.

16. a. 1   b. 5   c. 10

d. 10   e. 5   f. 1

17. a. Starting with the second row, add two consecutive entries to get, in the next row, the

entry "between" the two entries. The next row is 1 7 21 35 35 21 7 1, and the row

after, 1 8 28 56 70 56 28 8 1. There are many patterns, including the sums of the

rows. Samples—Symmetry in each row, diagonal patterns (including 1-3-6-10-15

giving the triangular numbers), sum of the numbers in the nth row = 2^{n-1}, if desired,

the relationship to the coefficients in the expansion of $(x + y)^n$.

b. The 1-5-10-10-5-1 row tells the number of combinations of increasing size, given 5

objects. The 1-6-15- and so on row would then tell that, given 6 objects, there is 1

combination of size 0, 6 combinations of size 1, 15 combinations of size 2, 20 combinations of size 3, 15 combinations of size 4, 6 combinations of size 5, and 1 combination of size 6.

Supplementary Learning Exercises for Section 33.2

1. $8 \cdot 10 \cdot 10 \cdot 10 \cdot 10 \cdot 10 = 8,000,000$.

2. It depends. Although there are 400 possible codes ($4 \cdot 10 \cdot 10$), you may have 100 or more books in a particular category. It would be safer to use more digits to extend your code. If every category of books includes fewer than 100 books, then you are safe.

3. $20 \cdot 19 \cdot 18 \cdot 17 \cdot 16 \cdot 15 = 27,907,200$ different orders! If all you care about is the choices of CDs, without concern about the order in which they're placed, there are "only" $_{20}C_6 = 38,760$ choices.

4. Taking into account the number of ways each part of the committee can be chosen, and the fact that every part can go with each of the other parts, there are $2 \cdot 3 \cdot {}_6C_4 \cdot {}_9C_4 = 2 \cdot 3 \cdot 15 \cdot 126 = 11,340$ ways in which the committee can be formed.

5. $13 \cdot {}_{15}C_2 \cdot 9 = 13 \cdot 105 \cdot 9 = 12,285$ possible different committees

6. There are $_{52}C_5$ different 5-card hands. The three face cards can occur in $_{12}C_3$ ways, and the other two cards, which must come from the 40 non–face cards, can occur in $_{40}C_2$ ways. The probability, then, is $\dfrac{_{12}C_3 \cdot {}_{40}C_2}{_{52}C_5} = \dfrac{220 \cdot 780}{2,598,960} \approx 0.066$.

7. a. $10 \cdot 26 \cdot 26 \cdot 26 \cdot 10 \cdot 10 = 17,576,000$, although some of the 3-letter choices might not be allowed.

    b. $10 \cdot 26 \cdot 25 \cdot 24 \cdot 9 \cdot 8 = 11,232,000$ but again some of the 3-letter choices might not be allowed.

8. a. $_8C_4 = 70$

    b. $\dfrac{_5C_3}{_8C_3} = \dfrac{10}{56} = \dfrac{5}{28} \approx 18\%$

    c. $\dfrac{_5C_3 \cdot {}_3C_2}{_8C_5} = \dfrac{30}{56} = \dfrac{15}{28} \approx 54\%$

9. Two balls can be chosen in $_9C_2 = \frac{9 \cdot 8}{2 \cdot 1} = 36$ possible outcomes. This problem is complicated because there are so many ways that you might get $10 or more.

    Draw two $5 balls from the four $5 balls: $_4C_2 = 6$ outcomes.
    Draw a $10 ball (2 ways) and one of the other 8 balls: $2 \times 8 = 16$ outcomes.
    So the probability of drawing at least $10 is $\frac{22}{36} = \frac{11}{18}$.